SOURCES FOR THE HISTORY OF EDUCATION

SOURCES FOR THE HISTORY OF EDUCATION

*A list of material (including school books)
contained in the Libraries of the Institutes and Schools
of Education, together with works from the Libraries of
the Universities of Nottingham and Reading*

Edited by
Dr. C. W. J. HIGSON, M.A., F.L.A.,
Librarian, School of Education, University of Leicester

1967
THE LIBRARY ASSOCIATION

Published by
The Library Association
7 Ridgmount Street, Store Street,
London, W.C.1

© DR. C. W. J. HIGSON, 1967

Text set in 10 point Times New Roman,
'Monotype' Series 327, and Index in 9 point

Printed and bound in England by
STAPLES PRINTERS LIMITED
at their Rochester, Kent, establishment

TABLE OF CONTENTS

Contents

PREFACE

Since the provincial Institutes and Schools of Education were set up in England after the last war, they have built up libraries not unworthy to stand beside the older library of the University of London Institute of Education. Both London and the newer libraries have regarded it as part of their function to collect older material useful for research in the history of education, and some have quite considerable collections of this kind. The combined holdings of the fifteen education libraries represented in this catalogue give a very extensive coverage of the field. Fortunately, we have been enabled to extend the coverage still further by receiving permission to incorporate entries relating to material in the Reading University Library and in the Briggs Collection of old school books at the University of Nottingham. We are grateful to the respective librarians.

As there has not hitherto been anything remotely resembling a complete bibliography of those British books and pamphlets which serve as source-material for the history of education, we feel that there should be a welcome for a publication which does not fall too far short of that ideal, and which throws in some foreign publications for good measure. The state of bibliography in this field leaves much to be desired. Many of the publications listed here cannot be found in any bibliography relating to education. Some of the titles – and many of the editions – are not in the catalogue of the British Museum. Whatever may be said about the limitations of this catalogue, it can at least be said that it supplies a want. Its usefulness is enormously increased by the fact that it gives locations of copies, and thus facilitates inter-library loan of a wide range of books which hitherto had not been readily accessible to scholars.

Tribute must be paid to the scholarly work of Dr. Winifred Higson, Librarian of the University of Leicester School of Education, who over the years has edited a number of sectional lists for private circulation, and has now crowned her task by preparing the present catalogue for publication.

C. B. FREEMAN

Chairman, Librarians of Institutes of Education
Hull, January 1966

INTRODUCTION

THE Union List here published is a product of what has been called 'Bibliography by correspondence', and the majority of the works listed have not been examined by the editor. Entries from the participating libraries vary in fullness, but wherever possible enough of the title is quoted to show the scope and purpose of the work. The editor has not had the leisure to do as much research as she would have liked, and standard works such as the *Dictionary of national biography* and the *Cambridge bibliography of English literature* have usually been accepted as authorities. For a few early works Stationers' register dates are given.

The list includes books on education, school textbooks and children's books published, or first published, from the fifteenth century until 1870, and government publications relating to education issued up to 1918, these last in a separate section. For non-government publications there is a broad division by period, with educational treatises, textbooks and children's books listed alphabetically by author, or by title if anonymous. From 1801 textbooks and children's books are given in a separate sequence, owing to their considerable number.

Entries for individual works give (a) Reference number, (b) Author, (c) Date of first edition or of the composition of the work (where known) in round brackets, (d) Title, statement of edition, etc., (e) Locations. Under the earliest period in which a work appeared contemporary editions are listed fully, and so are modern editions. References are made to editions appearing in the later periods covered by the list, and full entries are given in the appropriate period. References are *not* made from later editions to earlier ones, but the original publication date indicates where entries or references may be found.

Since it is hoped that the list will be useful to students at various levels, it was decided to include modern editions of works, as well as early editions, but, while most modern editions are represented, the full holdings in this field of some libraries are not shown. Modern editions of children's classics are not included. With a few exceptions the list includes only works in the possession of the participating libraries by the end of 1964. Subsequent accessions may be listed in a supplement.

Source material for the history of education can also be found incidentally in such works as autobiographies, not specifically connected with education, but the listing of these has not been attempted, although many may be found in the stock of the libraries concerned.

The subject index refers to books dealing with specific aspects of education. Books dealing with the broad field of education are not entered there, and must be sought in the appropriate sections. Subject indexing from book titles is full of pitfalls, and the editor has probably fallen into many of them. Nevertheless she thought that a subject index added to the usefulness of the work sufficiently to be worth attempting despite the dangers.

Books included in this list will usually be available for lending, at the discretion of the librarian, through the Inter-Library Loan System, with the exception of those in the Briggs Collection at Nottingham University. By the terms of the bequest these books may not leave the library.

C. W. J. HIGSON
Leicester, January 1966

LOCATION LIST

The following location symbols are used to represent the participating libraries:

BI	University of Birmingham Institute of Education
BR	University of Bristol Institute of Education
CA	Cambridge Institute of Education
DU	University of Durham Institute of Education
HU	University of Hull Institute of Education
LEE	University of Leeds Institute of Education
LEI	University of Leicester School of Education
LI	University of Liverpool Institute of Education
LO	University of London Institute of Education
MA	University of Manchester School of Education
NE	University of Newcastle upon Tyne Institute of Education
NO	University of Nottingham Institute of Education
NoU	Briggs Collection, University of Nottingham Library
RE	University of Reading Education Library
*ReU	University of Reading Library
SH	University of Sheffield Institute of Education
SO	University of Southampton Institute of Education

*Many of the books originally in the University of Reading Main Library have now been transferred to the Education Library.

SECTION A

Books published, or first published, in the 15th-17th Centuries

(with a few earlier works)

1. Individual authors

A1 [A.B.C., Paternoster, and other prayers, in Latin]. Antwerp, J. van Gaesbeeck [*ca.* 1620]. NoU

A2 A.B.C. (1538?) The ABC both in Latyn & Englyshe: being a facsimile reprint of the earliest extant English reading book... E. Stock, 1889. [Originally printed by Thomas Petyt, probably about 1538.] HU LEI LO NO NoU

AENEAS SYLVIUS. *See* Pius II, *pope*

A3 AESOP. Aesopi Phrygis fabulae graecae et latine, cum aliis quibusdem opusculis... Basle, 1606. NoU

A4 AESOP. Aisopou muthoi, sun tois epigrammasin... [Greek script] in usum scholae regiae Westmonast. Redmayne, 1671. LEE

A5 AESOP. Fabularum Aesopicarum delectus. [Edited by Anthony Alsop.] Oxford, Sheldonian Theatre, 1698. [Greek, Latin, Hebrew and Arabic texts.] LEI

A6 AINSWORTH, Robert, 1660–1743. (1698) The most natural and easy way of institution. 2nd ed., 1736. *See* B21

A7 ALBRECHT, Georg, *pastor of Geildorff.* Biblisches A B C = und Namen = Büchlein... Nuremberg, Endter, n.d. [16–?]. LEI

A8 [ALDRICH, Henry], 1647–1710. (1691) Artis logicae compendium. 1723; *and another ed.* 1793. *See* B24–25

A9 [ALDRICH, Henry]. Artis logicae rudimenta. 1828. *See* D29

A10 [ALER, Paul], 1656–1727. (1687) Gradus ad Parnassum. 1729. *See* B26; *and another ed.* 1802. *See* D30

A11 ALEXANDER, Johann, *of Berne.* (Eng. 1693) Synopsis algebraica. 2nd ed. 1709. *See* B27

A12 [ALLESTREE, Richard], 1619–1681. (1660) The gentleman's calling. R. Norton for T. Garthwait, 1667. HU

A13 [ALLESTREE, Richard], do., *another ed.* 1705. *See* B28

A14 [ALLESTREE, Richard]. (1673) The ladies calling, in two parts. By the author of the Whole duty of man, etc. 4th imp. Oxford, at the Theater, 1676. HU

A15 [ALLESTREE, Richard]. (1658) The whole duty of man. 1733; *and another ed.* 1756. *See* B29–30. *Latin translation:* Officium hominis. 1704. *See* B31

[*Note:* All the above works attributed to Allestree are also attributed to other authors.]

A16 [ALSOP, Anthony], d. 1726, *ed.* Fabularum Aesopicarum delectus. *See* A5 Aesop

A17 ARETINUS, *otherwise* Leonardo Bruni, 1369–1444. (1405?) De studiis et literis. *See* A450 Woodward, W. H., *ed.*

A18 ARNAULD, Antoine, 1612–1694. (1684) Défense de Mr. Arnauld... contre la Réponse au livre des vrayes et des fausses idées. Cologne, N. Schouten, 1684. LEI

A19 [ARNAULD, Antoine, & NICOLE, Pierre]. (1662) La logique. 9e éd., 1718. *See* B39

A20 ARRIGHI, Ludovico degli, *called* Vincentino, d. *ca.* 1527. (1522) The first writing book. An English translation and facsimile text of Arrighi's *Operina*... O.U.P., [etc.], 1955. HU LEI NE RE

Artis logicae compendium. *See* B24 Aldrich, H.
Artis logicae rudimenta. *See* D29 Aldrich, H.

A21 ASCHAM, Roger, 1515–1568. English works... Edited by W. A. Wright. C.U.P., 1904. HU LEE LEI NE RE SH SO

A22 ASCHAM, Roger. (1576) [Letters] Disertissimi viri Rogeri Aschami... familiarum epistolarum libri tres... aedita studio et labore E. Grantae... F Caldocki, [1576]. NoU

A23 ASCHAM, Roger, do. Rogeri Aschami epistolarum libri quatuor. 1703. *See* B41

A24 ASCHAM, Roger. (1570) The scholemaster. Edited with notes by John E. B. Mayor. Bell & Daldy, 1863. HU LEI; Bell, 1895. LO; 1907. ReU; 1911. LO; 1934. NO

A25 ASCHAM, Roger. The scholemaster. First edition 1570, collated with the second edition 1571, by Edward Arber. Arber, 1870. LO; Birmingham [Constable], 1870. NE; Arber, 1903. ReU

A26 ASCHAM, Roger. The schoolmaster. Cassell, 1888. LEE; 1890. SH; 1909. RE

A27 ASCHAM, Roger. The scholemaster, revised by J. Upton. 1711; *and another ed.* 1743. *See* B42–43

A28 ASCHAM, Roger. (1545) Toxophilus. Edited by Edward Arber. Murray, 1868. NO

A29 AULNOY, Marie Cathérine Jumel de Berneville, *comtesse d'*, 1650?–1705. (1700?) Les contes des fées. 1766. *See* B47

A30 AYRES, John, *fl.* 1680–1700, *penman.* (1688) The tradesman's copy-book, or apprentices companion... Crouch, 1688. NoU

A31 BACON, Francis, 1561–1626. The physical and metaphysical works of Lord Bacon, including his Dignity and advancement of learning... and his Novum organum... By Joseph Devey. Bohn, 1860 LEI

A32 BACON, Francis. (1605) The advancement of learning... Edited by W. A. Wright. 2nd ed. Oxford, Clarendon Pr., 1873. LEE; 3rd ed. 1885. LEI; 5th ed. 1926. HU NE RE

A33 BACON, Francis. The advancement of learning. [Edited by G. W. Kitchen.] Dent, 1915, repr. 1950. LEE SH; repr. 1954. BI NO

A34 BACON, Francis. (1620) Novum organum, edited by Thomas Fowler. 2nd ed. Oxford, Clarendon Pr., 1889. LO

A35 BAKER, Humphrey, *fl.* 1562–1587. (1561–2) [The well springe of sciences, which teacheth the perfect worke and practise of Arithmeticke... *ca.* 1600?.] NoU

A36 [BAKER, Thomas], 1656–1740. (1699) Reflections upon learning, wherein is shown the insufficiency thereof... By a gentleman. 2nd ed. Bosvile, 1700. BI; 3rd ed. 1700. LEI; 4th ed. 1708, *and* 5th ed. 1714. *See* B57

A37 BARROW, Isaac, 1630–1677. (1655) Euclidis elementorum libri XV. *See* A164, *and* B340 Euclid

A38 BARTHOLOMEW, *Anglicus, fl.* 1230–1250. Medieval lore from Bartholomew Anglicus. By Robert Steele... De la More Pr., 1905. [Selections from 'De proprietatibus rerum', 1535 ed.] LEI

A39 BELLAMY, Edward, *translator.* (1698) Examen de ingenios. *See* A229 Huarte de San Juan

BELLIUS, Martin, *pseud. See* Chateillon, S.

BERNEVILLE, Marie Cathérine Jumel de, *comtesse d'Aulnoy. See* Aulnoy, *comtesse d'.*

A40 BIBLE. *Old Testament. Proverbs.* Solomon's proverbs, English and Latin, alphabetically collected for help of memory. In English by H.D. [i.e. Henry Danvers] and since made Latin by S. Perkins... 1684. NoU

A41 BIRMINGHAM. Free school. (1552) The charter of the free school for the inhabitants of Birmingham, founded and endowed by King Edward the Sixth, 2d January 1552. Longman, 1830. HU

A42 BONCLE, Seth, *ed.* Vestibulum technicum. 1682. *See* A389 Vestibulum

A43 BOORDE, Andrew, 1490?–1549. (1542?) The wisdom of Andrew Boorde. Edited... by H. Edmund Poole... Leicester, Backus, 1936. [An abridged version of the 'Dyetary of health'.] LEI

A44 BOSSUET, Jacques Bénigne, 1627–1704. (1681) Discours sur l'histoire universelle... Edition augmentée des variantes. Paris, Librarie de Hautcoeur, 1826. LEI

A45 BOSSUET, J. B. (Written 1670–9) Lettres sur l'éducation du Dauphin... Introduction et notes de E. Lévesque. Paris, Bossard, 1920. LEI

A46 BOYER, Abel, 1667–1729. (1694) The complete French master. 19th ed. 1761, *and* 24th ed. 1779. *See* B139

A47 BOYER, Abel. (1699) Le dictionnaire royal. Nlle. éd. 1773. *See* B140

A47a BRIGGS, Henry, 1561–1630. Mathematical tables. 1705. *See* B958 Sherwin, H.

A48 BRINSLEY, John, 1564?–16–? (1622) A consolation for our grammar schooles... New York, Scholars' facsimiles and reprints, 1943. BR CA HU LEE LEI LO NE NO RE SH

A49 BRINSLEY, John. (1612) Ludus literarius, or the grammar schoole. T. Man, 1612. OX; 1627. ReU

A50 BRINSLEY, John. Ludus literarius... Edited... by E. T. Campagnac. Liverpool U.P., 1917. [Reprint of 1627 ed.] HU LEI LO RE ReU SO

A50a BROWN, Thomas, 1663–1704, *trans.* (1695) A new and easy method to understand the Roman history... Done out of the French [of the abbé de Fourcroy], with very large additions and amendments, by T. Brown. 1697. NoU; *another ed.* [1731?] *See* B400

A51 BROWNE (*or* Brown), Richard, *English master at Rugby.* (1700) The English school reformed. 7th ed. 1722. *See* B152

BRUNI, Leonardo, *d'Arezzo. See* Aretinus

A52 BUGENHAGEN, Johann, 1485–1558. (1531) Der Keyserliken Stadt Lübeck Christlike Ordeninge. (*in* Heppe, H., Das Schulwesen des Mittelalters. Marburg, Elwert, 1860.) LEI

A53 BURGERSDYCK, Franco, 1590–1629. (Eng. ed. 1637) Institutionum logicarum libri duo. Ad juventutem Cantabrigiensem. Cambridge, J. Hayes, 1680. LEI

A54 BURNET, Gilbert, 1643–1715. (Written *c.* 1668) Thoughts on education. 1761. *See* B160

A55 [BUSBY, Richard], 1606–1695. (1647?) Graecae grammatices rudimenta, in usum scholae Westmonasteriensis. J. Redmayne, 1671. LEI; 1689. NoU; 1707. *See* B163

A56 [BUSBY, Richard]. Grammatica Busbeiana. 1702; *and another ed.* 1789. *See* B164

A57 [BUSBY, Richard]. Rudimentum grammaticae Latinae metricum. 1729. *See* B165; *another ed.* 1810. *See* D166

A58 BUXTORF, Johannes, 1564–1629. (3rd ed. 1617) Epitome grammaticae Hebraeae... ad publicum scholarum usum proposita... Ed. 3a. Basle, 1617. NoU

A59 BUXTORF, Johannes, do., *another ed.*, 1716. *See* B174

A60 BUXTORF, Johannes. (1609) Thesaurus grammaticus linguae sanctae Hebraeae... Ed. quinta. Basle, impensis haered. Ludovici Regis, 1651. LEI

CALASANZIO, Jose, *saint. See* Jose, *saint*

A61 CALVIN, Jean, 1509–1564. [Selections.] *See* A437 Eby, F., *ed.*

A62 CAMBRIDGE. University. (1679) A projecte conteyninge the state, order and manner of governemente of the University of Cambridge: as now it is to be seen in the three and fortieth yeare of the raigne of our most Gracious and Soveraigne Lady Queen Elizabeth. Cambridge, 1679. BR

A63 CAMBRIDGE. University. *St. John's college.* Admissions to the college of St. John the Evangelist in the University of Cambridge. Part 1. January 1629/30–July 1665. C.U.P., 1882. LO

A64 [CAMDEN, William], 1551–1623. (1595) Institutio Graecae grammatices compendiaria, in usum scholae Westmonasteriensis. 1608. NoU; *another ed.* 1656. NoU; *another ed.* 1658. NoU; *another ed.* 1681. NoU

A65 [CAMDEN, William], do., *other eds.* 1701, 1725, 1763, 1779, 1793. *See* B175–176

A66 [CAMDEN, William]. Camdenus illustratus. 4th ed. 1750. *See* B177

A67 CASA, Giovanni della, 1503–1556. (1558) Galateo . . . From the Italian [by Richard Graves]. 1774. *See* B186

A68 CASAUBON, Meric, 1599–1671, *ed.* (1651) Publ. Terentii comoediae VI. 1681. *See* A380 Terence

CASTALIO, Sebastian. *See* Chateillon, Sebastien

A69 CASTIGLIONE, *conte* Baldassare, 1478–1529. (It. 1528; Eng. 1561) The book of the courtier. [Translation by Sir Thomas Hoby.] Dent, 1928, repr. 1948. HU LEE LEI NO RE SH SO

A70 CATHOLICON Anglicum: an English–Latin wordbook, dated 1483. Edited . . . by S. J. H. Heritage. Trübner for E.E.T.S., 1881. LEI

A71 CATO, Dionysius. Cato construed; or, a familiar and easie interpretation upon Catos morall verses. First doen in Laten and Frenche by Maturinus Corderius, and now newly englished . . . A. Maunsell, 1584. NoU

A72 CATO, Dionysius. Catonis disticha de moribus . . . [with translation by C. Hoole] . . . 1722; *and another ed.* 1749. *See* B190

A73 CAXTON, William, 1422?–1491. (1477?) Book of curtesye. Edited by F. J. Furnivall. E.E.T.S., 1868, repr. 1932. LEI

A74 CAXTON, William. The book of curtesye . . . [Facsimile ed.] Cambridge, 1907. NoU

A75 CELLARIUS, Christophorus, 1638–1707. (1686?) Geographia antiqua recognita denuo . . . [Edited by S. Patrick]. Ed. altera. 1745. *See* B191

CHALES, Claude François Milliet de. *See* Milliet de Chales, Claude François

A76 CHARLES II, *king of England. Charters.* The charter . . . impowering Erasmus Smith Esq., to erect grammar schools in . . . Ireland . . . 1724. *See* B200

A77 CHARRON, Pierre, 1541–1603. (Fr. 1601; Eng. 1697) Of wisdom . . . Made English by George Stanhope. 2nd ed. 1707. *See* B201

A78 CHÂTEILLON (*or* Castalio), Sebastien, 1515–1563. (1552?) Youth's scripture-remembrancer . . . Now attempted in an English dress . . . by D. Bellamy. 1743. *See* B202

Children's petition. *See* Lex Forcia

Christianis litteratum magistris de ratio discendi. *See* Jouvency, Joseph de

A79 [CLARK (*or* Clarke), John], *fl.* 1630–1650. (1629?) Formulae oratoriae in usum scholarum concinnatae . . . Accessit Dux poeticus . . . Ed. undecima. 1672. NoU

A80 [CLARK (*or* Clarke), John]. (1638) Phraseologia puerilis; sive elegantiae sermonis Latine pariter atque Anglicani . . . or, Selected Latine and English phrases . . . 4th ed. enl. by the author . . . and W.R. J.R. for Francis Eglesfield, 1670. HU

Clavis Homerica. *See* Roberti, Antonius

A81 CLERK, William. A dictionarie in English and Latine for children. Now augmented by W. Clerk. 1616. *See* A421 Withals, J.

A82 CLUVER, Philipp, 1580–1622. (1624) Introductionis in universam geographiam, tam veterem quam novam, libri VI. Leyden, Elzevir, 1629. LEE

A83 COCKER, Edward, 1631–1675. (1678) Arithmetick: being a plain and familiar method . . . Perused and published by John Hawkins . . . [22nd ed.] Tracy, 1697. NoU

A84 COCKER, Edward, do., 29th ed. 1711; 37th ed. 1720; 44th ed. [172–]; 45th ed. [1731]; 46th ed. [1736?]; 55th ed. 1758. *See* B231

A85 COCKER, Edward. (1685) Decimal arithmetick. 3rd ed. 1703; 5th ed. 1720; 6th ed. 1729. *See* B232

A86 COCKER, Edward. (1704) English dictionary. 2nd ed. 1715; 3rd ed. 1724. *See* B233

A87 COCKER, Edward. (1675) Morals, or, the Muses spring-garden . . . 1675. NoU

A88 COCKER, Edward. (1672) Multum in parvo, or the pen's gallantry. Invented, written and engraved by Edward Cocker. [*ca.* 1680.] NoU

A89 COCKER, Edward. (1661) Penna volans; or, the young man's accomplishment. [1661.] NoU

A90 COCKER, Edward. (1667?) The clarks tutor . . . being the remains of . . . E. Wingate . . . With a convenient copy book . . . By E. Cocker. 1671. NoU

A91 COLES, Elisha, 1640?–1680. (1677) A dictionary, English–Latin, and Latin–English . . . 3rd ed. R.E. for Tho. Guy, 1692. LEI

A92 COLES, Elisha. (1676) An English dictionary . . . 1717; *and another ed.* 1732. *See* B235

A93 COMENIUS, John Amos (*otherwise* Jan Amos Komensky), 1592–1670. Opera didactica omnia. Amsterdam, 1657. ReU

A94 COMENIUS, J. A. Opera didactica omnia. Editio anni 1657 lucis ope expressa. Prague, Academia Scientiarum Bohemoslovenica, 1957. 3 vols. [Facsimile of the 1657 Amsterdam ed.] HU LO

A95 COMENIUS, J. A. Veškeré spisy. Vydává Ustředni spolek jednot učitelských na Moravě. (Vols. 1, 4, 9, 10, 17.) Brno, 1912–1938. 5 vols. LEI

Sv. I: Problemata miscellanea. Sylloge quaestionum controversarum. Theatrum universitatis rerum. Physicae synopsis. Pansophiae prodromus. Conatuum pansophicorum dilucidatio. Faber fortunae. 1914

Sv. IV, oddil 2: Didactica magna. Informatorium scholae materna. 2nd ed., 1938

Sv. IX: De studii pansophici impedimentis. Laborum scholasticorum in illustri Patakino gymnasio Continuatio. Vydání spisu Fortiova a Erasmova. Fortius redivivus. Praecepta morum. Leges scholae bene ordinatae. Schola ludus. Coronis. 1915

Sv. X: Orbis pictus. 1929

Sv. XVII: Rád Jednoty. Haggaeus. Otázky o Jednotě. Ohlášeni. Cesta pokoje. 1912

A96 COMENIUS, J. A. [Selections]. Comenius, [edited] by M. W. Keatinge. New York, McGraw, 1931. HU ReU

A97 COMENIUS, J. A. Selections. Introduction by Jean Piaget. Paris, Unesco, 1957. CA LEI RE

A98 COMENIUS, J. A. [Didactica magna]. (1657) Lehrkunst; herausg. von J. Leutbecher. Leipzig, Baensch, 1855. LO

A99 COMENIUS, J. A. The great didactic. [Edited by] M. W. Keatinge. Black, 1896. BI LEE NE NO SH; 2nd ed, 1910. HU LEI LO RE SO; 1921. SH

A100 COMENIUS, J. A. La grande didactique: introduction et traduction par J. Piobetta. Paris, P.U.F., 1952. LO SO

A101 COMENIUS, J. A. (1631) Janua aurea reserata quatuor linguarum, sive compendiosa methodus Latinam, Germanicam, Gallicam et Italicam linguam perdiscendi. [—], Elsevir, 1640. LO; another ed., J. de Tournes, 1643. OX

A102 COMENIUS, J. A. Janua linguarum reserata ... The gate of languages unlocked ... formerly translated by Tho. Horn: afterwards much corrected and amended by Joh. Robotham: now carefully reviewed by W. D. To which is premised a Portal. W. Slater, 1650. LEE NoU

A103 COMENIUS, J. A. Janua linguarum trilinguis; sive Johannis-Amos Comenii Janua linguarum novissime ab ipso authore recognita, aucta, emendata: adjunctis metaphrasi graeca et anglicana versione. Daniel, 1662. LEE; 1670. NoU

A104 COMENIUS, J. A. Janua linguarum, cum versione Anglicana. 1665. ReU

A105 COMENIUS, J. A. Janua linguarum reserata, cum Graeca versione Theodori Simonii Holrati, innumeris in locis emendata a Stephano Curcellaeo ... Amsterdam, D. Elzevir, 1665. HU

A106 COMENIUS, J. A. Eerste deel der schoolgeleertheyd, genoemt het portael ... Amsterdam, 1673. NoU

A107 COMENIUS, J. A. Vestibulum ... wherein the sense of Janua linguarum is contained. 1682. See A389 Vestibulum technicum

A108 COMENIUS, J. A. [Linguarum methodus novissima]. (1648) The analytical didactic ... Translated from the Latin with introduction and notes by V. Jelinek. Chicago, Univ. of Chicago Pr., 1953. [Chap. X of the main work.] BI HU LEE NE NO RE SH SO

A109 COMENIUS, J. A. (Written 1623) The labyrinth of the world and the paradise of the heart, edited and translated by Count Lützow. 2nd ed., Sonnenschein, 1902. LEE LO SH

A110 COMENIUS, J. A., do., another ed. Translated by M. Spinka. Chicago, National Union of Czechoslovak Protestants in America, 1942. LEI

A111 COMENIUS, J. A. [Orbis pictus]. (1653) An incomplete Orbis pictus ... printed in 1653. Edited ... by G. H. Turnbull. [Reprinted from Acta Comeniana, vol. 1, pt. 1, 1957.] HU SH

A112 COMENIUS, J. A. Orbis sensualium pictus quadrilinguis ... pictura et nomenclatura, germanica, latina, italica et gallica ... Nuremberg, 1679. NoU

A113 COMENIUS, J. A. Orbis sensualium pictus ... Joh. Amos Comenius's Visible world ... Translated into English by Charles Hoole. 1682. NoU

A114 COMENIUS, J. A., do., 11th ed., 1729, and 12th ed., 1777. See B237

A115 COMENIUS, J. A. Orbis pictus. Prague, J. Pospisila, 1896. LO

A116 COMENIUS, J. A. Neuer Orbis pictus für die Jugend ... eingerichtet von J.E.G. 1842. See D519 Gayler, J. E.

A117 COMENIUS, J. A. (1639–1643) The Pansophiae diatyposis and its continuation. [Reprinted from Acta Comeniana, vol. 1, pt. 2, 1957. Includes: Templi sapientiae. Templi pansophici delineatio scenographica. Scenographiae pansophicae pars II.] HU SH

A118 COMENIUS, J. A. (1643) Two pansophical works: 1. Praecognita. 2. Janua rerum (1643); edited by G. H. Turnbull. Prague, Ceská Akademia, 1851. LEE ReU SH

A119 COMENIUS, J. A. (1645) Rules of life. Mallalieu, 1865. BR LEE NE

A120 COMENIUS, J. A. (1656) Schola ludus, seu encyclopaedia viva, h.e. januae linguarum praxis comica ... Amsterdam, 1657. NoU

A121 COMENIUS, J. A. Scholarum novi ordinis formator. Prague, Státní Pedagogické Nakladatelství, 1957. LO

A122 COMENIUS, J. A. (Written 1628) The school of infancy. An essay on the education of youth during their first six years ... Mallalieu, 1858. BI LO

A123 COMENIUS, J. A., do., another ed. Edited ... by W. S. Monroe. Boston, Heath, 1896. LEE

A124. COMENIUS, J. A., do., another ed. Edited by E. M. Eller. Chapel Hill, Univ. of N. Carolina Pr., 1956. CA HU LEI LO RE SH

A125 COMENIUS, J. A. (Written 1641) The way of light; translated by E. T. Campagnac. Liverpool U.P., 1938. LEE LO RE

A126 COMMANDINE, Frederico, 1509–1575, trans. Euclide's Elements. See B341–342 Euclid Considerations concerning free schools. See Wase, Christopher

A127 CONYBEARE, John, fl. 1580–1594. Letters and exercises of the Elizabethan schoolmaster John Conybeare ... Edited by F. C. Conybeare. Frowde, 1905. BR HU ReU

A128 CORDIER, Mathurin, 1479/80–1564. Cato construed; or, a familiar and easie interpretation upon Catos morall verses. First doen into Laten and Frenche by Maturinus Corderius, and now newly englished ... Maunsell, 1584. NoU

A129 CORDIER, Mathurin. (1564) Maturinus Corderius's School-colloquies English and Latine, divided into several clauses; wherein the propriety of both languages is kept . . . By Charles Hoole. S. Griffin for the Company of Stationers, 1657. HU

A130 CORDIER, Mathurin. Corderii colloquiorum centuria selecta . . . By John Clarke. 1718; 5th ed., 1730; 26th ed., 1783. *See* B252

A131 CORDIER, Mathurin. Une centurie des colloques de Cordier . . . [Edited by John Stirling.] 1739. *See* B253

A132 CORDIER, Mathurin. Colloquiorum Maturini Corderii centuria una . . . Amsterdam, 1742. *See* B254

A133 COURCELLES, Stephen, 1586–1658, *ed.* Janua linguarum reserata . . . innumeris in locis emendata a Stephano Curcellaeo . . . 1665. *See* A105 Comenius, J. A.

A134 CULMANN, Leonhard, 1497–*post* 1549. (1554) Sententiae pueriles, Anglo–Latinae. [Translated by] C. Hoole. 1717; *and another ed.*, 1728. *See* B263

A135 DANET, Pierre, d. 1709. (Eng. 1700) A complete dictionary of the Greek and Roman antiquities . . . J. Nicholson, 1700. NoU

A135a DANET, Pierre, *ed.* (1675?) Fabulorum Aesopiarum libri quinque . . . 1722. *See* B267 Phaedrus

A136 DANVERS, Henry, d. 1687, *ed.* (1676) Solomon's proverbs, English and Latin, alphabetically collected for help of memory. In English by H.D. and since made Latin by S. Perkins . . . 1684. NoU

D'AULNOY, *comtesse. See* Aulnoy, Marie Cathérine Jumel de Berneville, *comtesse d'*

A137 DEFOE, Daniel, 1661?–1731. (1697) An essay upon projects. Cassell, 1887. [Includes 'Of academies'.] LEI

A138 [DELAMOTHE, N. G.] (1592) The French alphabet . . . together with The Treasure of the French tongue . . . A. Miller, 1647. NoU
DESAINLIENS, Claude. *See* Holyband, C.

A139 DESCARTES, René, 1596–1650. (1637) The geometry of . . . Translated from the French and Latin by David Eugene Smith and Marcia L. Latham; with a facsimile of the first edition, 1637. N.Y., Dover, 1954. LEI SO
Dictionarie in English and Latine for children. *See* Withals, John

A140 DICTIONARIUM etymologicum, philologicum, phraseologicumque . . . Cui annectuntur a fronte, Catalogus auctorum nomina recensens: a calce, Dictionarium propria nomina complectens . . . Jo. Field, 1664. HU

A141 DICTIONARIUM historico-geographico-poeticum: in quo debita serie tractantur propria nomina . . . Una cum minutiorum tractatuum appendicibus non contemnendis. Jo. Field, 1664. HU
Dives pragmaticus. *See* Newbery, Thomas

A142 [DODWELL, Henry], 1641–1711. (1692) Praelectiones academicae in schola historices Camdeniana. Cum appendice. Oxford, Sheldonian theatre, 1692. LEI

A143 [DORRINGTON, Theophilus], d. 1715. (1692–1695) The excellent woman described by her true character and their opposites. Watts, 1692, [&] Wyat, 1695. 2 vols. LO

A144 DUGARD (*or* Du-Gard), William, 1606–1662. (1654) Graecae grammatices rudimenta; in usum Scholae Mercatorum Sciss. 1654. NoU

A145 DUGARD, William. (1648) Rhetorices elementa, quaestionibus et responsibus explicata . . . Ed. sexta. 1660. NoU

A146 DURY (*or* Durie), John, 1596–1680. (1649–1650) The reformed-school: and The reformed librarie-keeper . . . By John Durie. Rob. Littleberrie, 1651. [Typescript copy, page for page and line for line.] HU

A147 DURY, John. The reformed school; edited by H. M. Knox. Liverpool U.P., 1957. CA HU LEE LEI NO SH

A148 EACHARD (*or* Echard), Laurence, 1670?–1730, *trans.* Terence's Comedies made English. 1694. *See* A381 Terence

A149 EDWARD VI, *king of England. Charters.* The charter of the Free school . . . of Birmingham . . . 1552. *See* A41 Birmingham

A150 ELYOT, *Sir* Thomas, 1499?–1546. (1531) The boke named The Governour. New ed. by A. T. Eliot. Newcastle, J. Hervarian, 1834. RE

A151 ELYOT, *Sir* Thomas, do., *another ed.* Edited from the first edition of 1531 by H. H. S. Croft. Kegan Paul, 1883. 2 vols. LO

A152 ELYOT, *Sir* Thomas, do., *another ed.* With introduction by Foster Watson. Dent (pref. 1907). BI HU LEE LEI LO SH SO

A153 ENGLISH. (1683) An English introduction to the Latin tongue, for the use of the lower forms in Westminster School. E. Redmayne, 1683. NoU

A154 ENGLISH, do., *another ed.*, 1704. *See* B329 Epigrammatum delectus. *See* Nicole, Pierre, *comp.*

A155 ERASMUS, Desiderius, 1466?–1536. Desiderius Erasmus concerning the aim and method of education, by W. H. Woodward. C.U.P., 1904. [Contains translations of 'De ratione studii', 'De pueris instituendis', and extracts from other works.] BI HU LEE LEI LO NE NO RE SH

A156 ERASMUS, Desiderius. (1516) Colloquia. Nunc emendatior. Cum omnium notis. Amsterdam, L. Elzevir, 1650. LEI

A157 ERASMUS, Desiderius. Colloquia familiaria. Cum omnium notis. Amsterdam, Jo. Lausonius, 1635. HU

A158 ERASMUS, Desiderius. Colloquia selecta . . . with an English translation . . . By John Clarke. 14th ed., 1757; 19th ed., 1775; 20th ed., 1782. *See* B334

A159 ERASMUS, Desiderius. The colloquies of . . . concerning men, manners and things. Translated into English by N. Bailey, and edited . . . by E. Johnson. Gibbings, 1900. 3 vols. LEI

A160 ERASMUS, Desiderius. [Letters]. (1511–1527) Erasmus and Cambridge. The Cambridge letters of Erasmus, translated by D. F. S. Thomson. [Edited] by H. C. Porter. Toronto, Toronto U.P., 1963. LEI

A161 ERASMUS, Desiderius. [De pueris instituendis]. (1529) The education of children, translated by Richard Sherry. *See* A368 Sherry, R.

A162 ERASMUS, Desiderius. (1531) Züchtiger Sitten, zierlichen Wandels und höfflicher Geberden der Jugent . . . Nach der kürtze so vil der gemeynen Jugent dienlich new verteutscht. [Colophon: Getruckt zu Strassbur bey Hans Preussen. Im Weinmont. MDXXXI.] Berlin, Erasmusdruck, [1938]. [Facsimile reprint.] LEI

A163 ERONDELL, Peter. [Selections from The French garden]. *See* A435 Byrne, M. St. C., *ed.*

A164 EUCLID. Euclidis elementorum libri XV breviter demonstrati, opera Is. Barrow. Cambridge, 1655. NoU

A165 EUCLID. The elements of Euclid explain'd by C. F. M. de Chales . . . done into English . . . Oxford, 1685. NoU

Excellent woman described. *See* Dorrington, T.

A165a FABER, Tanaquil (*otherwise* Tannaguy Lefebvre), 1615–1672. A compendious way of teaching ancient and modern languages. [Edited] by J. T. Philipps. *See* B821 Philipps, J. T.

A166 FAMILIARES. (1677) Familiares colloquendi formulae. Ed. 23a. 1724. *See* B350

A167 FARNABY, Thomas, 1575?–1647. [Index rhetoricus]. (1625) Maximam partem ex Indice rhetorico Farnabii deprompta . . . 13th ed., 1737. *See* B351

A168 FARNABY, Thomas. (1641) Systema grammaticum. 1641. NoU

A169 FARNABY, Thomas. (1651) Publ. Terentii Comoediae VI, cum notis Th. Farnaby . . . 1681. *See* A380 Terence

A170 FENELON, François de Salignac de la Mothe-, 1651–1715. (1699) The adventures of Telemachus . . . Done into English. 1766. *See* B355

A171 FENELON, F. de S. de la M.-. (1687) De l'éducation des filles. Paris, P. Aubouin, 1687. OX

A172 FENELON, F. de S. de la M.-., do., Nlle éd. Paris, 1719. *See* B356

A173 FENELON, F. de S. de la M.-. Instructions for the education of a daughter. Translated . . . by George Hickes. 1707; 1713; 1721; 1750; 1797. *See* B357–358

A174 FENELON, F. de S. de la M.-. Treatise on the education of daughters. Translated . . . by T. F. Dibdin. 1805. *See* C446

A175 FENELON, F. de S. de la M.-. On the education of daughters. 1812. *See* C447

A176 FENELON, F. de S. de la M.-. De l'éducation des filles; publié . . . par Armand Gaste. Paris, Belin, 1884. LO

A177 FENELON, F. de S. de la M.-., do., *another ed.* Paris, Firmin-Didot, 1892. LEI

A178 FENELON, F. de S. de la M.-., do., *another ed.* Publié . . . par A. Cherel. Paris, Hachette, 1920. HU

A179 FENELON, F. de S. de la M.-., do., *another ed.* Publié . . . par P. Rousselet. Paris, Delagrave, 1922. RE

A180 FENELON, F. de S. de la M.-. Nouveaux dialogues des morts . . . 1727. *See* B359

A181 FENELON, F. de S. de la M.-. Pious reflections . . . 1823. *See* D438

A182 FENELON, F. de S. de la M.-. Tales and fables . . . 1736. *See* B360

A183 FESTEAU, Paul, *fl.* 1667–1693. (1667) Nouvelle grammaire françoise . . . 4ème éd. Londres, Newcomb, 1679. NoU

A184 FIFTEENTH century school book: from a manuscript in the British Museum (MS Arundel 240). Edited by William Nelson. Oxford, Clarendon Pr., 1956. [Passages for translation into Latin, written down by a teacher of grammar at Magdalen School, Oxford, *ca.* 1494–95, with specimens of Latin versions.] CA HU LEE LEI NE RE ReU SO

A185 FLEURY, Claude, 1640–1723. (1687?) Traité du choix et de la méthode des études. Brussels, Fricx, 1687. LO

A186 FLEURY, Claude, do., Nlle. éd. corr. 1740. *See* B385

A187 FONTAINE, Jean (*otherwise* Johannes Fontanus). (1605) Hortulus puerorum pergratus ac perutilis, latinè discentibus . . . Petit jardin, pour les enfants, fort agréable & profitable pour aprendre le latin . . . Paris, P. L. Febvrier, 1617. ReU
Formulae oratoriae in usum scholarum concinnatae. *See* Clark, John.

A188 [FOURCROY, *abbé de*] (Eng. 1695) A new and easy method to understand the Roman history . . . by way of dialogue, for the use of the Duke of Burgundy. Done out of French, with very large additions and amendments, by T. Brown. R. Wellington, 1617 [i.e. 1697]. NoU; *another ed.* [17–]. *See* B400

A189 [FOURCROY, *abbé de*]. Méthode pour apprendre facilement l'histoire romaine. [170–?]. *See* B399

A190 [FRANKLIN (*or* Francklin), Richard]. (1633) Orthotonia, seu tractatus de tonis in lingua graecanica . . . Scriptus per R.F. . . . et nunc secundum in lucem editus. 1633. NoU

A190a FREIND, John, 1675–1728, *ed.* (1696?) Aeschinous Ho Kata Ktesiphontos, *kai* Demosthenou Ho peri Stephanou logos . . . 1715. *See* B11 Aeschines
French alphabet. *See* Delamothe, N. G.

A191 FUGGER, Wolffgang, *fl.* 1551–1553. (1553) Handwriting manual entitled A practical and well-grounded formulary for divers fair hands . . . Translated by Frederick Plaat . . . O.U.P., 1960. LEI

A192 FULLER, Thomas, 1608–1661. (1655) The history of the University of Cambridge. 1840. *See* C500

A192a GALFRIDUS, *grammaticus.* Promptorium parvulorum. *See* A354

A193 GARRETSON, John. (1683) English exercises. 15th ed., 1719, *and* 19th ed., 1743. *See* B408

A193a GAUTRUCHE [*or* Gaultruche, Galtruchius], Pierre, 1602–1681. (1668) . . . Mathematicae totius . . . clara, brevis & accurata institutio. In gratiam studiosae juventutis adornata. M. Clarke for R. Green, 1683. HU
Gentleman's calling. *See* Allestree, R.

A194 GILBERT, *Sir* Humphrey, 1539?–1583. (*c.* 1570?) Queen Elizabethe's Achademy... Edited by F. J. Furnivall. E.E.T.S., 1869. LEI OX

GLANVILLE, Bartholomew de, *fl.* 1230–1250. *See* Bartholomew, *Anglicus*

A195 GOBINET, Charles. (Fr. 1687) The instruction of youth in Christian piety. 1803. *See* C529

A196 GODWYN, Thomas, d. 1642. (1614) Romanae historiae anthologia recognita et aucta. An English exposition of the Roman antiquities... for the use of Abingdon schoole. Newly revised and inlarged by the author. Oxford, Cripps, 1631. LEE; do., 1642. HU; London, Cripps, 1661. LEI; 1674. NoU

A197 GORDON, Patrick, 1635–1699. (1693) Geography anatomiz'd. 11th ed., 1728, *and* 13th ed., 1733. *See* B455

A198 GRACIAN, Baltasar, 1601–1658. (1647?) The oracle: a manual of the art of discretion. 'Oraculo manual y arte de prudencia.' The Spanish text and a new English translation... [Ed.] by L. B. Walton. Dent, 1953. LEI

Gradus ad Parnassum... Ab uno e Societate Jesu. *See* Aler, P.

Graecae grammatices rudimenta in usum Scholae Westmonasteriensis. *See* Busby, R.

A199 GRANT, Edward, 1540?–1601, *ed.* Disertissimi viri Rogeri Aschamum... familiarum epistolarum libri tres... [1576.] *See* Ascham, R.

Greek and Roman history illustrated by coins and medals. *See* Walker, Obadiah

Guardian's instructions. *See* Penton, Stephen

A200 GUARINO, Battista, 1434?–?1460. (1459) De ordine docendi et studendi. *See* A450 Woodward, W. H., *ed.*

A201 GUAZZO, Stefano, 1530–1593. (It. 1574; Eng. 1581–1586) The civile conversation... The first three books translated by George Pettie, anno 1581, and the fourth by Barth. Young, anno 1586. With an introduction by Sir Edward Sullivan. Constable, 1925. 2 vols. LEE LEI

A202 GUEVARA Y DE NORONA, Antonio de, 1480?–1545. (Sp. 1529; Eng. 1557) The diall of princes. Translated by Sir Thomas North. Being select passages... [ed.] by K. N. Colvile. P. Allan, 1919. LEI

A203 GUILLAUME, de Tournai. (*c.* 1250) The De instructione puerorum of William of Tournai, [edited by] James A. Corbett. Notre Dame, Indiana, Mediaeval Institute, 1955. HU LEI

A204 HALE, *Sir* Matthew, 1609–1676. (Written *c.* 1673) The counsels of a father. 1821. *See* D587

A205 HALIFAX, George Savile, *marquis of*, 1633–1695. (1688) The lady's new-year gift... 11th ed., 1734. *See* B483

A206 HALL, John, 1627–1656. (1649) The advancement of learning. Edited by A. K. Croston. Liverpool U.P., 1953. HU LEE LEI NO SH

A207 HALL, Thomas, 1610?–1665. (1654?) Vindiciae literarum, the school guarded: or, the excellency and usefulness of humane learning in subordination to divinity... Whereunto is added, an examination of John Websters delusive Examen of academies. Webb, [etc.], 1655. LEE

A207a HALLEY, Edmund, 1656–1742. Mathematical tables. 1705. *See* B958 Sherwin, H.

A208 HAWKINS, John, d. 1692. Cocker's arithmetick... perused and published by John Hawkins. *See* A83 Cocker, E.; B231 Cocker, E.

A209 HAWKINS, John. Cocker's decimal arithmetick. *See* B232 Cocker, E.

A210 HEEREBORD, Adrian. (1651?) 'ΕΡΜΗΝΕΊΑ logica, seu synopseos logicae burgersdicianae explicatio... Ed. nova... Accedit... Praxis logica. Cambridge, J. Hayes, 1680. LEI

A211 HERBERT, Edward, *1st baron Herbert of Cherbury*, 1583–1648. A dialogue between a tutor and his pupil. 1768. *See* B508

A212 HERNE, Samuel. (1677) Domus carthusiana; or, an account of the most noble foundation of the Charter-house... in London... with the life and death of Thomas Sutton Esq., the founder thereof... Marriott, 1677. BI

A213 HEWES (*otherwise* Huise), John, *fl.* 1624–1633. (1633) Florilegium phrasicon. Inlarged... by A. Ross. 1650. NoU

History of the seven champions of Christendom. *See* Johnson, Richard

A213a HILL, Joseph, 1625–1707, *ed.* (1663) Cornelii Schrevelii Lexicon manuale. 1774. *See* B933 Schrevelius, C.

A214 HOADLEY, Samuel, 1643–1705. (1683?) The natural method of teaching. 9th ed., 1737. *See* B520

A215 HOBY, *Sir* Thomas, 1530–1566, *trans.* The book of the courtier. *See* A69 Castiglione

A216 HOLDSWORTH, Richard, 1590–1649. Directions for a student in the universitie. [Printed from a MS. in Emmanuel Coll., Cambridge, in Fletcher, H. F. The intellectual development of John Milton. Vol. 2. 1961.] LEI

A217 HOLYBAND, Claudius, *originally* Claude de Sainliens, *fl.* 1564–1593. (1566, probably in error for 1576) The French Littelton. The edition of 1609. With an introduction by M. St. Clare Byrne. C.U.P., 1953. BR HU LEE LEI NO RE

A218 HOLYBAND, Claudius. [Selections from The French schoolemaister, The French Littelton, and Campo di fior.] *See* A435 Byrne, M. St. C., *ed.*

A219 HOOLE, Charles, 1610–1667. (1656) The common accidence examined and explained. 5th ed., 1661. NoU

A220 HOOLE, Charles, do., *another ed.*, 1757. *See* B530

A221 HOOLE, Charles. (1660) A new discovery of the old art of teaching schoole, in four small treatises. Edited by E. T. Campagnac. Liverpool U.P., 1913. BR HU LEE LO SO

A222 HOOLE, Charles. (1650) Terminationes ex exempla declinationum & conjugationum... 1752. *See* B531

A223 HOOLE, Charles, *ed. and trans.* (1659) Catonis disticha de moribus... [etc.] [with translations by] C. Hoole. 1722; *and another ed.*, 1749. *See* B532

A224 HOOLE, Charles. (1663?) Publ. Terentii Comoediae sex, Anglo-Latinae; in usum ludi-discipulorum . . . Six comedies, in English and Latine . . . By Charles Hoole. Company of Stationers, 1663. HU

A225 HOOLE, Charles. (1658) Orbis sensualium pictus . . . Joh. Amos Comenius's Visible world . . . Translated into English by Charles Hoole . . . 1682. NoU

A226 HOOLE, Charles, do., 11th ed., 1729, and 12th ed., 1777. See B533

A226a HOOLE, Charles. (1657) Maturinus Corderius's School-colloquies English and Latine . . . By Charles Hoole. Company of Stationers, 1657. HU

A227 HOOLE, Charles. (1658) Sententiae pueriles, Anglo-Latinae. Quae diversis authoribus olim collegerat Leonard Culman; et in vernaculum sermonem nuperrime transtulit Carolus Hoole . . . 1717; and another ed., 1728. See B534

A228 HORMAN, William, d. 1535. (1519) Vulgaria. First printed by Richard Pynson in 1519; now reprinted with an introduction by M. R. James. Oxford, for the Roxburghe Club, 1926. HU

Hortulus puerorum. See Fontaine, J.

A229 HUARTE DE SAN JUAN (otherwise Juan Huarte, or Juan Huarte y Navarro), 1526?–1592. (Sp. 1575; Eng. 1594 and 1698) Examen de ingenios; or, the tryal of wits, discovering the great differences of wits among men, and what sort of learning suits best with each genius. Made English . . . by Mr. Bellamy . . . R. Sare, 1698. LEI

A230 HUARTE DE SAN JUAN, do., another ed., 1734. See B540

HUISE, John, fl. 1624–1633. See Hewes, John

A231 HUME, Alexander, fl. 1574–1630. (c. 1620?) Of the orthographie and congruitie of the Britan tongue; a treates . . . for the schooles. Edited from the original MS. . . . by H. B. Wheatley. E.E.T.S., 1865. HU; 1925 reprint. LEI

A232 IGNATIUS, of Loyola, saint, 1491–1556. St. Ignatius and the 'Ratio studorium', edited by E. A. Fitzpatrick. Translations: The constitutions, part IV, by M. H. Mayer; The Ratio studorium, by A. R. Ball. N.Y., McGraw, 1933. HU

Institutio Graecae grammatices compendiaria. See Camden, W.

A233 ISOCRATES. Logoi kai epistolai. Orationes et epistolae. Cum latina interpretatione Hieronymi Wolfii . . . Editio postrema . . . Cambridge, J. Hayes, 1686. LEI

A234 ISOCRATES. Isocratis Orationes tres . . . item Plutarch Chaeronensis De liberorum educatione libellus & Pythagorae Carmina aurea. Cum annotationibus M. Guilielmi Diezii . . . Ulm, Kühn, 1678. LEI

A235 J., philomath. (1682) A practical grammar, or, the easiest and shortest way to initiate young children in the Latin tongue. Cockerill, 1682. LEE

A236 JANEWAY, James, 1636?–1674. (1671) A token for children. [17–.] See B559; another ed., 1825. See D716

A237 JOHN, of Salisbury, 1115?–1180. The Metalogicon . . . a twelfth-century defense of the verbal and logical arts of the trivium, translated . . . [and edited] by D. McGarry. Berkeley, California U.P., [etc.], 1955. ReU; 1962. HU LEI

A238 [JOHNSON, Richard, 1573–1659?] (c. 1597) History of the seven champions of Christendom. [18–.] See D725

A239 JOSE, de Calasanz, saint, 1556–1648. San Jose de Calasanz: su obra, escritos: estudio pedagógico y selección de escritos por el padre György Santha . . . Madrid, Biblioteca de autores cristianos, 1956. LEI

A240 [JOUVENCY, Joseph de], 1643–1719. (1692?) Christianis litteratum magistris de ratione discendi et docendi. Paris, 1692. NoU

A241 JUSTINUS, Marcus Junianus. . . . Ex Trogi Pompeii historiis externis libri XLIIII. Omnia quam diligentissime ex variorum exemplarium collatione recensita & castigata. E. Horton for W. Whitwood, 1686. HU

A242 K., P. (1686) Nomenclatura trilinguis Anglo-Latino-Graeco. See A325 Nomenclatura; and B775

A243 KAIKA'US IBN ISKANDER, prince of Gurgān. (1082) A mirror for princes: the Qābus nāma . . . Translated from the Persian by Reuben Levy. Cresset Pr., 1951. LEI

Katharinenbuch. See Schneuwly, Peter

A244 KEN, Thomas, 1637–1711. (1674) A manual of prayers for the use of the scholars of Winchester College. (17–?); and 23rd ed., 1728. See B579

A245 KERSEY, John, 1616–1690, ed. Mr. Wingate's arithmetick . . . Inlarged . . . revis'd . . . and improved . . . by John Kersey. 13th ed., [1713]; 15th ed., 1726; 18th ed., 1751; 19th ed., 1760. See B1150–1151 Wingate, E.

KING EDWARD VI SCHOOL, Birmingham. See Birmingham. Free school

A246 KNOX, John, 1505–1572. (Written 156–?) The book of discipline [in his History of the Reformation in Scotland; ed. by W. C. Dickinson. 1949. Vol. 2]. LEI

Ladies calling. See Allestree, R.

A247 LAMY, Bernard, 1640–1715. (167–?) La réthorique; ou, l'art de parler. 5e éd. 1725. See B611

A248 LANCELOT, Claude, 1615?–1695. Mémoires touchant la vie de Monsieur de S. Cyran. 1738. See B612

A249 [LANCELOT, Claude]. (Fr. 1655) Nouvelle méthode pour apprendre facilement la langue grecque. Nlle. éd. 1754. See B613

A250 [LANCELOT, Claude]. A new method of learning with facility the Greek tongue . . . Translated . . . by T. Nugent. 1797. See B616

A251 [LANCELOT, Claude]. The abridgment of the new method of learning . . . the Greek tongue . . . 1749. See B615

A252 [LANCELOT, Claude]. A treatise upon Greek accents. Translated from the Nouvelle méthode grecque. 1729. See B614

A253 [LANCELOT, Claude]. (Fr. 1660) Nouvelle méthode de Messieurs de Port Royal pour apprendre facilement . . . la langue italienne. 4e éd., 1736. *See* B617

A254 [LANCELOT, Claude]. (Fr. 1644) A new method of learning with facility the Latin tongue . . . Translated . . . by T. Nugent. 1803; *and* 1816. *See* D794

LANDRY, Geoffroy de la Tour. *See* La Tour Landry, G.

A255 LANGSTON, John, 1641?–1704. (1675) Lusus poeticus latino-anglicanus, in usum scholarum, or, the more eminent sayings of the Latin poets collected . . . 1675. NoU

A256 LA TOUR LANDRY, Geoffroy de, *fl.* 1371. (Fr. *c.* 1371/2; Eng. 1484) The book of the Knight of the Tower, Landry, which he made for the instruction of his daughters. By way of selection. Now done into English by Alexander Vance. Dublin, Moffatt, [etc.], 1868. LEI

A257 LA TOUR LANDRY, Geoffroy de, do., *another ed.* Translated from the original French into English in the reign of Henry VI, and edited . . . by Thomas Wright. E.E.T.S., 1868. LEI; Rev. ed., 1906. HU

A258 LA TOUR LANDRY, Geoffroy de. The booke of thenseygnementes and techynge that the Knyght of the Toure made to his doughters, edited . . . by G. B. Rawlings. Newnes, 1902. [An abridged reprint of Caxton's translation, 1484.] HU LEI

A259 LA TOUR LANDRY, Geoffroy de. The book of the Knight of La Tour-Landry. Edited by G. S. Taylor. Hamilton, [*c.* 1929?] LEE

A260 LE CLERC, Jean, 1657–1736. (Lat. 1698; Eng. 1699) A compendium of universal history: from the beginning of the world, to the reign of the Emperor Charles the Great. Written originally in Latin. Done into English. Gillyflower, [etc.], 1699. LEI

A261 [LEEDS (*or* Leedes), Edward]. More English examples to be turned into Latin. 2nd ed. (By E.L.). 1688. NoU

A262 LEEDS (*or* Leedes), Edward], do., 14th ed., 1742. *See* B630

LEFEBVRE, Tannaguy. *See* Faber, Tanaquil

A263 LE GRAND, Antoine, d. 1699. (1672) Institutio philosophiae secundum principia D. Renati Descartes . . . in usum juventutis academicae. Ed. 3a. 1675. NoU

A264 LEUSDEN, Jan, 1624–1699. (1675?) Compendium graecum Novi Testamenti. 5th ed. Rob. Clavel, 1691. LO

A265 LEUSDEN, Jan, *ed.* Johannis Buxtorfii Epitome grammaticae . . . emendata a Johanne Leusden. Ed. 4a. 1716. *See* B653

A266 LEX. (1698) Lex Forcia: being an address to the several societies for the reformation of manners . . . That such a care may be taken of the education of young schollars, that a more . . . virtuous disciplining them . . . may be brought into our schools . . . Published and propagated, but not written, by W.C., gent. A Baldwin, [*c.* 1699]. [A revision of 'The Children's petition', 1669.] HU

A267 LEYBOURN, William, 1626–1716. (1667) Arithmetical recreations . . . 2nd ed. H. Brome, 1676. NoU

A268 'A LIBRARY for younger schollers', compiled by an English scholar-priest about 1655. Edited . . . by Alma De Jordy and H. F. Fletcher. Urbana, Univ. of Illinois Pr., 1961. [Compiler may have been Thos. Barlow, bp. of London, and formerly Bodley's Librarian.] HU LEI LO

A269 [LILY, William], 1468?–1522. (*c.* 1540) Brevissima institutio: seu, Ratio grammatices cognoscende, ad omnium utilitatem praescripta, quam solam Regia Maiestas in omnibus scholis profitendam praecipit. Wolf, 1569. NoU

A270 LILY, William, do., *another issue.* Norton, 1663. NoU

A271 LILY, William, do., *another issue.* Oxford, Sheldonian Theatre, 1672. NoU

A272 LILY, William, do., *another issue.* Norton, 1673. NoU

A273 LILY, William, do., '2nd ed.' Oxford, Sheldonian Theatre. 1675. NoU

A274 LILY, William, do., *another ed.* [Edited by John Ward]. 1765. *See* B655

A275 LILY, William. Lilies Rules construed. 9th ed. . . . Whereunto are added T. Robertsons Heteroclites, the Latin syntaxis, Qui mihi. T. Dawson, 1603. NoU

A276 LILY, William, do., *another ed.* Assignes of R. Norton, 1642. NoU

A277 LILY, William. A shorte introduction of grammar. With an introduction by V. J. Flynn. N.Y., Scholars' facsimiles and reprints, 1945. [Facsimile reprint of 1567 ed.] HU LEE LEI SO

A278 LILY, William, do., *another ed.* Oxford, at the Theatre, 1673. NoU

A279 LILY, William, do., *another ed.* Norton, 1673. NoU

A280 LILY, William, do., '2nd ed.'. Oxford, at the Theatre, 1675. NoU

A281 LILY, William, do., '3rd ed.'. Oxford, at the Theater, 1679. LEE

A282 LILY, William, do. Buckley & Longman, 1743; 1753; 1765; 1771; 1784. *See* B657–658

A283 LILY, William, do. [Printed by Edw. Baines, Leeds, *c.* 1800.] *See* D822

A284 LILY, William. Propria quae maribus, Quae genus . . . [Edited by John Ward]. 1763 *and* 1778. *See* B656

A285 LINGUAE Latinae rudimenta concinnata ex Grammatica Lithocomo-Vossiana, in usum gymnasii Roterodami . . . Rotterdam, widow of A. Munnix, 1671. LEI

A286 LITHOCOMUS, Ludolphus, *ed.* (1644?) Grammatica Latine, [by Voss]. *See* A285

A287 LOCKE, John, 1632–1704. On politics and education. Edited by H. R. Penniman. N.Y., Van Nostrand, 1947. HU

A288 LOCKE, John. The educational writings. Edited by J. W. Adamson. E. Arnold, 1912. LO; 2nd ed., C.U.P., 1922. HU LEI NE NO RE SH

A289 LOCKE, John. (1690) An essay concerning human understanding. In four books. 2nd ed., with large additions. A. & J. Churchill, [etc.], 1694. NO

9

A290 LOCKE, John. (1692/3) Some thoughts concerning education. A. & J. Churchill, 1693. BI; 3rd ed., enl., 1695. HU

A291 LOCKE, John, do., *another ed.* [Edited] by E. Daniel. National Society's depository, 1880. BI LO

A292 LOCKE, John, do., *another ed.* Ward, Lock, [188–?] LO

A293 LOCKE, John, do., *another ed.* [Edited] by R. H. Quick. Rev. ed., C.U.P., 1884. BR HU LEE LEI NE RE SH SO

Logique, ou l'art de penser. *See* Arnauld, A., and Nicole, P.

LOYOLA, Ignatius of, *saint. See* Ignatius, *of Loyola, saint*

A294 LUTHER, Martin, 1483–1546. (1524) An die Radherrn aller stedte deutsches lands: das sie Christliche schulen auffrichten und hallten sollen. Wittemberg. M.D.xxiiii. [Facsimile reprint.] Zschopau, Raschke, 1883. LEI

A295 LUTHER, Martin. [Selections]. *See* A437 Eby, F., *ed.*

A296 MAINTENON, Françoise d'Aubigné, *marquise de*, 1635–1719. [Letters, etc.] *See* B678–680

A297 MAKIN, Bathsua, *fl.* 1649–1673. (1673) An essay to revive the ancient education of gentlewomen. T. Parkhurst, 1673. ReU

A298 MAUGER, Claude, *fl.* 1650–1702. (1653) French grammar enriched with 50 new short dialogues... 4th ed., 1662. NoU; 11th ed., Bentley & Magnes, 1684. LEI

A299 MEGGOTT (*or* Meggot), Richard, d. 1692. (1676) A sermon preach'd to those who had been scholars of St. Paul's school, London... St. Paul's Day, 1675/6. 1676. ReU

A300 [MELANCHTHON, Philip], 1497–1560. (152–?) Grammatica graeca... Frankfurt, P. Brubachus, 1544. LO

A301 MILLIET DE CHALES, Claude François, 1611–1678, *ed.* (1672?) The elements of Euclid explained. *See* A165 Euclid

A302 MILTON, John, 1608–1674. (Written 1644; pub. 1673) Tractate on education. A facsimile reprint from the edition of 1673. Edited by Oscar Browning. 1883. BI CA HU LEI LO NE RE SH SO

A303 MILTON, John, do., *another ed.* Edited... by E. E. Morris. Macmillan, 1895. HU LEE LO NE NO SO

A304 MILTON, John. Milton on education. The tractate *Of education*, with supplementary extracts from other writings of Milton; edited... by O. M. Ainsworth. New Haven, Yale U.P., 1928. HU

A305 MILTON, John. Paradise regain'd... with a tractate on education. 1756. *See* B725

Modest plea for infants baptism. *See* Walker, William

A306 MONTAIGNE, Michel Eyquem de, 1533–1592. The teacher's Montaigne, [edited] by G. E. Hodgson. Blackie, 1915. BI NE

A307 MONTOYA, Pedro Lopez de, b. 1542. (1595?) Libro de la buena educacion y enseñança de los nobles. [*In* Los ideas pedagógicas del Dr. Pedro Lopez de Montoya... por R. Rodriguez Hernandez. Madrid, Inst. San Jose de Calasanz, 1947.] LEI

More English examples to be turned into Latin. *See* Leeds, Edward

A308 MORLEY, Thomas, 1557–1604? (1597) A plain and easy introduction to practical music, edited by R. Alec Harman. Dent, 1952. CA

A309 MOTIVES grounded upon the word of God... for the present founding an university in the metropolis London... By a true lover of his nation. [*In* A contribution to the history of University College, London, by H. Gollancz. 1930. First published 1647.] LEI

A310 MOXON, Joseph, 1627–1700. (1654) A tutor to astronomie and geographie; or, an easy and speedy way to know the use of both the globes, coelestial and terrestrial. 2nd ed., J. Moxon, 1670. OX

A311 MULCASTER, Richard, 1530?–1611. The educational writings of... abridged and arranged... by James Oliphant. Glasgow, Maclehose, 1903. BI HU LEI LO NE RE SH

A312 MULCASTER, Richard. (1582) Elementarie; edited... by E. T. Campagnac. Oxford, Clarendon Pr., 1925. HU LEE LO NE NO SH SO

A313 MULCASTER, Richard. (1581) Positions... With an appendix... by R. H. Quick. Longman, 1888. BI BR HU LEE LO SH

A314 NEVILLE, Alexander, 1544–1614. (1575) Kettus, sive de furoribus Norfolciensium Ketto duce liber unus. H. Binneman, 1582. HU NoU

New and easie institution of grammar. *See* Taylor, Jeremy

A315 NEW England primer. (*c.* 1683?) The New England primer: a history of its origin... with a reprint of the unique copy of the earliest known edition (1727)... Edited by P. L. Ford. N.Y., Columbia Univ. Teachers College, 1962. LEI NE

A316 NEW England primer. The New England primer enlarged... (Twentieth century reprint). Ginn, [19–]. [Reprinted from a copy published between 1785 and 1790.] LEI

A317 A NEWE book of copies, 1575. A facsimile of a unique Elizabethan writing book in the Bodleian Library, Oxford. Edited... by B. Wolpe. O.U.P., 1962. [Originally printed by Thomas Vautrouillier.] LEI

New method of learning with facility the Greek/Latin tongue. *See* Lancelot, C.

A318 [NEWBERY, Thomas], *fl.* 1563. (1563) A booke in Englyshe metre, of the great merchaunt man called 'Dives pragmaticus...', 1563... With an introduction by P. E. Newbery; and remarks... by H. C. Wyld. Manchester U.P., 1910. [John Rylands facsimiles.] NoU

A319 NEWTON, John, 1622–1678. (1676) The English academy: or, a brief introduction to the seven liberal arts... to which is added the necessary arts and mysteries of navigation, dyaling [etc.] ... 2nd ed., Tho. Passenger, 1693. HU

A320 NEWTON, John. (1671) An introduction to the art of rhetorick... Tho. Passenger, 1671. NoU

A321 NICHOLLS, William, 1664–1712. (1698) The advantage of a learned education, being a sermon at the cathedral church of St. Paul preach'd St. Paul's Day, 1697/8, before the gentlemen educated at that school. 1697/8. ReU

A322 [NICOLE, Pierre], 1625?–1695, *comp.* (Fr. 1659; Eng. 1683) Epigrammatum delectus ex omnibus tum veteribus, tum recentioribus poetis accurate decerptus... Quibus hac quarta editione, subjungitur alterius delectus specimen... in usum Scholae Etonensis. Sam. Smith, 1689. HU NoU

A323 NICOLE, Pierre, do., Ed. nona. 1724. *See* B770

A324 NOMENCLATOR trilinguis. (1699?) Ed. tertia. 1713. *See* B773

A325 NOMENCLATURA trilinguis Anglo-Latino-Graeca... Composed... by P.K. 1688. NoU

A326 do., 6th ed., 1704. *See* B775

A327 [NORRIS, John], 1657–1711. (1694) Spiritual counsel; or, the father's advice to his children... W. Hunt, 1694. NoU

A328 NORTH, *Sir* Thomas, 1535?–1601, *trans.* The diall of princes. *See* A202 Guevara y de Noroña, A. de

A329 NORTHUMBERLAND, Henry Percy, 9*th earl of*, 1564–1632. (1609) Advice to his son, 1609. Edited... by G. B. Harrison. Benn, 1930. LEI

A330 [NOWELL, Alexander], *dean of St. Paul's.* ... [Greek script.] Christianae pietatis prima institutio, ad usum scholarum Graece et Latine scripta. 1638. NoU

Nouvelle méthode de Messieurs de Port Royal. *See* Lancelot, C., *and* A331

A331 NOUVELLE méthode pour apprendre facilement et en peu de temps la langue allemande. [La méthode de Messieurs de Port-Royal.] Nlle. éd. Zurich, Gesner, 1687. LO

O.W. *See* Walker, Obadiah

A332 OCLAND (*or* Ockland), Christopher, d. 1590. (1580) Anglorum praelia, ab anno Domini 1327 ... usque ad 1558 carmine summatim perstricta... Hiis A. Neuilli Kettum adjunximus. R. Nuberie ex assig. H. Bynneman, 1582. [*Includes his Eirenarchia, sive Elizabetha.*] HU NoU

Of education, especially of young gentlemen. *See* Walker, Obadiah

Orthotonia. *See* Franklin, Richard

A333 OSBORNE, Francis, 1593–1659. (1656) Advice to a son. New ed., with an introduction and notes by... E. A. Parry. D. Nutt, 1896. LEI

A334 OUGHTRED, William, 1575–1660. (1657) Trigonometria. Johnson, 1657. NoU

A335 P., R. (1674) A sermon preach'd 27 Jan. 1673/4 before persons who have had their education in St. Paul's school. 1674. [Possibly by Richard Pye.] ReU

P.K. *See* K., P.

A336 PACIO DE BERIGO, Giulio, 1550–1635. (1597?) ... Institutiones logicae, in usum scholarum Bernensium editae. Berne, 1600. NoU

PACIUS, Julius. *See* PACIO DE BERIGO, Giulio.

A337 PARLIAMENT. An ordinance for the ejecting of scandalous, ignorant and insufficient ministesr [*sic*] and school-masters. Tuesday August 29. 1654. W. du-Gard and H. Wills, 1654. LEE

A338 PEACHAM, Henry, 1576?–1643? (1622) ... Compleat gentleman, 1634. With an introduction by G. S. Gordon. Oxford, Clarendon Pr., 1906. [Facsimile reprint.] LEI

A339 PENTON, Stephen, 1639–1706. (1688) The guardian's instruction; or, the gentleman's romance. Written for the diversion and service of the gentry. Reprinted from the edition of 1688, with an introduction by H. H. Sturmer. F. E. Robinson, 1897. HU LEI

PERCY, Henry, 9*th earl of Northumberland. See* Northumberland, Henry Percy, 9*th earl of*

A340 PERKINS, S., *trans.* Solomon's proverbs. *See* A136 Danvers, H.

A341 PERRAULT, Charles, 1628–1703. (Fr. 1697; Eng. 1729?) Tales of passed times, by Mother Goose... 7th ed., 1796. *See* B806

A342 PERRAULT, Charles. Popular tales. Edited from the original editions... by Andrew Lang. Oxford, Clarendon Pr., 1888. LEI

A343 PETTIE, George, 1548–1589, *trans.* The civile conversation of M. Steeven Guazzo... *See* A201 Guazzo, Stefano

A344 PHAIRE (*otherwise* Phaer, *or* Phayer), Thomas, 1510?–1560. (1544) The boke of chyldren. [Edited by A. V. Neale and H. R. E. Wallis.] Edinburgh, Livingstone, 1955. LEE; 1957. LEI

A345 [PHILLIPS, John]. (1682) Speculum crapegownorum: or, an old looking-glass for the young academicks, new foyl'd... By a guide to the inferiour clergy. 2nd ed. corr. and enl. E. Rydal, 1682. LEI

A346 PIUS II, *pope*, 1405–1464. (Written 1450) De liberorum educatione; a translation, with an introduction, by J. S. Nelson. Washington, Catholic University of America, 1940. [Latin text, with parallel English trans.] HU; *see also* A450 Woodward, W. H., *ed.*

A347 PLATTER, Thomas, 1507?–1582. (1582) The autobiography of Thomas Platter, a schoolmaster of the sixteenth century, translated from the German by... [E. A. McCaul]. Wertheim, 1839. LEE LO

A348 PLUTARCH. De liberorum educatione libellus... [*In* Isocratis Orationes tres... Cum annotationibus M. Guilielmi Diezii... Ulm, Kühn, 1678.] LEI

Poetae minores Graeci. *See* Winterton, R.

A349 POMEY, François Antoine, 1618–1673. (Fr. 5th ed. 1697; Eng. 1694) The Pantheon... 4th ed., 1705; 19th ed., 1757; New ed. rev., 1795. *See* B845

A350 POMFRET, Samuel, 1650–1722. A sermon preach'd to young people. 2nd ed., 1698. NoU

PORT ROYAL, Messieurs de. *See* Arnauld, Antoine; Lancelot, Claude, *and* A433 Barnard, H. C., *ed.*; A436 Cadet, Felix, *ed.*

A351 PRACTICAL. (1682) Practical grammar, or, the easiest and shortest way to initiate young children in the Latin tongue. By J., *philomath.* Cockerill, 1682. LEE

Praelectiones academicae in schola historicae Camdeniana. *See* Dodwell, H.

A352 PRIDEAUX, Mathias, 1622–1646? (1648) An easy and compendious introduction for reading all sorts of histories: etc. ['3rd' ed.]. Oxford, L. Lichfield, 1655. LO

A353 PRIMER. (1546) The Primer set furth by the kinges maiestie & his clergie ... Imprinted at London ... by Richard Grafton ... 1546. Reprinted ... [1722]. *See* B858

A354 PROMPTORIUM parvulorum. (*c.* 1440) Promptorium parvulorum sive clericorum, dictionarius Anglo-Latinus princeps, auctore Fratre Galfrido Grammatico dicto ... circa A.D. MCCCCXL ... Recensuit Albertus Way. Camden Soc., 1865. HU

Proteus vinctus. *See* Willis, Thomas

R.P. *See* P., R.

A355 RABELAIS, François, 1494?–1553. The teacher's Rabelais; prepared by Geraldine Hodgson. Blackie, 1904. HU

A356 RAINOLDE, Richard, d. 1606. (1563) The foundacion of rhetorike. With an introduction by F. R. Johnson. N.Y., Scholars' facsimiles and reprints, 1945. HU LEE LEI

A357 RALEIGH, *Sir* Walter, 1552?–1618. (1632) Instructions to his sonne, and to posterity. P. Davies, 1927. [Reprinted from the 1632 ed.] LEI

A358 RAY, John, 1627–1705. (1675) Nomenclator classicus, sive dictionariolum trilingue ... 4th ed., 1703. *See* B872

Reflections upon learning. *See* Baker, T.

A359 RHODES, Hugh, *fl.* 1550–1555. (1550?) The boke of nurture, or schoole of good manners: for men, servants, and children, with Stans puer ad mensam. Newly corrected ... Imprinted at London ... by H. Iackson. 1577. [Facsimile reprint, with preface by F. J. Furnivall. 1868.] LEI

A360 ROBBE, Jacques. (1678) Méthode pour apprendre facilement la géographie. 2e partie [only]. Paris, Dupuis, 1678. [Contains Books 3–5 and a short manual of navigation.] SH

A361 [ROBERTI, Antonius]. (1638) Clavis Homerica. Editio ultima ... opera G. Perkins ... A. Crook, 1673. NoU

SAVILE, George, *marquis of Halifax. See* Halifax, George Savile, *marquis of*

A362 ROBINSON, Hugh, 1584?–1655. (2nd ed., 1658) Scholae Wintonensis phrases latinae. 2nd ed., 1658. NoU; 11th ed., 1685. ReU

Rudimentum grammaticae Latinae metricum. *See* Busby, R.

A363 RUGGLE, George, 1575–1622. (1630) Ignoramus. Ed. 6a, 1731. *See* B912

A364 SADOLETO, Jacopo, 1477–1547. (1533) Sadoleto on education: a translation of the De pueris recte instituendis ... [Edited] by E. T. Campagnac and K. Forbes. O.U.P., 1916. BI BR HU LEE LO NO RE SH

SAINLIENS, Claude de. *See* Holyband, C.

SAINT JOHN'S COLLEGE, Cambridge. *See* Cambridge. University. *St. John's College*

A365 SCHNEUWLY, Peter, 1539?–1597. (1577) [Schulordnung und Satzungen der nüwen ufgerichten und reformierten schul zy Fryburg im Uchtland.] Das sogennante Katharinenbuch vom Jahre 1577 ... zum ersten Male herausgegeben von F. Heinemann ... Freiburg i.Ue., Universitäts-Buchhandlung, 1896. LO

A366 SCHREVELIUS, Cornelis, 1615?–?1664. (1654) Lexicon manuale graeco–latinum & latino–graecum ... Ed.nova., 1774. *See* B933

A367 [SERGEANT, John], 1622–1707. (1657) The mystery of rhetorick unveiled ... By John Smith, of Montague Close, Southwark. 10th ed., 1721. *See* B942

A367a SHARP, Abraham, 1651–1742. Mathematical tables. 1705. *See* B958 Sherwin, H.

A368 SHERRY [*or* Shirrye], Richard, *fl.* 1550. (1550) A treatise of schemes and tropes, 1550, and his translation of The education of children, by Desiderius Erasmus. A facsimile reproduction ... Gainesville, Scholars' facsimiles and reprints, 1961. LEI

A368a SHIRLEY, James, 1596–1666. An essay towards an universal and national grammar. 1726. *See* B959

Short dictionarie for yonge beginners. *See* Withals, John

Short introduction of grammar. *See* Lily, W.

SILVIUS, Aeneas. *See* Pius II, *pope*

A368b SLEIDAN [*or* Sleidanus], Johannes, 1506–1556. De quatuor imperiis. [*In* Select parts of Grey's Memoria technica. 1786?] *See* B972

SMITH, John, *of Montague Close, Southwark. See* Sergeant, John.

Sons patrimony. *See* Woodward, Hezekiah.

Speculum crape-gownorum. *See* Phillips, John

Spiritual counsel. *See* Norris, John

A369 SPRAT, Thomas, 1635–1713. (1667) History of the Royal Society. Edited ... by J. I. Cope and H. W. Jones. St. Louis, Washington Univ. studies; London, Routledge; 1959. [Facsimile reprint of 1667 ed.] LEI

A370 STANBRIDGE, John, 1463–1510. (Written 1508?) The Vulgaria of John Stanbridge [1519 edition] and the Vulgaria of Robert Whittinton. Edited ... by B. White. E.E.T.S., 1932. CA LEE LEI

A371 STANHOPE, George, 1660–1728, *trans.* (1697) Of wisdom ... Written originally by the Sieur de Charron ... Made English by George Stanhope ... 2nd ed., 1707. *See* B201 Charron, P.

A372 STOCKWOOD, John, d. 1610. (1592) Questiones et responsiones grammaticales ... T. Dawson for Io. Harrisone, 1592. NoU

A373 STOCKWOOD, John. (1590?) The treatise of the figures at the end of the rules of construction in the Latin grammar, construed ... 1713, *and another ed.*, 1738. *See* B1008

A373a STURM, Johannes, 1507–1589. Epistolae generosissimi viri Io. Sturmii et ceterorum ad Rogerum Aschamum. *See* A431; B41

A374 STURM, Johann Christoph, 1635–1703. (Germ. 2nd ed. 1695; Eng. 1700) Mathesis enucleata; or, the elements of the mathematicks... Made English by J.R. and R.S.S. Knaplock, [etc.], 1700. LEI

A375 STURTEVANT, Simon. (1597) The Latin nomenclator, containing simple, primitive and meere latine words. n.p., 1597. NoU

SYLVIUS, Aeneas. *See* Pius II, *pope*

A376 TABULAE abcdariae pueriles... n.p., [*c.* 1540]. NoU

A377 TACQUET, Andreas, 1611–1660. (2nd ed. 1665) Elementa geometriae planae ac solidae... Ed. nova. Amsterdam, Wetstein, 1683. LEI

A378 [TAYLOR, Jeremy], 1613–1667. (1647) A new and easie institution of grammar. In usum juventutis cambro-britannicae... 1647. NoU

A379 TERENCE. Comoediae sex, Anglo-Latinae; in usum ludi-discipulorum... Six comedies, in English and Latine... By Charles Hoole. Company of Stationers, 1663. HU

A380 TERENCE. Comoediae IV, cum notis Th. Farnaby et M.C.Is:F. [i.e., Meric Casaubon]. Amsterdam, J. Van Waesberghe, 1681. LEI

A381 TERENCE. Comedies made English, with his life... by several hands [i.e., L. Eachard and others]. A. Small and T. Childe, 1694. LEI

A381a TROTTI DE LA CHETARDIE, Joachim. (Fr. 1684) Small tract of instruction for the conduct of young ladies. *See* B537 Fénelon

A382 UDALL, Nicholas, 1505–1556. (1553?) Roister Doister... Edited... by Edward Arber. Arber, 1869. [English reprints.] LEI

A383 VAREN, Bernhard [*otherwise* Bernhardus Varenius], 1622?–1650. (1650) A compleat system of general geography. 2nd ed., 1734. *See* B1066

A384 VARILLAS, Antoine, 1626?–1696. (1684) La pratique de l'éducation des princes. Amsterdam, Wetstein & Desbordes, 1684. LEI LO

A385 VENERONI, Giovanni [*otherwise* Jean Vigneron], 1642–1708. The complete Italian master. 1814. *See* D1395

A386 VENERONI, Giovanni. Grammaire française et italienne... 1804–1805. *See* D1396

A387 VERGERIO [*or* Vergerius], Pier Paolo, 1349–post 1419. (1392) De ingenuis moribus. *See* A450 Woodward, W. H.

A388 VESALIUS, Andreas, 1514–1564. (1543) On the human brain; translated and edited by C. Singer. O.U.P., 1952. [Translation of a section of his 'De humani corpore fabrica'.] BR

A389 VESTIBULUM technicum, or, an artificial vestibulum wherein the sense of Janua linguarum [of Comenius] is contained... Revised and corrected by Seth Boncle... 1682. NoU

VIGNERON, Jean. *See* Veneroni, Giovanni

VINCENTINO. *See* Arrighi, L. degli

A390 VIVES, Juan Luis, 1492–1540. De disciplinis libri XII: septem de corruptis artibus, cinque de tradendis disciplinis. Leyden, J. Maire, 1636. HU

A391 VIVES, J. L. (1531) Vives on education. A translation of De tradendis disciplinis, together with an introduction by Foster Watson. C.U.P., 1913. BI BR HU LEE LEI LO NE RE SH SO

A392 VIVES, J. L. [Exercitatio linguae Latinae]. (1539) Tudor schoolboy life; the dialogues of... Translated with an introduction by Foster Watson. Dent, 1908. BI CA HU

A393 VIVES, J. L. The instruction of a Christian woman, [etc.]. *See* A449 Watson, F., *ed.*

A394 VOSSIUS, Gerardus (*otherwise* Gerard John Vos), 1577–1649. Elementa rhetorica... Editio ... auctior. 1771. *See* B1069

A395 VOSSIUS, Gerardus. (1607) Latina grammatica, ex decreto D. D. Holl. West-Frisiaeque ordinum, in usum scholarum adornata... Editio altera, aliquot in locis castigatior priori; notis vero longe auctior. Leyden, Bonaventura & Abr. Elzevir, 1628. *With* Latina syntaxis, editio altera, 1628, *and* Latina prosodia, 1628. HU

A396 VOSSIUS, Gerardus, do. *See also* A285 Linguae Latinae rudimenta concinnata ex Grammatica Lithocomo-Vossiana

W., O. *See* Walker, Obadiah

W., T. *See* Willis, Thomas

W., W. *See* Walker, William

A397 WAKE, *Sir* Isaac, 1580?–1632. (1607) Rex Platonicus. 5th ed., 1636. ReU

A398 [WALKER, Obadiah], 1616–1699. (1692) The Greek and Roman history illustrated by coins and medals... Necessary for the instruction of youth... By O.W. G. Croom for Wm. Miller and Chris. Wilkinson, 1692. LEI NoU

A399 [WALKER, Obadiah]. (1673) Of education. Especially of young gentlemen. 3rd impression with additions. Oxford, The Theater, 1677. LEI; Oxford, printed at the Theater for Amos Curteyne, 1683. BI; 5th impression, Oxford, A. Curteyne, 1687. HU LEE LO; 6th ed., 1699. ReU

A400 WALKER, William, 1623–1684. (1670) A dictionarie of English and Latine idiomes wherein phrases of the English and Latine tongue answering in parallels each to the other are ranked under seuerall heads alphabeticallie set. Jos. Clarke, [1670]. HU NoU

A401 [WALKER, William]. (1677) A modest plea for infants baptism... By W. W., B. D. Cambridge, J. Hayes for H. Dickinson, 1677. LEI

A402 WALKER, William. A new dictionary of English particles with a praxis upon the same. (1653.) NoU

A403 WALKER, William. (1669) Some improvements to the art of teaching. 8th ed., 1717, *and* 9th ed., 1730. *See* B1082

A404 WALKER, William. (1655) A treatise of English particles... with a praxis upon the same. Whereunto is affix't Idiomatologiae anglo-latine specimen... 1655. NoU

A405 WALKER, William, do., 7th ed. T.N. for Rob. Pawlet, 1679. HU

A406 WALKER, William, do., 13th ed., 1706, *and* 15th ed., 1720. *See* B1083

A406a WALLIS, John, 1616–1703. Mathematical tables. 1705. *See* B958 Sherwin, H.

A407 [WASE, Christopher], 1625?–1690. (1678) Considerations concerning free-schools, as settled in England. Oxford, The Theatre, 1678. [Xerographic copy.] HU LEE LEI LO NE SH

A408 WASE, Christopher. (1660) Methodi practicae specimen. An essay of a practical grammar . . . 8th ed., 1682. NoU

A409 WEBSTER, John, 1610–1682. (1654) Academiarum examen, or the examination of academies. G. Calvert, 1654. ReU

A410 WELLS, Edward, 1667–1727. (1698) Elementa arithmeticae et speciosae. Ed. altera. 1726. See B1117

A411 WHITTINGTON (otherwise Whittinton, or Whytynton), Robert, fl. 1512–1554. (1520) The Vulgaria of John Stanbridge and the Vulgaria of Robert Whittinton. Edited . . . by B. White. E.E.T.S., 1932. CA LEE LEI

Whole duty of man. See Allestree, R.

WILLIAM, of Tournai. See Guillaume, de Tournai

A412 [WILLIS, Thomas, M.A.], 1582–1660? (1655) Proteus vinctus. Sive aequivoca sermonis anglicani, ordine alphabetico digesta, et latine reddita . . . Authore T.W. . . . 1655. NoU

A413 WILSON, Thomas, 1525?–1581. (1553) Arte of rhetorique. Edited by G. H. Mair. Oxford, Clarendon Pr., 1909. [Reprint of 1585 ed.] LEI

A414 WINGATE, Edmund, 1596–1656. (1667?) The clarks tutor for arithmetic and writing . . . being the remains of . . . E. Wingate . . . With a convenient copy book . . . By E. Cocker. 1671. NoU

A415 WINGATE, Edmund. (1630) [A treatise of common arithmetick]. [1670?] [t.p. and one sheet of first gathering missing.] NoU

A416 WINGATE, Edmund. Mr. Wingate's Arithmetick . . . 6th ed. Revised . . . by J. Kersey. 1673. NoU; 8th ed., 1683. NoU

A417 WINGATE, Edmund, do., 13th ed., 1713, and 15th ed., 1726. See B1150

A418 WINGATE, Edmund. A plain and familiar method for attaining the knowledge and practice of common arithmetic. 18th ed., 1751, and 19th ed., 1760. See B1151

A419 WINTERTON, Ralph, ed. (1635) Poetae minores Graeci: Hesiodus, Theocritus, Moschus [etc.] Quibus subjungitur, eorum potissimum quae ad philosophiam moralem pertinent, index utilis. Accedunt etiam nunc primam observationes Radulphi Wintertoni in Hesiodum. Cambridge, T. and J. Buck and R. Daniel, 1635. HU

A420 [WINTERTON, Ralph?]. Poetae minores Graeci, selecti & emendati. 1728. See B840 Poetae

A421 [WITHALS, John], fl. 1553–1556. (1553) A dictionarie in English and Latine for children. Now augmented by W. Clerk. 3rd ed., [1616]. NoU

A422 WOLF, Hieronymus, 1516–1580, ed. Isocratis Orationes et epistolae. See A233 Isocrates

A423 WOOD, Anthony à, 1632–1695. (1691–1692) Athenae Oxoniensis . . . A new edition . . . by Philip Bliss. 1813–1820. 4 vols. ReU

A424 [WOODWARD, Hezekiah (or Ezekias)], 1590–1675. (1640) A sons patrimony and daughters portion . . . in two volumes: In the first, the parent is taught his duty . . . In the second, the child is taught to know himself and God . . . T. Underhill, pr., 1643. [Contents: A childes patrimony, printed by I. Legatt, 1640; A child's portion, printed by I. Leggatt, 1640.] HU

A425 WOTTON, Sir Henry, 1568–1639. A philosophical survey of education; or moral architecture. With The aphorisms of education. Edited by H. S. Kermode. Liverpool U.P., [etc.], 1938. HU

A426 WOTTON, Henry, fl. 1672, incumbent of Wrentham. (Written 1672) An essay on the education of children . . . 1753. See B1164

A427 WOTTON, William, 1666–1726. (1694) Reflections upon ancient and modern learning . . . 3rd ed., 1705. See B1166

A428 YCIAR, Juan de, fl. 1549–1550. (1548) A facsimile of the 1550 edition of Arte subtilissima, with a translation by Evelyn Shuckburgh . . . O.U.P., 1960. LEI

A429 YOUNG. (1664) The young clerk's companion, or a manual for his daily practice . . . Collected by an able and learned practitioner for his private use, but now communicated for a general good. J. Streater, J. Flesher and H. Twyford, 1667. LO

A430 ZWINGLI, Huldreich (or Ulrich), 1484–1531. On the education of youth. See A434 Bromiley, G., ed.

2. Collections

A431 ACKER, Henry, ed. Epistolae generosissimi viri Io. Sturmii et ceterorum ad Rogerum Aschamum . . . Jena, 1912. LO

A432 AUSTIN, Thomas, ed. Two fifteenth-century cookery-books. Harleian MS.279 (ab. 1430) and Harl. MS. 4016 (ab. 1450), with extracts from . . . [other MSS.]. E.E.T.S., 1888. LEI

A433 BARNARD, H. C., ed. The Port Royalists on education: extracts from the educational writings of the Port-Royalists . . . C.U.P., 1918. HU LEE LO NE RE

A434 BROMILEY, Geoffrey, ed. Zwingli and Bullinger. S.C.M. Pr., 1953. [Includes Zwingli's 'On the education of youth'.] LEI

A435 BYRNE, M. St. Clare, ed. The Elizabethan home, discovered in 2 dialogues [by Claudius Hollyband and Peter Erondell]. Etchells & Macdonald, 1925. [Selections from: The French schoolemaister, 1573, The French Littleton, 1566, and Campo di fior, 1583, by Hollyband; The French garden, 1605, by Erondell.] LEI

A436 CADET, Felix, ed. Port-Royal education: Saint-Cyran; Arnauld; Lancelot; Nicole; De Saci; Guyot; Coustel; Fontaine; Jacqueline Pascal. Extracts, with an introduction, by F. Cadet. Translated . . . by A. D. Jones. Sonnenschein, 1898. BI HU LEE LEI LO NE RE SH

A437 EBY, Frederick, ed. Early Protestant educators: the educational writings of Martin Luther, John Calvin, and other leaders of Protestant thought. N.Y., McGraw, 1931. HU

A438 FURNIVALL, F. J., ed. The Babees book . . . The Bokes of nurture of Hugh Rhodes and John Russell . . . Wynkyn de Worde's Boke of keruynge . . . etc., etc. With some forewords on education in early England. E.E.T.S., 1868. HU LEE LEI NoU RE

A439 FURNIVALL, F. J. The Babees' book: medieval manners for the young; done into modern English from Dr. Furnivall's texts by Edith Rickert. Chatto & Windus, 1908. HU LEI RE

A440 FURNIVALL, F. J. Queene Elizabethes Achademy, by Sir Humphrey Gilbert. A Booke of precedence, The ordering of a funerall, etc. Varying versions of The Good wife, The Wise man, etc. . . . With essays on early Italian and German books of courtesy by W. M. Rossetti and E. Oswald. E.E.T.S., 1869. LEI OX

A441 The PARENTS' friend; or, extracts from the principal works on education from the time of Montaigne to the present day . . . J. Johnson, 1802. 2 vols. HU

A442 PHILIPPS, Jenkin Thomas, ed. A compendious way of teaching antient and modern languages, formerly practised by . . . Tanaquil Faber . . . to which are added some tracts and observations on the same subject by several eminent men . . . See B821

A443 PRACTICAL wisdom; or, the manual of life. The counsels of eminent men to their children . . . Coburn, 1824. [Extracts from Sir Walter Raleigh, Lord Burleigh, Sir Henry Sidney, Earl of Strafford, Francis Osborn, Sir Matthew Hale, etc.] LEI

A444 ROWLAND, E., ed. A pedagogue's commonplace book: being extracts from works written in the mother tongue by men of the sixteenth and seventeenth centuries. Dent, 1925. BR LEI

A445 SCOTLAND. General register house. Acts of the Parliament and of the Privy Council of Scotland relative to the establishing and maintaining of schools from the year MCCCCXCVI to the year MDCXCVI. [Edinburgh], General register house, [1839?]. BR LEI

A446 STEELE, R., ed. The earliest arithmetics in English. E.E.T.S., 1922. [Contains: The craft of numbrynge and The art of nombryng (15th C.); Accomptynge by counters (16th C.); etc.] LEE LEI

A447 TORRANCE, Thomas F., ed. and trans. The school of faith: the catechisms of the reformed church, [1541–1648]. J. Clarke, 1959. LEI

A448 TURNBULL, G. H., ed. Hartlib, Dury and Comenius: gleanings from Hartlib's papers. Liverpool U.P., 1947. BI BR HU LEE LEI LO NE RE SH SO

A449 WATSON, Foster, ed. Vives and the Renascence education of women. E. Arnold, 1912. [Extracts from Vives, Richard Hyrde, Sir Thomas More and Sir Thomas Elyot.] BI HU LEE LEI LO

A450 WOODWARD, W. H., ed. Vittorino da Feltre and other humanist educators: essays and versions . . . C.U.P., 1897. [Contains translations of: De ingenuis moribus, by P. P. Vergerius; De studiis et literis, by Lionardi Bruni d'Arezzo; De liberorum educatione, by Aeneas Sylvius; and De ordine docendi et studendi, by Battiste Guarino.] BI HU LEE LEI LO NE RE SH SO

A451 WRIGHT, Thomas, ed. A volume of vocabularies, illustrating the condition and manners of our forefathers, as well as the history of the forms of elementary education . . . from the tenth century to the fifteenth . . . 2nd ed., priv. print., 1882. LEI

A452 WRIGHT, Thomas, ed. A second volume of vocabularies . . . Priv. print., 1873. LEI

A453 YOUNG, Robert Fitzgibbon, ed. Comenius in England. The visit of Jan Amos Komensky . . . to London in 1641–1642 . . . as described in contemporary documents, selected, translated, and edited . . . O.U.P., 1932. [Extracts from Comenius, Dury, J. Collier, Hartlib.] LEI

Books published, or first published, 1701-1800

1. Individual authors

Abridgment of the new method of learning . . . the Greek tongue. *See* B615 Lancelot, C.

B1 An ABSTRACT of the case of Mr. Freeman's foundation of fellowships and scholarships in Clare Hall . . . 1749. NoU

The Academic. *See* Green, J.

B2 The ACCIDENCE, or, first rudiments of the Latin tongue, for the use of youth. New ed. rev. Eton, T. Pote, pr., 1791. HU

The Accidence; or, first rudiments of English grammar. *See* Devis, E.

Account of charity schools. *See* Society for the promotion of Christian knowledge

Account of the chief truths of the Christian religion. *See* D216 A Catachetical instruction

B3 An ACCOUNT of the eight parts of speech. For the use of Merchant-Taylors School. 15th ed., 1764. NoU

B4 ACCOUNT of the institution and regulations of the Guardians of the Asylum, or house of refuge . . . for the reception of orphan girls, etc. Printed by order of the Guardians, 1793. MA

B5 ACKWORTH SCHOOL. Reports on the state of Ackworth School, 1780–1812. Ackworth, The School, [1780–1812]. LEE

B6 ACKWORTH SCHOOL. Rules for the government of Ackworth School, established for the education of children who are members of the Society [of Friends] and whose parents are not in affluent circumstances. J. Phillips, pr., 1790. LEE; 1795. HU

B7 ADAMS, John, 1662–1720. (1702) A sermon preach'd at St. Paul's cathedral 8 December 1701. T. Bennet, 1702. ReU

B8 ADAMS, John, 1750?–1814, *comp.* The English Parnassus. 1789. NoU

B9 An ADDRESS to the Hibernian Society; with a plan of education in a Letter to the provost and fellows of Trinity College, Dublin. By M—. S—. Dublin, 1758. HU

Adèle et Théodore. *See* B414 Genlis, *comtesse de*

B10 [ADKIN, Lancaster]. (1785?) Proceedings for Sundays [*sic*] schools, and a plan of that in St. Stephen's, Norwich, established 1785. Norwich, W. Chase, pr., n.d. *with* The Sabbath: a sermon to promote the establishment of Sunday-schools. Norwich, J. Crouse and W. Stevenson, [1785]. HU

Adventures of the six princesses of Babylon. *See* Peacock, L.

Advice to a young student. *See* Waterland, D.

B11 AESCHINES. Ho Kata Ktesiphontos, *kai* Demosthenous Ho peri Stephanou logos. Interpretationem Latinam . . . adjecerunt P. Foulkes, J. Freind. In usum scholae Etonensis. J. Bowyer, 1715. HU

B12 AESCHYLUS. Choephoroi. 1729. *See* B1129 Westminster School. Treis tragoediai

B13 AESOP. Fabularum Aesopiarum libri quinque . . . Oxford, 1757. NoU

B14 AESOP. Fabulae Aesopi selectae, or select fables of Aesop; with an English translation . . . by H. Clarke. 9th ed., 1784. NoU

B15 [AIKIN, John], 1747–1822. (1784) The calendar of nature; designed for the instruction and entertainment of young persons. 2nd ed., J. Johnson, 1785. ReU

B16 AIKIN, John. (1788) England delineated; or, a geographical description of every county in England and Wales . . . 2nd ed., Bensley, 1790. LEI

B17 AIKIN, John. (1793) Letters from a father to his son, on various topics, relative to literature and the conduct of life. Written in the years 1792 and 1793. J. Johnson, 1793. LEI; 3rd ed., 1796. NoU

B18 [AIKIN, John, and BARBAULD, Anna Letitia]. (1792–1796) Evenings at home; or, the juvenile budget opened. Johnson, 1798–1800. 6 vols in 3. ReU

B19 AIKIN, J., and BARBAULD, A. L., do., *another set*. Vols 1, 3, 4, 5. [Vol. 1, 3rd ed; vols 3 and 4, 10th ed.; vol. 5, 2nd ed.] 1795–1814. NoU

B20 AIKIN, J., and BARBAULD, A. L., do., 5th ed. Johnson, 1805; 13th ed., 1823; 18th ed., 1858; Edinburgh, 1868; Kendrick, n.d. *See* D21

B21 AINSWORTH, Robert, 1660–1743. (1698) The most natural and easy way of institution, by making a domestic education less chargeable to parents, and more easy and beneficial to children. 2nd ed., E. Curll, 1736. LEE

B22 ALDERSON, James. (1793) Orthographical exercises: in a series of moral letters . . . 5th ed., with additions. J. Scatchard, etc., [179–?] HU

B23 ALDERSON, James, do., 14th ed., rev. and corr., 1818. *See* D28

B24 [ALDRICH, Henry], 1647–1710. (1691) Artis logicae compendium. Oxford, Sheldonian Theatre, 1723. LEE

B25 ALDRICH, Henry. Artis logicae compendium, in usum juventutis academicae. New ed., Oxford, J. Fletcher, 1793. LO

B26 [ALER, Paul], 1656–1727. (1687) Gradus ad Parnassum; sive novus synonymorum, epithetorum, phrasium poeticarum, ac versuum thesaurus . . . Ab uno e Societate Jesu. Ilive, 1729. LEI

B27 ALEXANDER, Johann. (Eng. 1693) Synopsis algebraica . . . Ed. secunda, emendatior. Cui adjungitur appendix per H. Ditton. In usum utriusque scholae mathematicae apud Hospitium-Christi Londinensis. Christ's Hospital, 1709. LEI

B28 [ALLESTREE, Richard], 1619–1681. (1660) The gentleman's calling. Written by the author of *The whole duty of man*. Eliz. Pawlet, 1705.   LEI

B29 [ALLESTREE, Richard]. (1658) The whole duty of man. Oxford, John Eyre, 1733.   LO

B30 [ALLESTREE, Richard], do., *another ed.* Assigns of J. & D. Eyre for the booksellers, 1756. LEI

B31 [ALLESTREE, Richard], do., *Latin trans.* (1704) Officium hominis . . . Liber hic ex lingua Anglicana in Latinam, eo praecipue consilio traductus est, quo juvenes in ludis literariis versantes, simul & moribus instituantur, & in lingua Latina proficiant. Eliz. Pawlet, 1704.   LEI

B32 AMBROSE. (1796) Ambrose and Eleanor . . . Translated by Lucy Peacock. 3rd ed., 1807. *See* D38

B33 [AMHURST, Nicholas], 1697–1742. (1721) Terrae-filius: or, the secret history of the University of Oxford; in several essays. To which are added remarks upon a late book, entitled, *University education*, by R. Newton. Francklin, 1726. [First collected ed.] LEE; 3rd ed., Francklin, 1754. LEI ReU

B34 L'AMI des enfans, avec des fables convenables à leur âge. Par M. l'Abbé de —— . . . Nouvelle édition. Copenhagen, Philibert, 1766.   LEI

Ami des enfans. *See* Berquin, A.

Amico de' fanciulli. *See* Berquin, A.

B35 AMUSMENS sérieux et comiques; ou nouveau recueil de bons-mots . . . à l'usage de ceux qui veulent apprendre la françois, ou l'anglois. The Hague, I. Vaillant, 1719.   LEI

B36 ANDRES, Bonaventura, *ed.* (1783) Quintilians Pädagogik und Didaktik mit Anmerkungen herausgegeben von Bonaventura Andres . . . Wirzburg, T. Göbhardt, 1783.   LEI

B37 ANGELICA's ladies' library; or, parents' and guardians' present . . . J. Hamilton and Mrs. Harlow, 1794.   LEI

Annales de la vertu. *See* Genlis, *comtesse de*

Answer to an anonymous letter to Dr. Lowth. *See* Lowth, R.

B38 ANTHOLOGIA. (1724?) Anthologia sive epigrammatum graecorum ex anthologia edita Bodleiana, aliisque autoribus delectus, in usum scholae Westmonasteriensis. Oxford, 1724. NoU; *another ed.*, London, 1790. NoU

Appeal to the publick from an unappellate tribunal. *See* Brooke, H.

B39 [ARNAULD, Antoine], 1612–1694, and [NICOLE, Pierre], 1625–1695. (1662) La logique, ou l'art de penser . . . 9e ed. revûe & de nouveau augmentée. Amsterdam, veuve Paul Marret, 1718.   LEI

Art of being easy at all times. *See* Deslandes, A.

B40 ART. (1770?) The art of teaching in sport; designed as a prelude to a set of toys, for enabling ladies to instill the rudiments of spelling, reading, grammar, and arithmetic, under the idea of amusement. J. Marshall, [1770?].   LEI

[Later called The friend of mothers. Attributed by Mrs. Trimmer, in *The Guardian of education*, to Mrs. Lovechild (i.e., Lady Fenn).]

Artis logicae compendium. *See* Aldrich, H.

B41 ASCHAM, Roger, 1515–1568. (1576) Rogeri Aschami epistolarum libri quatuor. Accessit Joannis Sturmii, aliorumque, ad Aschamum anglosque alios eruditos epistolarum liber unus. Editio novissima, prioribus auctior. [Edited by W. Elstob.] Oxford, Lichfield, 1703.   LEI

B42 ASCHAM, Roger. (1570) The scholemaster: or, a plain and perfect way of teaching the learned languages. Now corrected and revis'd . . . by J. Upton. Tooke, 1711.   BI

B43 ASCHAM, Roger. The scholemaster . . . Now revised a second time, and much improved, by J. Upton. Innys, 1743.   BI

B44 ASH, John, 1724?–1779. (1763) Grammatical institutes: or, an easy introduction to Dr. Lowth's English grammar; designed for the use of schools . . . 7th ed., rev., Dilly, 1775. SH; New ed., printed for the booksellers, 1794. HU; New ed., rev., corr. and enl., Smeaton, 1794.   LEI

[Originally had title: The easiest introduction to Dr. Lowth's English grammar.]

B45 ASH, John. (1777) Sentiments on education, collected from the best writers . . . E. and C. Dilly, 1777. 2 vols. HU LEE

B46 ASTRONOMY for school-boys; or, an introduction to the central machine, vulgarly called the whirling-table.   Northampton, [no pub.], 1766. [Includes also: Experimental philosophy for school-boys.] LEI

AUBIGNE, Françoise d', *marquise de Maintenon*. *See* Maintenon, *marquise de*

B47 AULNOY, Marie Cathérine Jumel de Berneville, *comtesse d'*, 1650?–1705. (1700?) Les contes des fées. Première partie. Amsterdam, Rey, 1766. LEI

B48 [AUNEUIL, Louise de Bossigny, *comtesse d'*] (1703) La tirannie des fées détruite. Nouveaux contes . . . par Mad. la Comtesse D. L. Amsterdam, Michel Le Cene, 1730. ReU

Babes in the wood. *See* Children in the wood

B49 BAILEY, Nathan (*or* Nathaniel), d. 1742. (1706?) English and Latine exercises for school-boys, comprising all the rules of syntaxis . . . 7th ed., Holland, 1727. LEE NoU; 12th ed., corr., R. Ware, 1750. HU; 17th ed., corr. and impr., Rivington, [etc.], 1786.   LEI

B50 BAILEY, Nathan (1721) An universal etymological English dictionary . . . 6th ed. with considerable improvements. Knapton, [etc.], 1733.   LEE

B51 [BAILEY, Nathan]? Dictionarium rusticum. 1717. *See* B1163 Worlidge, J.

B52 BAILEY, Nathan, *ed.* (2nd ed. 1724) Cato's Distichs *de moribus*, with a numerical *clavis*, and construing and parsing index . . . To which is added, an English translation of Erasmus's commentaries on each distich. For the use of schools. 5th ed., corr. and impr., D. Browne, 1757.   HU

B53 BAILEY, Nathan, *trans.* (1725) The colloquies of Desiderius Erasmus concerning men, manners and things. Translated into English by N. Bailey, and edited with notes by the Rev. E. Johnson. Gibbings, 1900. 3 vols. LEI

B54 BAILEY, Nathan, *ed.* Ovid's Metamorphoses, in fifteen books: with the arguments and notes of John Minellius translated into English. To which is marginally added a prose version ... For the use of schools. 4th ed., W. Innys, [etc.], 1756. HU

B55 BAILEY, Nathan, *ed.* (1726) Ovid's Tristia, in five books: with the arguments and notes of John Minellius, translated into English. To which is added a prose version ... For the use of schools. 2nd ed. ... 1740. NoU

B56 BAKER, Thomas, 1656–1740. History of the College of St. John the Evangelist, Cambridge. Edited by J. E. B. Mayor. C.U.P., 1869. 2 vols. [Edited from manuscript.] LO ReU

B57 [BAKER, Thomas]. (1699) Reflections upon learning, wherein is shewn the insufficiency thereof ... 4th ed. By a gentleman. Bosvile, 1708. LEE; 5th ed., Knapton & Wilkin, 1714. LO

B58 BANKS, Robert, *vicar of Hull.* Letter to Henry Newman, May 17th, 1712. [Photostat copy of a letter from the vicar of Holy Trinity, Hull, to Henry Newman of the S.P.C.K., describing the charity school in Hull.] HU

B59 BANSON, William. (170–?) The writing master's arithmetick: wherein are set several questions in all the common and useful rules, both in whole numbers and fractions, vulgar and decimal. To be wrought by the scholar. 2nd ed. London, for Jos. Button, New-Castle upon Tine, and D. Midwinter in St. Paul's Churchyard, 1718. HU

B60 [BARBAULD, Anna Letitia], 1743–1825. (1780–1781) Hymns in prose for children. 19th ed., 1818. *See* D71

B61 BARBAULD, Anna Letitia]. Hymns in prose for children ... New impr. ed., [1872?]. NoU

B62 BARBAULD, Anna Letitia. (1778?) Lessons for children of three years old. Pt. 1. 1788. NoU

B63 BARBAULD, Anna Letitia, do., *other eds.* 1812; 1818–1820; 1821–1825; 1840; New ed., 1851. *See* D73

B64 BARBAULD, Anna Letitia. Leçons pour les enfans depuis l'âge de deux ans jusqu'à cinq ans. Ouvrage en deux parties. Traduit ... par M. Pasquier. Vol. 1. Darton & Harvey, 1793. BI; Vol. 2. 1793. ReU

B65 BARBAULD, Anna Letitia, do., *another ed.* ... en quatre parties. 1816. *See* D73a

B66 [BARBAULD, Anna Letitia]. Instructive lessons for children. [18–]. *See* D74

B67 [BARBAULD, Anna Letitia]. More instructive lessons for children. [18–]. *See* D75

B68 BARBAULD, Anna Letitia. A new sequel to Lessons, adapted for children from four to seven years old. Nottingham, Sutton, 1796. BI

B69 [BARBAULD, Anna Letitia]. Evenings at home. *See* B18 Aikin, J., and Barbauld, A. L.

B70 BARCLAY, James, *fl.* 1743–1774. (1754) The Greek rudiments ... after the plan of Mr. Ruddiman's Latin rudiments. Edinburgh, Ruddiman, 1754. NoU

B71 BARCLAY, James. (1743) A treatise on education: or, an easy method of acquiring language, and introducing the children to the knowledge of history, geography ... [etc.]. Edinburgh, Symmes, 1743. LEE ReU

B72 BARCLAY, Rachel, *comp.* (1795) Poems intended to promote piety and virtue in the minds of young people. 2nd ed., Phillips, 1797. BI NoU [1st ed. had title: Select pieces of poetry ...]

B73 [BARNARD, *Sir* John], 1685–1764. (1740) A present for an apprentice. 1852. *See* D81

B74 BARNARD, Thomas, *master of the Free School at Leeds.* (1742) An historical character relating the holy and exemplary life of the Right Honourable the Lady Elizabeth Hastings: to which are added, I: One of the codicils of her last will ... II: Some of the observations resulting therefrom; III: A schedule of her principal charities ... Leeds, Swale, 1742. BR LEE SO

B75 BARNARD, William, 1697–1768. A sermon preached at Christ-Church, Dublin, on the 10th day of May, 1752, before the Incorporated society for promoting English Protestant schools in Ireland. By William, lord bishop of Derry ... With a continuation of the society's Proceedings, to 25th March 1752. Dublin, Powell for the society, 1752. LEI

B76 BARNES, Joshua, 1654–1712. (1715) Euripidis tragoediae Medea et Phoenissae graeco-latinae. Accessit ejusdem vita ... Authore J. Barnesio. In usum scholarum. 1715. NoU

B77 BARROW, Isaac, 1630–1677. (1655) Euclide's Elements. *See* B340 Euclid

B78 BARRUEL, Augustin, *abbé*, 1741–1820. (1797) [Mémoires du Jacobinisme]. Ancien projet des Sophistes, dans l'établissement de nouvelles écoles pour le Peuple. [*c.* 1815?] *See* C80

B79 BASEDOW, Johann Bernhard, 1723–1790. (1771) Agathokrator; oder, von Erziehung künftiger Regenten, nebst Anhang und Beylagen. Leipzig, 1771. LO

B80 BASEDOW, J. B. (1791) Beyträge zur Lebensgeschichte Joh. Bernh. Basedows aus seinen Schriften und andern ächten Quellen gesammlet [von Heinrich Rathmann]. Magdeburg, 1791. LO

B81 BASEDOW, J. B. (1770–1774) Des Elementarbuchs für Jugend und für ihre Lehrer und Freunde in gesitteten Ständen erster [– dritter] Stück. Bremen & Altona, 1770. LO

B82 BASEDOW, J. B. Des Elementarwerks erster [– vierter] Band. Dessau, 1774. 4 vols. LO

B83 [BASEDOW, J. B.]. Manuel élémentaire d'éducation ... Berlin, etc., Author, 1774. 3 vols. LEI

B84 BASEDOW, J. B. Kupfertafeln zum Elementarbuch für die Jugend ... [by D. N. Chodiewiecki]. Altona & Bremen, 1770–1774. 2 vols. NoU

B85 BASEDOW, J. B. Kupfersammlung zu J. B. Basedows Elementarwerke für die Jugend ... [by Chodiewiecki]. Berlin and Leipzig, 1774. OX

B86 BASEDOW, J. B. (1770) Das Methodenbuch für Väter und Mütter der Familien und Völker. 2. Aufl. Leipzig, 1771. LO

B87 BASEDOW, J. B. (1777) Practische Philosophie für alle Stände. Dessau, 1777. 2 vols. LO

B88 BASEDOW, J. B., and CAMPE, Joachim Heinrich. Pädagogische Unterhandlungen. Band I [only]. Dessau, 1777. LO

B89 [BAXTER, Andrew], 1686–1750. (Lat. 1738; Eng. 1740) Matho; or, the cosmotheoria puerilis, a dialogue in which the first principles of philosophy and astronomy are accommodated to the capacity of young persons ... Translated and enlarged by the author in two volumes. Miller, 1740. LEE

BAYLEY, Nathaniel. *See* Bailey, Nathan

BEAUMONT, Jeanne Marie Le Prince de. *See* Le Prince de Beaumont, J. M.

B90 BEAUTIES of fables: in verse: selected to form the judgment, direct the taste, and improve the conduct of youth. Smeaton, [1780?]. BI

B91 The BEE. (1795) 6th ed., 1811. *See* D95

B92 BELL, Andrew, 1753–1832. (1797) An experiment in education. *For subsequent editions, under various titles, see* C93–C103

B93 BELLAMY, Daniel, b. 1687, *ed. and trans.* Fifty instructive and entertaining fables of Phaedrus, in Latin, French and English, attempted after a new method, for the more speedy improvement of youth in schools. Knapton, [etc.], 1734. BR

B93a BELLAMY, Daniel, *ed. and trans.* Youth's scripture-remembrancer; or, select Bible stories written originally in Latin by S. Castalio for the use of foreign schools. And now attempted in an English dress ... by D. Bellamy. Robinson, Chapelle & Leake, 1743. [Translated from Bk. I of the Dialogi sacri.] BI

BELLEGARDE, Jean Baptiste Morvan de. *See* Morvan de Bellegarde, J. B.

BELLIUS, Martin, *pseud. See* Chateillon, Sebastien

B94 BEMMELEN, J. van. (179–?) Leçons faciles & instructives, destinées à être traduites en hollandais ou en anglais ... 2e éd. corr. Leyden, Honkoop, n.d. [Inscription dated 1802.] LEI
Benefits and duties of the members of Christ's Kingdom. *See* Robinson, John

B95 [BENNETT, John], *fl.* 1782–1788. (1788) Strictures on female education; chiefly as it relates to the culture of the heart ... By a clergyman of the Church of England. Author, [1788]. BI HU LEE

B96 BENNETT, John, *curate of St. Mary's, Manchester.* (1785) The advantages of Sunday schools: a discourse preached for the benefit of that ... charity at St. Mary's church in Manchester. To which is prefixed some account of the origin, design, and progress of this institution. Manchester, Wheeler, 1785. ReU

B97 BENTHAM, Jeremy, 1748–1832. (1776–1789) A fragment on government, and An introduction to the principles of morals and legislation; edited ... by W. Harrison. Oxford, Blackwell, 1948. LEI SO

B98 BENTLEY, Cl., *ed.* Phaedri Aug. Caesar Fabularum Aesopiarum libri quinque ... 1762. *See* B815 Phaedrus

B99 BERINGTON, Joseph, 1746–1827. (1788) An essay on the depravity of the nation, with a view to the promotion of Sunday schools, etc. ... Birmingham, M. Swinney; London, Robinson; 1788. HU

B100 BERKENHOUT, John, 1730?–1791. (1790) A volume of letters from Dr. Berkenhout to his son at the university. Cambridge U.P. for T. Cadell, 1790. LO

B101 BERNARD, Thomas. (1736) The advantages of learning, a sermon preach'd 12 Aug. 1736. 1736. ReU

B102 BERNARDIN DE SAINT-PIERRE, Jacques Henri, 1737–1814. (Fr. 1788; Eng. 1795?) Paul and Virginia. Translated from the French of Bernardin Saint-Pierre; by Helen Maria Williams ... 4th ed. Vernor & Hood, 1799. LEI

B103 BERNOULLI, Jacques, 1654–1705. (1713) Ars conjectandi, opus posthumum. Accedit, Tractatus de seriebus infinitis, etc. Basle, Impensis Thurnisiorum, 1713. LO

B104 BERQUIN, Arnaud, 1749–1791. (1782–1783) L'ami des enfans. Tomes I–IV. Londres, Stockdale, [etc.], 1787. LEE

B105 BERQUIN, Arnaud. L'ami des enfans. Nlle. éd. revue et corrigée ... par Nicolas Salmon. Londres, J. Johnson, [etc.], 1798. 4 vols. LEI

B106 BERQUIN, Arnaud. The children's friend. Translated by the Rev. Mark Anthony Meilan. Printed for the translator, 1786. 24 vols. in 12. ReU

B107 BERQUIN, Arnaud. The children's friend. Being a selection from the works of M. Berquin. 3rd ed. 1798. NoU; new ed., 1804. *See* D103

B108 [BERQUIN, Arnaud]. L'amico de' fanciulli, o sia, Il morale instruttore ... [Trans. into Italian by G. Buccarelli and F. Sastres, and introduced into England by G. Ernst.] London, Hooper, 1788. 4 vols. LO

B109 [BERQUIN, Arnaud]. (1792) The looking-glass for the mind. A reprint of the edition of 1792, with the original illustrations by Bewick. With an introduction by Charles Welsh. Griffith, Farran, etc., 1885. LEI

B110 BERQUIN, Arnaud. The looking-glass for the mind; or, intellectual mirror: being an elegant collection of the most delightful little stories and interesting tales. Dove, [1796]. LEE

B111 [BERQUIN, Arnaud], do., 9th ed., 1803; 10th ed., 1806; 23rd ed., 1862. *See* D104

B112 BERQUIN, Arnaud. (1796) The blossoms of morality ... [2nd ed.]. 1796. NoU

B113 BERQUIN, Arnaud, do., 8th ed., 1828. *See* D105

[These two abridgments of Berquin's *Ami des enfans* have been ascribed to 'The Rev. Mr. Cooper', but were probably edited by Richard Johnson.]

B114 BERQUIN, Arnaud. (1788) The friend of youth, by Mark Anthony Meilan; being a sequel to The children's friend ... partly translated from Mr. Berquin, and other French and German writers, and partly original, being written by the editor himself. *See* B715 Meilan, M. A.

B115 BERQUIN, Arnaud. (1791) Le petit Grandisson. Traduction libre du hollandais. 3e éd., 1801. *See* D106

B116 BERQUIN, Arnaud. (1776) Romances. Paris, Moutardier, 1796. ReU

B117 BERRIMAN, William, 1688–1750. (1742) Youth the proper season of discipline, a sermon preach'd before the Society corresponding with the Incorporated Society ... in Dublin, March 23, 1741–2. Downing, 1742. LEI ReU

B118 BETZKY, Ivan Ivanovich. Les plans et les statuts, des différents établissements ordonnés par Sa Majesté Impériale Catherine II pour l'éducation de la jeunesse . . . Ecrits en langue russe . . . & traduits en langue françoise . . . par Mr. Clerc. Amsterdam, M. M. Rey, 1775. 2 vols. LEI

B119 BIBLE. A new hieroglyphical Bible for the amusement and instruction of children; being a selection of the most useful lessons, and most interesting narratives; scripturally arranged . . . embellished with familiar figures, and striking emblems . . . [Pref. 1794.] [t.p. torn and publisher's name wanting]. LEI

B120 BIBLE. A curious hieroglyphick Bible. 20th ed., 1812; The modern hieroglyphical Bible, n.d. *See* D109–110

B121 BIELFELD, Jacob Friedrich, *baron*, 1711?– 1770. (Fr. 1768?) The elements of universal erudition . . . Translated . . . by W. Hooper. Dublin, Saunders, [etc.], 1771. 3 vols. BI

B122 BISSE, Thomas, d. 1731. (1725) Publick education, particularly in the charity schools; a sermon preach'd at St. Philip's church in Birmingham, August 9, 1724 . . . W. & J. Innys, 1725. BI ReU

B123 BISSET, James, 1762–1832. (1800) Juvenile reduplications; or, the new 'House that Jack built' . . . Birmingham, 1800. NoU

BLACKISTON, *Dr. See* Blackstone, Charles

B124 [BLACKSTONE, Charles], b. 1720. A reply to Dr. Golding's and Dr. Lowth's answers to the anonymous letter. By a Wykehamist. R. Baldwin, 1759. HU

B125 BLACKWALL, Anthony, 1674–1730. (1718) An introduction to the classics . . . Mortlock, [etc.], 1718 LEI; 2nd ed., Mortlock, [etc.], 1719. LO; 5th ed., with additions and an index. C. Rivington, 1737. HU LEE

B126 BLAIR, Hugh, 1718–1800. (Lectures 1783) An abridgement of: Lectures on rhetoric. For the use of schools. 1824. *See* D120a

B127 BLAIR, Robert, 1699–1746. The poems of Thomas Gray and Robert Blair, arranged for the use of young people. [18–]. *See* D121

BLAKISTON, *Dr. See* Blackstone, Charles

Blind child. *See* Pinchard, *Mrs.*

Blossoms of morality. *See* Berquin, A.

B128 BOBBIT, Richard. (1781?) Arithmetic methodised: or, a regular treatise of arithmetic, applied to the most useful branches of trade . . . with . . . a course of book-keeping by single entry. Newcastle, Author, [etc.], 1781. HU

BONNOT DE CONDILLAC, Etienne. *See* Condillac, Etienne Bonnot de

B129 BONNYCASTLE, John, 1750?–1821. (1782) An introduction to algebra; with notes and observations: designed for the use of schools and places of public education. 2nd ed., J. Johnson, 1788. HU; 4th ed., 1796. NoU

B130 BONNYCASTLE, John, do., 12th ed., 1822, *and* new ed. enl., 1833. *See* D127

B131 BONNYCASTLE, John. (1786) An introduction to astronomy. 7th ed., 1816. *See* D128

B132 BONNYCASTLE, John. (1782) An introduction to mensuration and practical geometry with notes, containing the reason of every rule. 4th ed., 1794. NoU; 5th ed., corr., J. Johnson, 1798. BR

B133 BONNYCASTLE, John, do., 11th ed., 1816, *and* 13th ed., 1823. *See* D129

B134 BONNYCASTLE, John. (2nd ed. 1780) The scholar's guide to arithmetic. 5th ed., 1788. NoU

B135 [BOREMAN, Thomas], *ed.* (1736) A description of a great variety of animals and vegetables . . . adapted . . . especially for the entertainment of youth . . . T. Boreman, 1736. NoU

B136 BOS, Lambert, 1670–1717. (Latin 1714?) The antiquities of Greece. New ed., 1805. *See* D133

BOSSIGNY, Louise de, *comtesse d'* Auneuil. *See* Auneuil *comtesse d'*

B137 BOUDIER DE VILLEMERT, Pierre-Joseph. (1758) L'ami des femmes, ou, La philosophie du beau sexe. 3e éd., Paris, [privately printed], 1766. LO

BOUREAU DESLANDES, André François. *See* Deslandes, A.

B138 BOURN, Samuel, 1689–1754. (1748) Religious education begun and carried on in three catechisms . . . Birmingham, Robinson, 1748. BI

B139 BOYER, Abel, 1667–1729. (1694) The complete French master for ladies and gentlemen . . . 19th ed., Ballard, [etc.], 1761. LEI; 24th ed., E. Barnard, [etc.], 1779. ReU

B140 BOYER, Abel. (1699) Le dictionnaire royal, françois–anglois et anglois–françois . . . Autrefois composé à l'usage de feu S.A.R. le duc de Glocester [*sic*] par M. A. Boyer. Nlle. éd., soigneusement revue, corrigée, & augmentée . . . par J. C. Prieur. C. Bathurst, [etc.], 1773. 2 vols. LEI

B141 BOYER, Abel, *trans.* The adventures of Telemachus. *See* B355 Fénelon

B142 BRADFORD, Samuel, 1652–1731. (1709) Unanimity and charity, the character of Christians, a sermon preach'd June 16, 1709. J. Wyat, 1709. ReU

B143 [BRIDLE, John], *D.D.* (1758) A letter to the Reverend Dr. Lowth . . . in vindication of the conduct of the Fellows of New College in Oxford, in their late election of a Warden of Winchester. R. Baldwin, 1758. HU

B144 [BRIDLE, John] (1758) A short address to the Society of New College in Oxford. Occasioned by a paragraph in a late dedication. J. Staples, 1758. HU

B145 BRIGGS, Henry, 1561–1630. Mathematical tables. *See* B958 Sherwin, H.

B146 BRIGHTLAND, John, *fl.* 1711. (1711) A grammar of the English tongue, with the arts of logic, rhetorick, poetry, etc. Also useful notes giving the grounds and reason of grammar in general. The whole making a compleat system of an English education. 3rd ed., Author, 1714. LEE NoU

Britain's remembrancer, *author of. See* Burgh, J.

B147 BROKESBY, Francis, 1637–1714. (1701) A letter of advice to a young gentleman at the university. To which are subjoined, directions for young students. [No publisher], 1701, repr. 1751. BI

B148 [BROOKE, Henry], 1694–1757. An appeal to the publick from an unappellate tribunal. Or an impartial enquiry into the rise, progress and extent of visitatorial power, in a letter to a member of the House of Commons, by a senior fellow of a college in Oxford. Roberts, 1740. LEE

B149 BROOM, Thomas. (1791?) Sketches of female education, partly original and partly selected from the most approved authors for the instruction and amusement of young ladies, both in public seminaries and private families. Law, 1791. BI

B150 BROWN, John, 1715–1766. Sermons on various subjects. Davis & Reymers, 1764. BI

B151 BROWNE, John. Letter to Catherine, Empress of Russia. [Copy of 2 pp. of a MS. at Cambridge.] London, 1766. LO

B152 BROWNE (or Brown), Richard, *English master at Rugby*. (1700) The English school reformed; containing I. Rules shewing the nature of vowels . . . Lastly, An accidence adapted to our English tongue. 7th ed., corr. By R. Brown. T. Norris, 1722. HU

BRULART DE SILLERY, *Mme*. *See* Genlis, *comtesse de*

BRYDALL, John. *See* Bridle, J.

B153 BUCCARELLI, Giovanni Battista, *trans*. L'amico de' fanciulli. *See* B108 Berquin, A.

B154 BUCHANAN, James, *fl*. 1753–1766. (1753) The complete English scholar, in three parts. Containing a new . . . method of instructing children . . . in the English tongue, and of learning grammar in general, without the help of Latin. A. Millar, 1753. HU

B155 BURGESS, D. (1759) The entertainer; or, youth's delightful preceptor. To which is prefixed, A plan of education, from the Chevalier Ramsay . . . And an appendix, containing rules for reading and study . . . from the learned Mr. Locke . . . Berwick, R. Taylor, pr., 1759. LEI

B156 BURGESS, D. The York entertainer; or, youth's delightful preceptor . . . York, 1759. NoU

B157 BURGH, James, 1714–1775. (1747) Thoughts on education . . . By the author of Britain's remembrancer. London, Freer, 1747. LEE; Edinburgh, 1747. HU

B158 BURMANN, Pieter, 1668–1741, *ed*. Quintilian's De institutione oratoria. *See* B863 Quintilian

B159 [BURN, John], 1744?–1802. (1766) A practical grammar of the English language: in which the several parts of speech are clearly and methodically explained . . . together with rules of composition . . . For use in schools. 2nd ed., Glasgow, D. Reid, pr., 1772. HU

B160 BURNET, Gilbert, 1643–1715. (1761) Thoughts on education. By the late Bishop Burnet. Now first printed from an original manuscript. D. Wilson, 1761. BI HU LEE

B161 BURTON, J., *of Rochester?* (1793) Lectures on female education and manners. 2nd ed., Johnson, 1793. 2 vols. BI; 3rd ed., Dublin, J. Milliken, 1794. SH; 4th ed., Dublin, Milliken, 1796. LEE

B162 [BURTON, Nicholas]. (1702) Figurae grammaticae & rhetoricae Latino carmine donatae . . . Cum indice figurarum etymologico. In usum Regiae Scholae Dunelmensis. Leigh & Midwinter, 1702. LEI

B163 [BUSBY, Richard], 1606–1695. (1647?) Graecae grammatices rudimenta. In usum Scholae Regiae Westmonasteriensis. Wm. Redmayne, 1707. HU

B164 BUSBY, Richard. (1702 in this form) Grammatica Busbeiana, auctior et emendatior, i.e. Rudimentum grammaticae graeco-latinae metricum. In usum nobilium puerorum in Schola Regia Westmonasterii. Redmayne, 1702. LEI; G. Ginger, 1789. HU

B165 [BUSBY, Richard]. (1688) Rudimentum grammaticae Latinae metricum, in usum Scholae Regiae Westmonasteriensis. Barker, 1729. LEI; *another ed.*, 1810. *See* D166

B166 BUTLER, Joseph, *bp. of Durham*, 1692–1752. (1745) A sermon preached in the parish-church of Christ Church, London; on Thursday May 9th, 1745. Being the time of the yearly meeting of the children educated in the charity-schools . . . To which is annexed an account of the Society for promoting Christian knowledge. S.P.C.K., 1745. BI

B167 [BUTLER, S.], *of Bristol*. (1753?) An essay upon education, by a gentleman of Bristol. Owen, Robinson, [etc.], [1753?]. BR

B168 BUTLER, William, *writing master*, d. 1822? (2nd ed. 1795) Arithmetical questions. 5th ed., 1811, *and* 10th ed., 1829. *See* D171

B169 BUTLER, William. (1799) Chronological, biographical, historical and miscellaneous exercises. 7th ed., 1823. *See* D172

B170 BUTLER, William. (1798) Exercises on the globes and maps. 6th ed., 1814, *and* 12th ed., 1831. *See* D173

B171 BUTTERWORTH, Edmund, *writing master*. Butterworth's text copies. Set 2nd, 1799. NoU

B172 BUTTERWORTH, Edmund. Butterworth's universal penman, or, the beauties of writing delineated . . . [Edinburgh?], [1785]. NoU

B173 BUTTON, Edward. (1739) Rudiments of ancient history, sacred and prophane . . . Dublin, Faulkner, 1740. BI

B174 BUXTORF, Johannes, 1564–1629. (3rd ed. 1617) Epitome grammaticae Hebraeae, breviter & methodice ad publicum scholarum usum proposita . . . Jam variis in locis a mendis typographicis emendata . . . a Johanne Leusden. Ed. quarta. Leyden, S. Luctmans, 1716. LEI
Calendar of nature. *See* Aikin, J.

B175 [CAMDEN, William], 1551–1623. (1595) Institutio graecae grammatices compendiaria in usum Regiae Scholae Westmonasteriensis . . . W. Norton, 1701. HU; Norton, 1725. LEE

B176 CAMDEN, William, do. [Edited by John Ward.] Buckley & Longman, 1763. HU; Buckley & Longman, 1779. LEI; Buckley & Longman, 1793. LEE

B177 CAMDEN, William. Camdenus illustratus, sive graeca grammatica luculenta . . . 4th ed., Brotherton, 1750. [An adaptation of the Institutio.] LEE

B178 CAMPE, Joachim Heinrich, 1764–1818. (Germ. 1779; Eng. 1781–1788) The new Robinson Crusoe . . . 2nd ed., Vols. 1 and 2 [of 4]. 1789. NoU

B179 CAMPE, J. H. Le nouveau Robinson. 4th ed., 1814. *See* D204

B180 CAMPE, J. H., and BASEDOW, Johann Bernard. Pädagogische Unterhandlungen. *See* B88 Basedow, J. B., and Campe, J. H.

B181 CAPPE, Catherine. (1800) An account of two charity schools for the education of girls; and of a female friendly society in York: interspersed with reflections on charity schools and friendly societies in general. York, Johnson, [etc.], 1800. LEE

B182 CARACCIOLI, Louis Antoine de, *marquis*, 1721–1803. (1759) Le véritable mentor, ou, l'éducation de la noblesse. Liège, Bassompière; Brussels, J. van den Berghen; 1759. HU

B183 [CARACCIOLI, L. A. de]. (1786) La vie de Madame de Maintenon, institutrice de la royale maison de Saint-Cyr. Paris, Buisson, 1786. LEI

CARITAT DE CONDORCET, Antoine Nicolas de. *See* Condorcet, A. N. de Caritat, *marquis de*

B184 CARPENTER, Thomas. (1796) The scholar's spelling assistant. New ed., 1833, *and* new ed., 1839. *See* D210

B185 CARTER, Benjamin, *fl.* 1716–1722. (1718) The excellency of friendship, a sermon preach'd at the parish-church of St. Saviour in Southwark, 17 Nov. 1718, at the first general meeting of the gentlemen educated at the Free-School of the said parish. J. Wyat, 1718. ReU

B186 CASA, Giovanni della, 1503–1556. (It. 1558) Galateo: or, a treatise on politeness and delicacy of manners. Addressed to a young nobleman. From the Italian [by Richard Graves]. Dodsley, 1774. LEI

CASTALIO, Sebastian. *See* Chateillon, S.

B187 A CATECHETICAL instruction: being an account of the chief truths of the Christian religion. New ed., 1821. *See* D216

Catechistical explanation of the dayly and Sunday offices. *See* Creffeild, E.

B188 CATLOW, Samuel. (1793) Observations on a course of instructions, for young persons in the middle classes of life. Johnson, & Knott, 1793. LEE

B189 CATO, Dionysius. Cato's Distichs *de moribus*, with a numerical *clavis*, and construing and parsing index . . . To which is added, an English translation of Erasmus's commentaries on each distich. For the use of schools. 5th ed., corr. and impr. By N. Bailey. D. Browne, 1757. HU

B190 CATO, Dionysius. 1. Catonis disticha de moribus. 2. Dicta insignia septem sapientium Graeciae. 3. Mimi Publiani, sive Senecae proverbia, Anglo-Latino . . . [with translation by] C. Hoole . . . 1722. NoU; 1749. NoU

B191 CELLARIUS, Christophorus, 1638–1707. (1686?) Geographia antiqua recognita denuo . . . 5a ed. plurimis locis aucta & immutata. Huic demum 6a ed . . . chartas . . . duplicemque indicem . . . addidit, totam recensuit, & scholarum usui accommodavit Samuel Patrick. Ed. altera & castigatior. S. Ballard, [etc.], 1745. LEI

B192 CHAMBAUD, Louis. (1751) Fables choisies, à l'usage des enfans, et des autres personnes qui commencent à apprendre la langue françoise . . . Nlle. éd. rev. & corr. Londres, C. Nourse, 1786. LEI

B193 CHAMBAUD, Louis. (1750) A grammar of the French tongue, with a prefatory discourse, containing an essay on the proper method for teaching and learning that language. 5th ed., rev. and corr., A. Millar and T. Cadell, 1769. HU

B194 CHAMBAUD, Louis. (1750) Thèmes françois & anglois. Or, French and English exercises. 2nd ed., Millar, 1764. LEI

B195 CHAPMAN, George, 1723–1806. (1773) A treatise on education, with a sketch of the author's method. 3rd ed. enl., Cadell, 1784. LEE

B196 CHAPMAN, George. A treatise on education. In two parts. With the author's method of instruction while he taught the school of Dumfries. And a view of other books on education. 4th ed. Author, 1790. BI HU LEE LEI LI

B197 CHAPMAN, John, 1704–1784. (1752) The ends and uses of charity-schools for poor children. A sermon preach'd April 30, 1752, being the time of the yearly meeting . . . B. Dod, 1752. ReU

B198 CHAPONE, *Mrs.* Hester, 1727–1801. (1773) Letters on the improvement of the mind, addressed to a young lady. 1773. 2 vols. ReU; new ed., Walter, 1787. LEE; Walter, 1797. LO

B199 CHAPONE, *Mrs.* Hester, do., *another ed.*, 1811, *and* 1829; 8th ed., 1848. *See* D230

B200 CHARLES II, *king of England. Charters.* The charter . . . impowering Erasmus Smith Esq., to erect grammar schools in the Kingdom of Ireland, and to endow the same . . . Together with an Act of Parliament for the further application of the said charity. Dublin, Erasmus Smith charity trustees, 1724. BI

B201 CHARRON, Pierre, 1541–1603. (Fr. 1601; Eng. 1697) Of wisdom. Three books. Written originally in French, by the Sieur de Charron. With an account of the author. Made English by George Stanhope . . . 2nd ed. corr. Book 1 [only]. R. Bonwick, [etc.], 1707. LEI

Charters of the Collegiate church . . . [Manchester]. *See* Manchester. *Charters*

B202 CHATEILLON, Sebastien, 1515–1563. (1552?) Youth's scripture-remembrancer; or, select Bible stories written originally in Latin by S. Castalio for the use of foreign schools. And now attempted in an English dress . . . by D. Bellamy . . . Robinson, Chapelle & Leake, 1743. [Translated from Bk. 1 of the Dialogi sacri.] BI

B203 CHATHAM, William Pitt, *earl of*, 1708–1778. Letters written to his nephew Thomas Pitt. 1805. *See* C255

B204 CHESTERFIELD, Philip Dormer Stanhope, *4th earl of*, 1694–1773. (4th ed., 1775.) The accomplished gentleman. (1847?) *See* D237

B205 CHESTERFIELD, *earl of*. (1800) The elements of a polite education; carefully selected from the Letters . . . to his son. Edited by G. Gregory. R. Phillips, [1800]. LEE; 2nd ed., Phillips, [1800]. BI LO; 1802. *See* D238

B206 CHESTERFIELD, *earl of.* (1774) Lord Chesterfield's maxims, or, a new plan of education, on the principles of virtue and politeness . . . Being the substance of . . . letters to his son . . . 1777. NoU

B207 CHETWOOD, Knightly, 1650–1720. (1701) A sermon preach'd Dec. 6, 1700. 1701. ReU

B208 CHILDREN IN THE WOOD. The history of the two children in the wood. Warrington, [17–?]. NoU
Children's friend. *See* Berquin, A.

B209 The CHILDREN's magazine, or, monthly repository of instruction and delight. February and October, 1799. NoU

B210 The CHILD's first book. New ed., 1820. *See* D250

B211 CHILD's. (1743) Child's new play-thing; being a spelling-book intended to make the learning to read a diversion instead of a task . . . 7th ed., Ware, 1760. BI

B212 [CHODOWIECKI, Daniel Nikolaus], 1726–1801. (1770–1774) Kupfertafeln zum Elementarbuch für die Jugend, ihre Eltern und Freunde in gesitteten Ständen [von J. B. Basedow]. Altona and Bremen, 1770–1774. 2 vols. NoU

B213 [CHODOWIECKI, D. N.]. Kupfersammlung zu J. B. Basedows Elementarwerke für die Jugend und ihre Freunde . . . Berlin and Leipzig, 1774. OX

B214 CHURCH, Thomas, 1707–1756. A sermon preached in the parish-church of Christ-Church, London, on Thursday May the 2nd 1751 . . . [with] An account of the Society for promoting Christian knowledge. B. Dod, 1751, HU

B215 CICERO, Marcus Tullius. Opuscula: hoc est, Cato major, seu, de senectute. Laelius, seu, de amicitia. Paradoxia. Somnium Scipionis. Praefigitur ejusdem M. T. Ciceronis vita literaria. Editio altera recognita. Eton, 1789. NoU

B216 CICERO, M. T. Select orations, translated into English [by Wm. Duncan]; with the original Latin . . . and notes . . . designed for the use of schools, as well as private gentlemen. G. Keith, 1756. LEI
Circle of the sciences. Vol. 6. *See* Newbery, J., Geography made familiar and easy

B217 CLAGETT [*or* Claggett], Nicholas, *bp of Exeter*, d. 1746. (1739) A sermon preach'd May 3, 1739, on behalf of the charity schools in and about London and Westminster. 1739. ReU

B218 CLAIRAUT, Alexis Claude, 1713–1765. (1749) Elémens d'algèbre . . . 4e éd., Paris, 1768. BI

B219 CLARKE, H., *teacher of the Latin language.* Fabulae Aesopi selectae, or select fables of Aesop; with an English translation . . . 9th ed., 1784. NoU

B220 CLARKE, John, 1686–1734, *master of Hull grammar school.* (1731) An essay upon study. Wherein directions are given for the due conduct thereof, and the collection of a library, proper for the purpose . . . Bettesworth, 1731. HU LEE; 2nd ed., Bettesworth, 1737. BI

B221 CLARKE, John. (1720) An essay upon the education of youth in grammar-schools . . . J. Wyat, 1720. HU; 2nd ed., with very large additions. Bettesworth, 1730. LEE ReU

B222 CLARKE, John, *trans.* (1734) C. Crispi Sallustii Bellum Catalinarium et Jugurthinum; cum versione libera . . . I.e., The history of the wars . . . to which is prefixed a large dissertation upon the usefulness of translations of classic authors. 4th ed. W. Clarke, 1745. HU

B223 CLARKE, John, *trans.* (1732) C. Suetonii Tranquilli XII Caesares . . . or, The lives of the twelve first Roman emperors . . . with a free translation . . . Bettesworth & Hitch, 1732. HU; 2nd ed., Bettesworth & Hitch, 1739. HU

B224 CLARKE, John, *trans.* (1718) Corderii colloquiorum centuria selecta; or, a select century of Cordery's colloquies: with English translation as literal as possible, design'd for the use of beginners in the Latin tongue. York, Grace White for Tho. Hammond, jun., 1718. HU; 5th ed., Bettesworth & Hitch, 1730. LEE; 26th ed., 1783. NoU

B225 CLARKE, John, *trans.* (1720) Erasmi colloquia selecta; or, the select colloquies of Erasmus. With an English translation . . . 14th ed., W. Clarke, 1757. LEI; 19th ed., 1775. NoU; 20th ed., Gloucester, R. Raikes; London, Rivington, etc.; 1782. HU

B226 CLARKE, John, *trans.* (1722) Eutropii historiae Romanae breviarum, cum versione Anglica . . . Or Eutropius's compendious history of Rome: together with an English translation . . . notes and an index . . . York, Chas. Bourne for Tho. Hammond, 1722. HU NoU; 2nd ed., York, Gent, 1728. LEE

B227 CLAVERING, Robert, 1671–1747. (1733) A sermon preach'd April 5, 1733, at the yearly meeting of the children educated in the charity-schools . . . 1733. ReU
CLAVILLE, Charles François Nicolas Le Maître de. *See* Le Maitre de Claville, C. F. N.

B228 CLAYTON, Robert, 1695–1758. (1740) The religion of labour, a sermon preach'd . . . before the Incorporated society for promoting English Protestant schools in Ireland. Dublin, Grierson, 1740. LEI ReU
CLERC, Nicolas Gabriel, *aft.* Leclerc. *See* Leclerc, N. G.

B229 CLOWES, J., *trans.* (1797) Pious reflections, for every day in the month. 1823. *See* D269

B230 CLUTTON, John. (1795) Two addresses: one to the children belonging to the Charity School, Birmingham; the other to the apprentices educated therein. Birmingham, M. Swinney, pr., 1795. HU
Cobwebs to catch flies. *See* Fenn, E.

B231 COCKER, Edward, 1631–1675. (1678) Arithmetick: being a plain and familiar method . . . Perused and published by John Hawkins . . . 29th ed., 1711. NoU; 37th ed., Tracy, 1720. LEI; 44th ed., carefully corrected and amended by George Fisher . . . E. Midwinter, [172–]. HU NoU; 46th ed., [1736?]. NoU; 55th ed., 1758. NoU

B232 COCKER, Edward. (1685) Decimal arithmetick . . . Perused, corrected, and published by John Hawkins. 3rd ed., 1703. NoU; 5th ed., 1720. NoU; 6th ed., J. Darby, [etc.], 1729. HU LEI NoU

B233 COCKER, Edward. (1704) Cocker's English dictionary; containing, an explanation of the most refined and difficult words and terms . . . Publish'd from the author's copy. 2nd ed., very much enlarged and altered, by John Hawkins, 1715. NoU; 3rd ed., T. Norris and A. Bettesworth, 1724. HU

B234 COKE (or Cooke), master of Thame school, d. 1795. (1785) A poetical essay on the early part of education; to which is prefixed an enquiry into the discipline of the ancients, with some observations on that part of our public schools. Oxford, Clarendon Pr., 1785. HU

B235 COLES, Elisha, 1640?–1680. (1676) An English dictionary, explaining the difficult terms that are used in divinity, husbandry, physick . . . and other arts and sciences . . . R. Bonwick, [etc.], 1717. HU; another ed., newly corrected, and much improved. Walthorn, [etc.], 1732. LEE

B236 COMBE, Edward, trans. The art of being easy at all times. See B286 Deslandes, A.

B237 COMENIUS, John Amos, 1592–1670. (Lat. 1654; Eng. 1658) Orbis sensualium pictus . . . John Amos Comenius's Visible world . . . Translated into English by Charles Hoole . . . 11th ed., 1729. NoU; 12th ed., corr. and enl., Leacroft, 1777. BI HU LEE ReU

B238 COMPAGNE. (1791?) La compagne de la jeunesse, ou entretiens d'une institutrice avec son élève. Londres, Edwards, 1791. 2 vols. LEI

B239 COMPARET, J. A. (176–?) Education morale. Ou, réponse à cette question proposée en 1765, par la Société des Arts et Sciences de Harlem. Geneva, Pellet, 1770. LO

B240 A COMPENDIOUS history of England, from the invasion by the Romans to the beginning of the year 1789 . . . 1789. NoU

B241 The COMPLETE letter-writer; or, polite English secretary . . . To which is prefixed, a plain and compendious grammar of the English tongue . . . 17th ed., 1785. NoU

B241a CONCIONES et orationes ex historicis latinis excerptae . . . in usum Scholae Westmonasteriensis . . . 1713. NoU; J. Tonson and J. Watts, 1727. LEI

B242 CONDILLAC, Etienne Bonnot de, 1715–1780. (1775?) Cours d'étude pour l'instruction du Prince de Parme. Geneva, F. Dufart, 1789. 16 vols. LO

B243 CONDORCET, Antoine Nicolas de Caritat, marquis de, 1743–1794. (1792) Report on the general organization of public instruction. See B1172 De la Fontainerie, F., ed.

B244 CONDORCET, marquis de. (1799) A sure and easy method of learning to calculate. 1815. See C305

B245 The CONSTRUCTION of the Latin verse-grammar. For the use of the lower forms in Westminster School. Barker, 1729. LEI; 1810. See D290

Conversations and amusing tales. See English, Harriet

B246 CONYBEARE, John, 1692–1755. (1733) Scripture difficulties consider'd, a sermon preach'd 31 Aug. 1732 in the cathedral church of St. Peter, Exon. . . . at the anniversary meeting of the gentlemen educated at the Free-School there. Knapton, 1733. ReU

B247 COOKE, Thomas. (1771?) The universal letter-writer. [c. 1838.] See D297

COOKE, William. See Coke, W.

B248 [COOPER, Rev. Mr.], pseud.? (1761) A new history of England, from the invasion of Julius Caesar to the present time . . . J. Newbery, 1763. NoU

B249 COOPER, Rev. Mr., do., 15th ed., 1809, and 21st ed., 1830. See D298

B250 [COOPER, Rev. Mr.], trans. (1796) The blossoms of morality. See B112 Berquin, A.

B251 [COOPER, Rev. Mr.], trans. (1792) The looking-glass for the mind. See B109–110 Berquin, A.

[Mr. Cooper's initials are given variously as C., J., S., and W. D. The name may be a pseudonym of Richard Johnson, 1734–1793.]

B252 CORDIER, Mathurin, 1479/80–1564. (1564) Corderii colloquiorum centuria selecta; or, a select century of Cordery's colloquies: with English translation as literal as possible, design'd for the use of beginners in the Latin tongue. By John Clarke. York, G. White for T. Hammond, 1718. HU; 5th ed., London, Bettesworth & Hitch, 1730. LEE; 26th ed., 1783. NoU

B253 CORDIER, Mathurin. Une centurie des colloques de Cordier; or, a century of the colloquies of Corderius. For the use of schools. [Edited by John Stirling.] Wilcox, 1739. BI

B254 CORDIER, Mathurin. Colloquiorum Maturini Corderii centuria una; cum Erasmi Roterodami Colloquiis selectis . . . in usum scholarum. Amsterdam, 1742. NoU

B255 CORSINO, Edoardo (or Odoardo), 1702–1763. (1731?) Institutiones mathematicae ad usum scholarum piarum . . . Florence, Paperini, 1731. LEI

B256 COTES, E., schoolmaster. An English dictionary, explaining the difficult terms . . . Newly corrected, and much improved. Wilkin, [etc.], 1732. LEE

B257 [COTTON, Nathaniel], 1705–1788. (1751) Visions in verse, for the entertainment and instruction of younger minds. 9th ed., rev. and enl., Dodsley, 1796. LEI; new ed., Vernor & Hood, [etc.], 1798. BI LEE

B258 COWLEY, J., ed. A new and easy introduction to the study of geography. See B542 Huebner, Johann

COURCELLES, Anne Thérèse de Marguenat de, marquise de Lambert. See Lambert, marquise de

B259 COX, Thomas, rector of Stock-Harvard. (1712) The necessity of a right understanding . . . a sermon preach'd at the parish-church of Bishop Stortford, 26 Aug. 1712, at the annual meeting of the gentlemen educated in that school. Knaplock, 1712. ReU

B260 COZENS, Alexander, d. 1786. A new method of assisting the invention in drawing original compositions of landscape. [c. 1780.] NoU

B261 [CREFFEILD, Edward]. (1713) A catechistical explanation of the dayly and Sunday offices and rubricks of the common-prayer. Carefully adapted to the capacities of the younger and meaner sort . . . And humbly recommended to the use of charity schools . . . S. Keble, 1713. LEI

B262 Croft, George, *master of Beverley school.* (1775) General observations concerning education, applied to the author's method in particular. Hull, J. Ferraby, 1775. BR; *typescript copy,* HU

B262a Crosby, T., *ed.* (1799?) The tutor's assistant. *See* B1084

B263 Culmann, Leonhard, 1497–post 1549. (1554; Eng. 1658) Sententiae pueriles, Anglo-Latinae. Quae diversis authoribus olim collegerat Leonard Culman; et in vernaculum sermonem nuperrime transtulit Carolus Hoole . . . Sentences for children, English and Latin . . . S. Collins, 1717. HU; 1728. NoU

B264 Cunn, Samuel, *fl.* 1715–1720, *ed.* Euclid's Elements of geometry. *See* B575 Keill, J.

B265 Curray, Edward. (1732?) Sententiae selectae. Or, a collection of miscellaneous sentences . . . in prose and verse, English and Latin . . . T. Cobb, 1732. ReU

B266 Curtis, William. (1713) The peace-offering . . . a sermon encouraging . . . the decent appearance . . . of the charity children at divine service . . . preach'd June 25, 1713 at a meeting . . . at St. Mary Tower in Ipswich, for the support of the charity-schools there. J. Wyat, 1713. ReU
Cyclomathesis. *See* Emerson, William

B267 Danet, Pierre, d. 1709, *ed.* (1675?) Phaedri Augusti Caesari liberti Fabulorum Aesopiarum libri quinque: interpretatione & notis illustravit Petrus Danet . . . J. & B. Sprint, [etc.], 1722. LEI

B268 [Darrell, William], 1651–1721. (Pt. 1, 4th ed., 1709; Pts. 2–3, 1713) The gentleman instructed, in the conduct of a virtuous and happy life. In three parts. 9th ed., E. Smith, 1727. LEE

B269 Darrell, William, do., 11th ed. To which is added, a word to the ladies. D. Midwinter, 1738. LEE LO

B270 Darwin, Erasmus, 1721–1802. (1797) A plan for the conduct of female education in boarding schools. Derby, J. Drewry for J. Johnson, 1797. HU LEE LEI SH; 1798. ReU

B271 Daubeny, Charles, 1745–1827. (1799) A letter to Mrs. Hannah More, on some part of her . . . 'Strictures on female education' . . . J. Hatchard, 1799. BR

B272 Daubichon, J. An English exercise-book, to translate into French. 3rd ed., Dublin, 1768. NoU

D'Aubigné, Françoise, *marquise de Maintenon. See* Maintenon, *marquise de*

D'Aulnoy, Marie Cathérine Jumel de Berneville, *comtesse. See* Aulnoy, *comtesse d'*

David Simple, *author of. See* Fielding, Sarah

B273 Davidson, Robert. (1738?) A new guide to geography. For the use of schools. By the author of Geography epitomiz'd. Ware, 1738. LEE

B274 Davies, T., *schoolmaster.* The newest reading made completely easy: or, an introduction to reading the Holy Bible . . . New ed., Gainsborough, 1794. NoU

B275 Davys, P. (1790) Adminiculum puerile; or, a help for schoolboys . . . For the use of St. Patrick's school. Dublin, Cross, 1790. BI

B276 Dawes, *Sir* William, 1671–1724. (1704) The excellency and usefulness of wisdom . . . a sermon preach'd at Bishops Starford [*sic*] church, 17 Aug. 1703. At a feast for the encouragement of the school there. T. Speed, 1704. ReU

B277 Dawes, *Sir* William. (1713) The excellency of the charity of charity schools, in a sermon preach'd May 27, 1713, at the anniversary meeting . . . London and Westminster, A. Speed, 1713. ReU

B278 Dawes, *Sir* William. (1706) The nature and excellency of the duty of alms-giving, a sermon preach'd at the parish church of St. Giles in the Fields Nov. 17, 1706 on behalf of the charity-schools settled in that parish. 2nd ed., 1707. ReU

B279 Day, Thomas, 1748–1789. (1783–1789) The history of Sandford and Merton. 1787–1789. 3 vols. NoU

B280 Day, Thomas, do., 11th ed., 1802; 1803; 9th ed., 1812; 1816; 1818; Edinburgh, n.d.; 1887. *See* D334
Defence of the conduct of the Warden of Winchester. *See* Golding, Christopher

B281 Defoe, Daniel, 1661?–1731. (Written 1729) The compleat English gentleman. Edited for the first time from the author's autograph manuscript in the British Museum . . . by Karl D. Bülbring. Nutt, 1890. LEE LEI

B282 [Defoe, Daniel]. (1715–1718) The family instructor. 1809. *See* D335

B283 Defoe, Daniel. (1719) The history of Robinson Crusoe. [18–.] *See* D336

B284 Defoe, Daniel. (1719–1725) The life and adventures of Mr. Duncan Campbell [etc.]. 1841. *See* C356
De Luc, Jean André, *the elder. See* Luc, J. A. de

B285 Demosthenes. [De corona]. Ho peri Stephanou logos. *See* B11 Aeschines
Description of a great variety of animals and vegetables. *See* Boreman, Thomas

B286 [Deslandes, André], *fl.* 1713–1740. (Fr. 1715) The art of being easy at all times, and in all places. Written chiefly for the use of a lady of quality. Made English from the French original by Edward Combe. Rivington, 1724. LEE

B287 [Devis, Ellen [*or* Ellin].] (1775) The accidence; or, first rudiments of English grammar. Designed for the use of young ladies. With an appendix . . . By a Lady. Author, 1775. HU

B288 Devis, Ellen, do., 15th ed., 1814. *See* D343

B289 Dialogue sur l'ortographie . . . par M——. The Hague, 1736. NoU
Dialogues concerning education. *See* Fordyce, David
Dialogues on the passions. *See* Forrester, James
Dialogues on the uses of foreign travel. *See* Hurd, Richard
Dictionarium rusticum. *See* Worlidge, John
Dictionnaire historique d'éducation. *See* Fillassier, J. J.

B290 Diderot, Denis, 1713–1784. (Written *c.* 1776) Plan of a university for the Russian government. *See* B1172 De la Fontainerie, E., *ed.*

B291 DILWORTH, Thomas, d. 1780. (1740) A new guide to the English tongue, in five parts. New ed. corr. Printed for the booksellers, 1795. LEE

B292 DILWORTH, Thomas. (1743) The schoolmaster's assistant; being a compendium of arithmetic, both practical and theoretical . . . 13th ed., H. Kent, 1765. LEI; 18th ed., R. & H. Causton, 1773. HU ReU; New ed., Osborne & Griffin, 1787. LEE; 25th ed., 1795. NoU

B293 DIONYSIUS, *Periegetes*. Oikoumenes Periegesis, sive Dionysii Geographia; emendata & locupletata, additione scil. *Geographiae hodiernae* . . . ab Edu. Wells. [At head of title: Tes palai kai tes nun.] Ed. 5a, T. Wood, 1738. HU

Dissertation upon the way of teaching the Latin tongue. *See* Ruddiman, Thomas

B294 DITTON, Humphrey, 1675–1715, *ed.* (1693) Synopsis algebraica: opus posthumum Johannis Alexandri . . . Editio secunda, emendatior. Cui adjungitur appendix per Humfredum Ditton. In usum utriusque scholae mathematicae apud Hospitium-Christi Londinense. Christ's Hospital, 1709. LEI

B295 DITTON, Humphrey. [Preface to] Arithmetick both in the theory and practice. *See* B515 Hill, J.

B296 DIXON, Henry, *schoolmaster at Bath.* (1728) The English instructor; or, the art of spelling improved. Being a more plain, easy, and regular method of teaching young children, than any extant . . . London, J. Hazard; Bath, J. Leake; 1728. HU

B297 DODD, William, 1729–1777. (1795) The beauties of history; or, pictures of virtue and vice . . . 2nd ed., Vernor & Hood, 1796. BI

B298 DODDRIDGE, Philip, 1702–1751. (1743) The principles of the Christian religion, expressed in plain and easy verse. 1811. *See* D350

B299 DODDRIDGE, Philip. (1732) Sermons on the religious education of children, preached at Northampton. R. Holt, 1732. BR; 3rd ed., Fenner, 1743. LEI

B300 [DODSLEY, Robert], 1703–1764. (1748) The preceptor: containing a general course of education. Vol. 1 [only]. Dodsley, 1748. NoU; 5th ed., J. Dodsley, 1769. 2 vols. LEE LO; 6th ed., Dodsley, 1775. 2 vols. BI ReU; 7th ed., Dodsley, 1783. 2 vols. LEI; 8th ed., Dodsley, 1793. 2 vols. HU NoU

B301 DODSON, James, *ed.* A plain and familiar method for attaining the knowledge and practice of common arithmetic, [by E. Wingate]. 19th ed., by James Dodson. *See* B1151 Wingate, E.

B302 DODWELL, William, 1709–1785. (1758) A sermon preached in the parish-church of Christ-Church, London . . . May the 11th, 1758: being the time of the yearly meeting . . . To which is annexed an account of the Society for promoting Christian knowledge. B. Dod, 1758. HU

B303 DOWNES, Robert, *bishop of Raphol.* (1750) A sermon preach'd . . . 25 March, 1750, before the Incorporated society for promoting English Protestant schools in Ireland. 1750. ReU

B304 DOWNMAN, Hugh, 1740–1809. (1774–1776) Infancy, or, the management of children: a didactic poem in six books. 5th ed., Edinburgh, Bell & Bradfute, [etc.], 1790. BI; 7th ed., 1809. *See* C372

Ducks and green peas. *See* Lund, John

DU FRESNOY, Nicholas Lenglet. *See* Lenglet du Fresnoy, N.

DU MARTRE, Antoine Pyron. *See* Porny, Marc Antoine, *pseud.*

B305 [DUNCAN, William], 1717–1760, *trans.* (1756) Cicero's Select orations, translated into English; with the original Latin . . . and notes . . . designed for the use of schools, as well as private gentlemen. G. Keith, 1756. LEI

B306 DUNDAS, John. (1709?) The method of procedure by presbyteries, in settling of schools in every parish . . . Edinburgh, Anderson, 1709. LEE

B307 DUNSTER, Samuel, 1675–1754. (1707) Wisdom and understanding . . . a sermon preach'd 10 Feb., 1707, before the gentlemen educated at Merchant-Taylors' school. 2nd ed. ReU

B308 DYCHE, Thomas, *fl.* 1707–1719. (1707) A guide to the English tongue. In two parts. 48th ed., corr., C. & R. Ware, 1767. LEI; 52nd ed., 1769. NoU; 56th ed., Ware, 1771. BI; enl. ed., 1811. *See* D368

B309 DYCHE, Thomas. (6th ed., 1735) Vocabularium Latiale; or, a Latin vocabulary. In two parts . . . 13th ed., corr., B. Law, [etc.], 1788. HU

B310 DYCHE, Thomas. The youth's guide to the Latin tongue: or, an explication of Propria quae maribus, Quae genus, and As in praesenti . . . 3rd ed., Ware, 1748. LEI

E.R. *See* R., E.

B311 EASY lessons for beginners. 1797. NoU

Easy lessons for young children. *See* Trimmer, S.

B312 [EDGEWORTH, Maria], 1767–1849. (1795) Letters for literary ladies. To which is added, An essay on the noble science of self-justification. 2nd ed., J. Johnson, 1799. LO

B313 EDGEWORTH, Maria. (1795–1796?) The parent's assistant; or, stories for children. 3rd ed., Johnson, 1800. 6 vols. NoU; 3rd ed., Vol. 4 [only]. 1800. SO

B314 EDGEWORTH, Maria, do., 4th ed., 1804; New ed., 1834; New ed., 1855; New ed., 1897. *See* D385

B315 EDGEWORTH, Maria. Simple Susan. [From The Parent's assistant.] 1846, *and* 1858. *See* D387

B316 EDGEWORTH, Richard Lovell, 1747–1817, and EDGEWORTH, Maria. (1798) Practical education. J. Johnson, 1798. 2 vols. BR HU NO RE ReU

B317 EDGEWORTH, R. L., and EDGEWORTH, Maria, do., 2nd ed., 1801. *See* C399

B318 EDGEWORTH, R. L., and EDGEWORTH, Maria, do., *with title:* Essays on practical education. 3rd ed., 1811; New ed., 1815; 1822. *See* C399

Elegant epistles. *See* Knox, V.

Elegant extracts. *See* Knox, V.

Elements of the Latin language. *See* Valpy, R.

B319 ELLIS, William, *of King's College, Aberdeen.* (1782) A collection of English exercises. 6th ed., 1813. *See* D398

B320 [ELPHINSTON, James], 1721–1809. Plan of education at Mr. Elphinston's Academy, Kensington. [No publisher], [1764]. BI

B321 ELRINGTON, Thomas, 1760–1835, *ed.* (1788) Euclid's Elements of geometry. New ed., 1856. *See* D400

B322 [ELSTOB, William], 1673–1715, *ed.* (1703) Rogeri Aschami epistolarum libri quatuor. Accessit Joannis Sturmii aliorumque ad Aschamum anglosque alios eruditos epistolarum liber unus. Editio novissima, prioribus auctior. Oxford, Lichfield, 1703. LEI

B323 EMBLEMS for the entertainment and improvement of youth: containing hieroglyphical and enigmatical devices, relating to all parts and stations of life . . . The whole curiously engraved on 61 copper plates. Thos. Green, [*c.* 1728]. [Inscription dated 1728.] LEI; [1750?] NoU

B324 EMERSON, William, 1701–1782. (1763) Cyclomathesis; or, an easy introduction to the several branches of the mathematics . . . Nourse, 1763. BI

B325 ENFIELD, William, 1741–1797. (1780) Exercises in elocution; selected from various authors . . . Intended as a sequel to a work entitled *The Speaker* . . . A new edition, to which are added Counsels to young men, in a letter from a father to his son. J. Johnson, 1798. MA

B326 ENFIELD, William. (1774) The speaker; or, miscellaneous pieces, selected from the best English writers . . . with a view to facilitate the improvement of youth in reading and speaking. 8th ed., Dublin, J. Rice, 1793. LO; New ed., London, 1799. NoU

B327 ENFIELD, William, do., Stereotype ed., 1808; 2nd ed., Gainsborough, 1812; New ed., 1810. *See* D401

B328 [ENGLISH, Harriet]. (1799) Conversations and amusing tales offered to the publick for the youth of Great Britain. Hatchard, 1799. LEI NoU

B329 ENGLISH. (1683) An English introduction to the Latin tongue, for the use of the lower forms in Westminster School. 1704. NoU

B330 ENTERTAINING. (1790?) Entertaining fables for the instruction of children. Embellished with cuts. Derby, J. Drewry, [1790?]. NoU

B331 ENTICK, John, 1703?–1773. (1764) The new spelling dictionary. New ed., 1778. NoU; *another issue*, 1781. NoU

B332 ENTICK, John, do., Stereotype ed., [180–]; Abridged ed., 1813. *See* D404

B332a ENTICK, John, *ed.* (1774) Cornelii Schrevelii Lexicon manuale graeco-latinum & latino-graecum: studio atque opera Josephi Hill, necnon Johannis Entick . . . auctum . . . Editio nova multo auctior & emendatior. Bowyer, [etc.], 1774. LEI

EPEE, Charles Michel, *abbé de l'*. *See* L'Epée, C. M.

B333 EPICTETUS. To tou Epiktetou encheiridion [Greek script] ex editione Joannis Upton accurate expressum. Glasgow U.P., 1758. LEE

Epigrammatum delectus. *See* Nicole, Pierre

B334 ERASMUS, Desiderius, 1466?–1536. (1516) Colloquia selecta . . . with an English translation . . . By John Clarke. 14th ed., W. Clarke, 1757. LEI; 19th ed., 1775. NoU; 20th ed., Rivington, [etc.], 1782. HU

B335 ERASMUS, Desiderius. Colloquiorum Maturini Corderii centuria una; cum Erasmi Roterodami Colloquiis selectis . . . in usum scholarum. Amsterdam, 1742. NoU

B336 ERASMUS SMITH CHARITY. The charter of H.M. King Charles II . . . impowering Erasmus Smith Esq., to erect grammar schools in the Kingdom of Ireland, and to endow the same . . . Together with an Act of Parliament for the further application of the said charity. Dublin, Erasmus Smith charity trustees, 1724. BI

B337 ERNST, George, *ed.* (1788) L'amico de' fanciulli, o sia, il morale instruttore . . . [Translated into Italian from Berquin's 'Ami des enfans' by G. Buccarelli and F. Sastres, and introduced into England by G. Ernst.] Hooper, 1788. 4 vols. LO

Essay on charity and charity schools. *See* Mandeville, B.

B338 ESSAY. (1711) An essay upon education; shewing how Latin, Greek and other languages may be learn'd more easily, quickly and perfectly than they commonly are. Tho. Baker, 1711. HU

Essay upon education, by a gentleman of Bristol. *See* Butler, S.

Estimate of the religion of the fashionable world. *See* More, H.

B339 ETHICES compendium in usum juventutis academicae, auctius & emendatius editum. Cui accedit Methodus argumentandi aristotelica. Oxford, E. Broughton, 1745. LEI

B340 EUCLID. Euclide's Elements; the whole fifteen books compendiously demonstrated: with Archimedes's Theorems . . . To which is annex'd Euclide's Data . . . By Isaac Barrow . . . The whole revis'd. By Thomas Haselden. Midwinter & Ward, [etc.], 1732. LEE

B341 EUCLID. Elements of geometry, from the Latin translation of Commandine. To which is added, a treatise of the nature of arithmetic of logarithms . . . [etc.] by Doctor J. Keil . . . The whole revised by S. Cunn. 5th ed., Osborn, 1745. LEI

B342 EUCLID. Elementorum libri priores sex, item undecimus et duodecimus, ex versione Federici Commandini . . . [revised] a Roberto Simson. Glasgow U.P., 1756. LEI

B343 EUCLID. Elektra. *See* B1129 Westminster School

B344 EURIPIDES. Euripidis tragoediae Medea et Phoenissae graeco-latinae. Accessit ejusdem vita, variis narrationibus et digressionibus olim disjuncta jam denua in unum collecta. Authore J. Barnesio. In usum scholarum. 1715. NoU

B345 EURIPIDES. [Greek script] Phoenissae. Ad fidem manuscriptorum emendata et brevibus notis . . . instructa [by R. Porson]. In usum studiosae juventutis. G. Wilkie, 1799. LEI

B346 EUTROPIUS. Historiae Romanae breviarium, cum versione anglica . . . Or, Eutropius's compendious history of Rome: together with an English translation . . . by John Clarke. York, C. Bourne for T. Hammond, 1722. Hu NoU; 2nd ed., York, Gent, 1728. LEE

Evenings at home. *See* Aikin, John, and Barbauld, A. L.

B347 EVES, *Mrs.* [Georgiana?]. (1800) The grammatical play-thing. Birmingham, 1800. NoU

B347a EXEMPLA minora: or, new English examples to be turned into Latin; adapted to the Latin grammar, lately printed at Eton. For the use of the lower forms. [Edited by T. Morell.] New ed., rev., Eton, J. Pote, 1761. HU; new ed., 1817; 1821; 1831. *See* D420a

B347b EXAMPLA moralia: or, third book of new English examples, to be rendered into Latin . . . [Edited by T. Morell.] New ed, Eton, 1789. NoU; new ed., 1815. *See* D420b

B348 EXERCISES. (1744?) Exercises instructive and entertaining, in false English; written with a view to perfect youth in their mother tongue . . . 8th ed., Leeds, Binns, 1799. LEE; 7th ed. [*sic*], 1802. *See* D423

Expence of university education reduced. *See* Newton, R.

Fable of the bees. *See* Mandeville, B.

B349 FACCIOLATUS, Jacobus [*otherwise* Jacopo Facciolati], 1682–1769. (1757) Fasti gymnasii Patavini. 1757. 2 vols. ReU

B350 FAMILIARES. (1677) Familiares colloquedin formulae, in usum scholarum concinnatae . . . Ed. 23a. 1724. NoU

Family instructor. *See* Defoe, D.

B351 FARNABY, Thomas, 1575?–1647. [Troposchematologia]. (1648) Maximam partem ex indice rhetorico Farnabii deprompta . . . 13th ed., Walthoe, 1737. LEE

B352 FARTHER. (1776) Farther English examples; or, book of cautions for children, in rendering English into Latin . . . New ed., Eton, T. Pote, pr., 1792. LEE NoU; new ed., 1818. *See* D432

   [A sequel to *Exempla moralia*.]

Father's instructions. *See* Percival, T.

B353 FAWCETT, John, *D.D.*, 1740–1817. (1778) Advice to youth; or, the advantages of early piety . . . Leeds, [1778]. NoU

Female mentor. *See* Honoria, *pseud.*

B354 FEMALE tuition; or, an address to mothers, on the education of daughters. Murray, 1784. LEE

B355 [FENELON, François de Salignac de la Mothe-], 1651–1715. (Fr. 1699) The adventures of Telemachus, the son of Ulysses. In xxiv books. Written by the Archbishop of Cambray. To which is added, The adventures of Aristonous. Done into English by Mr. Littlebury and Mr. Boyer . . . Vol. 1, 17th ed., rev.; Vol. 2, 18th ed. J. Brotherton, [etc.], 1766. 2 vols. LEI

B356 FENELON, F. de S. de la M.-. (1687) De l'éducation des filles . . . Nlle. éd. Augmentée d'une lettre du même auteur à une dame de qualité sur l'éducation de M—— sa fille unique. Paris, J. Mariette, 1719. LEI; Nlle. éd., 1729. LI

B357 [FENELON, F. de S. de la M.-]. Instructions for the education of a daughter, by the author of Telemachus. To which is added, A small tract of instructions for the conduct of young ladies of the highest rank. With suitable devotions annexed. Done into English, and revised by Mr. George Hickes. Bowyer, 1707. BI; 3rd ed., Bowyer, 1713. BI; 4th ed., Bowyer, 1721. LEE; Glasgow, Foulis, 1750. HU

B358 [FENELON, F. de S. de la M.-]. Instructions for the education of a daughter. Translated from the French of the author of Telemachus . . . Hull, J. Ferraby; London, G. G. & J. Robinson; 1797. HU

B359 FENELON, F. de S. de la M.-. Nouveaux dialogues des morts, Contes & fables, avec un Abrégé des vies des anciens philosophes, & un recueil de leurs plus belles maximes. Composés pour l'éducation d'un prince. Amsterdam, R. & J. Wetstein, & G. Smith, 1727. 3 vols in 1. LEI

B360 FENELON, F. de S. de la M.-. The tales and fables of the late Archbishop and Duke of Cambray, author of Telemachus, in French and English . . . now published for the use of schools . . . by N. Gifford . . . 1736. NoU

B361 [FENN, Eleanor, *lady*], 1743–1813. (1783?) Cobwebs to catch flies. New ed., 1829 *and* 1833; *also* Second series., new ed., (1867?). *See* D438a

B362 FENN, Eleanor, *lady*. [Children's books]. *For other undated and nineteenth-century editions of her children's books, see* D439–444

B363 [FENN, Eleanor, *lady*]? The art of teaching in sport. [1770?] *See* B40 Art

B364 FENNING, Daniel, *fl.* 1754–1775. (1754) The British youth's instructor; or, a new and easy guide to practical arithmetic. Hodges, 1754. LEE; 4th ed., corrected and improved, S. Crowder, 1762. HU; 11th ed., by W. Burbidge, 1787. NoU

B365 FENNING, Daniel, do., *another ed.*, 1806; *and* 13th ed., 1866. *See* D446

B366 FENNING, Daniel. (1754?) A new and easy guide to the use of globes. 9th ed., 1809. *See* D447

B367 FENNING, Daniel. (1765) The schoolmaster's most useful companion, and scholar's best instructor in the knowledge of arithmetic: in two parts. Part I, Containing the first principles of arithmetic . . . Part II, Comprehending a short and simple sketch of book-keeping . . . 4th ed., corr., impr. and greatly enlarged by H. Marshall. Crowder, 1788. BR

B368 FENNING, Daniel. (1756) The universal spelling book; or, a new and easy guide to the English language. New ed., Millar, Law & Cater, 1790. BI

B369 FENNING, Daniel, do., York, 1805; *Stereotype ed.*, [1820]; *another ed.*, Derby, 1837. *See* D448

B370 FENNING, Daniel. Wogan's improved universal spelling book. Dublin, [1841?]; new ed., [1846?]. *See* D449

B371 FENNING, Daniel. (1758?) The young algebraist's companion; or, a new and easy guide to algebra . . . designed for the use of schools . . . 4th ed., corr., Robinson, [etc.], 1772. LEI

B372 FENNING, Daniel, do., new 2nd ed., 1808. *See* D450

B373 FENNING, Daniel. (1772?) The young measurer's complete guide; or, a new and universal treatise of mensuration... Crowder, [1772?] BI

B374 FICHTE, Johann Gottlieb, 1762–1814. The educational theory of... 1926. *See* C448

B375 [FIELD, William], 1768–1851. (1798) An introduction to the use of globes. 2nd ed., 1801. *See* D457

B376 [FIELDING, Sarah], 1710–1768. (1749) The governess; or, the little female academy. Calculated for the entertainment of young ladies in their education. By the author of David Simple. 4th ed., Millar, 1758. LEE LO; 5th ed., 1768. NoU; 7th ed., rev., Rivington, 1789. LEI

Figurae grammaticae & rhetoricae. *See* Burton, N.

B377 [FILLASSIER, Jean Jacques], 1736?–1806. (1771) Dictionnaire historique d'éducation; où, sans donner de préceptes, on se propose d'exercer & enrichir toutes les facultés de l'âme et de l'esprit, en substituant les exemples aux leçons... Paris, Vincent, 1771. 2 vols. HU

FISHER, Anne, *aft. Mrs.* Slack. *See* Slack, A.

B378 FISHER, George, *accomptant.* (1719) Arithmetick in the plainest and most concise methods hitherto extant. With new improvements for dispatch of business in all the several rules.... 10th ed., carefully corrected, with large additions. C. Hitch and L. Hawes, 1759. HU

B379 FISHER, George. (1731 or earlier) The instructor; or, young man's best companion. Containing spelling, reading, writing, and arithmetic... [etc., etc.]. 27th ed., 1788. NoU; *another ed.*, J. Taylor, 1789. LEI; 28th ed., Johnson, 1798. LEE

B380 FISHER, George, do.... To which is added, The Family's best companion... and A compendium of the sciences of geography and astronomy... New ed., London, W. Osborne and T. Griffin; Gainsborough, Mozley; 1797. HU

B381 FISHER, George, do. New ed., corrected... by N. Downes. [*c.* 1800]. NoU

B382 FISHER, George, *ed.* Cocker's Arithmetick ... 44th ed., carefully corrected and amended by George Fisher. Midwinter, [172–]. HU NoU

B383 [FITZGERALD, Thomas], *ed.* M. V. Martialis Epigrammata. In usum scholae Westmonasteriensis. Ed. altera. 1740. NoU

B384 [FLETCHER, Ann, *and others*]. (1796–1798?) The study of history rendered easy, by a plan founded on experience. Vol. 1, England; vol. 2, Rome; vol. 3, France. Authors, 1798–1801. 3 vols. HU

B385 FLEURY, Claude, 1640–1723. (1687?) Traité du choix et de la méthode des études. Nlle. éd., corr., Paris, Martin, 1740. LEI

B386 FLORIAN, Jean Pierre Claris de, 1755–1794. (Fr. 1792) Select fables. 1806. *See* D476

B387 FLORUS, Lucius Annaeus. Rerum Romanorum epitome. Or, an abridgment of the Roman history... By John Stirling. Author, 1738. LEI

B388 FONTENAY, *M. de.* (1746) Lettres sur l'éducation des princes; avec une lettre de Milton ou il propose une nouvelle manière d'élever la jeunesse d'Angleterre. [Ecrites à M. le duc de Chartres.] Edinburgh, J. Trueman, 1746. RE

B389 FOOD. (2nd ed., 1758) Food for the mind: or, a new riddle-book. Compiled for the use of... good boys and girls... By John-the-giant-killer, Esq. T. Carnan and E. Newbery, 1778. [Actually facsimile reprint by the Leadenhall Pr., 1899.] LEI

B390 [FORDYCE, David], 1711–1751. (1745) Dialogues concerning education. [Vol. 1.] [No publisher], 1745. BI HU LEE LEI ReU

B391 [FORDYCE, David]. Dialogues concerning education. Vol. 2. 1748. BI HU ReU

B392. FORDYCE, David. Dialogues concerning education. 3rd ed., E. Dilly, 1757. 2 vols. LO

B393 FORDYCE, James, 1720–1796. (1777) Addresses to young men. 3rd ed., T. Cadell, 1789. 2 vols. in 1. LEI

B394 FORMEY, Jean Henri Samuel, 1711–1797. Conseils pour former une bibliothèque peu nombreuse mais choisie. 2e éd. Berlin, Hande & Spener, 1756. LO

B395 FORMEY, J. H. S. Traité d'éducation morale, qui a remporté le prix de la Société des sciences de Harlem, l'an 1765, sur cette question: Comment on doit gouverner l'esprit et le coeur d'un enfant, pour le rendre heureux & utile. Liège, Desoer, 1773. ReU

B396 [FORRESTER, James]. (1748) Dialogues on the passions, habits, and affections peculiar to children. R. Griffiths, 1748. HU

B397 FOULKES, Peter, 1676–1747, *ed.* (1715) Aeschinous Ho Kata Ktesiphontos, *kai* Demosthenous Ho peri Stephanou logos. Interpretationem Latinam... adjecerunt P. Foulkes, J. Freind. In usum scholae Etonensis. J. Bowyer, 1715. HU

B398 [FOUNDLING HOSPITAL]. A copy of the royal charter, establishing an hospital for the maintenance and education of exposed and deserted young children. Osborn, 1739. LEE

B399 [FOURCROY, —, *abbé de*] Méthode pour apprendre facilement l'histoire romaine. Amsterdam, Tielenburg, [170–?]. LO

B400 FOURCROY, —, *abbé de.* [A new and easy method to understand the Roman history... by way of dialogue, for the use of the Duke of Burgundy. Done out of French... by Mr. Tho. Brown.] [17–?] [Lacks t.p.; possibly 8th ed., 1731.] LEI

B401 FRANCKE, August Hermann, 1663–1727. Pädagogische Schriften... Herausgegeben von D. G. Kramer. 2. Ausg. Langensalza, Beyer, 1885. LEI

B402 FRANCKE, A. H. (Germ. 1701; Eng. 1705) Pietas Hallensis: or, a publick demonstration of the foot-steps of a divine being yet in the world: in an historical narration of the orphan-house, and other charitable institutions, at Glaucha near Hall in Saxony... J. Downing, 1705. LEI

B403 FRANCKE, A. H. Pietas Hallensis... 2nd ed. With a preface written by Josiah Woodward. R. Burrough, 1707, *with* Pietas Hallensis, part 2, for the years 1707 and 1708, 2nd ed., 1716, *and* Pietas Hallensis, part 3, 1716. HU

B404 FRANKLIN, Benjamin, 1706–1790. Benjamin Franklin on education. Edited with an introduction and notes by J. H. Best. New York, Columbia Univ. Teachers Coll., 1962. LEI

B405 FRANKLIN, Benjamin. (1751) Sketch of an English school. 1819. *See* C474

B406 FREE, John. (1789) Young gentleman's and lady's geography. In two parts . . . To which is added, Dionysius, translated into blank verse . . . 2nd ed., with additions. Wm. Baynes, [etc.], 1792. HU

FRESNOY, Nicholas Lenglet du. *See* Lenglet du Fresnoy, Nicholas

Friend of mothers. *See* Art of teaching in sport

Friendly instructor. *See* Harrison, Elizabeth

B407 GARNIER, Jean Jacques. De l'éducation civile. Paris, Vente, 1765. LO

B408 GARRETSON, John. (1683) English exercises for school-boys to translate into Latin, comprizing all the rules of grammar . . . 15th ed., corr., J. & B. Sprint, [etc.], 1719. HU; 19th ed., W. Innys, [etc.], 1743. NoU

B409 GASTRELL, Francis, 1662–1725. (1707) [Christian institutes]. The faith and duty of a Christian. 1825. *See* D513

B410 GASTRELL, Francis. (1707) The religious education of poor children recommended, in a sermon preach'd in the parish church of St. Sepulchres, June 5, 1707 . . . at the anniversary meeting of the gentlemen concerned in promoting the charity-schools . . . Bowyer, and Clement, 1707. LEE ReU

B411 GAULTIER, Camille, 1745–1818. (Fr. 1789?) Complete course of geography by means of instructive games. 1817. *See* D517

B412 GAULTIER, Camille. (1800–1801) A method of making abridgments. 1800–[1801]. *See* D518

B413 A GENERAL view of English pronunciation, to which are added, easy lessons for the use of the English class. Edinburgh, 1784. NoU

B414 GENLIS, Stéphanie Félicité du Crest de Saint-Aubin, comtesse de, 1746–1830. (Fr. 1782; Eng. 1783) Adèle et Théodore; ou, lettres sur l'éducation. Paris, Lambert & Baudouin, 1782. 3 vols. LO; *another ed.*, Maestricht, Dufour & Roux, 1783. 3 vols. LEE

B415 GENLIS, comtesse de. Adèle et Théodore . . . Tome 2. 1822. *See* C517

B416 GENLIS, comtesse de. Adelaide and Theodore; or, letters on education. Translated from the French. Bathurst & Cadell, 1783. 3 vols. LEI; 3rd ed., corrected and amended, Cadell, 1788. 3 vols. HU LO

B417 [GENLIS, comtesse de.] (1781) Annales de la vertu, ou, cours d'histoire à l'usage des jeunes personnes, par l'auteur du Théâtre d'éducation. Paris, 1781. 3 vols. NoU; *another ed.*, Paris, Dufour & Roux, 1786. 3 vols. LEI

B418 GENLIS, comtesse de. (1790) Discours sur l'éducation de M. le Dauphin et sur l'adoption; par Mme. de Brulart . . . Paris, Onfroy, [etc.], 1790. LEI

B419 GENLIS, comtesse de. (1799) La Bruyère the less. 1801. *See* D522

B420 GENLIS, comtesse de. (1791) Leçons d'une gouvernante à ses élèves, ou, fragmens d'un journal qui a été fait pour l'éducation des enfans de Monsieur d'Orléans. Paris, Onfroy, [etc.], 1791. LO

B421 GENLIS, comtesse de. Lessons of a governess to her pupils; or, journal of the method adopted . . . in the education of the children of M. d'Orleans . . . Translated from the French. [Robinson, 1792.] 3 vols. BI

B422 GENLIS, comtesse de. A new method of instruction for children from five to ten years old. 1800. NoU

B422a [GENLIS, comtesse de]. (Fr. 1780; Eng. 1781) Théâtre pour servir à l'éducation. Paris, Lambert & Baudouin, 1780. 4 vols. LEI

B423 GENLIS, comtesse de., do., Nlle. éd., 1829. *See* D523

B424 GENLIS, comtesse de. The theatre of education: a new translation from the French of Madame la Marquise de Silléry, late Madame la Comtesse de Genlis. Walter, 1787. 4 vols. LEE

B425 [GENLIS, comtesse de]. (Fr. 1784; Eng. 1785) Les veillées du château. 1814. *See* D524

B426 GENLIS, comtesse de. Tales of the castle; or, stories of instruction and delight. Being Les veillées du château . . . translated into English by Thomas Holcroft. 3rd ed., 1787. 5 vols. ReU; 4th ed., Robinson, 1793. 5 vols. LEI; 8th ed., 1806. *See* D525

B427 The GENTLEMAN and lady's key to polite literature. [17–?]. NoU

Gentleman instructed. *See* Darrell, Wm.

GENTLEMAN OF BRISTOL, pseud. *See* Butler, S.

Gentleman's calling. *See* Allestree, R.

B428 GENTLEMAN'S. (1715) The Gentleman's library: containing rules for conduct in all parts of life. 3rd ed., corr. and enl. Written by a gentleman. W. Mears, D. Browne, 1734. HU

Geographia classica. *See* Moll, H.

B429 GEOGRAPHISCHER Calender. (1776) Zu einer höchstleichten Erlernung der Geographie eingerichteter Calender, nebst historischen Einschaltungen und 365 geographischen Aufgaben für die Jugend aufs Jahr Christi 1777. Hamburg, J. C. Brandt, [pref. 1776]. LEI

B430 GEOGRAPHY. (2nd ed., 1794) Geography and history selected by a lady. 7th ed., 1808, *and* 10th ed., 1815. *See* D528

B431 GEOGRAPHY for youth. New ed., 1797. NoU

Geography made familiar and easy. *See* Newbery, John.

B432 [GERARD, Alexander], 1728–1795. (1755) Plan of education in the Marischal College and University of Aberdeen, with the reasons of it. Drawn up by order of the faculty. Aberdeen, J. Chalmers, pr., 1755. LEI

B433 [GERDIL, Giacinto Sigismondo], 1718–1802. (1763) Réflexions sur la théorie, & la pratique de l'éducation, contre les principes de Mr. Rousseau. Par le P.G.B. Turin, Reycends, and Guibert, 1763. LEI

B434 GERDIL, G. S. (1765) Reflections on education. 1765. 2 vols in 1. ReU

B435 GIBERT, Balthazar, 1662–1741. (1727) Observations addressées à Mr. Rollin, ancien recteur, et professeur royal, sur son Traité de la manière d'enseigner et d'étudier les belles-lettres. Paris, L'Hermite, 1727. LO

B436 GIBSON, Edmund, 1669–1748. (1716) The peculiar excellence and reward of supporting schools of charity. A sermon preach'd at the anniversary meeting of the charity schools ... London and Westminster, May 24, 1716. 1716. ReU

B437 GIFFORD, N., ed. (1736?) The tales and fables of the late archbishop and duke of Cambray, author of Telemachus [i.e. Fénelon], in French and English ... now published for the use of schools ... 1736. NoU

B438 [GILPIN, William], 1724–1804. (1798) [Moral contrasts]. A memoir of Naimbanna. 1843. See D531

B439 GILPIN, William. (1791) A sermon preached ... May 18, 1791. New ed., 1825. See C524

B440 GISBORNE, Thomas, 1758–1846. (1797) An enquiry into the duties of the female sex. 2nd ed., corr., Cadell & Davies, 1797. LEI LO

B441 GLASSE, Samuel, 1735–1812. (1774?) A sermon preached before the ... Marine Society, at St. Andrew's church, Holborn, on occasion of their anniversary meeting, on Thursday 10th February 1774. 3rd ed. Dodsley, 1777. LEI

B442 GLASSE, Samuel. (1778) A sermon preached before the ... Marine Society at St. Andrew's church, Holborn, on occasion of their anniversary meeting, on Thursday 19th March, 1778. To which is added, an abstract of the Proceedings of the Marine Society, from its first institution ... Dodsley, 1778. LEI

B444 [GOLDING, Christopher]. (1758) A defence of the conduct of the Warden of Winchester College in accepting of that wardenship. Occasioned by a letter to the Rev. Dr. Lowth, and written by himself. R. & J. Dodsley, 1758. HU; 2nd ed., corr., 1759. HU

B445 [GOLDSMITH, Oliver], 1728–1774. (1764) An history of England in a series of letters from a nobleman to his son. 1771. 2 vols. NoU

B445 GOLDSMITH, Oliver, do., 1807; 1819; 1821; 1832; 1845; 1854; 1865. See D538–541

B446 GOLDSMITH, Oliver. (1774) History of Greece, abridged. 1804; 1812; 1838. See D542

B447 GOLDSMITH, Oliver. (1769; abridged ed. 1772) Dr. Goldsmith's Roman history, abridged by himself for the use of schools. 1793. NoU

B448 GOLDSMITH, Oliver, do., new ed., 1817; [182–]; [184–?]. See D543

B449 [GOLDSMITH, Oliver]? (1765) Goody Two-shoes. See Goody Two-shoes

B450 GOLDSMITH, Oliver? (1762) A pretty book of pictures for little masters and misses. 15th ed., 1867. See D544

B451 GOODY Two-shoes. (1765) Facsimile reproduction of the edition of 1766. With an introduction by Charles Welsh. Griffith & Farran, 1881. LEI NoU ReU; 1882. HU LEE

B452 GOODY Two-shoes. The history of Goody Two-shoes. 1806. See D554

B453 GOOLE, John. (1721) An answer to a scandalous pamphlet intitul'd 'The present state of the free-school at Witney in the county of Oxford, etc.'. Oxford, S. Fletcher, 1721. HU

B454 GORDON, George, ed. Astronomical dialogues between a gentleman and a lady ... by John Harris. 2nd ed., corrected by George Gordon. Bettesworth & Batley, 1729. HU

B455 GORDON, Patrick, 1635–1699. (1693) Geography anatomiz'd; or, the geographical grammar ... 11th ed., Knapton, [etc.], 1728. LEI; 13th ed., 1733. NoU

Governess, or the little female academy. See Fielding, Sarah

Gradus ad Parnassum ... Ab uno e Societate Jesu. See Aler, Paul

B456 GRAECAE. (1721?) Graecae grammaticae compendium. [For the use of Westminster School.] G. & G. Ginger, 1794. HU

B457 GRAECAE grammaticae rudimenta, in usum regiae scholae Etonensis. Ed. nova, recognita et aucta. Eton, J. Pote, 1768. LEI; another ed., 1772. HU

Graecae grammatices rudimenta. See Busby, R.

B458 GRAHAM, Mrs. Catherine, form. Mrs. Catherine Macaulay, 1731–1791. (1790) Letters on education ... C. Dilly, 1790. HU LEE

Grammatical exercises. See Ruddiman, T.

B459 [GRAVES, Richard], 1715–1804, trans. (1774) Galateo: or, a treatise on politeness and delicacy of manners. Addressed to a young nobleman. From the Italian of Monsig. Giovanni de la Casa. J. Dodsley, 1774. LEI

B460 GRAY, Thomas, 1716–1771. The poems of Thomas Gray and Robert Blair, arranged for the use of young people. [18–?] See D563

B461 [GREEN, John], 1706?–1779. (1750) The academic, or a disputation on the state of the University of Cambridge ... C. Say, 1750. LEI

B462 GREENWOOD, James, d. 1737. (1711) An essay towards a practical English grammar, describing the genius and nature of the English tongue ... 2nd ed., with additions. J. Clark, 1722. HU; 3rd ed., 1729. NoU

B463 GREENWOOD, James. (3rd ed., 1713) The London vocabulary, English and Latin: put into a new method ... Adorned with pictures ... 14th ed., Hawes, [etc.], 1763. BI; 15th ed., 1767. NoU; 17th ed., Rivington, [etc.], 1777. LEI; 18th ed., Rivington, [etc.], 1782. BI; 19th ed., Rivington, [etc.], 1785. LEE NoU; 20th ed., Rivington, [etc.], 1791. BI; 21st ed., Longman, [etc.], 1797. HU

B464 GREENWOOD, James, do., another ed., 1802; 25th ed., 1814; New ed. rev., 1836. See D564

B464a GREGORY, George, 1754–1808, ed. (1800) The elements of a polite education, carefully selected from the Letters of the late Rt. Hon. Philip Dormer Stanhope, Earl of Chesterfield, to his son. R. Phillips, [1800]. LEE; 2nd ed., Phillips, [1800]. BI LO; 1802. See D566

B465 GREGORY, John, 1724–1773. (1774) A father's legacy to his daughters, by the late Dr. Gregory of Edinburgh. New ed., A. Strahan and T. Cadell, [etc.], 1797. LEI LO

B466 GREIG, John, 1759–1819. (2nd ed., 1800) The young ladies' new guide to arithmetic. New ed., 1816. *See* D569

B467 GREY, G. (1773) Epitome of the annals of Great-Britain . . . useful for youth at schools . . . Newcastle, Author, 1773. LEI; 2nd ed., Newcastle, 1777. NoU

B468 GREY, Richard, 1694–1771. (1730) Memoria technica: or, a new method of artificial memory, applied to, and exemplified in chronology, history, geography, astronomy . . . 3rd ed., corr., Stagg, 1737. LEI

B469 GREY, Richard. Memoria technica . . . To which are subjoined Lowe's Mnemonics delineated. New ed., 1819. *See* D570

B470 GREY, Richard. Select parts of Grey's Memoria technica; to which are added, J. Sleiden. De quatuor imperiis; and the general divisions of ancient and modern geography . . . [1786?] NoU

B471 GREYBEARD, *Sir* Gregory, *pseud.* Tommy and Billy, the brothers; or, the oak and the acorn . . . Gainsborough, 1792. NoU

B472 GREYBEARD, *Sir* Gregory. The two boys, and the bird's nest . . . [Gainsborough, 1792]. NoU

B473 GRIVEL, Guillaume. Théorie de l'éducation; ouvrage utile aux pères de famille et aux instituteurs. 2e éd., Paris, Moutard, 1783. 3 vols. LEE

B474 GRUBB, Sarah, 1756–1790. (1792) Some account of the life and religious labours of Sarah Grubb. With an appendix, containing an account of Ackworth School, Observations on Christian discipline, and extracts from many of her letters. [Edited by Lindley Murray.] Dublin, R. Jackson, 1792. LEE LEI

B475 GRUBB, Sarah. Some remarks on Christian discipline, as it respects the education of youth. Whitby, T. Webster, pr., 1798. HU

B476 GUIDE for the child and youth . . . By T.H. 1774. NoU

B477 GUTHRIE, William, 1708–1770. (1770) A new geographical . . . grammar. 21st ed., 1808. *See* D577

B478 GUTHRIE, William. (1785) An atlas to Guthrie's Geographical grammar. 1804. *See* D578

B479 GUTSMUTHS [*or* GuthsMuths], Johann Christian Friedrich, 1759–1839. (Germ. 1793) Gymnastics for youth: or a practical guide to healthful and amusing exercises for the use of schools . . . Freely translated from the German of C. G. Salzmann. J. Johnson, 1800. [Wrongly attributed to Salzmann by the translator.] LEI

B480 GUY, John, *schoolmaster.* (1796) Miscellaneous selections: or, the rudiments of useful knowledge . . . designed for senior scholars in schools . . . Bristol, Author, 1796. 2 vols. LEI

B481 H., T., *M.A., teacher of a private school.* (1725) A guide for the child and youth . . . 1774. NoU

B482 H., T. A short way to know the world: or, the rudiments of geography . . . 2nd ed., T. Osborne, 1712. ReU

B483 HALIFAX, George Savile, *marquis of,* 1633–1695. (1688) The lady's new-year gift: or, advice to a daughter . . . 11th ed., exactly corrected, Midwinter, 1734. LEE

B484 HALLEY, Edmund, 1656–1742. . . . Method for constructing the logarithms. *See* B958 Sherwin

B485 HALLIFAX, Charles. Familiar letters on various subjects of business and amusement. Written . . . with a view, chiefly, to form the style of the younger part of both sexes . . . 2nd ed., rev. and corr., R. Baldwin, 1754. LEI

B486 [HAMILTON, Joseph], *ed.* (14th ed., 1801) Johnson's dictionary of the English language in miniature . . . New ed., 1827. *See* D598

B487 HAMPTON, Barnaby. (1704) Prosodia construed, and the meaning of the most difficult words therein contained, plainly illustrated; being an addition to the construction of Lilie's Rules, and of the necessary use. W. Norton, 1704. HU; 1733. NoU

B488 HANBURY, William, 1725–1778. (1767) The history of the rise and progress of the charitable foundations at Church-Langton, [Leics.]. Dodsley, 1767. LEI

B489 HANWAY, Jonas, 1712–1786. (1786) Domestic happiness promoted. New ed., 1811. *See* D600

B490 HARDY, James, *teacher of mathematics.* (1760?) The elements or theory of arithmetic: containing all its rules . . . and the doctrine of the circulates and logarithms: demonstrated in a new and familiar method. As also practical arithmetic . . . Author, 1760. HU NoU

B491 HARLEM. Société des arts et sciences. [Prize essays]. *See* B239 Comparet, J. A.; B395 Formey, J. H. S.

B492 HARRIS, John, 1667–1719. (1719) Astronomical dialogues between a gentleman and a lady: wherein the doctrine of the sphere, uses of the globes, and the elements of astronomy and geography are explain'd; in a pleasant, easy and familiar way . . . 2nd ed., corrected by George Gordon. A Bettesworth and J. Batley, 1729. HU

B493 [HARRISON, *Mrs.* Elizabeth], *fl.* 1724–1756. (2nd ed., 1741) The friendly instructor; or, a companion for young ladies and young gentlemen . . . With a recommendatory preface by P. Doddridge . . . 9th ed., 1784. 2 vols. NoU

B494 HARRISON, *Mrs.* Elizabeth, do., new ed., 1836. *See* D610

B495 HARRISON, *Mrs.* Elizabeth, do., *abridged ed. with title* Familiar dialogues between children. 1815. *See* D611

B496 HASELDEN, Thomas, d. 1740, *ed.* Euclide's Elements . . . By Isaac Barrow. The whole revised. By Thomas Haselden. Midwinter & Ward, [etc.], 1732. LEE

B497 HAWKINS, John, d. 1692. Cocker's arithmetick. *See* B231 Cocker, E.

B498 HAWKINS, John. Cocker's Decimal arithmetick. *See* B232 Cocker, E.

B499 HAWNEY, William. (1717) The complete measurer; or, the whole art of measuring. In 2 parts . . . 16th ed., Rivington, 1789. BI

B500 HAWNEY, William, do., [revised] by Thomas Keith. Enlarged by Samuel Maynard. 1839. *See* D758 Keith, T.

B501 HAY, William, 1695–1755, *trans.* Martial's select epigrams . . . Translated and imitated by W. Hay . . . With an appendix of some by Cowley and other hands. 1755. NoU

B502 HAYTER, Thomas, 1702–1762. (1754) A sermon preach'd before the Society corresponding with the Incorporated Society in Dublin for promoting English Protestant working-schools in Ireland, May 2, 1753. 1754. ReU

B503 HEDERICH, Benjamin, 1675–1748. (1722?) Lexicon manuale Graecum . . . Recensitum et plurimum auctum a Sam. Patrick . . . Ed. altera. H. Knaplock, [etc.], 1739. LEI

B504 HELME, Elizabeth, d. 1816. (1798) Instructive rambles in London, and the adjacent villages. Designed to amuse the mind, and improve the understanding of youth. Vol. 1 [only]. Longman, 1798. BI

B505 HELVETIUS, Claude Adrien, 1715–1771. (1773) De l'homme, de ses facultés intellectuelles et de son éducation. Ouvrage posthume . . . Tome premier [of 2]. Londres, Société typographique, 1773. LEI

B506 HENLEY, John, 1692–1756. (1719) The complete linguist, or, an universal grammar of all the considerable tongues in being. 1719. 9 pts. in 2 vols. ReU

B507 HENSON, John, *master of the Free school in Nottingham.* (1756) A compendium of English grammar . . . Nottingham, [1756]. NoU

B508 HERBERT, Edward, *1st baron Herbert of Cherbury*, 1583–1648. (1768) A dialogue between a tutor and his pupil. Bathoe, 1768. LEE

B509 HERBERT, Elizabeth. [Part of MS. copy book, inscribed 'Elizabeth Herbert, her book. 1789'.] LEI

B510 HERRING, Thomas, 1693–1757. (1741) A sermon preach'd before the Society corresponding with the Incorporated society in Dublin for promoting English Protestant working-schools in Ireland, March 18, 1740/41. 1741. ReU

B511 HEWLETT, John, 1762–1844. An introduction to reading and spelling. 4th ed., 1798. NoU

B512 [HICKES, George], 1624–1715. The gentleman instructed, [by William Darrell. Dedication by George Hickes]. *See* B268–269 Darrell, W.

B513 HICKES, George, *trans.* (1707) Instructions for the education of a daughter, by the author of Telemachus [i.e., Fénelon]. To which is added, A small tract of instruction for the conduct of young ladies of the highest rank [by Trotti de la Chétardie]. With suitable devotions annexed. Done into English, and revised by Mr. George Hickes. Bowyer, 1707. BI; 3rd ed., Bowyer, 1713. BI; 4th ed., Bowyer, 1721. LEE

B514 HICKES, George. Instructions for the education of daughters, by M. Fénelon . . . Translated from the French and revised by George Hickes. Glasgow, R. & A. Foulis, 1750. HU
Hieroglyphical Bible. *See* Bible

B515 HILL, John. (1712) Arithmetic both in the theory and practice made plain and easie . . . 2nd ed. With the addition of several algebraical questions. [Preface by Humphrey Ditton.] Midwinter, 1716. LEI

B516 HILL, 'Sir' John, 1716?–1775. (1754) On the management and education of children: a series of letters written to a neice [*sic*]. By the Hon. Juliana-Susannah Seymour [i.e., John Hill]. Baldwin, 1754. HU LEE

B517 HINCHCLIFFE, John, 1731–1794. (1786) A sermon preach'd June 1st, 1786, being the time of the yearly meeting of the children educated in charity schools in and about . . . London. 1786. ReU

B518 The HISTORY of all nations. Giving a brief and entertaining account of . . . every country throughout the known world . . . To which is added a short and easy introduction to geography . . . Designed for the use of schools. New, enl. ed. London, G. G. & J. Robinson; Newcastle, S. Hodgson; 1800. HU
History of England in a series of letters from a nobleman to his son. *See* Goldsmith, O.

B519 HISTORY. (1798?) The History of Martin and James. 1833. *See* D631

B519a HISTORY. (1791?) The History of the Davenport family. [18–]. *See* D636
History of the two children in the wood. *See* Children in the wood

B520 HOADLY, Samuel, 1643–1705. (1683?) The natural method of teaching. Being the accidence in questions and answers, explained, amended, abridged, and fitted to the capacity and use of the lowest form . . . 9th ed., yet more fitted for the use of the lowest form. T. Astley, 1737. HU
Hogarth moralized. *See* Trusler, J.

B520a HODSON, Thomas. (1800) The accomplished tutor. Vol. 1. 3rd ed., 1836. *See* D642

B521 HOLCROFT, Thomas, 1745–1809, *trans.* (1785) Tales of the castle. *See* B426 Genlis, *Mme. de*

B522 HOLDERLIN, Friedrich, 1770–1843. (1797–1801) Briefe zur Erziehung, zusammengestellt von K. Lothar Wolf. Marburg, Simons, 1950. [From *Hyperion* and letters to his brother.] LEI

B523 HOLLAND, Thomas, and HOLLAND, John, 1766–1826. (3rd ed., 1798) Exercises for the memory and understanding. 4th ed., 1805. *See* D665

B524 HOLMES, John, b. 1702, *master of the grammar school, Holt.* (1738) The art of rhetoric made easy; or, the elements of oratory briefly stated for . . . the studious youth of Great Britain and Ireland: in two books . . . the second containing the substance of Longinus's celebrated treatise on the sublime . . . A. Bettesworth and C. Hitch, 1739. [Bk. 2 has separate t.p. dated 1738.] Hu NoU

B525 HOLMES, John. (1751) The grammarian's geography and astronomy ancient and modern, exemplified in the use of globes . . . In two parts. Particularly adapted to the capacities of young gentlemen studying the classicks . . . C. Hitch and L. Hawes, 1751. LEI

B526 HOLMES, John. (1735) The Greek grammar; or, a short, plain, critical and comprehensive method of learning the Greek tongue . . . Author, and A. Bettesworth, [etc.], 1735. HU; 7th ed., rev. and corr., L. Hawes, [etc.], 1771. LEI

B527 HOLMES, John. (Pre-1733) A new grammar of the Latin tongue . . . freed from the many obscurities . . . and errors, which render the common grammar an insufferable impediment to the progress of education . . . 3rd ed., corr., Author, [etc.], 1747. HU

HOLROYD, Maria Josepha, *afterwards* Lady Stanley of Alderley. *See* Stanley, M. J.

B528 [HOME, Henry], *Lord Kames*, 1696–1782. (1781) Loose hints upon education, chiefly concerning the culture of the heart. Edinburgh, J. Bell, 1781. BI HU LEE; 2nd ed., enl., Edinburgh, J. Bell, [etc.], 1782. LO

B529 [HONORIA, *pseud.*]. (1793–1796) The female mentor; or, select conversations. Cadell & Davies, 1798. 2 vols. LO

B530 HOOLE, Charles, 1610–1667. (1656) The common accidence examined and explained by short questions and answers . . . Written heretofore, and made use of in *Rotherham School*, and now published for the profit of young beginners in that and other schools. T. Longman, 1757. HU NoU

B531 HOOLE, Charles. (1650) Terminationes ex exempla declinationum & conjugationum, in usum grammaticastrorum . . . This impression . . . accommodated as well to the *new* as to the *old* edition of the Grammar . . . Longman, 1752. *With his* Propria quae maribus, Quae genus, and As in praesenti, Englished and explained . . . Longman, 1752. HU

B532 HOOLE, Charles, *ed. and trans.* (1659) 1. Catonis disticha de moribus. 2. Dicta insignia septem sapientum Graeciae. 3. Mimi Publiani, sive Senecae proverbia, Anglo-Latino . . . [with translation by] C. Hoole . . . 1722. NoU; *another ed.*, 1749. NoU

B533 HOOLE, Charles, *trans.* (1658) Orbis sensualium pictus . . . John. Amos Comenius's Visible world . . . Translated into English by Charles Hoole . . . 11th ed., 1729. NoU; 12th ed., corr. and enl., S. Leacroft, 1777. BI HU LEE ReU

B534 HOOLE, Charles, *trans.* (1658) Sententiae pueriles, Anglo-Latinae. Quae diversis authoribus olim collegerat Leonard Culman; et in vernaculum sermonem nuperrime transtulit Carolus Hoole . . . Sentences for children, English and Latin . . . S. Collins, 1717, HU; *another ed.*, 1728. NoU

B535 HOOPER, William. (1774) Rational recreations, in which the principles of numbers and natural philosophy are . . . elucidated by a series of . . . experiments. Vol. 4 [only]. L. Davis, 1774. LO

HOPKINS, Mary, *aft. Mrs.* Pilkington. *See* Pilkington, M.

B536 HOPPUS, E. (10th ed., 1777) Practical measuring made easy . . . by a new set of tables . . . 12th ed., improved., Rivington, [etc.], [178–?]. LEI

B537 HORNE, George, 1730–1792. (1786) Sunday schools recommended in a sermon preached at the parish church of St. Alphege, Canterbury, on Sunday, Dec. 18th, 1785 . . . with an appendix concerning the method of forming and conducting an establishment of this kind . . . Oxford, O.U.P., 1786. BI ReU

B538 HOWARD, J., *engraver*. The writing-master's assistant in all the hands necessary for gentlemen, or men of business. Written by P. Roberts. Engraved by J. Howard. Sold by Mr. Marks and Mr. Parker, [*c.* 177–?]. LEI

B539 HOWARD, John, 1726?–1790. (1789) An account of the principal lazarettos in Europe . . . Warrington, W. Eyres, pr., 1789. LEI

B540 HUARTE DE SAN JUAN, 1526?–1592. (Sp. 1575) A treatise of the education and learning proper for the different capacities of youth . . . Principally extracted from the 'Examen de ingenios' of . . . Dr. John Huartes . . . [etc.]. Rivington, 1734. LEE

B541 HUDSON, Peter. (1755) The French scholar's guide: or, an easy help for translating French into English . . . Designed for the use of schools, as well as private learners . . . 8th ed., corr. and enl., G. Keith, 1780. LEI

B542 HUEBNER, Johann, *the elder.* (Germ. 1722) A new and easy introduction to the study of geography, by way of question and answer, principally designed for the use of schools . . . Written originally . . . by the late . . . Mr. Hubner, and now faithfully translated . . . 3rd ed., carefully revised and corrected by J. Cowley. T. Cox and J. Hodges, 1746. [From Huebner's 'Kurze Fragen aus der neuen und alten Geographie'.] HU

B543 HUMPHREYS, Samuel, 1698?–1738, *trans.* (1733) Spectacle de la nature: or, nature display'd. [By N. A. Pluche.] *See* B838 Pluche, N. A.

B544 HUNTLEY, Thomas. (1780) A grammar of the Latin tongue: in which the four principal parts of grammar . . . are distinctly treated of . . . 2nd ed. Compiled for the use of schools. Cirencester, S. Rudder, 1794. HU

B545 [HURD, Richard], 1720–1808. (1764) Dialogues on the uses of foreign travel; considered as a part of an English gentleman's education: between Lord Shaftesbury and Mr. Locke. By the editor of 'Moral and political dialogues'. London, Millar; Cambridge, Thurlbourn & Woodyer; 1764. LEE; Dublin, P. Wilson, 1764. HU

B546 HUTTON, Charles, 1737–1823. (1770?; 3rd ed., 1796) The compendious measurer. 5th ed., 1803. *See* D691

B547 HUTTON, Charles, *ed.* Select exercises for young proficients in the mathematicks . . . by Thomas Simpson. New ed., to which is prefixed an account of the life and writings of the author, by Charles Hutton. F. Wingrave, 1792. HU

Hymns in prose for children. *See* Barbauld, A. L. Impartial by-stander's review of the controversy concerning the wardenship of Winchester College. *See* Speed, John

B548 INCORPORATED SOCIETY IN DUBLIN FOR PROMOTING ENGLISH PROTESTANT WORKING SCHOOLS IN IRELAND. An account of the proceedings of the . . . society from February 6th, 1733, on which day the Royal Charter was opened, to the 6th of March following. In two letters published by order of the society. Dublin, The Society, 1734. LEE

B549 INCORPORATED Society in Dublin for Promoting English Protestant Working Schools in Ireland. A brief account of the proceedings of the . . . society . . . Dublin, 1735. ReU

B550 INCORPORATED Society in Dublin for Promoting English Protestant Working Schools in Ireland. A continuation of the proceedings . . . 1738–1740. Dublin, G. Grierson, 1740. LEI ReU

B551 INCORPORATED Society in Dublin for Promoting English Protestant Working Schools in Ireland. A copy of His Majesty's royal charter for erecting English Protestant schools in the Kingdom of Ireland . . . [1733]. Dublin, Grierson, 1735. LEI

B552 INCORPORATED Society in Dublin for Promoting English Protestant Working Schools in Ireland. An abstract of His Majesty's royal charter for erecting and promoting English Protestant schools in Ireland. Dublin, [1753?]. ReU

B553 INCORPORATED Society in Dublin for Promoting English Protestant Working Schools in Ireland. Continuation of the proceedings. *See* B75 Barnard, W. 1752; *and* B771 Nicolls, S. 1749.

B554 INDENTURE relative to a free school in Great Greenford. Founded by E. Betham. Harrow, 1781. BI

B555 INFANT'S library. Book 1: [Illustrated alphabet]. [*c.* 1800]. NoU; Book 9. [17–?]. NoU; A short history of England for the Infant's library. [*c.* 1800]. NoU

Institutio Graecae grammatices compendiaria. *See* Camden, W.

Instructions for the education of a daughter. *See* Fénelon

Instructive lessons for children. *See* Barbauld, A. L.

Introduction to history ancient and modern. *See* Randall, J.

B556 INTRODUCTION. (1758) An introduction to the Latin tongue, for the use of youth. New ed., revised and correctly printed. Eton, J. Pote, 1765. HU; new ed., rev., Eton, J. Pote, 1771. LEI

B557 INTRODUCTION, do., new ed., Eton, 1802; York, 1803; Eton, 1850. *See* D704

Introduction to the study of philosophy. *See* Johnson, Samuel, 1696–1772

Introduction to the use of globes. *See* Field, Wm.

J.J. *See* Jennings, John

B558 JACKSON, John, *curate of Dursley.* (1710) The blessedness of communicating to the charity-schools, as a sermon preach'd at Dursley, Feb. 19, 1710, on the design of erecting a charity-school in that town. 1710. ReU

B559 JANEWAY, James, 1636?–1764. (1671) A token for children: being an account of the conversion, holy and exemplary lives, and joyful deaths, of several young children. [17–?]. NoU

B560 JEFFERSON, Thomas, 1743–1826. Crusade against ignorance: Thomas Jefferson on education. Edited . . . by Gordon C. Lee. New York, Columbia Univ. Teachers Coll., 1961. LEI

B561 [JENNINGS, John], d. 1723. (1721) Logica in usum juventutis academicae. Autore J.J. Northampton, Raikes & Dicey, 1721. LEI

B562 JENNINGS, John. (1721) Miscellanea in usum juventutis academicae. Pars I. Autore J.J. Northampton, Raikes & Dicey, 1721. LEI

B563 JOHNSON, Richard, d. 1721. (1706) Grammatical commentaries: being an apparatus to a new national grammar: by way of animadversion upon the falsities . . . and defects of Lilly's system now in use . . . Author, 1706. HU LEI NoU

JOHNSON, Richard, 1734–1793. *See* Cooper, *Rev. Mr., pseud.?*

B564 [JOHNSON, Samuel], 1699–1772. (1743) An introduction to the study of philosophy: exhibiting a general view of all the arts and sciences, for the use of pupils. Rivington, 1744. LEE

B565 JOHNSON, Samuel, 1709–1784. (1755) A dictionary of the English language . . . Abstracted from the folio edition by the author . . . 9th ed., Rivington, [etc.], 1790. LEI

B566 JOHNSON, Samuel. Johnson's dictionary of the English language in miniature. New ed., 1827. *See* D727

B567 JOHNSON, Samuel. Comprehensive Johnson's dictionary. 1851. *See* D726

B568 JOHNSON, Thomas, *fl.* 1688–1718. (3rd ed., 1706) Novus graecorum epigrammatum & poemation delectus, cum nova versione et notis. In usum scholae Etonensis. Ed. tertia. Smith & Walford, 1706. LEI; Ed. 7a, 1732. NoU

B569 JONES, Evan. The young geographer and astronomer's best companion. 1773. NoU

B570 JONES, J. A step towards an English education in two essays on the excellency of geography. 2nd ed., Bristol, B. Hickey, pr., 1740. ReU

B571 JONES, Stephen, 1763–1827. (1790) A general pronouncing and explanatory dictionary of the English language. New ed., 1813, *and* 1824. *See* D731

B572 [JONES, William], *of Nayland,* 1726–1800. (1775?) Letters from a tutor to his pupils. Robinson, 1780. LEI ReU

Juvenile olio, *Author of. See* Mavor, W. F.

Juvenile speaker. *See* Weightman, Mary

B573 K., P. (1686) Nomenclatura trilinguis Anglo-Latino-Graeca . . . 6th ed., carefully revised and corrected by R.C. . . . G. Conyers, 1704. HU

KAMES, Henry Home, *lord. See* Home, H.

B574 KAYE, Richard. (1778) A sermon preached before the . . . Marine Society at St. Stephen's church, Walbrook, on occasion of their anniversary meeting, on Tuesday, 8th April, 1777. Dodsley, 1778. LEI

B575 KEILL, John, 1671–1721, *ed.* (1715) Euclids Elements of geometry, from the Latin translation of Commandine. To which is added, a treatise of the nature of logarithms . . . [etc.], by Doctor J. Keil . . . The whole revised by S. Cunn. 5th ed., Osborn, 1745. LEI

B576 KEIR, James, 1735–1820. (1791) An account of the life and writings of Thomas Day, Esq. Stockdale, 1791. LEI

B577 KEITH, Thomas, 1759–1824. (1798) The complete measurer. New ed., 1839. *See* D758

B578 KEITH, Thomas. (1788) The complete practical arithmetician. 5th ed., 1811. *See* D759

B579 KEN, Thomas, 1637–1711. (1674) A manual of prayers for the use of the scholars of Winchester College, and all other devout Christians. [17–?]. NoU; 23rd ed., 1728. NoU

B580 [KENDALL, Edward Augustus], 1776?–1842. (1798) Keeper's travels in search of his master. 14th ed., 1826, *and another ed.*, 1850. *See* D763

B581 KENNETT, White, 1660–1728. (1706) The charity of schools for poor children recommended in a sermon preach'd . . . 1706 . . . J. Downing, 1706. BI ReU

B582 KENNETT, White. (1710) The Christian scholar. 22nd ed., 1823. *See* D766

B583 KER, John, d. 1741. (1708–1709) Selectarum de lingua Latina observationum libri duo . . . J. Hartley, 1708–1709. 2 vols. HU LEE

B584 KERR, William, *fl.* 1727–1750. (1727) Un recueil tiré des autheurs françois, tant en prose qu'en vers, pour l'utilité de la jeunesse qui désire de s'avancer dans la langue françoise. Par Guillaume Kerr. Edinburgh, Baskett, 1727. LEE

B585 [KILNER, Dorothy], 1755–1836. (1783?) Anecdotes of a boarding school; or, an antidote to the vices of those useful seminaries, by M.P. Marshall, [178–]. BI HU [Hull copy inscribed Jan. 1, 1787.]

B586 [KILNER, Dorothy]. (1799) The rational brutes. 1816. *See* D770

B587 [KILNER, Dorothy]. (*c.* 1785?) The village school. New ed., 1828, *and* 1831. *See* D771

B588 [KILNER, Mary Jane], b. 1753. (*c.* 1783?) Memoirs of a peg top. New ed., 1828. *See* D772

B589 KIRKBY, John, 1705–1754. (1746) A new English grammar; or, guide to the English tongue . . . Manby & Cox, 1746. LEI

B590 KNIGHT, Samuel, 1675–1746. (1724) The life of Dr. John Colet, dean of S. Paul's . . . and founder of S. Paul's School: with an appendix containing some account of the masters and more eminent scholars of that foundation . . . J. Downing, 1724. LEE LEI NE

B591 KNIGHT, Samuel, do., 2nd ed., 1823. *See* C762

B592 KNIGHT, Samuel. (1726) The life of Erasmus . . . wherein an account is given of . . . the state of religion and learning at that time in both our universities . . . Cambridge, Crownfield, pr., 1726. LEI

Knight of the rose. *See* Peacock, Lucy

B593 KNIPE, Rest. (1783) A course of lectures: containing remarks upon the government and education of children, thoughts upon the present plan of education, and an essay upon elocution . . . Edinburgh, Author, 1783. LO SO

B594 KNOX, Vicesimus, 1752–1821. (1778–1779) Essays, moral and literary. 16th ed., 1808. *See* C763

B595 KNOX, Vicesimus. (1781) Liberal education; or, a practical treatise on the methods of acquiring useful and polite learning. C. Dilly, 1781. OX; 5th ed., C. Dilly, 1783. CA NE SH; 6th ed., Dilly, 1784. LEE; 7th ed., Dilly, 1785. LEI; 9th ed., 1788. 2 vols. ReU; vol. 1, 9th ed., vol. 2, 10th ed., 1788–1789. 2 vols. NO; 10th ed., Dilly, 1789. 2 vols. BI HU ReU; 11th ed., Dilly, 1795. 2 vols. LO

B596 [KNOX, Vicesimus], *compiler*. Elegant epistles: being a copious collection of familiar and amusing letters, selected for the improvement of young persons . . . New ed., impr. and enl., Longman, [etc.], 1794. LEI

B597 [KNOX, Vicesimus], *compiler*. Elegant extracts; or, useful and entertaining pieces of poetry . . . New ed., 1790. NoU

B598 [KNOX, Vicesimus], *compiler*. Elegant extracts; or, useful and entertaining passages in prose . . . for the improvement of scholars. 2nd ed., [1783?]. 4 books in 1 vol. NoU; [5th?] ed., Longman, 1794. 4 books in 2 vols. NoU; new ed., Dilly, [179–?]. LEI

B599 [KNOX, Vicesimus], *compiler*. The poetical epitome; or, elegant extracts from the larger volume, for the improvement of scholars . . . 1791. NoU

B600 KNOX, Vicesimus, *compiler*, do., *another ed.*, 1807. *See* D784

L. D., *madame la comtesse. See* Auneuil, *comtesse d'*

LA CASA, Giovanni de. *See* Casa, Giovanni della

B601 LA CHALOTAIS, Louis René de Caradeuc de, 1701–1785. (1763) Essai d'éducation nationale, ou plan d'études pour la jeunesse. [No publisher], 1763. HU

B602 LA CHALOTAIS, L. R. de C. de. Essay on national education; or, plan of studies for the young. Translated and with an historical introduction by H. R. Clark. Arnold, 1934. BI BR HU LEE LEI LO MA NE NO RE SH SO; *another ed. See* B1172 De la Fontainerie, F., *ed.*

LA CHETARDIE, Joachim Trotti de. *See* Trotti de la Chétardie, J.

B602a LADDER to learning. 16th ed., 1841; 17th ed., 1845. *See* D1378 Trimmer, S., *ed.*

Ladies' library. *See* Wray, Mary

LADY, A., *pseud. See under the titles of the works*

B603 LA FITE, Marie Elisabeth de. (1787) Eugénie et ses élèves; ou, lettres et dialogues à l'usage des jeunes personnes. Paris, Onfroy, & Née de la Rochelle, 1787. 2 vols. LEI

B604 LA FITE, M. E. de. (1790) Réponses à démêler; ou, essai d'une manière d'exercer l'attention. On y a joint divers morceaux, qui ont pour but d'instruire ou d'amuser les jeunes personnes. Londres, Murray, 1790. LEE

LA MADELEINE, Louis Philipon de. *See* Philipon de la Madeleine, L.

B605 LAMBERT, Anne Thérèse de Marguenat de Courcelles, *marquise de*, 1674–1733. Lettres sur la véritable éducation. Amsterdam, Bernard, 1729. LEE

B606 LAMBERT, *marquise de*. Réflexions nouvelles sur les femmes; et Lettres sur la véritable éducation. Amsterdam, P. Humbert, 1732. LO

B607 LAMBERT, *marquise de.* Avis d'une mère à son fils et à sa fille. 3e éd., Paris, Ganeau, 1734. LO

B608 LAMBERT, *marquise de.* Letters to her son and daughter, on true education, etc. Translated by Mr. Rowell. M. Cooper, 1749. LEI

B609 LAMBERT, *marquise de.* Counsels of a mother to her son and daughter. Translated from the French by Alfred Haggard. Hodsoll, 1885. LEI

B610 LAMBERT, Joseph, 1654–1722. La manière de bien instruire les pauvres, et en particulier les gens de la campagne. Ouvrage utile à tous les pauvres . . . même utile aux riches. 4e éd., Luxembourg, A. Chevalier, 1737. LO

B611 LAMY, Bernard, 1640–1715. (167–) La réthorique; ou, l'art de parler. 5e éd., revûe & augmentée, ou l'on a ajouté des Nouvelles réflexions sur l'art poétique. The Hague, P. Gosse, 1725. LEI

B612 LANCELOT, Claude, 1615?–1695. Mémoires touchant la vie de Monsieur de S. Cyran, pour servir d'éclaircissement à l'histoire de Port-Royal. Cologne, aux dépens de la Compagnie, 1738. 2 vols. LEI

B613 [LANCELOT, Claude]. (Fr. 1655) Nouvelle méthode pour apprendre facilement la langue grecque . . . Nlle. éd., corr. & augm. de nouveau. Paris, vve. Brocas & D. J. Aumont, [etc.], 1754. LEI

B614 [LANCELOT, Claude]. A treatise upon Greek accents. Translated from the Nouvelle méthode grecque, written by the Messieurs of Port-Royal. To which is prefixed a Character of the most valuable Greek authors. Lintot, 1729. LEE

B615 [LANCELOT, Claude]. The abridgment of the New method of learning easily and expeditiously the Greek tongue; translated from the French of Messieurs de Port Royal, with considerable improvements. To which is added, an abridgment of the Greek roots. For the use of schools. J. Nourse, & G. Hawkins, 1749. HU NoU

B616 [LANCELOT, Claude]. A new method of learning with facility the Greek tongue . . . Translated from the French of the Messieurs de Port Royal, by T. Nugent. New ed., Wingrave, 1797. HU LEI

B617 [LANCELOT, Claude]. (Fr. 1660) Nouvelle méthode de Messieurs de Port Royal pour apprendre facilement & en peu de temps la langue italienne. 4e éd., revüe, corrigée, & augmentée . . . Amsterdam, F. l'Honoré, 1736. LEI

B618 LANGE, Joachim, 1670–1744. Easy and pleasant Latin conversations . . . Republished by J. Ryland . . . Dilly, 1769. NoU

LANGLET DU FRESNOY, Nicholas. *See* Lenglet du Fresnoy, N.

B619 LANGLEY & Co., *firm.* Langley's introduction to running hand. [17–?]. NoU

B620 LANTHENAS, François. Bases fondamentales de l'instruction publique et de toute constitution libre; ou, Moyens de lier l'opinion publique . . . Paris, Imprimerie du Cercle Social, 1793. BI

B621 LA PLACE, Pierre Antoine de, 1707–1793. (1792?) Le Valère-Maxime françois, livre classique pour servir à l'éducation de la jeunesse et de l'adolescence françoise . . . Paris, Didot, 1792. 2 vols. LEI

B622 LA SALLE, Jean-Baptiste de, 1651–1719. (Written 1695, pub. 1720) Conduite des écoles chrétiennes. Edition du manuscrit français . . . Introduction et notes comparatives avec l'édition princeps de 1720 par F. Anselme. Paris, Procure Générale, [1951?]. LO

B623 LA SALLE, J.-B. de. The conduct of the schools. Translation and introduction by F. de la Fontainerie. New York, McGraw, 1935. HU LEE

B624 LA SALLE, J.-B. de. Letters and documents. Edited by W. J. Battersby. Longmans, 1952. HU LEE LEI RE

Latin grammar for the use of Christ's Hospital. *See* Penn, James

B625 LAW. (1759) The Law and equity of the late appointment of a Warden of Winchester considered. S. Hooper, 1759. HU

B626 LAYNG, Henry, *fl.* 1744–1754. (1754) The rod, a poem in three cantos. Oxford, W. Jackson, 1754. HU

B627 LECLERC, Nicolas Gabriel, 1726–1798, *trans.* Les plans et les statuts, des différents établissements ordonnés par Sa Majesté Impériale Cathérine II pour l'éducation de la jeunesse . . . Ecrits en langue russe par M. Betzky & traduits en langue françoise . . . par Mr. Clerc. Amsterdam, M. M. Rey, 1775. 2 vols. LEI

B628 LECOUTZ DE LEVIZAC, Jean Pons Victor. (1797) A theoretical and practical grammar of the French tongue. 3rd ed., 1806, *and* 20th ed., 1835. *See* D807

B629 LECTURES on astronomy and natural philosophy for the use of children. Bath, 1794. NoU

B630 [LEEDS, Edward]. (2nd ed., 1688) More English examples to be turned into Latin . . . for the use of young beginners at Bury School. 14th ed. with large additions. C. Bathurst, 1742. HU

B631 [LE FRANCOIS, *abbé*]? Méthode abrégée et facile pour apprendre la géographie . . . Nlle. éd., revûe, corrigée & augmentée. Paris, Savoye, 1751. LEI

B632 LE MAITRE DE CLAVILLE, Charles François Nicolas. (*c.* 1734) Traité du vrai mérite de l'homme, considéré dans tous les âges & dans toutes les conditions: avec des principes d'éducation propres à former les jeunes gens à la vertu. 2e éd., Paris, Saugrain, 1736. LO; 4e éd., Paris, Saugrain, 1740. 2 vols. LEE; *another ed.*, Suivant la dernière édition de Paris. Liège, Collette, 1745. 2 vols in 1. HU

B633 LENGLET DU FRESNOY, Nicholas, 1674–1755. (Eng. 1742?) An abridgment of ancient geography. 2nd ed., 1829. *See* D811

B634 LENGLET DU FRESNOY, Nicholas. (1736) Géographie des enfans, ou méthode abrégée de la géographie. Divisée par leçons . . . 4e éd. augm., Paris, Rollin, & De Bure, 1740. LEI

B635 LENGLET DU FRESNOY, Nicholas. Geography for children; or, a short and easy method of teaching and learning geography . . . Translated from the French . . . 18th ed., 1794. NoU; 20th ed., 1799. NoU

B636 LENGLET DU FRESNOY, Nicholas, do., 22nd ed., 1806, *and* 31st ed., 1829. *See* D812

B637 LENGLET DU FRESNOY, Nicholas. (Fr. 1713) New method of studying history . . . In two volumes . . . Vol. 1. Originally written in French by M. Langlet du Fresnoy . . . The whole made English by Richard Rawlinson. W. Burton, 1728. LEI

B638 LENGLET DU FRESNOY, Nicholas. (1737–) Principes de l'histoire pour l'éducation de la jeunesse. Par années & par leçons. Quatrième année, qui contient l'histoire générale & particulière de France. Amsterdam, aux dépens de la Compagnie, 1738. LEI

B639 LENOIR [*or* Le Noir], P. V. (1800) The logographic emblematical English spelling book, or a method of teaching children to read. T. Boosey, 1800. BR

B640 [L'EPEE, Charles Michel de], *abbé*, 1712–1789. La véritable manière d'instruire les sourds et les muets, confirmée par une longue expérience. Par l'abbé ———. Paris, Nyon, 1784. [2nd rev. ed. of his *Institution des sourds et muets*, first pub. 1776.] LO

B641 LE PRINCE DE BEAUMONT, Jeanne-Marie, 1711–1780. Le magasin des adolescents. 1822. *See* D815

B642 LE PRINCE DE BEAUMONT, J.-M. (1756) Magazin des enfans, ou dialogues entre une sage gouvernante & plusieurs de ses élèves de la première distinction . . . Leyden & The Hague, Luzac & Van Damme, & P. F. Gosse, 1777. 4 vols. in 2. LEI

B643 LE PRINCE DE BEAUMONT, J.-M., do., *another ed.*, Metz, 1821. *See* D816

B644 LE PRINCE DE BEAUMONT, J.-M. The young misses magazine . . . Translated from the French . . . Vol. 2 [trans. of vols. 3–4 of the French]. Glasgow, Mundell, 1800. LEI

B645 LE PRINCE DE BEAUMONT, J.-M. (1750–1755) Le nouveau magasin françois; ou, bibliothèque instructive et amusante, 1750, 1751, 1752. Londres, F. Changuion, [etc.], 1750–1752. 3 vols. LEI

B646 LESSING, Gotthold Ephraim, 1729–1781. (Germ. 1780) The education of the human race. Translated by the Rev. Fred. W. Robertson. 4th ed., rev., Kegan Paul, 1896. BR HU

Lessons for children. *See* Barbauld, A. L.

B647 LESSONS. (1717?) Lessons for children, historical and practical, to which are added, some prayers, and the chief rules for spelling and dividing words into syllables . . . Drawn up for the use of a charity school in the country. 4th ed., J. Downing, 1725. HU

B648 LESSONS historical and chronological. Printed for private use. Taunton, T. Norris, pr., 1792. HU

B649 LESSONS in geography. [178–]. [Apparently issued without title-page.] HU

B650 A LETTER from a father to his daughter at a boarding school. Robinson, 1774. LEE

B651 A LETTER to a schoolmaster in the country, from his friend in town, relative to Mr. Sheridan's Scheme of education. Dublin, 1758. HU

Letter to the Rev. Dr. Lowth. *See* Bridle, John

B652 A LETTER to the scholars of Eaton, occasioned by . . . Dr. Snape's letter to the Bishop of Bangor. By D.H. 1717. ReU

Letters for literary ladies. *See* Edgeworth, M.

Letters from a tutor to his pupils. *See* Jones, William

B653 LEUSDEN, Jan, 1624–1699, *ed.* Johannis Buxtorfii Epitome grammaticae Hebraeae, breviter & methodice ad publicum scholarum usum proposita . . . Jam variis in locis a mendis typographiciis emendata . . . a Johanne Leusden. Ed. quarta. Leyden, S. Luctmans, 1716. LEI

LEVIZAC, Jean Pons Victor Lecoutz de. *See* Lecoutz de Levizac, J. P. V.

B654 LIEBERKUHN, Philipp Julius. Versuch über die anschauende Erkenntnis: ein Beitrag zu Theorie des Unterrichts. Züllichau, auf Kosten der Waisenhaus und Frommannischen Buchhandlung, 1782. LO

B655 LILY, William, 1468?–1522. (*c*. 1540). Brevissima institutio, seu ratio grammatice cognoscendae . . . [Edited by John Ward]. Buckley & Longman, 176[5]. HU

B656 LILY, William. Propria quae maribus, Quae genus, As in praesenti, Syntaxis, Qui mihi, construed. Buckley & Longman, 1763. HU; Buckley & Longman, 1778. LO

B657 LILY, William. A short introduction to grammar . . . Buckley & Longman, 1743. LEI; *another ed.*, Buckley & Longman, 1753. BI

B658 LILY, William. A short introduction of grammar . . . [Edited by John Ward]. Buckley & Longman, 1765. HU; *another ed.*, 1771. BR; *another ed.*, Buckley & Longman, 1784. LO

B659 LITTLEBURY, Isaac, *fl.* 1399–1709, *trans.* The adventures of Telemachus. *See* B355 Fénelon

B660 LIVRE pour apprendre à lire aux enfans . . . Paris, Jouenne, [1726]. LO

B661 [LOCKMAN, John], 1698–1771. (3rd ed., 173–) A new history of England, by question and answer. Extracted from the most celebrated English historians; particularly M. Rapin de Thoyras. Dublin, G. Faulkner, 1741. HU; 8th ed., London, 1752. NoU; 23rd ed., Longman, [etc.], 1794. LEI

B662 [LOCKMAN, John]. [173–]. A new Roman history, by question and answer . . . Extracted from ancient authors, and the most celebrated among the modern . . . By the author of the History of England by question and answer. 2nd ed., Astley, 1740. LEI; 11th ed., 1791. NoU

Logica in usum juventutis academicae. Autore J.J. *See* Jennings, J.

Logique, ou l'art de penser. *See* Arnauld, A., and Nicole, P.

B663 LONGINUS. Treatise on the sublime. *See* B524 Holmes, J.

Looking glass for the mind. *See* Berquin, A.
Loose hints upon education. *See* Home, Henry

B664 LOVE, John, 1695–1750. (1733) Two grammatical treatises: viz. 1. Animadversions on the Latin grammar lately published by Mr. Robert Trotter . . . By Mr. John Love, schoolmaster at Dumbarton. 2. A dissertation upon the way of teaching that language . . . By another hand, [i.e., Thomas Ruddiman]. Edinburgh, 1733. HU

Lovechild, *Mrs.*, *pseud*. *See* Fenn, E.

Lovechild, Solomon, *pseud*. *See* Fenn, E.

B665 LOWE, Solomon, *fl*. 1723–1737. (1724) A grammar of the Latin tongue. J. Wyat, [etc.], 1726. HU

B666 LOWE, Solomon. (1737) Mnemonics delineated. *See* D570 Grey, R.

B667 [LOWTH, Robert], 1710–1787. (1759) An answer to an anonymous letter to Dr. Lowth; concerning the late election of a Warden of Winchester College. A. Millar, 1759. HU

B668 LOWTH, Robert. (1758) The life of William of Wykeham, bishop of Winchester. Collected from records, registers, manuscripts, and other authentic evidences. A. Millar, & R. & J. Dodsley, 1758. HU LI; *also* Supplement to the first edition, containing the corrections and additions of the second edition. 1759. HU

B669 [LOWTH, Robert]. (1762) A short introduction to English grammar; with critical notes. New ed., corr., A. Millar, [etc.], 1767. HU; new ed., 1787. NoU; new ed., printed for the booksellers, 1789. LEI; new ed., J. Dodsley and T. Cadell, 1791. HU

B670 LUC, Jean André de, *the elder*. (1799) Lettres sur l'éducation religieuse de l'enfance. Précédées et suivies de détails historiques . . . Berlin, Librairie du Bureau des Arts. [1800]. HU

B761 [LUND, John]. (1777) Ducks and green peas. [18–?]. *See* D848

B672 LUPTON, William, 1676–1726. (1718) The necessity of positive duty . . . a sermon preach'd June 5, 1718, at the anniversary meeting of the children . . . in charity schools . . . 1718. ReU

Lusus Westmonasterienses. *See* Prior, Robert

B673 LYONS, Israel, d. 1779. (1735) The scholar's instructor, an Hebrew grammar. Cambridge, 1735. NoU

M., T. *See* Morell, Thomas

M.P., *pseud*. *See* Kilner, Dorothy

MACAULAY, *Mrs*. Catherine, *later* Graham. *See* Graham, C.

B674 [MADDOX, Isaac], 1697–1759. (1740) A sermon preach'd before the Society corresponding with the Incorporated society in Dublin for promoting English Protestant working-schools in Ireland, March 19, 1739/40 . . . M. Downing, 1740. LEI ReU

MADELEINE, Louis Philipon de la. *See* Philipon de la Madeleine, L.

B675 [MAESE, Sarah]. The school: being a series of letters between a young lady and her mother. 1766. NoU

B676 MAGAZINE. (1703) Magazine; or, animadversions on the English spelling, by G.W. (1703). Introduction by David Abercrombie. Los Angeles, W. A. Clark memorial lib., 1958. [Possibly by John White.] HU

B677 MAIDWELL, Lewis. (1705) An essay upon the necessity and excellency of education, 1705. Introduction by J. M. Patrick. Los Angeles, Augustan reprint soc., 1955. [Facsimile reprint.] HU

B678 MAINTENON, Françoise d'Aubigné, *marquise de*, 1635–1719. Lettres et entretiens sur l'éducation des filles. Recueillis et publiés pour la première fois par M. Th. Lavallée. Paris, Charpentier, 1861. 2 vols. LO

B679 MAINTENON, *marquise de*. Extraits de ses lettres, avis, entretiens, conversations, et proverbes sur l'éducation, précédés d'une introduction par O. Gréard. 7e éd., Paris, Hachette, 1912. LEI

B680 MAINTENON, *marquise de*. Recueil des instructions que Madame de Maintenon a données aux demoiselles de St. Cyr, d'après un manuscrit originel et inédit . . . Paris, Dumoulin, 1908. LEE LEI LO

B681 MALEZIEU, Nicholas de, 1650–1729. Elémens de géométrie de Monseigneur le duc de Bourgogne. Nlle. éd., revue, corrigée et augmentée d'un traité des logarithmes par M. de Malezieu . . . Paris, Ganeau, [etc.], 1722. LEI

B682 MANCHESTER. *Charters*. The charters of the collegiate church, the free grammar school, the blue coat hospital, [Manchester], and the last will and testament of the late Catherine Richards, with ancient curiosities. Manchester, Falkner, Dawson, 1791. LEE

B683 [MANDEVILLE, Bernard], 1670–1733. (1714–1723) The fable of the bees; or, private vices publick benefits. With an essay on charity and charity schools . . . 3rd ed., Tonson, 1724. LEE; 4th ed., Tonson, 1725. LEI

B684 MANDEVILLE, Bernard. The fable of the bees: or private vices, publick benefits. With a commentary critical, historical, and explanatory by F. B. Kaye. Oxford, Clarendon pr., 1924, repr. 1957. 2 vols. [Includes the Essay on charity and charity schools.] HU

B685 MANGEY, Thomas, 1688–1755. (1726) The gospel preach'd to the poor: a sermon preach'd June 2, 1726, at the annual meeting of . . . charity schools . . . 1726. ReU

B686 [MANGNALL, Richmal], 1769–1820. (1798) Historical and miscellaneous questions. Stockport, 1798. NoU

B687 MAGNALL, Richmal, do., 5th ed., 1806; 6th ed., 1808; 7th ed., 1809; new ed., 1825; new ed., 1828; rev. ed., 1834; rev. ed., 1844; new ed., n.d.; rev. ed., [187–?]. *See* D868

B688 MANN, Isaac, *bp. of Cork & Ross*. [Pre-1780] A familiar exposition of the Church catechism. 24th ed., 1825. *See* D870

B689 MANSON, David, 1726–1792. (1764?) Directions to play the literary cards: invented for the improvement of children in learning and morals, from their beginning to learn the letters, till they become proficients in spelling, reading, parsing, and arithmetic. [Belfast?], printed for the author, 1764. [With set of 119 cards.] HU

B690 MANSON, David. (1762?) A new pocket dictionary, or, English expositor . . . Belfast, 1762. NoU

B691 MANSON, David. (*c.* 1760) A new spelling book. 1839. *See* D871

B692 MAPLETOFT, John. (1755) The practice of a college and the visitor's decision concerning it, submitted to the consideration of the public, in behalf of founders or benefactors, and of scholars in the University of Cambridge . . . 1755. ReU

B693 MARINE SOCIETY. Abstract of the proceedings, from its first institution . . . 1778. *See* B442 Glasse, S.

B694 MARKHAM, Robert. (1779) A sermon preached before the . . . Marine Society at St. George's church, Hanover-Square, on occasion of their anniversary meeting, on Tuesday, 13th April, 1779. Oliver, 1779. LEI

B695 MARKHAM, William. (1720?; 5th ed., 1738) An introduction to spelling and reading English: being the most plain and easy method of teaching young children to read . . . 34th ed., Gainsborough, H. Mozley, 1790. ReU

B696 MARKHAM, William, do., *another ed.*, Morpeth, 1824. *See* D885

B697 MARMONTEL, Jean François, 1723–1799. Marmontel's tales, selected and abridged . . . by Mrs. Pilkington. Vernor & Hood, 1799. ReU

B698 MARSHALL, Charles. A practical introduction to arithmetic; or, the teacher of arithmetic's assistant . . . 1774. NoU

B699 MARSHALL, H., *ed.* The schoolmaster's most useful companion, by Daniel Fenning . . . 4th ed., corrected, improved and greatly enlarged by H. Marshall. Crowder, 1788. BR

B700 MARTIAL. Epigrammata. In usum scholae Westmonasteriensis. Ed. altera. [Edited by T. Fitzgerald.] 1740. NoU

B701 MARTIAL. Select epigrams . . . Translated and imitated by W. Hay . . . With an appendix of some by Cowley and other hands. 1755. NoU

MARTRE, Antoine Pyron du. *See* Porny, Marc Antoine, *pseud.*

B702 MARTYN, Thomas, 1735–1825, *trans.* (1785) Letters on the elements of botany, addressed to a young lady . . . By Jean Jacques Rousseau. Translated into English by Thomas Martyn. 3rd ed., B. White, 1791. OX

B703 MASON, John, 1706–1763. (1748) Essays on poetical and prosaic numbers, and elocution. 2nd ed., Buckland & Waugh, 1761. NO

B704 MASON, John. (1745) A treatise of self-knowledge. 11th ed., Buckland, 1784. LO

B705 MASSON, Arthur, *fl.* 1755–1779. A collection of prose and verse, from the best English authors, for the use of schools. New and much enlarged ed. Air [*sic*], J. & P. Wilson, pr., 1796. HU

B706 MASTERS, Robert, 1713–1798. (1753) History of the College of Corpus Christi and the Blessed Virgin Mary in the University of Cambridge. 1753. ReU

Matho. *See* Baxter, Andrew

B707 MAVOR, William Fordyce, 1758–1837. (1798) The British Nepos. 2nd ed., 1800. NoU

B708 MAVOR, W. F., do., 7th ed., 1806; 13th ed., 1829. *See* D900

B708a MAVOR, W. F. (1780?) The English spelling book. *For 19th century editions see* D903

B709 MAVOR, W. F. (1800) Natural history for the use of schools . . . 1800. NoU

B710 MAVOR, W. F. Histoire naturelle, à l'usage des écoles . . . 1801. *See* D905

B711 MAVOR, W. F. The elements of natural history. 9th ed., 1816. *See* D904

B712 MAVOR, W. F. (1780?) Universal stenography. 8th ed., 1807. *See* D908

B713 [MAVOR, W. F.] (1798) Youth's miscellany; or, A father's gift to his children. Consisting of original essays, moral and literary, tales, fables, reflections, etc. . . . By the author of The juvenile olio . . . Newbery, 1798. BI

B714 MAVOR, W. F., *ed. and trans.* (1800) Select lives of Plutarch . . . abridged from the original for the use of schools. New eds., 1806 [*and*] 1823. *See* D909

B715 MEILAN, Mark Anthony, *fl.* 1774–1812, *ed.* (1788) The friend of youth; being a sequel to The Children's friend . . . consisting of apt stories, entertaining dialogues, and moral dramas . . . partly translated from Mr. Berquin and other French and German writers, and partly original, being written by the editor himself . . . Vols. 5–10. T. Hookham, 1788. 6 vols in 3. LEI

B716 MEILAN, M. A., *trans.* The children's friend. *See* B106 Berquin, A.

B720 MEMOIRS. (1799 or earlier) Memoirs of Dick, the little poney. 1806. *See* D920

Méthode abrégée et facile pour apprendre la géographie. *See* Le François, *abbé.*

Méthode pour apprendre facilement l'histoire romaine. *See* Fourcroy, *abbé de*

Methods used for erecting charity-schools. *See* Society for promoting Christian knowledge

B721 MILLS, Henry. (1732) An essay on generosity and greatness of spirit. The builders of colleges, hospitals and schools, prais'd and commended. The invaluable blessing of a sound, useful and pious education: especially that of school learning; with a particular view to Archbp. Whitgyft's foundation, in Croydon, Surry. J. Pemberton, 1732. LO

B722 MILLS, Henry. (1741) Pueritiae formandae artifex. J. Pemberton, 1741. HU

B723 MILNER, John, *D.D.*, *fl.* 1729–1757. (1743) Reflections on human life: a sermon preached in St. Thomas's on New-Year's-Day, MDCCXLIII. For the benefit of the charity-school in Gravel-Lane, Southwark . . . J. Noon, & M. Fenner, 1743. LEI

B723a [MILNER, John]. (1729) A practical grammar of the Latin tongue . . . Gray, 1729. LEE

B724 MILNS, William, b. 1760? (1794) The well-bred scholar, or practical essays on the best methods of improving the taste, and assisting the exertions of youth in their literary pursuits. S. Gosnell, pr., 1794. HU; Rivingtons, [etc.], 1794. LO

B725 MILTON, John, 1608–1764. (Tractate 1673) Paradise regain'd . . . To which is added Samson Agonistes; and Poems upon several occasions; with a Tractate on education. J. & R. Tonson, 1756. LEI

B726　MIRABEAU, Honoré Gabriel Riquetti, *comte de*, 1749–1791. (1791) Discours sur l'éducation nationale. Projet de Décret sur l'organisation des écoles publiques. Paris, 1791. LO

Miscellanea in usum juventutis academicae... Autore J.J. *See* Jennings, J.

B727　[MOLL, Herman], d. 1732. Geographia classica: the geography of the ancients so far described as is contain'd in the Greek and Latin classicks... 2nd ed., 1717. NoU; 5th ed., 1727. NoU

B728　MOLL, Herman. Thirty-two new and accurate maps of the geography of the ancients as contained in the Greek and Latin classicks... 1731. NoU

B729　MONRO, George. (1712) An essay upon Christian education; shewing the necessity and advantage of reading Christian authors in grammar-schools... J. Downing, 1712. LEI

B730　MORE, Hannah, 1745–1833. (1777) Essays on various subjects, principally designed for young ladies. 1777. ReU; 4th ed., Cadell, 1785. LEE

B731　MORE, Hannah, do., new ed., 1810. *See* D948

B732　MORE, Hannah. (1788) An estimate of the religion of the fashionable world. 5th ed., Cadell, 1793. LEE

B733　MORE, Hannah. The letters of Hannah More; selected with an introduction by R. B. Johnson. J. Lane, 1925. BR

B734　MORE, Hannah. (1793) Remarks on the speech of M. Dupont, made in the National Convention of France, on the subjects of religion and public education. Cadell, 1793. HU LEE; 2nd ed., Cadell, 1793. LEI LO

B735　MORE, Hannah. (1782) Sacred dramas: chiefly intended for young persons: the subjects taken from the Bible... 6th ed., Cadell, 1789. LEI

B736　MORE, Hannah, do., 16th ed., 1810. *and another ed.*, Chiswick, 1823. *See* D949

B737　MORE, Hannah. (1799) Strictures on the modern system of female education. Cadell & Davies, 1799. 2 vols. LEI; 2nd ed., Cadell & Davies, 1799. 2 vols. LEE SH; 3rd ed., Cadell & Davies, 1799. 2 vols. BR HU LO; 4th ed., Cadell & Davies, 1799. LO; 7th ed., 1799. 2 vols. NE NO ReU; 5th ed., Dublin, Porter, 1800. BI

B738　MORE, Hannah, do., 9th ed., 1801, 11th ed., 1811, [*and*] 12th ed., 1818. *See* C911

More English examples to be turned into Latin. *See* Leeds, Edward

More instructive lessons for children. *See* Barbauld, A. L.

B739　[MORELL, Thomas], 1703–1784, *ed.* Exempla minora; or, new English examples to be turned into Latin; adapted to the rules of the Latin grammar, lately printed at Eton. For the use of the lower forms. New ed., rev., Eton, J. Pote, 1761. HU

B740　[MORELL, Thomas], do., new ed., 1817; new ed., 1821; 1831. *See* D951

B741　[MORELL, Thomas], *ed.* Exempla moralia; or, third book of new English examples, to be rendered into Latin... New ed., Eton, 1789. NoU

B742　[MORELL, Thomas], do., new ed., rev., Eton, 1815. *See* D952

B743　MORELL, Thomas, *ed.* (1757) Sophocles Philoctetes [Greek script]... in usum scholae Etonensis. Longman, 1777. LEI

B744　MORLET, L. C. (1774?) Les beautés de l'histoire tirées des auteurs anciens & modernes de toutes les nations: ou essai sur l'éducation morale de la jeunesse... Nlle. éd., augm., Londres, P. Elmsly, 1784. LEI

B745　MORVAN DE BELLEGARDE, Jean Baptiste, 1648–1734. L'éducation parfaite. Amsterdam, 1710. ReU

B746　MORVAN DE BELLEGARDE, J. B. Les règles de la vie civile, avec des traits d'histoire, pour former l'esprit d'un jeune prince. The Hague, Guillaume de Voys, 1720. LO

B747　MOSER, C. F., and WITTICH, C. F. Der Landschullehrer. Ulm, 1798–1800. 3 vols. LO

B748　MOSS, Robert, 1666–1729. (1708) The providential division of men into rich and poor... a sermon preach'd in the parish church of St. Sepulchres, May 27, 1708... at the anniversary meeting of the chief promoters of the charity schools... R. Sare and J. Tonson, 1708. LEI ReU

B749　The MOTHER'S catechism. By a Reverend divine. Nottingham, 1717. NoU

MULSO, Hester, *aft.* Chapone. *See* Chapone, H.

B750　MURRAY, *Rev.* James, *of Newcastle*. The rudiments of the English tongue. 2nd ed., Newcastle, 1771. NoU

B751　MURRAY, Lindley, 1745–1826. (1797) English exercises, adapted to Murray's 'English grammar'. 10th ed., 1806; 33rd ed., 1825; 36th ed., 1827; Key to the exercises, 30th ed., 1853. *See* D967–968

B752　MURRAY, Lindley. (1795) An English grammar. 12th ed., York, 1805; new ed., 1808; 4th ed., 1819; 24th ed., 1813; 27th ed., 1815; 5th ed., York, 1824. *See* D969

B752a　MURRAY, Lindley. (1797) Abridgement of Murray's English grammar. *See* D966

B753　MURRAY, Lindley. (1799) The English reader; or, pieces in prose and poetry, selected from the best writers... With a few preliminary observations on the principles of good reading. York, Wilson, Spence & Mawman; London, Longman & Rees; 1799. LEE

B754　MURRAY, Lindley, do., 8th ed., 1809. *See* D970

B755　[MURRAY, Lindley], *ed.* (1792) Some account of the life and religious labours of Sarah Grubb. With an appendix, containing an account of Ackworth School, Observations on Christian discipline, and extracts from many of her letters. Dublin, R. Jackson, 1792. LEE LEI

B756 MURRY, Ann. (1778) Mentoria, or, the young ladies instructor: in familiar conversations, on moral and entertaining subjects. Calculated to improve young minds in the essential as well as ornamental parts of female education. 7th ed., C. Dilly, 1794. HU; 8th ed., C. Dilly, 1796. LEI

B757 MUSEUM. (c. 1758) A Museum for young gentlemen and ladies; or, a private tutor for little masters and misses. Containing a variety of useful subjects . . . 13th ed., Crowder, [1794]. HU; 15th ed., n.d. NoU

B758 NELSON, James, 1710–1794. (1753) An essay on the government of children, under three general heads, viz. health, manners, and education. Dodsley, 1753. BR; 3rd ed., Dodsley, 1763. BI LEE

B759 NELSON, Robert, 1665–1715. (1715) An address to persons of quality and estate. To which is added, an appendix of some original and valuable papers. R. Smith, 1715. LEE LEI

B760 Die NEUSTEN Erziehungsbegebenheiten, mit practischen Anmerkungen für das Jahr 1781. Zweiter Jahrgang. Erstes – drittes Stuck. Giessen, J. C. Krieger, 1781. LO

B761 A NEW English introduction to the Latin tongue . . . For the use of schools. 1735. NoU
New history of England. See Cooper, Rev. Mr.
New history of England by question and answer. See Lockman, J.

B762 A NEW invented horn-book. [17–?]. NoU

B763 A NEW lottery book of birds and beasts for children. Newcastle, 1771. NoU
New method of learning with facility the Greek tongue. See Lancelot, C.

B764 A NEW moral system of natural history, or, the beauties of nature displayed . . . Riley, 1789. (Historical pocket library, VI, Natural history.) LEE

B765 A NEW pocket companion for Oxford. New ed., 1785. ReU
New Roman history by question and answer. See Lockman, J.

B766 [NEWBERY, John], 1713–1767, ed.? (1746?) Geography made familiar and easy to young gentlemen and ladies. Being the sixth volume of the Circle of the sciences, etc. J. Newbery, 1748. LEI

B767 NEWBERY, John, ed. (1752) A spelling dictionary of the English language on a new plan. 5th ed., to which is prefix'd a compendious English grammar; with a concise historical account of the language. J. Newbery, 1755. NoU

B768 [NEWTON, Richard], 1676–1753. (1733) The expence [sic] of university education reduced: in a letter to A.B., Fellow of E.C. [i.e. Exeter College]. 2nd ed., Strahan, 1734. LEE

B769 NEWTON, Richard. (1726) University education; or, an explication and amendment of the statute which . . . prohibits the admission of scholars going from one society to another. 1726. ReU; 2nd ed., Strahan, 1733. LEE

B770 [NICOLE, Pierre], 1625?–1695, comp. (Fr. ed., 1659) Epigrammatum delectus ex omnibus tum veteribus, tum recentioribus poetis . . . Ed. nona. In usum scholae Etonensis. Innys, 1724. LEI
NICOLE, Pierre, joint author. See Arnauld, A., and Nicole, P.

B771 NICOLLS, Samuel. (1749) A sermon preach'd before the Society corresponding with the Incorporated society in Dublin for promoting English Protestant working schools in Ireland . . . 1749. [With] An abstract of His Majesty's royal charter for erecting and promoting English Protestant schools in Ireland, an alphabetical list of the members of the Incorporated society . . . [and] A continuation of the proceedings of the Incorporated society. Oliver, 1749. BI

B772 NOBLE, Edward. (1771) The elements of linear perspective demonstrated by geometrical principles . . . with an introduction containing . . . the elements of geometry . . . T. Davies, 1771. LEI

B773 NOMENCLATOR trilinguis, usitatoria rerum nomina continens . . . in puerorum ingenuorum gratiam qui cum Latinis Gallica conjungant. Ed. tertia. 1713. NoU

B774 NOMENCLATURA; or, nouns and verbs in English and Latin, to be formed and declined by children of the lowest forms. For the use of Eton-School. Eton, J. Pote, 1766. HU

B775 NOMENCLATURA. (1686) Nomenclatura trilinguis Anglo-Latino-Graeca; or, a short vocabulary, English, Latin, and Greek . . . Composed for the benefit of English youth, by P.K. 6th ed., carefully revised and corrected by R.C. . . . G. Conyers, 1704. HU
Nouvelle méthode de Messieurs de Port Royal. See Lancelot, C.

B776 NUGENT, Thomas, 1700?–1772, trans. (1763) Emilius; or, an essay on education, by J. J. Rouseau. J. Nourse, & P. Vaillant, 1763. 2 vols. HU

B777 NUGENT, Thomas, trans. (1746) A new method of learning with facility the Greek tongue . . . Translated from the French of the Messieurs de Port Royal. New ed., Wingrave, 1797. LEI

B778 NUGENT, Thomas, trans. (1746) A new method of learning with facility the Latin tongue . . . Translated from the French of the Messieurs de Port Royal. New ed., 1803; and another ed., 1816. See D997

B779 OBSERVATIONS. (1759) Observations on the present state of the English universities. Occasioned by Dr. Davies's account of the general education in them. M. Cooper, 1759. BR
Officium hominis. See Allestree, R.

B780 [OLLA podrida]. No place, [17–?]. NoU

B781 OURRY, J. A. (1788) The French scholar put to trial; or, questions on the French language . . . 2nd ed., 1794. NoU

B782 OVERBERG, Bernhard, 1754–1826. (1793) Anweisung zum zweckmässigen Schulunterricht für die Schullehrer im Fürstentum Münster. Besorgt von J. Esterhues. Paderborn, Schöningh, 1957. LEI

B783 OVID. Metamorphoses, in fifteen books: with the arguments and notes of John Minellius translated into English. To which is marginally added a prose version... For the use of schools. By Nathan Bailey. 4th ed., W. Innys, [etc.], 1756. HU

B784 OVID. Tristia, in five books: with the arguments and notes of John Minellius, translated into English. To which is added a prose version... For the use of schools. By N. Bailey. 2nd ed., 1740. NoU

B785 OXFORD. University. Corpus statutorum universitatis Oxoniensis. 1768. ReU

B786 OXFORD. University. Parecbolae, sive excerpta e corpore statutorum universitatis Oxoniensis. Accedunt Articuli religionis XXXIX ... In usum juventutis academicae. Oxford, Clarendon Pr., 1794. LEI

B787 The OXFORD magazine; or university museum. No. xxv, April 1770. By a society of gentlemen, members of the university of Oxford. LEI

B788 OXFORD verses. 1713–1761. 2 vols. ReU

P., M., *pseud. See* Kilner, Dorothy

P., P. *See* Poiret, Pierre

P.K. *See* K., P.

B789 PALEY, William, 1743–1805. (1790) Reading made completely easy. [*c.* 1855?]. *See* D1011

PANAGE, *pseud. See* Toussaint, François Vincent

B790 PARIS. Ecoles normales. Séances des Ecoles normales, recueillies par des sténographes, et revues par les professeurs. Tome 11. 2e éd., Paris, Imprimerie du Cercle-Social, An 9 [1800]. LO

B791 PARIS. Ecole royale militaire. Cours d'étude à l'usage des élèves de l'Ecole royale militaire. Paris, Nyon, 1777–1787. 44 vols. [Abrégé de l'histoire naturelle, tome premier, pour la première année de philosophie. 1777 – do., tome second, pour la seconde année de philosophie. 1777 – Abrégé de l'histoire sainte et écclesiastique, première partie. 1786– Abrégé de l'histoire ancienne, en particulier de l'histoire grecque, suivi d'un abrégé de la fable. 3e éd., augm., 1787.] LO

B792 PARKYNS, *Sir* Thomas, 1664–1741. (2nd ed., 1716) A practical and grammatical introduction to the Latin tongue. By Sir Thomas Parkyns of Bunny Park, Bart. For the use of his sons and of Bunny School. 4th ed., with many additions. Nottingham, T. Osborne, [etc.], 1732. HU

B793 PARR, Samuel, 1747–1825. (1786) A discourse on education and on the plans pursued in charity–schools. Cadell & Evans, [1786]. LEE

Pastoral advice to young persons. *See* Woodward, Josiah

B794 PATRICK, Samuel, 1684–1748, *ed.* (1731) Christ. Cellarii Geographia antiqua recognita denuo ... Huic demum 6a ed.... chartas... duplicem indicem... addidit, totam recensuit, & scholarum usui accommodavit Samuel Patrick. Ed. altera & castigatior. S. Ballard, [etc.], 1745. LEI

B795 PATRICK, Samuel, *ed.* (1727?) Hederici Lexicon manuale Graecum... Recensitum et plurimum auctum a Sam. Patrick... Ed. altera. H. Knaplock, [etc.], 1739. LEI

B796 [PEACOCK, Lucy], *fl.* 1785–1816. (1785) The adventures of the six princesses of Babylon, in their travels to the temple of virtue... Author, 1785. ReU

B797 [PEACOCK, Lucy]. (1793) The knight of the rose. An allegorical narrative... designed for the amusement and moral instruction of youth. By the author of The Adventures of the six princesses of Babylon, etc.... Hookham & Carpenter, [etc.], 1793. LEI ReU

B798 PEACOCK, Lucy. (1794) The visit for a week. 4th ed., [1804]; 8th ed., 1815. *See* D1020

B799 PEACOCK, Lucy. Visite d'une semaine. 2e éd., 1817. *See* D1021

B800 PEACOCK, Lucy, *trans.* (1796) Ambrose and Eleanor... Translated by Lucy Peacock. 3rd ed., 1807. *See* D1022

B801 PEARSON, William, *archdeacon of Nottingham.* (1708) The duty of charity to the poor recommended, a sermon preach'd Dec. 22, 1707. 1708. ReU

PELHAM, Mary, *pseud. See* Kilner, Dorothy

B802 [PENN, James], 1727–1800. (1761) A Latin grammar for the use of Christ's Hospital. T. Hope, 1761. HU

B803 [PENNINGTON, Sarah, *lady*], d. 1763? (1761) An unfortunate mother's advice to her absent daughters, in a letter to Miss Pennington. 4th ed., Towers, 1767. LO; 5th ed., corr., J. Walter, 1770. LEI

B804 PERCIVAL, Thomas, 1740–1804. (2nd ed., 1776) A father's instructions; consisting of moral tales. 8th ed., 1793. ReU

B805 PERKS, William. (1792) The youth's introduction to geography; containing a description of the several empires, kingdoms and states in the world... The whole adapted to the capacity of youth. 2nd ed., enl. and impr. Author, & G. G. & J. Robinson, 1793. [1792 ed. has title: The youth's general introduction to Guthrie's geography.] HU

B806 PERRAULT, Charles, 1628–1703. (Fr. 1697; Eng. 1729?) Tales of passed times. With morals... Englished by R.S., gent. [i.e. R. Samber]... 7th ed., 1796. ReU

B807 PERRAULT, Charles. Histories, or tales of past times, told by Mother Goose with morals... Englished by G.M., gent. Newly edited by J. Saxon Childers. Nonesuch Pr., 1925. [Reprint of an edition dated 1719, probably in error for 1799.] LEI

B808 PERRIN, Jean Baptiste. (1774) The elements of French conversation. 18th ed., 1815; 26th ed., 1833. *See* D1039

B809 PERRIN, J. B. (1771) Fables amusantes. 16e éd., 1817. *See* D1040

B810 PERRIN, J. B. (1768) A grammar of the French tongue, grounded upon the decisions of the French Academy... 4th ed., B. Law, 1783. HU

B811 PERRIN, J. B. (1769) The practice of the French pronunciation alphabetically exhibited... With two spelling vocabularies, French and English. By John Perrin. 6th ed., B. & C. Law, 1795. HU

B812 PESTALOZZI, Johann Heinrich, 1746–1827. (1781) Lienhard und Gertrud. Hrsg. von A. Haller. Basle, Birkhäuser, 1946. LEI; Zurich-Erlenbach, 1945. SO

B813 PESTALOZZI, J. H. Leonard and Gertrude, translated and abridged by Eva Channing. Heath, 1885 [various reprint dates]. BI HU LEE LEI LO SH SO

Petit Grandisson. *See* Berquin, A.

B814 PHAEDRUS. Fabularum Aesopiarum libri quinque: interpretatione & notis illustravit Petrus Danet . . . J. & B. Sprint & S. Burrows, [etc.], 1722. LEI

B815 PHAEDRUS. Fabularum Aesopiarum libri quinque, editio altera . . . Huic editioni accessere Publii Syri et aliorum sententiae, ex recensione Cl. Bentlei. Eton, 1762. NoU

B816 PHAEDRUS. Fifty instructive and entertaining fables of Phaedrus, in Latin, French and English, attempted after a new method for the more speedy improvement of youth in schools, by D. Bellamy. J. J. & P. Knapton, [etc.], 1734. BR

B817 PHAEDRUS. Phaedri Fabulae; or, Phaedrus's Fables, with . . . improvements, in a method entirely new . . . For the use of schools. By J. Stirling . . . 13th ed., 1793. NoU

B818 PHAEDRUS. A poetical translation of the Fables of Phaedrus, with the appendix of Gudius, and an accurate edition of the original on the opposite page. To which is added a parsing index for the use of learners. By Christopher Smart. Dodsley, [etc.], 1765. NO

B819 PHILIPON DE LA MADELEINE, Louis. (1784?) De l'éducation des collèges. 1784. ReU

B820 PHILIPON DE LA MADELEINE, Louis. (1783) Vues patriotiques sur l'éducation du peuple, tant des villes que de la campagne. Lyons, 1783. ReU

B821 PHILIPPS, Jenkin Thomas, d. 1755. (1721) A compendious way of teaching antient and modern languages, formerly practised by . . . Tanaquil Faber . . . to which are added some tracts and observations on the same subject by several eminent men . . . Author, 1723. OX; 2nd ed., W. Meadows, 1727. LEE; 3rd ed., W. Meadows, 1728. HU; 4th ed., enl., Meadows, 1750. LEI LO ReU

B822 [PHILIPPS, J. T.], *ed.* (1726) An essay towards an universal and rational grammar, by J. Shirley. 1726. NoU

B823 PHILPOT, Stephen. (1747) An essay on the advantages of a polite education joined with a learned one. Philpot, 1747. LEE

B824 PICARDET, Henri-Claude. Essai sur l'éducation des petits enfans. Dijon, Hucherot, 1756. LO

B825 PILKINGTON, Mary, 1766–1839. (1799) Biography for girls; or, moral and instructive examples for the female sex. 3rd ed., 1800. ReU

B826 PILKINGTON, Mary. (1798) A mirror for the female sex. Historical beauties for young ladies . . . Designed principally for the use of ladies' schools. 2nd ed., Vernor & Hood, 1799. HU LEE

B827 PILKINGTON, Mary. (1800) New tales of the castle; or, the noble emigrants, a story of modern times. Vernor & Hood, 1800. ReU

B828 PILKINGTON, Mary. (1799) The spoiled child; or, indulgence counteracted. Vernor & Hood, 1799. BI

B829 PILKINGTON, Mary. (1798) Tales of the cottage; or, stories moral and amusing, for young persons. Vernor & Hood, 1798. ReU

B830 PILKINGTON, Mary, do., 5th ed., 1809. *See* D1061

B831 PILKINGTON, Mary. (1798) Tales of the hermitage. 2nd ed., 1809. *See* D1062

B831a PILKINGTON, Mary, *ed.* Marmontel's tales, selected and abridged . . . by Mrs. Pilkington. 1799. ReU

B832 [PINCHARD, *Mrs.*] (1791) The blind child; or, anecdotes of the Wyndham family. Written for the use of young people. By a lady. 5th ed., E. Newbery, 1798. ReU

B833 PINCHARD, *Mrs.*, do., 9th ed., 1809; new ed. [*c.* 1820?]. *See* D1063

B834 [PINCHARD, *Mrs.*]. (1794) The two cousins, a moral story, for the use of young persons . . . By the author of The blind child and Dramatic dialogues. E. Newbery, 1794. ReU

B835 PINEDA, Pedro. (Span. 1726) A short and compendious method for the learning to speak, read and write the English and Spanish languages. 1751. NoU

PITT, William, *earl of Chatham*. *See* Chatham, *earl of*

Plain hymn to Our Redeemer. *See* Society for the promotion of Christian knowledge

Plan of education at Mr. Elphinston's Academy. *See* Elphinston, James

Plan of education in the Marischal College. *See* Gerard, Alexander

B836 PLEASING. (1789) The Pleasing, interesting, and affecting history of Prince Lee Boo. 1816; *and another ed.*, Banbury, [18–?]. *See* D1093

Pleasing instructor, or entertaining moralist. *See* Slack, Anne

B837 PLUCHE, Noel Antoine, 1688–1761. (1751) La mécanique des langues et l'art de les enseigner. Paris, vve. Estienne, 1751. LEI

B838 PLUCHE, N. A. (Eng. 1733–1739) Spectacle de la nature; or, nature display'd, etc. Translated from the original French by Mr. [Samuel] Humphreys. Pemberton, [etc.], 1736–1740. 4 vols. [Vols. 1–3, 3rd ed., 1736–1740; vol. 4, 1st ed., 1739.] LO; 3rd ed., Pemberton, 1736–1739. 4 vols. ReU; 1770–1776. 6 vols. [Vols. 1–4, new ed., 1776; vols. 5–6, 5th ed., 1770.] NoU

B839 PLUTARCH. Select lives of Plutarch . . . abridged from the original for the use of schools. By W. F. Mavor. New eds., 1806 [*and*] 1823. *See* D1094

B840 POETAE minores Graeci, selecti & emendati . . . In usum scholarum. G. Innys & B. Motte, 1728. LEI

Poetical epitome. *See* Knox, V.

B841 POINTER, John, 1668–1754. (1718) Miscellanea in usum juventutis academica . . . 1718. NoU

B842 POINTER, John. (1749) Oxoniensis academia; or, the antiquities and curiosities of the University of Oxford. S. Birt & J. Ward, 1749. OX

B843 [POIRET, Pierre], 1646–1719. Les principes solides de la religion et de la vie chrétienne, appliqués à l'éducation des enfans, et applicables à toutes sortes de personnes. Par P.P. Amsterdam, Desbordes, 1705. LO

B844 POLITE. (c. 1763) The Polite lady; or, a course of female education. In a series of letters from a mother to her daughter. 2nd ed., corr., Newbery & Carnan, 1769. HU LEI

B845 POMEY, François Antoine, 1618–1673. (Eng. 1694) The Pantheon, representing the fabulous histories of the heathen gods and most illustrious heroes . . . Written for the use of the Dauphin. 4th ed. wherein the whole translation [by A. Tooke] is revised . . . For the use of schools. Clavell, 1705. LEI; 18th ed., S. Birt, [etc.], 1753. ReU; 19th ed., 1757. NoU; new ed., rev. and corr., 1794. HU

B846 PORNY, Marc Antoine, pseud. [i.e. Antoine Pyron du Martre]. (1780?) Grammatical exercises, English and French . . . 7th ed. . . . 1793. NoU

B847 PORNY, M. A. Modern letters in French and English . . . to which are annexed directions with regard to the proper form of writing to superiors, equals and inferiors. The whole designed for the instruction and improvement of . . . young gentlemen and ladies . . . By Mr. Porny, French-master at Eton-College. J. Nourse & S. Hooper, 1769. LEI

B848 [PORSON, Richard], 1759–1808, ed. (1799) . . . [Greek script]. Phoenissae [of Euripides]. Ad fidem manuscriptorum emendata et brevibus notis . . . instructa. In usum studiosae juventutis. G. Wilkie, 1799. LEI

Port Royal grammars. See Lancelot, C.

B849 POWELL, William Samuel, 1715–1775. (1774) An observation on the design of establishing annual examinations at Cambridge. Cambridge, [no publisher], [1774]. BI

Practical grammar of the English language. See Burn, John

B850 A PRACTICAL grammar of the Latin tongue . . . being a collection from those very learned masters, Sanctius, Perizonius, [etc.], drawn up at first to serve a private occasion of life, and now made publick, as a testimony of respect to British youth. [By John Milner.] Gray, 1729. LEE

Preceptor. See Dodsley, Robert

Present for an apprentice. See Barnard, Sir J.

B851 PRETTY. (1762) Pretty book of pictures for little masters and misses . . . 15th ed., 1867. See D1110

B852 PRICE, Richard, 1723–1791. (1787) The evidence for a future period of improvement in the state of mankind, with the means and duty of promoting it, represented in a discourse . . . to the supporters of a new academical institution among Protestant dissenters. H. Goldney, pr., 1787. MA

B853 PRIESTLEY, Joseph, 1733–1804. (1765) An essay on a course of liberal education for civil and active life. With plans of lectures on . . . history . . . To which are added, Remarks on a code of education, proposed by Dr. Brown, in a late treatise, entitled, Thoughts on civil liberty, etc. C. Henderson, [etc.], 1765. LEE OX

B854 PRIESTLEY, Joseph. (1788) Lectures on history . . . To which is prefixed, An essay on a course of liberal education. J. Johnson, 1788. 2 vols. LO; 3rd ed., Dublin, White & Byrne, 1791. LEI; Johnson, 1793. 2 vols. LEE

B855 PRIESTLEY, Joseph. (1778) Miscellaneous observations relating to education; more especially as it respects the conduct of the mind. To which is added, An essay on a course of liberal education for civil and active life. Bath, R. Cruttwell for J. Johnson (London), 1778. BR HU ReU; Cork, White, 1780. BI LEE LEI SH

B856 PRIESTLEY, Joseph. (1791) A particular attention to the instruction of the young recommended, in a discourse, delivered at the Gravel-pit Meeting in Hackney, December 4, 1791 . . . J. Johnson, 1791. LEI

B857 PRIEUR, J. C., ed. Le dictionnaire royal . . . Autrefois composé . . . par M. A. Boyer . . . Nlle. éd. . . . par J. C. Prieur. 1773. See B140 Boyer, A.

B858 PRIMER. (1546) The Primer set furth by the kinges maiestie & his clergie, to be taught, lerned, and red: and none other to be used thorowout all his dominions. Imprinted at London . . . by Richard Grafton . . . 1546. Reprinted without any alteration. [1722.] HU

B859 PRIMITIAE POETICES. (1733) Primitiae poetices: sive illustrium veterumque poetarum sententiae . . . ad alenda puerorum ingenia aptae . . . Ed. secunda. J. Pemberton, 1741. [With Mills, Henry. Pueritiae formandae artifex.] HU

Prince Lee Boo. See Pleasing, interesting, and affecting history of Prince Lee Boo

B860 [PRIOR, Robert]. (1730) Lusus Westmonasterienses, sive epigrammatum et poematum minorum delectus. Westminster, A. Campbell, 1730. HU

Proceedings for Sunday schools. See Adkin, L.

B861 PUBLIUS SYRUS. Sententiae. 1762. See B815 Phaedrus

PYRON DU MARTRE, Antoine. See Porny, Marc Antoine, pseud.

B862 QUATREMERE DE QUINCY, Antoine Chrysostôme, 1755–1849. (1791) Considérations sur les arts du dessin en France, suivies d'un plan d'académie, ou d'école publique, et d'un système d'encouragemens. Paris, Devaux, 1791. [Photocopy.] NE

B863 QUINTILIAN. De institutione oratoria, libri duodecim, cum notis et animadversionibus virorum doctorum, summa cura recogniti et emendati per Petrum Burmannum. Leyden, J. de Vivie, 1720. 2 vols. LEE

B864 QUINTILIAN. Quintilians Pädagogik und Didaktik mit Anmerkungen herausgegeben von Bonaventura Andres . . . Wirzburg, T. Göbhardt, 1783. LEI

B865 [R., E.]. (2nd ed., 1794) Geography and history, selected by a lady . . . 7th ed., 1808; [and] 10th ed., 1815. See D1119

B866 RAINE, Matthew. (1771) English rudiments, or, an easy introduction to English grammar for the use of schools. Darlington, J. Sadler, 1771. LO

B867 RAMSAY, Andrew Michael, 1686–1743. (1732) A plan of education. 3rd ed., Glasgow, Foulis, 1741. LEI

B868 [RANDALL, John]. (1749) An introduction to history antient and modern . . . Designed for the instruction of the young gentlemen of the Academy at Heath, near Wakefield, Yorkshire. To which is added, an account of that academy. J. & J. Rivington, 1749. HU

B869 RANDOLPH, Thomas. (1733) The advantages of publick education: a sermon preach'd in the cathedral-church at Canterbury on Thursday, Sept. 13, 1733. Fletcher, 1733. SH

B870 [RATHMANN, Heinrich], ed. Beyträge zur Lebensgeschichte Joh. Bernh. Basedows, aus seinen Schriften und andern ächten Quellen gesammlet. Magdeburg, 1791. LO

B871 RAWLINSON, Richard, 1690–1755, trans. New method of studying history. See B637 Lenglet du Fresnoy, N.

B872 RAY, John, 1627–1705. (1685) Nomenclator classicus, sive dictionariolum trilingue . . . 4th ed., J. Taylor, 1703. NoU

B873 RECUEIL. (1775) Recueil des chefs-d'oeuvre des plus célèbres beaux-esprits françois, tant en vers qu'en prose. Nlle. éd. augmentée. Edinburgh, Gordon & Murray, 1781. HU

B874 REEVE, Clara, 1729–1807. (1792) Plans of education; with remarks on the systems of other writers. In a series of letters . . . Hookham & Carpenter, 1792. LEI

Reflections upon learning . . . By a gentleman. See Baker, Thomas

Réflexions sur la théorie, & la pratique de l'éducation. See Gerdil, G. S.

B875 REGNY, —. (1792) On the means of securing to youth the advantages of their early education. With a specimen of the method, as applicable to the French language. By M. Regny. Author, [1792]. LEE

B876 REID, Thomas, 1710–1796. (1788) Essay on the active powers of the human mind. 1843. See C1203

B877 REID, Thomas. (1785) Essays on the intellectual powers of man. Edinburgh, Bell, 1785. LEE LEI

B878 RENNELL, Thomas, 1754–1840. (1799) A sermon preached in the cathedral church of St. Paul on June 6, 1799. Being the time of the yearly meeting . . . To which is annexed An account of the Society for Promoting Christian Knowledge. F. & C. Rivington, 1799. HU

Reply to Dr. Golding's and Dr. Lowth's answers to the anonymous letter. By a Wykehamist. See Blackstone, Charles

B879 RICHARDSON, John, F.S.A. A key to geography . . . to which are prefix'd, an easy introduction to decimal arithmetic and the extraction of roots . . . Sheffield, 1787. NoU

B880 [RIDLEY, James], 1736–1765. (1764) The tales of the genii; or, the delightful lessons of Horam the son of Asmar . . . By Sir Charles Morell [pseud.]. Vol. 3 [only]. 1781. (Entertaining museum, or Complete circulating library.) NoU

B881 RIOS, Angelique de los. L'encyclopédie enfantine. Edition augmentée. Dresden, 1780. NoU

RIQUETTI, Honoré Gabriel, comte de Mirabeau. See Mirabeau, comte de

B882 ROBERTS, P., b. 1760. The writing-master's assistant in all the hands necessary for gentlemen, or men of business. Written by P. Roberts. Engraved by J. Howard. Sold by Mr. Marks, and Mr. Parker, [c. 177–?]. LEI

B883 [ROBINSON, John], 1650–1723. (1714) The benefits and duty of the members of Christ's kingdom. A sermon preach'd in the parish-church of St. Sepulchre, May 20, MDCCXIV . . . at the anniversary meeting of the children educated in the charity schools . . . By the Lord Bishop of London. Downing, 1714. LEI ReU

B884 ROBINSON, John, schoolmaster, of London. The art of teaching the orthography, accent and pronunciation of the English language by imitation . . . T. Maiden, pr., for the author, 1800. HU

B885 ROLLIN, Charles, 1661–1741. (1726–1728) De la manière d'enseigner et d'étudier les belles-lettres. 2e éd., Paris, Estienne, 1748. 4 vols. LO

B886 ROLLIN, Charles. Supplément au traité de la manière d'enseigner et d'étudier les belles lettres. Paris, Estienne, 1734. LEE

B887 ROLLIN, Charles. Traité des études. Nlle. éd., 1845. See C1241

B888 ROLLIN, Charles. (1737) The method of teaching and studying the belles lettres . . . Translated from the French. 2nd ed., Bettesworth & Hitch, 1737. 4 vols. LEI; 3rd ed., vol. 1 [only], C. Hitch, 1742. LO; 6th ed., W. Strahan, 1769. 3 vols. LO NoU; Lackington, 1798. 4 vols. LEE

B889 ROLLIN, Charles. (1735) New thoughts concerning education. Done from the French, with notes. Bettesworth & Hitch, 1735. [Book 1 of The Method of teaching and studying the belles lettres.] LEE LO; Dublin, G. Risk, [etc.], 1738. HU

B890 ROUSSEAU, Jean Jacques, 1712–1778. Minor educational writings. Selected and translated by W. Boyd. Blackie, 1911. HU LEE LO SH; N.Y., Columbia univ. Teachers coll., 1962. CA LEI

B891 ROUSSEAU, J. J. Rousseau on education; edited by R. L. Archer. Arnold, 1912 [and reprints]. HU LEE LO SH SO

B892 ROUSSEAU, J. J. (1762) Emile, ou de l'éducation. Frankfurt, [no pub.], 1762. 4 vols. LEI

B893 ROUSSEAU, J. J., do., another ed., Amsterdam, Rey, 1774. 4 vols. RE

B894 ROUSSEAU, J. J., do., another ed., Londres [i.e. Paris], [1781]. Tome 1 [only]. LO

B895 ROUSSEAU, J. J., do., another ed., Paris, 1816. See C1251

B896 ROUSSEAU, J. J. L'élève de la nature. Nlle. éd., augmentée, Amsterdam, Rey, 1773. LEE

B897 ROUSSEAU, J. J. Emilius; or, an essay on education. Translated from the French by Mr. Nugent. J. Nourse & P. Vaillant, 1763. 2 vols. HU

B898 ROUSSEAU, J. J. Emilius and Sophia; or, a new system of education. Translated from the French... 2nd ed., Becket & De Hondt, 1763. 4 vols. BI; Becket & Baldwin, 1783. 4 vols. BI LEI

B899 ROUSSEAU, J. J. Emilius; or, a treatise of education. Translated from the French. Edinburgh, A. Donaldson, 1763. 3 vols. LEI; 1768. 3 vols. HU

B900 ROUSSEAU, J. J. Emilius and Sophia; or, a new system of education. Translated from the French... by the translator of Eloisa. New ed., Dublin, Potts, [etc.], 1779. 4 vols. LEE

B901 ROUSSEAU, J. J. Emile; or, concerning education: extracts... With an introduction and notes by J. Steeg. Translated by E. Worthington. Boston, Heath, 1883 [and reprints]. BI LEE SH

B902 ROUSSEAU, J. J. Emile; or, a treatise on education. Abridged, translated, and annotated by W. H. Payne. Appleton, 1892 [and reprints]. BI HU

B903 ROUSSEAU, J. J. Emile. [Translated by B. Foxley.] Dent, 1911 [and reprints]. BI HU LEE LEI LO NE NO RE SH SO

B904 ROUSSEAU, J. J. Emile for today... Selected, translated and interpreted by W. Boyd. Heinemann, 1956. LEE LEI RE SH

B905 ROUSSEAU, J. J. (Eng. 1785) Letters on the elements of botany, addressed to a lady... Translated into English by Thomas Martyn. 3rd ed., White, 1791. OX

B906 ROWELL, J., trans. (1749) Letters to her son and daughter, by the Marquise de Lambert. See B608 Lambert, Mme. de

B907 The ROYAL French grammar... 1720. NoU

B908 [RUDDIMAN, Thomas], 1674–1757. (1733) A dissertation upon the way of teaching the Latin tongue: wherein the objections raised against Mr. Ruddiman's and other such like grammars... are answered and confuted... Together with some critical remarks on the new Latin grammar composed by Mr. John Clarke, schoolmaster at Hull... Edinburgh, 1733. HU

B909 [RUDDIMAN, Thomas] Grammatical exercises; or, an exemplification of the several moods and tenses... Taken for the most part from Mr. Turner's *Exercises to the accidence*, and adapted to the method of the *Latin rudiments* published by T.R. Edinburgh, T. & W. Ruddiman, 1757. HU

B910 RUDDIMAN, Thomas. (1714) The rudiments of the Latin tongue; or, a plain and easy introduction to Latin grammar... 13th ed., Edinburgh, the Author, 1755. LEE

B911 RUDDIMAN, Thomas, do., *another ed.*, corrected and revised by A. Dun. 1803. See D1164 Rudimentum grammaticae Latinae metricum. See Busby, R.

B912 RUGGLE, George, 1575–1622. (1630) Ignoramus. Comoedia coram rege Jacobo primo et totius Angliae magnatibus, ab academicis cantabrigiensibus habita. Ed. sexta. Westminster, 1731. LEE

B913 RUMFORD, Benjamin Thompson, *count von*, 1753–1814. Essays political, economical, and philosophical. New ed., 1800–1802. See C1255

B914 RYLAND, John Collett, 1723–1792. An address to the ingenuous youth of Great-Britain, together with a body of divinity in miniature: to which is subjoined a Plan of education adapted to the use of schools, and which has been carried into execution during a course of near fifty years. H. D. Symonds, 1792. CA

B915 RYLAND, J. C., *ed.* (1769) Easy and pleasant Latin conversations, by Dr. Lange. Republished by J. Ryland... Dilly, 1769. NoU

B915a S., H. (1797?) The history of the Davenport family. [18–]. See D1169

B916 S., M. An address to the Hibernian Society; with a plan of education in a letter to the provost and fellows of Trinity College, Dublin. By M—S—. Dublin, 1758. HU

Sabbath: a sermon. See Adkin, L.

SAINT-AUBIN, Stéphanie Félicité du Crest de, *comtesse de Genlis. See Genlis, comtesse de

SAINT-PIERRE, Jacques Henri Bernardin de. See Bernardin de Saint-Pierre, J. H.

B917 SALISBURY SPELLING-BOOK. (1786) The Salisbury spelling-book... 12th ed., 1809. See D1173

B918 SALLUST. C. Crispi Sallustii Bellum Catilinarium et Jugurthinum; cum versione libera... By John Clarke. 4th ed., W. Clarke, 1755. HU

B919 SALMON, Nicholas, *fl.* 1773–1814. (1788) The complete system of the French language; or, a course of grammatical observations, wherein the great deficiencies of grammars, and even dictionaries, are supplied, etc. T. Spilsbury, pr., 1788. MA

B920 SALMON, Nicholas. (1787) A footstep to the French language; containing such observations as will facilitate the acquisition of it, and render its study less disgusting to beginners... Author, 1787. LEI

B921 SALMON, Nicholas, *ed.* L'ami des enfans, [par A. Berquin]. Nlle. éd., revue et corrigée par Nicolas Salmon. J. Johnson, [etc.], 1798. 4 vols. LEI

B922 SALMON, Thomas, 1648–1706. (1701) A discourse concerning the baptism and education of children... Whereunto are annexed proposals for the settlement of free-schools in all parishes for education of the children of the poor. B. Tooke, 1701. LEI

B923 SALMON, Thomas, 1679–1767. A new and historical grammar. 9th ed., 1764. NoU

B924 SALZMANN, Christian Gotthilf, 1744–1811. (1796) Conrad Kiefer; oder, Anweisung zu einer vernünftigen Erziehung der Kinder. Neue Ausg. Minden, Hufeland, 1879. LEI

B925 SALZMANN, C. G. Gymnastics for youth [wrongly ascribed to Salzmann]. See B479 Guts-Muths, J. C. F.

B926 SALZMANN, C. G. (1780) Krebsbüchlein; oder, Anweisung zu einer unvernünftigen Erziehung der Kinder. Neue Ausg. Minden, Hufeland, 1877. LEI

B927 SASTRES, Francesco, *trans.* L'amico de' fanciulli. See B108 Berquin, A.

B928 SCENES for children. By a lady. Loddon [*sic*], [17–?]. NoU

B929 SCHILLER, Friedrich v., 1759–1805. (Written 1795) Ueber die aesthetische Erziehung des Menschen... Mit einer Einführung von G. Ehrhart. Herford, Die Arche, 1948. LEI

B930 SCHILLER, Friedrich v. On the aesthetic education of man... Translated with an introduction by R. Snell. Routledge, 1954. BR HU LEE LEI RE SO

B931 SCHLEZ, Johann Ferdinand. (1795) Gregorius Schlaghart und Richard Lorenz, oder die Dorfschulen zu Langenhausen und Traubenheim. Erste Hälfte. Nuremberg, Felszecker, 1795. LO
School (The). See Maese, Sarah

B932 SCHOOLMISTRESS. (1778) The Schoolmistress for the poor. Edinburgh, Martins, 1778. BR

B933 SCHREVELIUS, Cornelis, 1615?–?1664. (1654) Cornelii Schrevelii Lexicon manuale graeco–latinum & latino–graecum: studio atque opera Josephi Hill, necnon Johannis Entick... auctum... Editio nova... multo auctior & emendatior. Bowyer, [etc.], 1774. LEI

B934 SCOT, Alexandre, comp. (1784?) Nouveau recueil: ou mélange littéraire, historique, dramatique et poétique, à l'usage des écoles... 3e éd., Londres, 1789. NoU

B935 SCOT, Alexandre. Rudiments and practical exercises for learning the French language. 1781. NoU

B936 SCOTT, William, fl. 1770–1793. Beauties of eminent writers; selected and arranged for the instruction of youth in the proper reading and reciting of the English language... Edinburgh, Hill, 1793. LEE

B937 SECKER, Thomas, 1693–1768. (1743) A sermon preach'd May 5, 1743, being the time of the yearly meeting of the charity schools... M. Downing, 1743. ReU

B938 SECKER, Thomas. (1757) A sermon preached before the society corresponding with the Incorporated society in Dublin, for promoting English Protestant working-schools in Ireland, at their general meeting... April 27, 1757. Oliver, 1757. BI ReU

B939 SELECTA ex Homeri Odyss., Hesiodo, [etc.], cum vulgata versione emendata, ac variis... notis. In usum Regiae Scholae Etonensis. Eton, J. Pote, 1762. HU

B940 SELECTA, do., another ed. with title Poeti Graeci. 1828–1849. See D1095 Poetae

B941 SELLON, William, minister at Clerkenwell. (1784) An abridgment of the Holy Scriptures. New ed., [c. 1820]. See D1201

B942 [SERGEANT, John], 1622–1707. (1657) The mystery of rhetorick unveiled... by John Smith, of Montague Close, Southwark... 10th ed., 1721. NoU

B943 SERIOUS. (1751) A Serious address to the educators of youth in Great Britain. Trye, 1751. LEE

B944 SERVICE, John Paterson. Recreation for youth: a useful and entertaining epitome of geography and biography... Kearsley, 1787. LEI
SEYMOUR, Juliana-Susannah, pseud. See Hill, 'Sir' John

B945 SHARP, Abraham, 1651–1742. Of constructing the natural sines. See B958 Sherwin, H.

B946 SHARP, William, 1719–1782. (1755) The amiableness and advantage of making suitable provision for the education and employment of poor children. A sermon preach'd at the parish-church of St. Martin in the city of Oxford, on Sunday, Sept. 28, 1755... Oxford, the Theatre for J. Fletcher, 1755. LEI

B947 SHAW, Peter, 1694–1763, ed. (1733) A compleat system of general geography, by Varenius... The whole revised and corrected by Peter Shaw. 2nd ed. Vol. 2 [only]. S. Austen, 1734. LEI

B948 SHAW, Samuel, schoolmaster of Tamworth. (1724) A short and plain syntax, for the instruction of children in the Latin tongue... For the use of Tamworth school. W. & J. Innys, 1724. HU

B949 SHELLEY, George, 1666?–1736? (1710?) Alphabets in all the hands, with great variety of capitals and small letters. Done for the use of the writing school of Christ's Hospital, London. [1718?] NoU

B950 SHELLEY, George. A supplement to Mr. Wingate's Arithmetic... 1704. NoU. For Wingate's Arithmetic including the Supplement, see B1150–1151 Wingate, E.

B951 SHERIDAN, Thomas, 1719–1788. (1756) British education; or, the source of the disorders of Great Britain. Dodsley, 1756. HU LEE SH ReU; Dublin, Faulkner, 1756. BI; new rev. ed., Dilly, 1769. LEI

B952 SHERIDAN, Thomas. (1775) Lectures on the art of reading, in two parts. 1781. ReU

B953 SHERIDAN, Thomas, do., 6th ed., 1805. See C1293

B954 SHERIDAN, Thomas. (1769) A plan of education for the young nobility and gentry of Great Britain... Dilly, 1769. HU LEE

B955 SHERLOCK, Thomas, 1678–1761. (1719) A sermon preach'd May 21, 1719. 1719. ReU

B956 [SHERLOCK, Thomas]. (1738) A sermon preach'd before the Society corresponding with the Incorporated society... for promoting English Protestant schools in Ireland, on Friday, March 17, 1737–8, by the Lord Bishop of Salisbury. 1738. ReU

B957 SHERWILL, Thomas. (1710) The great advantage of a right education, a sermon preach'd July 18, 1710, at Felstead in Essex... at the annual meeting of the scholars educated at that school. 1710. ReU

B958 SHERWIN, Henry. Mathematical tables, contrived after a most comprehensive method... With their construction and use. By Mr. Briggs, Dr. Wallis, Mr. Halley, Mr. Abr. Sharp. Seller & Price, 1705. LEE

B959 SHIRLEY, James, 1596–1666. (1726) An essay towards an universal and rational grammar. [Edited by J. T. Philipps]. 1726. NoU
Short account of the school in Kingswood. See Wesley, John

Short address to the Society of New College in Oxford. See Bridle, John

B960 SHORT and easy rules for attaining a knowledge of English grammar. To which are added a few letters for the formation of juvenile correspondence. Wallis, 1800. LEI; *another ed.,* 1801. *See* D1234

B961 SHORT (A) history of England, for the Infant's library. [*c.* 1800]. NoU

Short introduction of grammar. *See* Lily, W.

Short introduction to English grammar. *See* Lowth, R.

B962 SHORT. (1728) A short introduction to grammar; for the use of the lower forms, in the King's School at Westminster. Barker, 1731. LEI; 1781. NoU; *another ed.,* 1810. *See* D1236

B963 SHORT way (A) to know the world; or, the rudiments of geography ... by T.H. 2nd ed., T. Osborne, 1712. ReU

B964 SICARD, Roch-Ambroise, 1742–1822. (1800) Cours d'instruction d'un sourd-muet. [1801], *and* 2e ed., 1803. *See* C1301–1302

SILLERY, *marquise de. See* Genlis, *comtesse de*

B965 SIMPSON, Thomas, 1710–1761. (1752) Select exercises for young proficients in the mathematicks ... New ed., to which is prefixed an account of the life and writings of the author, by Charles Hutton. F. Wingrave, 1792. HU

B966 SIMSON, Robert, 1687–1768, *ed.* (1756) Euclidis Elementorum libri priores sex, item undecimus et duodecimus, ex versione latina Federici Commandini ... [revised] a Roberto Simson. Glasgow U.P., 1756. LEI

B967 SLACK, *Mrs.* Anne [*or* Ann], *formerly* Fisher, 1719–1778. The new English tutor. 18th ed., 1821. *See* D1248

B968 SLACK, *Mrs.* Anne. (1750) [A new grammar]. A practical new grammar, with exercises of bad English ... By A. Fisher. 10th ed., enl. and impr., M. Richardson, L. Hawes, & T. Slack, 1765. HU; 17th ed., Newcastle, Slack, 1778. NoU; 19th ed., 1780. NoU; 20th ed., Newcastle, T. Slack, 1781. OX; 24th ed., Newcastle, Hodgson, 1788. LEE

B969 SLACK, *Mrs.* Anne. Fisher's Grammar improved ... 35th ed., 1811. *See* D1249

B970 SLACK, *Mrs.* Anne. (1756) The pleasing instructor, or entertaining moralist ... to which are prefixed new thoughts on education. By A. Fisher. New ed., Robinson, 1785. HU; 2nd ed. [*sic*], Robinson, 1787. LO; new eds., 1805 and 1809. *See* D1250

B971 [SLACK, *Mrs.* Anne]. The young scholar's delight; or, familiar companion. Being the most easy introduction to learning and science. Newcastle, T. Slack, 1770. NE

B972 SLEIDAN, Johannes, 1506–1556. De quatuor imperiis. [*In* Select parts of Grey's Memoria technica.] [1786?]. NoU

B973 SMALRIDGE, George, 1663–1719. (1710) The royal benefactress; or, the great charity of educating poor children. In a sermon preached in the parish church of St. Sepulchre, June 1, 1710 ... at the anniversary meeting of the children educated in the charity-schools. J. Downing for Jonah Bowyer, 1710. HU ReU

B974 SMART, Christopher, 1722–1771. (3rd ed., 1775) Hymns for the amusement of children. Oxford, Blackwell for Luttrell society, 1947. [Facsimile of 3rd ed., 1775.] LEI

B975 SMART, Christopher, *trans.* (1765) A poetical translation of the fables of Phaedrus, with the appendix of Gudius, and an accurate edition of the original on the opposite page. To which is added a parsing index for the use of learners. Dodsley, [etc.], 1765. NO

B976 SMETHAM, Thomas. (1774) Practical grammar; or, an easy way to understand English ... To which is added, A poetical epitome of grammar ... and A short English grammar upon the plan of the Latin ... Dublin, P. Hoey, 1774. HU NoU

B977 SMITH, Charlotte, *formerly* Turner, 1749–1806. (1796) Rambles farther: a continuation of Rural walks: in dialogues. Intended for the use of young persons. Cadell & Davies, 1796. 2 vols. BI

SMITH, Erasmus. *See* Erasmus Smith charity

SMITH, John, *of Montague Close, Southwark, pseud. See* Sergeant, John

B978 SMITH, William, 1651?–1735. Annals of University-College. 1728. ReU

B979 SNAPE, Andrew, 1675–1742. (1711) A sermon preach'd in the parish-church of St. Sepulchre, May the 24th, 1711 ... at the anniversary meeting of the children educated in the charity schools ... Bowyer, 1711. LEE ReU

B980 SOCIETE DES ARTS ET SCIENCES DE HARLEM. [Prize essays]. *See* B239 Comparet, J. A.; B395 Formey, J. H. S.

B981 SOCIETY FOR BETTERING THE CONDITION OF THE POOR. Reports. 1798–1808. *See* C1332

B982 SOCIETY FOR PROMOTING CHRISTIAN KNOWLEDGE. Account of the charity schools in Great Britain and Ireland [title varies]. 5th ed., Downing, 1706. BI LEE; 6th ed., 1707. LEE; 7th ed., 1708. BI LEE ReU SH; 8th ed., 1709. LO ReU; 9th ed., 1710. ReU; 10th ed., 1711. ReU; 11th ed., 1712. HU ReU; 12th ed., 1713. LEI ReU; 13th ed., 1714. LEE

B983 SOCIETY for Promoting Christian Knowledge. An account of the methods whereby the charity-schools have been erected and managed. Downing, 1705. ReU; 1706. BR

B984 SOCIETY for Promoting Christian Knowledge. The methods used for erecting charity-schools, with the rules and orders by which they are governed ... Downing, 1715. LEE; 1716. HU

B985 SOCIETY for Promoting Christian Knowledge. An account of the Society for Promoting Christian Knowledge. Downing, 1738. LEI; Downing, 1739. ReU; Dod, 1751. LEE; Rivington, [1780]. LEI; 1805. *See* C1333

B986 SOCIETY for Promoting Christian Knowledge. A plain hymn to our Redeemer, containing the substance of Christian religion. More particularly recommended to the charity-schools. Wyat, 1707. LEE

B987 SOCIETY for Promoting Christian Knowledge. Prayers for the use of the charity schools. Downing, 1716. LEE

B988 SOCIETY for Promoting Christian Knowledge. The standing rules and orders of the Society . . . Downing, 1741. LEI

Some account of the life and religious labours of Sarah Grubb. *See* Murray, Lindley, *ed.*

B989 SOME few letters selected, from an account of work-houses and charity-schools for employment of the poor in England, with a preface to excite some such application of our charity in Ireland. Dublin, J. Hyde, 1728. LEE

B990 SOPHOCLES. Elektra. 1729. *See* B1129 Westminster School. Treis tragoediai

B991 SOPHOCLES. Philoctetes [Greek script] . . . In usum Scholae Etonensis. Curante T. Morell, S.T.P. Longman, 1777. LEI

B992 SOULES, François. (1784) A new grammar of the French language. Author, [1785?]. LO

Spectacle de la nature. *See* Pluche, N. A.

B993 [SPEED, John]. (1759) An impartial by-stander's review of the controversy concerning the wardenship of Winchester College. By Statutophilus. R. Baldwin, 1759. HU

Spelling dictionary of the English language. *See* Newbery, John, *ed.*

B994 STACKHOUSE, Thomas, 1756–1836. (1800) A new essay on punctuation: being an attempt to reduce the practice of pointing to the government of distinct and explicit rules . . . Author, 1800. LEE

B995 STAINFORTH, William. (1711) The duty of doing good recommended . . . a sermon preach'd March 30, 1711. 1711. ReU

B996 STANHOPE, Charles. (1786) The new polite tutoress; or, young ladies' best instructor. Containing a complete course of dialogues between a sensible governess and several of her pupils of the first rank . . . Hogg, [1786]. LEE LO

B997 STANHOPE, George, 1660–1728. (1705) The danger of hard-heartedness to the poor, a sermon preach'd May 31, 1705, at a meeting of the gentlemen concerned in promoting the charity schools . . . S. Keble, 1705. ReU

B998 STANHOPE, George, *trans.* Of wisdom . . . by the Sieur de Charron. 1707. *See* B201 Charron, P.

STANHOPE, Philip Dormer, *4th earl of Chesterfield. See* Chesterfield, *earl of*

B999 STANLEY, Maria Josepha, *lady Stanley of Alderley, formerly* M. J. Holroyd. The girlhood of Maria Josepha Holroyd (Lady Stanley of Alderley), Recorded in letters of a hundred years ago, from 1776 to 1796. Edited by J. H. Adeane. Longmans, 1896. LO

B1000 [STARS. A set of 40 cards, pricked to show position of stars in various constellations.] [*c.* 1800]. NoU

STATUTOPHILUS, *pseud. See* Speed, J.

B1001 STEDMAN, John. The study of astronomy adapted to the capacities of youth . . . Dilly, 1796. LEI

B1002 STIRLING, John, *fl.* 1735–1740. A short view of English grammar, in a method entirely new . . . For the use of schools. Author, 1735. HU

B1003 STIRLING, John. (1733) A system of rhetoric, in a method entirely new . . . For the use of schools. 3rd ed. T. Astley, 1740. HU

B1004 STIRLING, John, *ed.* Une centurie des colloques de Cordier; or, a century of the colloquies of Corderius . . . For the use of schools. Wilcox, 1739. BI

B1005 STIRLING, John, *ed.* L. Annaei Flori Rerum Romanorum epitome. Or, an abridgment of the Roman history . . . By John Stirling. Author, 1738. LEI

B1006 STIRLING, John, *ed.* (1739) P. Terentii Comoediae sex; or, the six comedies of Publius Terence . . . For the use of schools. 2nd ed., Rivington, [etc.], 1763. HU

B1007 STIRLING, John, *ed.* (1751) Phaedri Fabulae; or, Phaedrus's fables, with . . . improvements, in a method entirely new . . . For the use of schools. 13th ed., 1793. NoU

B1008 STOCKWOOD, John, d. 1610. (1590?; 1672) The treatise of the figures at the end of the rules of construction in the Latin grammar, construed . . . R. Norton, 1713. HU; 1738. NoU

B1009 STONHOUSE, *Sir* James, 1716–1795. (c. 1780) Prayers for the use of private persons . . . 21st ed., 1825. *See* D1277

B1010 STONHOUSE, *Sir* James. (1774) The religious instruction of children recommended. 1824, *and* 1827. *See* C1367

B1011 STRETCH, L. M. (1770) The beauties of history; or, pictures of virtue and vice, drawn from real life; designed for the instruction and entertainment of youth. 3rd ed., rev., corr. and enl. Dilly, 1777. 2 vols. HU; Lewis, 1817. *See* D1283

Strictures on female education. *See* Bennett, John
Study of history rendered easy. *See* Fletcher, Ann, *and others*

B1012 A SUBSCRIPTION to a school for the children of debtors, in the Fleet prison and Newgate. [Handbill]. 1796. NoU

B1013 SUETONIUS. C. Suetonii Tranquilli XII Caesars . . . or, the lives of the first twelve Roman emperors . . . with a free translation . . . By John Clarke. A. Bettesworth & C. Hitch, 1732. HU; 2nd ed., Bettesworth & Hitch, 1739. HU

B1014 SULZER, Johann Georg, 1720–1779. Anweisung zu Erziehung seiner Töchter. Zürich, Fuessli, 1781. LO

T.H. *See* H., T.

B1015 TABLES in arithmetic for the use of schools. Nottingham pr., [17–?]. NoU

B1016 TALBOT, James. (1707) The Christian school-master; or, the duty of those who are employ'd in the publick instruction of children: especially in charity schools . . . J. Downing, 1707. LEE ReU; 2nd ed., Downing, 1711. HU LEI

B1017 TALBOT, William, 1659?–1730. (1717) A sermon preach'd June 13, 1717 . . . at the anniversary meeting of the . . . charity schools . . . Downing, 1717. ReU

B1018 TALES of the arbor. 1800. [incomplete]. ReU

Tales of the genii. *See* Ridley, James
Tales of the hermitage. *See* Pilkington, Mary

B1019 TARDY, —, *abbé.* (1799) An explanatory pronouncing dictionary of the French language ... Author, & W. Clarke, 1799. LEE

B1020 TAYLOR, John, 1694–1761. (1752) The value of a child. 2nd ed., 1816. *See* C1398

B1021 TAYLOR, John, 1704–1766. (1749) A sermon preached at Bishop-Stortford on Tuesday, Aug. 22, 1749, the anniversary of the school feast. Cambridge U.P., 1749. LEI

B1022 TAYLOR, Samuel, *fl.* 1786–1816. (1786) Taylor improved. Universal stenography. 1830. *See* D1326

TEACHWELL, *Mrs., pseud. See* Fenn, E.

B1023 TERENCE. Comoediae sex; or, the six comedies of Publius Terence ... for the use of schools. By John Stirling, D.D. 2nd ed., Rivington, [etc.], 1763. HU

B1024 TERENCE. Elegantiae terentianae; or, the phrases of Terence. 1718. NoU
Terrae-filius. *See* Amhurst, N.

B1025 THACKER, Anthony. A miscellany of mathematical problems. In three volumes. Vol. 1 [only]. Birmingham, Aris, 1743. BI
Théâtre pour servir à l'éducation. *See* Genlis, *comtesse de*

B1026 THOMAS, John, 1691–1766. (1743) A sermon preach'd before the Society corresponding with the Incorporated society in Dublin for promoting English Protestant working-schools in Ireland, March 22, 1742–43. By John Thomas, D.D., dean of Peterborough ... M. Downing, 1743. LEI ReU

B1027 THOMAS, M. [Monsieur?]. Essai sur le caractère, les moeurs et l'esprit des femmes dans les différens siècles. Paris, Moutard, 1772. LO
THOMPSON, Benjamin, *count von Rumford. See* Rumford, *count von*
Thoughts on education, by the author of Britain's remembrancer. *See* Burgh, J.
Tirannie des fées détruite. *See* Auneuil, *comtesse d'*

B1028 TOOKE, Andrew, 1673–1712, *ed.* The Pantheon. *See* B845 Pomey, F. A.

B1029 TOOKE, Andrew, *ed.* A treatise of English particles. By William Walker. 15th ed., corrected by A. Tooke. *See* B1083 Walker, W.

B1030 TOUSSAINT, François Vincent, 1715–1772. (Fr. 1748; Eng. 1749) Manners. In three parts. By Panage. Translated from the French. 5th ed., Glasgow, R. Urie, 1770. LO

B1031 TOY-SHOP. (1795?) The Toy-shop; or, sentimental preceptor. 1830. *See* D1354

B1032 TRIMMER, *Mrs.* Sarah, 1741–1810. (1792) An abridgment of scripture history; consisting of lessons selected from the Old Testament; designed chiefly for charity schools, kitchens, and cottages. Longman, & Rivington, 1792. LEI

B1033 TRIMMER, *Mrs.* Sarah. (1786; 1798) The charity school spelling book. Part 1. 6th ed., Rivington, 1800. [1st ed. had title: Little spelling book.] BI HU; 10th ed., 1807, and new ed., 1818. *See* D1363

B1034 TRIMMER, *Mrs.* Sarah. The charity school spelling book. Part 2. 2nd ed., 1794. NoU; 5th ed., Rivington, 1800. HU; new ed., 1818. *See* D1364

B1035 TRIMMER, *Mrs.* Sarah. (1787?) Easy lessons for young children. 3rd ed., J. Johnson, 1792. [Cover title: Easy lessons. A sequel to Mrs. Trimmer's spelling book for young children.] LEI

B1036 TRIMMER, *Mrs.* Sarah. (1780?) An easy introduction to the knowledge of nature and reading of Holy Scriptures adapted to the capacities of children. 6th ed., 1789. NoU; 11th ed., 1802, *and* 17th ed., 1825. *See* D1365

B1037 TRIMMER, *Mrs.* Sarah. Introduction à la connaissance de la nature ... Traduite ... par C. Gros. 1837. *See* D1366

B1038 TRIMMER, *Mrs.* Sarah. (1786) Fabulous histories. Designed for the instruction of children, respecting their treatment of animals. 3rd ed., Longman, [etc.], 1788. BR LEI NoU; 4th ed., 1791. NoU; *later eds.,* 1809, 1821, 1838, 1840, etc. *See* D1367–1368

B1039 TRIMMER, *Mrs* Sarah. (1788–1789) Instructive tales. 3rd ed., 1815. *See* D1370

B1040 TRIMMER, *Mrs.* Sarah. A selection from Mrs. Trimmer's Instructive tales. 1823. *See* D1371

B1041 TRIMMER, *Mrs.* Sarah. (1787) The oeconomy of charity; or, an address to ladies concerning sunday-schools ... Longman, 1787. LEI; Dublin, White, [etc.], 1787. HU LEE; 1801. *See* C1426

B1042 TRIMMER, *Mrs.* Sarah. (1786–1788) [Prints with descriptions, as below]:

(*a*) [Illustrations to ancient history]. 1786–1788. 2 pts. in 1 vol. NoU; A series of prints of ancient history ... Marshall, [178–]. HU

(*b*) A description of a set of prints of ancient history, contained in a set of easy lessons. In two parts. Part I. Marshall, [178–]. HU

(*c*) A series of prints of English history. [1792]. NoU

(*d*) A series of prints of Roman history ... Marshall, [1789]. HU NoU

(*e*) A description of a set of prints of Roman history, contained in a set of easy lessons. Marshall, [1789]. HU NoU

(*f*) A series of prints taken from the New Testament. [1790]. NoU

B1043 TRIMMER, *Mrs.* Sarah, do., *for various 19th century eds. with varying titles, see* D1372

B1044 TRIMMER, *Mrs.* Sarah. (1792) Reflections upon the education of children in charity schools. 1792. ReU

B1045 TRIMMER, *Mrs.* Sarah. (1782–1784?) Sacred history, selected from the Scriptures. 7th ed., 1817. *See* D1373

B1046 TRIMMER, *Mrs.* Sarah. (2nd ed., 1787) The servant's friend. New ed., 1824. *See* D1374

B1047 TRIMMER, *Mrs.* Sarah. (1788) The sunday school catechist; consisting of familiar lectures, with questions for the use of visiters and teachers. Longman, 1788. LEI

B1048 TRIMMER, *Mrs.* Sarah. (1787) The two farmers. New ed., 1826. *See* D1377

B1049 TROTTER, Robert. (1732) Grammaticae Latinae compendium, ad puerorum captum summa ope concinnatum. In usum Scholae Dumfrisiensis. Edinburgh, T. Lumisden, & J. Robertson, 1732. HU

B1050 TROTTI DE LA CHETARDIE, Joachim. (Fr. 1684) Small tract of instruction for the conduct of young ladies of the highest rank. *See* B537 Fénelon

B1051 TRUSLER, John, 1753–1820. (1775?) The accomplished gentleman. [1847?]. *See* D1380

B1052 [TRUSLER, John]. (1768) Hogarth moralized ... Calculated to improve the minds of youth ... 1786. NoU

B1053 TRUSLER, John. (1790?) The progress of man and society. [1810]. *See* C1430

B1054 TURGOT, Anne-Robert-Jacques, 1727–1781. (*c.* 1775) The manner of preparing individuals and families to participate properly in a good social organization. *See* B1172 De la Fontainerie, F., *ed.*

B1055 TURNBULL, George. (1742) Observations upon liberal education in all its branches. Millar, 1742. LEI

B1056 TURNER, Richard, *the elder,* 1724?–1791. A view of the earth. 2nd ed., 1766. NoU

B1057 TURNER, Richard, 1753–1788. (1783?) An easy introduction to the arts and sciences. 10th ed., 1804. *See* D1385

B1058 TURNER, Richard. (1780) A new and easy introduction to universal geography, in a series of letters to a youth at school. 1780. NoU; 4th ed., improved and considerably enlarged by the author ... S. Crowder, 1789. BI HU; 14th ed., 1810. *See* D1386

B1059 TURNER, William, 1658?–1726. (1713) Exercises to the accidence. 1713. NoU

B1060 TURNER, William. Exercises to the accidence and grammar ... 9th ed. with additions. Ballard, & Longman, 1757. HU; 12th ed., Ballard, & Longman, 1770. LEI
Two cousins. *See* Pinchard, *Mrs.*

B1061 UFFENBACH, Zacharias Conrad von, 1683–1734. (Pub. 1753) Oxford in 1710, from the Travels of Z. C. von Uffenbach. Edited by W. H. Quarrell and W. J. C. Quarrell. Oxford, Blackwell, 1928. LEI
Unfortunate mother's advice to her absent daughters. *See* Pennington, S.

B1062 UPTON, James, 1670–1749, *ed.* (1726) Poikiae istoria [Greek script], sive novus historiarum fabellarumque delectus ... notis & versione illustravit Jacobus Upton ... J. Knapton, [etc.], 1726. LEI

B1063 UPTON, James, *ed.* (1711) The scholemaster. *See* B42–43 Ascham, R.

B1064 UPTON, John, 1707–1760, *ed.* (1739) To tou Epiktetou Encheiridion [Greek script], ex editione Joannis Upton accurate expressum. Glasgow, University Pr., 1758. LEE
V., R. *See* Valpy, R.

B1065 [VALPY, Richard], 1754–1836. The elements of the Latin language; or, an introduction to Latin grammar. [By R.V.] 3rd ed., Reading, Smart & Cowslade; London, Elmsly, [etc.]; 1790. LEI

B1066 VAREN, Bernhard [*otherwise* Bernhardus Varenius], 1622?–1650. (1650) A compleat system of general geography ... Improved and illustrated by Sir Isaac Newton and Dr. Jurin; and now translated ... by Mr. Dugdale. The whole revised and corrected by Peter Shaw. 2nd ed. Vol. 2 [only]. S. Austen, 1734. LEI

B1067 VAUGHAN, W. Advice to young gentlemen, concerning the conduct of life. In two parts. To which is added, An eminent gentleman's advice to his sons. B. Lintott, [17–]. [Dedicated to Wm. Bohun, of the Middle Temple, *fl.* 1702–1740.] LEI
Veillées du château. *See* Genlis, *comtesse de*

B1067a VENERONI, Giovanni [*otherwise* Jean Vigneron], 1642–1708. (Eng. 1729) The complete Italian master. 1814. *See* D1395
Véritable manière d'instruire les sourds et les muets. *See* L'Epée, *abbé*

VERNEY, George, 4th baron Willoughby de Broke. *See* Willoughby de Broke, *baron*

Vie de Mme. de Maintenon. *See* Caraccioli, *marquis de*

B1068 VIEYRA, Antonio, *prof. of Spanish.* (1767) A new Portuguese grammar. 7th ed., 1809. *See* D1399
VIGNERON, Jean. *See* Veneroni, G.

VILLEMERT, Pierre Joseph Boudier de. *See* Boudier de Villemert, P. J.
Visions in verse. *See* Cotton, Nathaniel

B1069 VOSSIUS, Gerardus [*otherwise* Gerard John Vos], 1577–1649. Elementa rhetorica, oratoriis ejusdem partitionibus accommodata inque usum scholarum emendatius edita. Editio prioribus accuratior et auctior. Eton, 1771. NoU

B1070 VYSE, Charles. (2nd ed., 1772) The tutor's guide. Being a complete system of arithmetic; with various branches in the mathematics ... 4th ed., Robinson, 1779. LEE; 6th ed., corr., Robinson, 1785. HU; 9th ed., Robinson, 1796. LEI

B1071 VYSE, Charles. The key to the Tutor's guide ... 3rd ed., Robinson, 1779. ReU; 5th ed., rev., Robinson, 1791. LEI

B1072 W., G. (1703) Magazine; or, animadversions on the English spelling (1703). Introduction by David Abercrombie. Los Angeles, Clark memorial lib., 1958. [Possibly by John White.] HU

B1073 WAKE, William, 1657–1737. (1715) The excellence and benefits of a religious education: a sermon preached in the parish church of St. Sepulchre, June the sixth, 1715 ... at the anniversary meeting of the children ... Downing, 1715. LEE ReU

B1074 WAKEFIELD, Priscilla, 1751–1832. (1796) An introduction to botany, in a series of familiar letters. Dublin, 1796. NoU; 5th ed., 1807, *and* 7th ed., 1816. *See* D1413

B1075 WAKEFIELD, Priscilla. (1794–1796) Leisure hours; or, entertaining dialogues . . . designed as lessons of morality for youth. 3rd ed., Darton & Harvey, 1798. 2 vols. BI; 5th ed., 1812, *and another ed.*, 1821, *see* D1415

B1076 WAKEFIELD, Priscilla. (1794) Mental improvement . . . New ed., impr. [18–]. *See* D1416

B1077 WALKER, John, 1674–1747. (1714) An attempt towards discovering an account of the numbers and sufferings of the clergy of the Church of England, heads of colleges, fellows, scholars, etc., who were sequester'd, harrass'd, etc., in the late times of the grand rebellion . . . W.S. for J. Nicholson, [etc.], 1714. LEI

B1078 WALKER, John, 1732–1807. (1791) The academic speaker; or, a selection of parliamentary debates, orations, odes, scenes and speeches, from the best writers. Proper to be read and recited by youth at school. Dublin, G. Burnet, [etc.], 1800. LO

B1079 WALKER, John. A key to the classical pronunciation of Greek and Latin proper names, in which the words are accented and divided into syllables as they ought to be pronounced. Robinson, & T. Caldwell, 1798. MA

B1080 WALKER, John, 1759–1830. (3rd ed., 1800) Elements of geography. 4th ed., 1805. *See* D1419

B1081 WALKER, John. [Atlas of maps engraved for Walker's Geography]. [*c.* 1800]. NoU

B1082 WALKER, William, 1623–1684. (1669) Some improvements to the art of teaching, especially in the first grounding of a young scholar in grammar-learning . . . 8th ed., 1717. NoU; 9th ed., Bettesworth, & Batley, 1730. BI HU OX

B1083 WALKER, William. (1655) A treatise of English particles . . . 13th ed., 1706. NoU; 15th ed., corrected and amended by A. Tooke. Baskett, 1720. LEI

B1084 WALKINGAME, Francis, 1723?–1783. (1751) The tutor's assistant: being a compendium of arithmetic . . . 3rd ed., Author, 1757. LEI; 5th ed., B. Dod & M. Walkingame, [176–]. HU; new ed., corrected . . . by T. Crosby. York, Wilson, Spence & Mawman, 1799. LEE

B1085 WALKINGAME, Francis, do., 55th ed., 1818; 62nd ed., 1823; *another ed.*, 1826; 71st ed., 1832; 74th ed., 1837; new ed., 1840 *and* 1841; new ed., [18–]. *See* D1423

B1086 WALKINGAME, Francis. A treatise on arithmetic . . . Revised by R. Langford. 1824. *See* D1422

B1087 WALL, Adam. An account of the different ceremonies observed in the Senate House of the University of Cambridge; together with tables of fees . . . and other articles relating to the customs of the University . . . Cambridge, Deighton, 1798. BI

B1088 WALLER, John. (1708) Religion and loyalty . . . a sermon preach'd 31 August, 1708. 1708. ReU

B1089 WALLIS, Edward. (1794) Wallis's tour through England and Wales. [1802?]. *See* D1426

B1090 WALLIS, John, 1616–1703. Logarithms, their invention and use. *See* B958 Sherwin, H.

B1091 WANOSTROCHT, Nicolas, 1745–1812. A classical vocabulary, French and English; to which is added a collection of letters, familiar and commercial . . . in both languages. 2nd ed., enlarged and improved, J. Boosey, 1785. LEI

B1092 WANOSTROCHT, Nicolas. (1780) A grammar of the French language, with practical exercises. 5th ed., J. Johnson, [etc.], 1795. LEI; 10th ed., 1807. *See* D1428

B1093 WANOSTROCHT, Nicolas. (1788) Petite encyclopédie des jeunes gens: ou définition abrégée des notions relatives aux arts et aux sciences . . . Galabin, for the author, 1788. LEI

B1094 WANOSTROCHT, Nicolas. (5th ed., 1797) Receuil choisi de traits historiques. Nlle. éd., 1833. *See* D1429

B1095 WARD, John, *of Chester*. (1709) The young mathematician's guide: being a plain and easy introduction to the mathematicks . . . 3rd ed., Horne, 1719. HU LEE; 5th ed., Bettesworth & Fayram, 1728. LEI; 10th ed., C. Hitch, [etc.], 1758. HU

B1096 WARD, John, *biographer*, 1679?–1758. (1740) The lives of the professors of Gresham College; to which is prefixed the life of the founder, Sir Thomas Gresham . . . John Moore, 1740. BI

B1097 [WARD, John], *grammarian, ed.* Brevissima institutio, seu ratio grammatice cognoscendae . . . Buckley & Longman, 176[5]. [Part of the revision of Lily.] HU

B1098 [WARD, John], *ed.* Institutio Graecae grammatices compendaria, in usum Regiae Scholae Westmonasteriensis. Buckley & Longman, 1763. HU; Buckley & Longman, 1793. LEE [Revision of Camden.]

B1099 [WARD, John], *ed.* Propria quae maribus, Quae genus, As in praesenti, Syntaxis, Qui mihi, construed. Buckley & Longman, 1763. HU; Buckley & Longman, 1778. LO [Part of revision of Lily.]

B1100 [WARD, John], *ed.* (1732) A short introduction of grammar . . . [Revision of Lily]. Buckley & Longman, 1765. HU; Buckley & Longman, 1771. BR; Buckley & Longman, 1784. LO; [*c.* 180–]. *See* D1433

[*Note:* The identification of the various John Wards is disputed.]

B1101 [WARDEN, John], *fl.* 1737–1753, *comp.* (1737?) A collection from the Spectator, Tatler, Guardian, Mr. Pope, Mr. Dryden, from Mr. Rollin . . . For the benefit of English schools. Newcastle upon Tyne, Author, 1752. HU NoU

B1102 [WATERLAND, Daniel], 1683–1740. (1730) Advice to a young student. With a method of study for the four first years. 2nd ed., J. Crownfield, 1730. HU; *another ed.*, 1755. ReU

B1103 WATERLAND, Daniel. (1723) Religious education of children . . . a sermon preach'd before the Society for promoting Christian knowledge, June 6, 1723. 1723. ReU

B1104 WATTS, Isaac, 1674–1748. (1715) Divine songs, attempted in easy language, for the use of children. 1776. ReU; Evans, [1790]. BI; 14th ed., Dublin, 1795. NoU; Rivington, 1821. *See* D1443

B1105 WATTS, Isaac. Divine and moral songs for children. 1811; 1841. *See* D1442

B1106 WATTS, Isaac. The first set of catechisms and prayers. Wellington, [*c.* 1810], *and* Derby, 1839. *See* D1444

B1107 WATTS, Isaac. The golden rule, an abstract from Dr. Isaac Watts. [180–]. *See* D1445

B1108 WATTS, Isaac. The historical catechism. Woodbridge, 1851. *See* D1446

B1109 WATTS, Isaac. (1741–1751) The improvement of the mind. *For 19th century editions, see* C1476

B1110 WATTS, Isaac. (1725) Logic; or, the right use of reason in the inquiry after truth . . . New ed., corr. Edinburgh, J. Dickson, & J. & J. Fairbairn, 1792. HU

B1111 WATTS, Isaac. (1728) Prayers composed for the use of children. Derby, [*c.* 1820?]. *See* D1447

B1112 WATTS, Isaac. (Written 1725?, pub. 1751) A treatise on the education of children and youth. 2nd ed. Buckland, 1769. BI BR ReU

B1113 WEBSTER, Noah, 1758–1843. (1782–1783) American spelling book. With an introductory essay by H. S. Commager. N.Y., Columbia univ. Teachers coll., 1962. [Facsimile reprint of 1831 edition.] HU LEI

B1114 WEBSTER, William, *writing master, fl.* 1715–1740. (1715) Arithmetick in epitome; in two parts. 2nd ed., C. King, [etc.], 1716. HU

B1115 WEEKBLAD voor kinderen, 1–53 [in 1 vol.]. Amsterdam, 1789. NoU

B1116 [WEIGHTMAN, Mary]. (1787) The juvenile speaker, or dialogues and miscellaneous pieces in prose and verse. 1787. NoU

B1117 WELLS, Edward, 1667–1727. (1698) Elementa arithmeticae et speciosae. In usum juventutis academicae. Editio altera, auctior. Knapton, [etc.], 1726. LEE LEI

B1118 WELLS, Edward. (1713?) The young gentleman's arithmetick, and geometry . . . 2nd ed., Knapton, 1723. HU LEE NoU

B1119 WELLS, Edward. (1712) The young gentleman's astronomy, chronology and dialling, containing such elements of the said arts or sciences, as are most useful and easy to be known. 3rd ed., rev. and corr. Knapton, 1725. 3 vols in 1. LEE; 4th ed., 1736. NoU

B1120 WELLS, Edward. (1712) The young gentleman's chronology, containing such chronological elements as are most useful and easy to be known. Knapton, 1712. HU

B1121 WELLS, Edward, *ed.* (1704) Oikoumenes Periegesis, sive Dionysii geographia emendata & locupletata, additione scil. *Geographie hodiernae* . . . Ed. quinta. T. Wood, pr., 1738. HU

B1122 WELLS, Zachary. (1705) The advantages of a learned and religious education, in a sermon preach'd 6 Dec., 1705, before the gentlemen educated at Eton College. 1705. ReU

B1123 WENDEBORN, Gebhardt Friedrich August, 1742-1811. (1774) An introduction to German grammar. 3rd ed., with additions and improvements. Author, 1797. [1st ed. had title: Elements of German grammar.] LEI

B1124 WESLEY, John, 1703–1791. Works, [edited by T. Jackson]. Vol. 13. 4th ed., 1841. *See* C1481; vol. 14. 1841. *See* D1453

B1125 [WESLEY, John]. A short account of the school in Kingswood, near Bristol. Bristol, F. Farley, 1749. [Facsimile reprint.] LO

B1126 WEST, Gilbert, 1703–1756. (1751) Education, a poem: in two cantos. Written in imitation of the style and manner of Spenser's Fairy queen. Canto the first. [All published.] M. Cooper, 1751. LEI

B1127 WESTMINSTER SCHOOL. Lusus Westmonasterienses, sive epigrammatum et poematum minorum delectus. [Edited by Robert Prior.] Westminster, A. Campbell, 1730. HU

B1128 WESTMINSTER SCHOOL. Lusus alteri Westmonasterienses . . . Oxford, 1863–1867. *See* C1486

B1129 WESTMINSTER SCHOOL. (1729) Treis tragoediai: Aischylou Choephoroi, Sophokleous Elektra, Euripidou Elektra. In usum Scholae Regiae Westmonasteriensis. Oxford, Clarendon Pr. for B. Barker, 1729. HU

B1130 WESTON, Thomas, *master of the academy at Greenwich, fl.* 1715–1728. A copy-book, written for the use of the young-gentlemen at the Academy at Greenwich. Fenwick Bull, [*c.* 1737]. HU

B1131 WESTON, Thomas. (1729?) A new and compendious treatise of arithmetic in whole numbers and fractions, vulgar and decimal . . . 2nd ed., Ward & Chandler, 1736. BI

B1132 WHISHAW, H. (1752) The great and important duty of training up children . . . in a sermon preached in the parish church of Lugwardine near Hereford on Sunday, March 1, 1752 . . . Knapton, 1755. BI

B1133 WHISTON, William, 1667–1752. (1705) A sermon preach'd in Cambridge, Jan. 25, 1705 . . . to which is added a particular account of the . . . charity-schools. 1705. ReU

B1134 WHITCHURCH [*or* Whitechurch], James Wadham. (1772) An essay upon education. Becket & Hondt, 1772. BI HU

B1135 WHITEHEAD, —, *of Newcastle.* (1777) The historian's pocket companion; or, memory's assistant. Newcastle, T. Angus for the author, 1777. LEI

Whole duty of man. *See* Allestree, R.

B1136 [WILCOCKS, Joseph], 1673–1756. (1739) A sermon preach'd before the Society corresponding with the Incorporated society in Dublin for promoting English Protestant working-schools in Ireland . . . March 17, 1738–9, by the Lord Bishop of Rochester. M. Downing, 1739. LEI ReU

B1137 WILCOCKS, Joseph, 1724–1791. (1792–1794) Roman conversations; or, a short description of the antiquities of Rome . . . 2nd ed . . . Bickerstaffe, 1797. 2 vols. LEI

B1138 WILKES, Wetenhall, *fl.* 1740–1747. (1740) A letter of genteel and moral advice to a young lady: being a system of rules and informations; digested into a new and familiar method, to qualify the fair sex to be useful, and happy in every scene of life. 5th ed., rev., corr. and enl., C. Hitch, 1748. LEI

B1139 WILKINSON, Robert, *fl.* 1794–1835, *publisher.* (1794) A general atlas. Wilkinson, 1794. NoU

B1140 WILLETS, William. Christian education of children. Author, 1750. LO

B1141 WILLIAMS, David, 1738–1816. (1789) Lectures on education. Read to a society for promoting reasonable and humane improvements in the discipline and instruction of youth. Bell, 1789. 3 vols. ReU; vols. 1 and 2 [only]. BI

B1142 WILLIAMS, David. (1774) A treatise on education . . . T. Payne, 1774. HU SH

B1143 WILLIAMS, Helen Maria, 1762–1827, *trans.* (1795?) Paul and Virginia. Translated from the French of Bernardin Saint-Pierre. 4th ed., Vernor & Hood, 1799. LEI

B1144 WILLIAMS, Peter. Letters concerning education: addressed to a gentleman entering at the university. 1785. ReU

B1145 WILLIS, Richard, 1664–1734. (1704) Sermon preach'd in the parish church of St. Andrew's, Holborn, June 8, 1704, at the first meeting of the gentlemen concerned in promoting the charity schools in and about the cities of London and Westminster. J. Downing, 1704. ReU

B1146 WILLOUGHBY DE BROKE, George Verney, *4th baron,* 1674–1728. (1712) The blessedness of doing good. A sermon preached in the parish church of St. Sepulchre, June the 12th, 1712 . . . at the anniversary meeting of the children educated in the charity-schools . . . J. Downing, 1712. LEI ReU

B1147 WILLYMOTT, William, d. 1737. (1703) English particles exemplify'd in sentences designed for Latin exercises; with the proper rendering of each particle inserted in the sentence. For the use of Eton School. London, Sam. Smith, [etc.]; Eton, J. Slatter; 1703. HU; 6th ed., Bathurst & Richardson, 1765. BI; 8th ed., 1771. NoU

B1148 WILSON, George. (1756) The youth's pocket-companion; or, universal preceptor. [1756?]. NoU; 2nd ed., J. Coote, 1759. LEI

B1149 WILSON, Thomas, 1663–1755. (1724) The true Christian method of educating the children of the poor and rich . . . in a sermon preach'd in the parish church of St. Sepulchre, at the anniversary meeting of the . . . charity schools . . . on May 28, 1724. 1724. ReU; 11th ed., 1824. *See* C1526

B1150 WINGATE, Edmund, 1596–1656. (1630) Mr. Wingate's Arithmetick: containing a plain and familiar method for attaining the knowledge and practice of common arithmetick . . . Inlarged . . . revis'd . . . and improved . . . by John Kersey. 13th ed. With a new supplement. By George Shelley. J. Phillips, [etc.], (1713). LEI; 15th ed., 1726. NoU

B1151 WINGATE, Edmund. A plain and familiar method for attaining the knowledge and practice of common arithmetic . . . 18th ed., wherein the additions and emendations made by Mr. John Kersey . . . and Mr. George Shelley . . . are introduced in their proper places. By James Dodson. Knapton, 1751. HU; 19th ed., Hitch, 1760 LEE

B1152 WISDOM. (3rd ed., 1791) Wisdom in miniature. 1821. *See* D1482

B1153 WISEMAN, Charles, *fl.* 1764–1778. (1764) A complete English grammar on a new plan. For the use of foreigners and such natives as would acquire a scientical knowledge of their own tongue . . . Nicol, 1764. LEI

B1154 WITHERSPOON, John, 1723–1794. (Am. ed. 1797) A series of letters on education . . . Bristol, James, 1798. BI [Ascription doubtful.]

B1155 WOLLSTONECRAFT, Mary, *aft,* Godwin, 1759–1797. (1788) . . . . Original stories. With six illustrations by William Blake. With an introduction by E. V. Lucas. H. Frowde, 1906. LEI NoU

B1156 WOLLSTONECRAFT, Mary. (1787) Thoughts on the education of daughters: with reflections on female conduct . . . Johnson, 1787. LEE

B1157 WOLLSTONECRAFT, Mary. (1792) A vindication of the rights of woman: with strictures on political and moral subjects. Vol. 1 [all pub.]. 2nd ed., Johnson, 1792. LEE

B1158 WOLLSTONECRAFT, Mary, do., *another ed.,* New York, 1856. *See* C1532

B1159 WOOD, James, 1760–1839. (1798) The elements of algebra. 3rd ed., 1801, *and* 7th ed., Cambridge, 1820. *See* D1488

B1160 WOODBRIDGE. *Free school.* Orders, constitutions, and directions, to be observed, for and concerning the free-school, in Woodbridge . . . Suffolk . . . Agreed at the foundation, 1662 . . . 2nd ed., enl., Woodbridge, Loder, 1796. [Contains 3 pp. dated 1806.] LEI

B1161 [WOODWARD, Josiah], *supposed author.* (1702) Pastoral advice to young persons. 20th ed., 1809. *See* D1494

B1162 WOODWARD, Josiah. [Preface to Francke's] Pietas Hallensis. *See* B403 Francke, A. H.

B1163 [WORLIDGE, John], *fl.* 1669–1698. (1704) Dictionarium rusticum, urbanicum et botanicum; or, a dictionary of husbandry, gardening, trade, commerce, and all sorts of country-affairs . . . 2nd ed., rev., J. Nicholson, [etc.], 1717. LEI [Also attributed to Nathaniel Bailey.]

B1164 WOTTON, Henry, *incumbent of Wrentham.* (Written 1672; pub. 1753) An essay on the education of children in the first rudiments of learning, together with a narrative of what knowledge, William Wotton, a child of six years of age, had attained unto, upon the improvements of those rudiments in the Latin, Greek and Hebrew tongues. Waller, 1753. LEE

B1165 WOTTON, William, 1666–1726. (1701) The history of Rome, from the death of Antoninus Pius to the death of Severus Alexander. Goodwin, 1701. LEI

B1166 WOTTON, William. (1694) Reflections upon ancient and modern learning. To which is now added a defense thereof, in answer to the objections of Sir W. Temple, and others . . . 3rd ed., Goodwin, 1705. LEE

B1167 [WRAY, Mary]. The ladies' library. Written by a lady. Sir R. Steele, 1714–1739. 2 vols. [Vol. 1, 1714; vol. 2, 5th ed., 1739.] LO

B1168 WRIGHT, George, *fl.* 1775–1787. (Post-1777) The young moralist, consisting of allegorical and entertaining essays, in prose and verse, compiled from various authors . . . 3rd ed., enl., H. Turpin, & J. Fielding, 1782. LEI

WYKEHAMIST, *pseud.* *See* Blackstone, Charles

B1169 YORKE, Henry Redhead, 1772–1813. (1800) Elements of civil knowledge. Dorchester, T. Lockett; London, W. I. Clement; 1800. [Described on half title as 'Moral nights. vol. 1'. Vol. 2 never pub.] HU

B1170 The YOUNG ladies' new guide to arithmetic. Being a short and useful selection . . . designed particularly for the use of ladies' schools and private teachers. Author, 1798. HU

Young scholar's delight. *See* Slack, Anne

Youth's miscellany. *See* Mavor, W. F.

B1171 ZOLLIKOFER, Georg Joachim, 1730–1788. Sermons on education. 1806. *See* C1555

2. Collections

B1172 DE LA FONTAINERIE, F., *ed. and trans.* French liberalism and education in the eighteenth century: the writings of La Chalotais, Turgot, Diderot and Condorcet on national education. N.Y., McGraw, 1932. HU

B1173 DICKINSON, W. C., *ed.* Two students at St. Andrews, 1711–1716; edited from the Devline papers. Edinburgh, Oliver & Boyd, 1952. [Consists mainly of letters by the tutor, James Morice.] BR

SECTION C

Books on education published, or first published,
1801-1870

C1 ABBOTT, Jacob, 1803–1879. (1833) The teacher; or, moral influences employed in the instruction and government of the young. Darton, [1833]. LEE; Revised by the Rev. Charles Mayo. Seeley, etc., 1834. LEI NE; Darton, [*c.* 1836]. HU

C2 ABBOTT, John Stevens Cabot, 1805–1877. The mother at home; or, the principles of maternal duty familiarly illustrated. Revised. R.T.S., [1833?]. LEI

C3 ABERCROMBIE, John, 1780–1844. (1830) Inquiries concerning the intellectual powers and the investigation of truth. 15th ed., Murray, 1857. LEI

ABERDARE, Henry Austin Bruce, 1*st baron*. *See* Bruce, Henry Austin

C4 ABERDEEN. Public meeting on national education, 1851. Report of the proceedings at a public meeting, held in the Mechanics' Hall, Aberdeen, 25th April 1851 on . . . national education. [From the 'Aberdeen Herald'.] Aberdeen, L. Smith, 1851. HU

C5 ABERDEENSHIRE. *Prison board.* Aberdeenshire reports on juvenile delinquency, 1845, 1848, 1851. HU

C6 ABRAHAM, J. H., *ed.* Juvenile essays: comprising . . . the first and second half-yearly prize compositions of the pupils belonging to the Milk Street Academy, Sheffield, to which is prefixed a brief history of education and a table of the system pursued in the above academy. W. Todd, 1805. SH

Academic errors. *See* Gilly, William Stephen

Account of public charities in England and Wales. *See* Wade, John

Account of the progress of Joseph Lancaster's plan for the education of poor children. *See* Lancaster, Joseph

C7 An ACCOUNT of the visit of his royal highness the Prince Regent and their imperial and royal majesties the Emperor of Russia and the King of Prussia to the University of Oxford in June MDCCCXIV. Oxford, Clarendon Pr., 1815. ReU

C8 ACKWORTH SCHOOL. Reports on the state of Ackworth school, 1780–1812. Ackworth, The school, [1780–1812]. LEE

C9 ACLAND, *Sir* Thomas Dyke, 1809–!898. (1857) Middle-class education. Scheme of the West of England examination and prizes . . . resolution of the Bath and West of England Agricultural Society thereon; Mr. Temple's scheme of examinations . . . Ridgway, 1857. BR

C10 ACLAND, *Sir* T. D. (1858) Some account of the origin and objects of the new Oxford examinations for the title of Associate in arts . . . 2nd ed., Ridgway, 1858. ReU

C11 ADAM, A. Mercer, *ed.* (1857) The Dumfries album. Dumfries, Dumfries & Maxwelltown Mechanics Institution, 1857. LEI

C12 ADAM, James. The knowledge qualification: a plan for the reciprocal extension of education and the franchise. Edinburgh, Tait, 1837. BI

C13 ADAMS, Francis, *ed.* The Elementary education act, 1870; with analysis, index and appendix. Simpkin, Marshall, 1870. BR

C14 ADAMS, John. (1850) Summary jurisdiction. A charge to the Grand Jury of the quarter sessions of the county of Middlesex . . . at the April session 1850. J. T. Norris, 1850. HU

C15 ADDERLEY, Charles Bowyer, 1*st baron Norton*, 1814–1905, and GRIFFITHS, William. (1843) Correspondence between Mr. Adderley and Mr. William Griffiths of Tutbury on the principles of Sir James Graham's scheme for national education. Painter, 1843. LEE

Address on national education . . . by the Principal of Magdalene Hall. *See* Macbride, John David

Admonitions for Sunday schools. *See* Waldo, Peter

Adèle et Théodore. *See* Genlis, *comtesse de*

C16 ADSHEAD, Joseph. On juvenile criminals, reformatories and the means of rendering the perishing and dangerous classes serviceable to the state. Manchester, Harrison, 1856. [Reprinted from the Transactions of the Manchester statistical society.] BR

C17 AETAS, *pseud.* The reform of the army, in connection with that of our public schools and universities. A letter addressed to the Right Honourable Lord Viscount Palmerston. Bell & Daldy, 1855. LO

C18 AIMÉ-MARTIN, Louis. (Fr. 1834) The education of mothers of families; or, the civilisation of the human race by women . . . Translated from the 3rd Paris edition, with remarks on the prevailing methods of education . . . by E. Lee. Whittaker, 1842. BI

C19 AKROYD, Edward, *M.P. for Huddersfield*. (1870) A paper, 'On the extension of the factory system of education to the agricultural classes in this country', at the education conference [of the National education union], held at Leicester, January 27, 1870. Also a letter on the same subject from the Hon. Edward Stanhope. Longmans, [etc.], [1870]. HU

C20 ALDERSON, *Sir* Edward Hall, 1787–1857. (1855) On the reform of youthful criminals by means of reformatory schools . . . being part of the charge of Mr. Baron Alderson to the Grand Jury of Yorkshire at the winter assize, 1854. Masters, 1855. LEE

C21 ALDIS, W. S. University tests. Cambridge, Association for the removal of religious disabilities from the universities, 1870. NE

C22 ALLEN, J. T. A vindication of the moral and religious instruction of the children of the poor; a sermon preached in the Collegiate Church of Manchester on . . . October 4th, 1819 . . . Manchester, Gleave, 1820. BI

Alma mater . . . By a Trinity man. *See* Wright, J. M. F.

C23 AMERICAN educational monthly. Vol. 2, no. 9, Sept. 1865. BI

C24 AMERICAN journal of education [*also known as* Barnard's American journal of education]. Vols. 1–5, 8, 10–12, 14–16, 18–21. 1856–1870. HU; Vols. 1–2, 5, 9, 1856–1860. NE; Vol. 1, no. 3, March 1856, vol. 5, nos. 13–15, June–Dec. 1858. BI

C25 AMERICAN journal of education. American pedagogy: education, the school, and the teacher, in American literature. Republished from Barnard's American journal of education. 2nd ed., Hartford (Conn.), Brown & Gross, 1876. LEI

C26 AMERICAN journal of education. Educational aphorisms and suggestions, ancient and modern. Part 1. Laurie's Educational depository, [1860]. NE; Lippincott, 1861. SH

C27 AMERICAN journal of education. (1862) English pedagogy: education, the school and the teacher, in English literature. 1st and 2nd series. 2nd ed., Hartford, Brown & Gross, 1876. LO

C28 L'AMI des hommes; ou, réflexions sur l'éducation commune, considérée dans ses rapports avec la morale et avec le bonheur du peuple. Lyons & Paris, Perisse, [etc.], 1831. [Reprinted from the Revue provinciale.] LEI

C29 AMOS, Andrew, 1791–1860. (1846) Four lectures on the advantage of a classical education, as an auxiliary to a commercial education. With a letter to Dr. Whewell upon the subject of his tract 'On liberal education'. Bentley, 1846. LEI

C30 ANALYTICAL digest. (1843) An analytical digest of the education clauses of the Factories Bill now before Parliament, with observations and objections; to which are added, Practical suggestions to the opponents of the bill, [by James Dinnis?] James Dinnis, 1843. HU LEI

C31 ANDERSON, Christopher, 1782–1852. (1828) Historical sketches of the ancient native Irish and their descendants; illustrative of their past and present state with regard to literature, education, and oral instruction. Edinburgh, Oliver & Boyd, 1828. LEI

C32 ANDERSON, George. The education of the working classes, and the best means of promoting it. A paper . . . Glasgow, Murray, 1857. LEE

C33 ANNALS of education. Sketches of Hofwyl, by Woodbridge. *See* C82 Barwell, L. M.
Anti-national education. *See* Simpson, James

C34 ANTROBUS, John. (1837) Parental wisdom; or, the philosophy and social bearings of education . . . 2nd ed., Saunders & Otley, 1850. [1st ed. had title: A philosophical and practical view of the social bearings and importance of education.] LEE

C35 An APPEAL to the public on behalf of a house of refuge for coloured juvenile delinquents. Philadelphia, T. K. & P. G. Collins, pr., 1846. HU

C36 APPLETON, Elizabeth. (1820) Early education; or, the management of children, considered with a view to their future character. Whittaker, 1820. HU SH; 2nd ed., Whittaker, 1821. LEE

C37 APPLETON, Elizabeth. (1815) Private education; or, a practical plan for the studies of young ladies. With an address to parents, private governesses, and young ladies. 2nd ed., rev. Colburn, 1816. HU

C38 [APPLEYARD, Ernest Sylvanus]. (1828) Letters from Cambridge, illustrative of the studies, habits, and peculiarities of the university. J. Richardson, 1828. LEI

C39 APPLICATION du système de Mettray aux colonies agricoles d'orphelins et d'enfants trouvés. [Paris, Claye, 1850]. BI

C40 AREY, Henry W. The Girard College and its founder: containing the biography of Mr. Girard, the history of the institution . . . etc. Philadelphia, Sherman, 1854. HU; 1869. LO

C41 ARNOLD, Matthew, 1822–1888. Democratic education; edited by R. H. Super. Ann Arbor, Univ. of Michigan Pr., 1962. [Contents: The popular education of France; The twice-revised code; The principle of examination; The code out of danger; Ordnance maps; Mr. Walter and schoolmasters' certificates; A French Eton.] All libraries

C42 ARNOLD, Matthew. Thoughts on education, taken from the writings of Matthew Arnold. Edited by Leonard Huxley. Smith, Elder, 1912. CA RE ReU SH

C43 ARNOLD, Matthew. (1869) Culture and anarchy: an essay in political and social criticism. Murray, 1920, repr. 1949. LEI; do., edited by J. Dover Wilson. C.U.P., 1932. NE; 2nd ed. C.U.P., 1935, repr. various dates. BR HU LEE LO NO RE SH

C44 ARNOLD, Matthew. (1864) A French Eton; or, middle-class education and the state. Macmillan, 1864. BI LEI; do., to which is added 'Schools and universities on the continent', published in 1868. Macmillan, 1892. CA HU LEE NE NO RE SH SO

C45 ARNOLD, Matthew. (1868) Higher schools and universities in Germany. [Originally part of 'Schools and universities on the continent.'] 2nd ed. Macmillan, 1874. SH; 1882. CA LEI; 1892. HU LEE

C46 ARNOLD, Matthew. Letters . . . 1848–1888; collected and arranged by George W. E. Russell. Macmillan, 1895. 2 vols. LEI SH

C47 ARNOLD, Matthew. (1861) The popular education of France: with notices of that of Holland and Switzerland. Longman, 1861. BI HU LEE LO NE ReU SH

C48 ARNOLD, Matthew. Reports on elementary schools, 1852–1882. Edited by Sir Francis Sandford. Macmillan, 1889. LEE SH; New ed. with additional matter and appendices and with an introduction by F. S. Marvin. H.M.S.O., 1908. HU LEI RE ReU SO; 1910. CA LEE

C49 ARNOLD, Matthew. (1868) Schools and universities on the continent. Macmillan, 1868. HU LEE LEI NE RE ReU SH

C50 [ARNOLD, Matthew]. (1862) The twice-revised code. Reprinted from 'Fraser's magazine'. Clowes, 1862. BI HU LEE

C51 ARNOLD, Thomas, 1795–1842. Arnold of Rugby: his school life and contributions to education; edited by J. J. Findlay. C.U.P., 1897, repr. 1925. [Includes his Sermons, and Educational essays.] LEI

C52 ARNOLD, Thomas. (1829–1834, 3 v.) Sermons preached mostly in the chapel of Rugby School. Vols. 1 and 2. 4th ed. Fellowes, 1845. BR

C53 [ARROWSMITH, J. H.] (1825) Essay on mechanics' institutions, with a particular relation to the Institute recently established in Bolton. Bolton, J. Yates, 1825. LO

ARTEGALL, pseud. See Williams, Jane

ASHLEY, Antony Ashley Cooper, lord. See Shaftesbury, earl of

C54 ASSOCIATED BODY OF CHURCH SCHOOLMASTERS IN ENGLAND AND WALES. (1862) The new Education code and its effects. Bolton, Winterburn, 1862. BI

C55 AUBERT, Mme. [Prospectus of a] Boarding-school for young ladies, conducted by Mme. Aubert, rue Basse-du-Rempart, no. 38, Passage Sandrié, à Paris. Paris, 1815. LO

C56 AUSTIN, Sarah, 1793–1867. (1857) Two letters on girls' schools, and on the training of working women. With additions. Chapman & Hall, 1857. HU

C57 AUSTIN, Sarah, trans. (Fr. 1831; Eng. 1834) Report on the state of public instruction in Prussia, by M. Cousin... Effingham Wilson, 1834. HU LEI LI; 2nd ed. 1836. LO SH

C58 [BABINGTON, Thomas], 1758–1837. (1814) A practical view of Christian education in its early stages. 3rd ed., Hatchard, 1817. BI BR; 8th ed., to which is added, A letter to a son soon after the close of his education... Hatchard, 1831. BI

C59 BACHE, Alexander Dallas, 1806–1867. (1839) Report on education in Europe, to the trustees of Girard College for Orphans. Philadelphia, privately printed, 1839. LEE LEI

C60 BAIN, Alexander, 1818–1903. (1859) The emotions and the will. Parker, 1859. BI

C61 BAIN, Alexander. (1855) The senses and the intellect. Parker, 1855. BI

C62 BAINES, Sir Edward, 1800–1890. (1854) Education best promoted by perfect freedom, not by state endowments. With an appendix containing official returns of education, in 1818, 1833, and 1851. J. Snow, 1854. LEI

C63 BAINES, Sir Edward. (1847?) A letter to the... Marquis of Lansdowne... on the government plan of education: with an appendix, containing the minutes of the Committee of Council on Education, in December 1846... 6th ed., Ward, & Simpkin, Marshall, 1847. NO

C64 BAINES, Sir Edward. (1846) Letters to the Right Hon. Lord John Russell... on state education... London, Simpkin, Marshall; Leeds, Baines & Newsome; [1846]. LEI RE; 2nd ed., Ward, 1847. BR; 5th ed., Ward, & Simpkin, Marshall, 1847. LEE ReU

C65 BAINES, Sir Edward. (1851) The life of Edward Baines, late M.P. for the borough of Leeds; by his son. Longman, 1851. LEE; 2nd ed., 1859. HU

C66 BAINES, Sir Edward. (1856) National education: remarks on the speech and plan of Lord John Russell. Ward, 1856. BI HU

C67 BAINES, Sir Edward. (1843) The social, educational, and religious state of the manufacturing districts; with statistical returns of the means of education and religious instruction in the manufacturing districts of Yorkshire, Lancashire, and Cheshire... Simpkin, Marshall, 1843. LEI ReU; 2nd ed., 1843. LEE

C68 BAKER, James. Military education; a letter to... Latimer Niveille, vice-chancellor of the university of Cambridge. Cambridge, Macmillan, 1861. BI

C69 BAKER, James. Military education in connection with the universities. Cambridge, Macmillan, 1861. BI

C70 BAKER, Thomas, 1656–1740. (1869) History of the College of St. John the Evangelist, Cambridge. Edited by J. E. B. Mayor. C.U.P., 1869. 2 vols. LO ReU

BALLYCONREE. Connemara orphans' nursery. See Connemara Orphans' Nursery

C71 BANISTER, Elizabeth Ruth. A letter to the Right Hon. Viscount Palmerston... on a new system of agriculture, drainage, and secondary punishment for juvenile criminals. Brighton, A. Wallis, 1853. HU

C72 [BARCLAY, Hugh], 1799–1884. Juvenile delinquency, its causes and cure; by a county magistrate. Edinburgh & London, Blackwood, 1848. HU

C73 BARNARD, Henry, 1811–1900. Henry Barnard on education. Edited by J. S. Brubacher. N.Y., McGraw, 1931. HU

C74 BARNARD, Henry. (1851) Practical illustrations of the principles of school architecture. Hartford; Case, Tiffany; 1851. LO; [2nd ed.], [Hartford, no pub.], 1854. BI

C75 BARNARD, Henry. School architecture. N.Y., Barnes, 1848. ReU

C76 BARNARD, Henry, ed. American journal of education. See C24 American journal of education

C77 BARNARD CASTLE. Victoria infant school. Report of 1852. Barnard Castle, Atkinson, 1852. BI

C78 BARRON, Henry Wenston. (1840) A few notes on the public schools and universities of Holland and Germany, taken during a tour in the summer of 1839. Ridgway, 1840. HU

C79 BARROW, William, 1754–1836. (1802) An essay on education; in which are particularly considered the merits and the defects of the discipline and instruction in our academies. Rivington, 1802. 2 vols. BI HU LEE LEI OX; 2nd ed., 1804. ReU

C80 BARRUEL, Augustin, *abbé*, 1741–1820. Ancien projet des Sophistes, dans l'établissement de nouvelles écoles pour le peuple; extrait des Mémoires du Jacobinisme, par M.l'Abbé Barruel, chapitre 17 du tome 1er. [1797]. Besançon, V. Couché, [*c*. 1815?]. HU

C81 BARRY, William. An essay on the most desirable plan for supplying innocent and elevating recreation for the working classes. Leeds, Walker, 1853. BI

C82 [BARWELL, *Mrs*. Louisa Mary], 1800–1885. (1842) Letters from Hofwyl, by a parent, on the educational institutions of De Fellenberg, with an appendix, containing Woodbridge's Sketches of Hofwyl, reprinted from the Annals of education. Longman, 1842. HU LEI ReU

C83 BARWELL, *Mrs*. L. M. (1837) Nursery government: or, hints addressed to mothers and nurserymaids on the management of young children. 2nd ed. corr. and enl., Chapman & Hall, 1845. HU

C84 BATEMAN, Josiah. (1839) La Martiniere: a reply to certain statements respecting the Bishop of Calcutta, contained in a work entitled 'Recent measures for the promotion of education in England'; [by Kay-Shuttleworth]. Hatchard, 1839. BR

C85 BATH, *district*. National schools. (1840) The case stated between the committee of the Bath District National Schools and the Rev. W. J. Brodrick, rector of Bath; with an appendix. Bath, H. E. Carrington, 1840. HU

C86 [BAUCLOS, Louis de]. Remarques sur la méthode de M. Jacotot, et sur ses deux ouvrages concernant l'enseignement de la langue maternelle et celui des langues étrangères. Brussels, Brest van Kempen, 1827. HU

C87 BEAMES, Thomas. A plea for educational reform. Ridgway, 1856. BI

C88 BEARD, Charles, 1827–1888. Port Royal: a contribution to the history of religion and literature in France. Longmans, 1861. 2 vols. HU

BEDE, Cuthbert, *pseud*. *See* Bradley, Edward

C89 BEGGS, Thomas. (1849) An inquiry into the extent and causes of juvenile depravity. Gilpin, 1849. BI LEI

C90 BEGGS, Thomas. Three lectures on the moral education of the people. Gilpin, 1847. HU

C91 [BEKKER, Ernst Immanuel]? Von deutschen Hochschulen allerlei: was da ist und was da sein sollte. Von einem deutschen Professor. Berlin, Reimer, 1869. [Ms. note in the book attributes it to E. I. Bekker.] LEI

C92 BELFAST. Presbytery. Report adopted by the Presbytery of Belfast on the changes in the national system of education. Belfast, News-letter office, 1867. LO

C93 BELL, Andrew, 1753–1832. The complete works. Edinburgh, Oliver & Boyd, 1832. BR

C94 BELL, Andrew. The practical parts of Lancaster's 'Improvements' and Bell's 'Experiment'; edited by D. Salmon. C.U.P., 1932. BI LEE LEI LO NE NO ReU SH

C95 BELL, Andrew. Dr. Bell's system of instruction, broken into short questions and answers ... compiled ... by F. Iremonger. *See* C703 Iremonger, F.

C96 BELL, Andrew. (1797) An experiment in education, made at the Male Asylum at Egmore, near Madras ... 2nd ed., Cadell & Davies, 1805. HU

C97 BELL, Andrew. An analysis of the experiment in education, made at Egmore, near Madras. 3rd ed., Cadell & Davies, 1807. LO

C98 BELL, Andrew. The Madras school; or, elements of tuition: comprising the analysis of an experiment, made at the male asylum, Madras ... Murray, [etc.], 1808. LEE NE RE ReU SH

C99 BELL, Andrew. Sketch of a national institution for training up the children of the poor ... Extracted from 'The Madras school'. Murray, [etc.], 1808. LEI

C100 BELL, Andrew. The report of the military male orphan asylum at Madras ... New ed., to which are subjoined additional documents and records ... Murray, [etc.], 1812. LEE SH

C101 BELL, Andrew. Elements of tuition. Part 1: The Madras school. New ed., 1813. ReU; Part 2: The English school, or, the history, analysis, and application of the Madras system of education to English schools. New ed. enl., Rivington, [etc.], 1814. HU

C102 BELL, Andrew. Instructions for conducting schools through the agency of the scholars themselves: comprising the analysis of an experiment in education ... 6th ed., Rivingtons, 1817. [Extracted from Elements of tuition.] BI

C103 BELL, Andrew. Mutual tuition and moral discipline: or, manual of instructions for conducting schools through the agency of the scholars themselves. 7th ed. For the use of schools and families. With an introductory essay on the object and importance of the Madras system of education ... G. Roake, [etc.], 1823. ReU

C104 BELL, Andrew. (1807) Extract of a sermon on the education of the poor under an appropriate system, preached at St. Mary's, Lambeth, 28 June, 1807. 2nd ed., Cadell & Davies, [etc.], 1807. NE

C105 BELL, Andrew. Letters to the Rt. Hon. Sir John Sinclair, Bart., on the Infant School Society at Edinburgh, etc. Rivington, [etc.], 1829. LO

C106 BELL, Andrew. (1808) The wrongs of children. Parts I and II [of 3]. Rivington, 1819. LEE

C107 [BELL, W. B.]. Lucus a non lucendo, education from non-educing; being observations on the present system of female education; with a plan for its permanent improvement. Vizetelly, pr., 1829. LEE

C107a BELLEMARE, Jean François. Le collège de mon fils. Paris, Dentu, 1827. LO

C108 BENNETT, William J. E. (1846) Crime and education: the duty of the state therein. W. J. Cleaver, 1846. LEE

C109 BENTHAM, Jeremy, 1748–1832. (1816) Chrestomathia; being a collection of papers, explanatory of the design . . . of the Chrestomathic day school . . . Payne, [etc.], 1816. LEE LEI ReU SH

C110 BENTHAM, Jeremy. Church-of-Englandism and its catechism examined: preceded by strictures on the exclusionary system, as pursued in the National Society's schools . . . Effingham Wilson, 1818 [printed 1817]. HU

C111 BENTLEY, Joseph. State of education, crime, etc., etc.; and proposed national training schools for England and Wales: or, education as it is; ought to be; and might be. Longmans, 1842. NO

C112 BERESFORD-HOPE, Alexander James, form. Hope, 1820–1887. The new government scheme of academical education for Ireland considered in a letter to a friend. Rivington, 1845. BI

BERGERON, P. Dubois. See Dubois-Bergeron, P.

C113 BERLYN, Peter, trans. Industrial instruction in England, being a report made to the Belgian government by the Chevalier de Cocquiel. Chapman & Hall, 1853. HU

C114 BERNARD, Sir Thomas, 1750–1818. (1812) The Barrington school: principles, practices, and effects, of the new system of instruction in facilitating the religious and moral instruction of the poor. Society for bettering the condition of the poor, 1812. BR SH; 1815. ReU

C115 BERNARD, Sir Thomas. (1809) The new school; being an attempt to illustrate its principles, detail, and advantages. Society for bettering the condition of the poor, 1809. HU LEE; 3rd ed., 1810. HU LEE NE

C116 BERNARD, Sir Thomas. (1809) Of the education of the poor; being the first part of a digest of the reports of the Society for bettering the condition of the poor, and containing a selection of those articles which have reference to education. Society for bettering the condition of the poor, 1809. HU LEE LEI SH

C117 BESANÇON. Ecoles d'enseignement mutuel. Prospectus: Ecole élémentaire d'après le système de l'enseignement mutuel, établie . . . sous la direction des sieurs Boichard et Robert, instituteurs brevetés. Besançon, Mourgeon, [1817]. HU

C118 BEVERLEY, Robert Mackenzie. (1833) A letter to . . . the Duke of Gloucester, chancellor, on the present corrupt state of the university of Cambridge. 2nd ed., Dinnis, 1833. LEI

C119 BIBER, George Edward, 1801–1874. (1830) Christian education; in a course of lectures, delivered in London, in spring 1829. Effingham Wilson, 1830. HU LEE

C120 BIBER, G. E. (1831) Henry Pestalozzi and his plan of education: being an account of his life and writings, with copious extracts from his works, and extensive details illustrative of the practical parts of his method. J. Souter, 1831. BR CA HU LEE LO NE RE SH; Sherwood, [etc.], 1833. LEI

C121 BIGGS, William. (1849) Report of a lecture upon national education, delivered on April 23rd, 1849. Leicester, Geo. Smallfield, [1849?] [Reprinted from the Leics. Mercury, April 28th, 1849.] LO

C122 BINNEY, Thomas, 1798–1874. (1847) Education. Jackson & Walford, 1847. [Two addresses given at Mill Hill School, 1842 and 1847.] HU

C123 BIRKS, Thomas Rawson, 1810–1883. (1862) The 'Great fact' on which the Revised Code rests . . . proved to be a gross fallacy . . . showing that one-half of the scholars in the inspected schools reach the first class. Clowes, pr., 1862. BI HU LEE

C124 BIRKS, T. R. (1862) The Revised Code: what would it do, and what should be done with it? In a letter to Earl Granville, K.G. Seeley, [etc.], 1862. BI HU LEE RE

C125 BIRMINGHAM. Corporation. Report of the Schools Inquiry Commission in relation to the free grammar school of King Edward VI, in Birmingham . . . Birmingham, The Corporation, 1866. BI

C126 BIRMINGHAM. General purposes committee. Free grammar school of King Edward VI, in Birmingham; report . . . for presentation at the special meeting of the council . . . July 1868. Birmingham, The Committee, 1868. BI

C127 BIRMINGHAM. General institution for the instruction of deaf and dumb children. Account of the institution established in Birmingham . . . including rules of the society, and a list of the patrons, officers and subscribers. Birmingham, [The Institution], 1814. BI

BIRMINGHAM. Hill-Top School. See Hill-Top School, Birmingham.

C128 BIRMINGHAM. King Edward VI School. The charter of the Free School for the inhabitants of Birmingham; founded and endowed by King Edward the Sixth, 2nd January 1552. Longman, 1830. HU

C129 BIRMINGHAM EDUCATIONAL ASSOCIATION. Statistical sectional committee. A report of an enquiry into the state of education of the children of the working classes in Birmingham as affected by the demand for labour . . . Simpkin, Marshall, [1857?]. BI

C130 BIRMINGHAM REFORMATORY INSTITUTION. Report of proceedings at a public meeting for establishing the Birmingham Reformatory Institution, with list of officers and subscriptions. Birmingham, J. W. Showell, pr., 1853. HU

BITZIUS, Albert. See Gotthelf, Jeremias, pseud.

BLACK, John, jt. author. See Campbell, Peter Colin and Black, John.

C131 BLACK, William Henry. Bibliothecae Colfanae catalogus: catalogue of the library in the Free Grammar School at Lewisham, founded by the Rev. Abraham Colfe in the year 1652. Worshipful company of leathersellers, 1831. HU ReU

C132 BLACKBURN, Thomas. (1836) A defence of the system adopted in the Corporation Schools of Liverpool. Liverpool, Wales & Baines, 1836. LEE

C133 BLACKIE, John Stuart, 1809–1895. On the advancement of learning in Scotland: a letter to the ... Lord Provost and Town Council of Edinburgh, patrons of the university. Edinburgh, Sutherland & Knox, 1855. HU

C134 BLACKIE, Thomas Morell. What is a boy? 2nd ed., Simpkin, Marshall, 1860. HU

BLAKE, Sophia Jex-. See Jex-Blake, Sophia

C135 BLAKESLEY, Joseph Williams. (1837) Thoughts on the recommendations of the Ecclesiastical Commission: particularly in reference to their probable influence on the state of the universities. In a letter to W. E. Gladstone. Rivington, 1837. BI

C136 BLISS, Philip, 1787–1857, ed. (1813–1820) Athenae Oxonienses ... by Anthony à Wood. A new edition ... by Philip Bliss. 1813–1820. 4 vols. ReU

C137 BLOMFIELD, Charles James, 1786–1857. (1839) Speech of the Lord Bishop in the House of Lords, July 5, 1839, on the government plan for promoting national education. Fellowes, [1839]. BI LEE

C138 [BLUNDELL, Bezer]. A brief memorial of Abingdon free grammar school, founded 1563 by John Royne ... Abingdon, J. G. Davis, 1863. HU

C139 BLUNT, Walter. Ecclesiastical restoration and reform. No. 1. Considerations and practical suggestions on church rates – parish officers – education of the poor – cemeteries. Masters, 1847. LEI

C140 BONALD, Louis Gabriel Ambroise, vicomte de, 1754–1840. Opinion de M. de Bonald, sur l'enseignement mutuel. Besançon, V. Couché, 1819. HU

C141 BOND, Elizabeth. (1814) Letters of a village governess; descriptive of rural scenery and manners; with anecdotes of Highland children ... Longman, 1814. 2 vols. BI

Book of Rugby School. See Goulburn, Edward Meyrick, ed.

C142 BOONE, James Shergold, 1799–1859. (1838) The educational economy of England. Part 1. On the external economy of education; or, the means of providing instruction for the people. Parker, 1838. LEI

C143 BOOTH, James, 1806–1878. Education and educational institutions considered, with reference to the industrial professions, and the present aspects of society. Parker, 1846. LO

C144 BOOTH, James. (1856) How to learn and what to learn. Two lectures advocating the system of examinations established by the Society of arts... With an appendix containing the programme of the examinations for 1857. 3rd ed., Bell & Daldy, 1857. LEI

C145 BOOTH, James. (1858) On the self-improvement of the working classes. An address delivered at the Leeds Mechanics' Institution, on the opening of the present session, Sept. 1858. Leeds, C. Goodall, pr., 1858. HU

BORSBEEK, Louis François de-Paule Marie Joseph de, comte Robiano. See Robiano Borsbeek, comte de

C146 BOSTON, Mass. School committee. Annual reports [for the years] 1857, 1864, 1868. Boston, Mudge, 1858–1869. 3 vols. BI

C147 BOUYER, Reynold Gideon, d. 1826. (1811) A comparative view of the two new systems of education for the infant poor ... Rivington, 1811. HU

C148 BOWLES, John, fl. 1793–1808. (1808) Education of the lower orders. A second letter to Samuel Whitbread, Esq., M.P.; containing observations on his Bill for the establishment of parochial schools ... Stockdale, 1808. HU LO

C149 BOWLES, John. (1807) A letter addressed to Samuel Whitbread, Esq., M.P., in consequence of the unqualified approbation expressed by him in the House of Commons of Mr. Lancaster's system of education ... Hatchard, [etc.], 1807. HU

C150 BOWLES, William Lisle, 1762–1850. [1818?] Thoughts on the increase of crimes, the education of the poor, and the national schools; in a letter to Sir James Mackintosh. Salisbury, Brodie & Dowding, [1818?]. HU

C151 BOWLES, W. L. (1818) Vindiciae Wyke-hamicae; or, a vindication of Winchester College: in a letter to Henry Brougham, Esq., occasioned by his letter to Sir Samuel Romilly, on charitable abuses. Longman, 1818. HU

C152 BOWSTEAD, J. and others. British schools best adapted to the educational wants of Wales. Carmarthen, Williams, 1855. BI

C153 BOYLE, William Robert Augustus, fl. 1837–1870. A practical treatise on the law of charities. Saunders & Benning, 1837. LO

C154 BRADLEY, Edward, 1827–1889. (1853–1856) The adventures of Mr. Verdant Green, an Oxford freshman, by Cuthbert Bede [pseud.]. Blackwood, [18—]. 3 vols. in 1. LEI

C155 BRANDRETH, Henry. On modern education: a letter to the Senate of the University of Cambridge. Macmillan, 1868. LO NE

C156 BRAY, Charles, 1811–1884. (1838) The education of the feelings: a system of moral training for the guidance of teachers, parents, and guardians of the young. 5th ed., Longmans, Green, 1894. SH

C157 BRAYLEY, Edward William, 1802–1870. The utility of the knowledge of nature considered: with reference to the introduction of instruction in the physical sciences into the general education of youth ... Baldwin & Cradock, 1831. BR

BRENTFORD. Wyke-House School. See Wyke-House School, Brentford

C158 BRERETON, Joseph Lloyd, 1822–1901. (1856) County education. A letter addressed to the Right Hon. Earl Fortescue. Ridgway, 1856. LEE

C159 BREWER, Thomas. (1858) Memoir of Mr. Walter Scott, citizen and plaisterer of London; with an account of the Blue Coat charity school, founded and endowed by him, in the town of Ross, Herefordshire. Mitchell, pr., 1858. LEI

C160 BREWER, Thomas. (1856) Memoir of the life and times of John Carpenter, town clerk of London ... and founder of the City of London School. Taylor, 1856. LO

Brief comments on the revised speech of the Rt. Hon. Robert Lowe. *See* Hume, Mary C.

Brief history of Christ's Hospital. *See* Wilson, John Iliffe

Brief memoir of James Davies. *See* Gabb, James Ashe

Brief memorial of Abingdon free grammar school. *See* Blundell, Bezer.

C161 BRISTED, Charles Astor, 1820–1874. Five years in an English university. 2nd ed., N.Y., Putnam, 1852. BI ReU

C162 BRITISH AND FOREIGN SCHOOL SOCIETY. Annual report. 20th, 1825. HU; 28th, 1833. LEE; 1862. HU

C163 BRITISH AND FOREIGN SCHOOL SOCIETY. Handbook of the Borough Road schools: explanatory of the methods of instruction adopted by the ... society. The Society, 1854. LO RE ReU SH

C164 BRITISH AND FOREIGN SCHOOL SOCIETY. (1816) Manual of the system of teaching reading, writing and arithmetic in the elementary schools of the ... society. 3rd ed., The Society. 1825. ReU

C165 BRITISH AND FOREIGN SCHOOL SOCIETY. Manual of the system of primary instruction, pursued in the model schools of the ... society. 1831. LEI; 1834. HU

BRITISH AND FOREIGN SCHOOL SOCIETY. *See also* Institution for promoting the British system of education; Royal Lancasterian Institution

C166 BRITISH ASSOCIATION FOR THE ADVANCEMENT OF SCIENCE. *Parliamentary committee.* Report to be presented ... at Glasgow, on the question, whether any measures could be adopted by the government or Parliament that would improve the position of science or its cultivation in this country. [Brit. Ass., 1855.] BI

C167 BRITISH MAGAZINE and monthly register of religious and ecclesiastical information, parochial history, and documents respecting the state of the poor, progress of education, etc. J. Turrill, 1832. LO

C168 BRODIE, *Sir* Benjamin Collins, 1783–1862. (1854) Psychological inquiries: in a series of essays intended to illustrate the mutual relations of the physical organization and the mental faculties. 2nd ed., Longmans, 1855. LO

C169 BROMBY, Charles Henry, 1814–1907. (1861) A letter to the Rt. Hon. Robert Lowe, M.P., containing strictures upon the false assumptions and inadequate remedies of the Revised education code. Simpkin, Marshall, [1861]. BI

C170 BROMBY, C. H. (1861) Revised educational code. A letter to the Right Hon. Lord Granville ... Simpkin, Marshall, 1861. BI LEE

C171 BROOKE, Samuel Roebuck, 1844–1898? Sam Brooke's journal: the diary of a Lancing schoolboy, 1860–1865. Friends of Lancing chapel, 1953. BR LEI

C172 BROUGHAM, Henry Peter, 1*st baron Brougham and Vaux*, 1778–1868. (1835) Address to the members of the Manchester Mechanics' Institution on ... 21st July, 1835, with a report of the proceedings of the general meeting. Manchester, The Institution, 1835. NE SH

C173 BROUGHAM, H. P. Addresses on popular literature, and on the monument to Sir Isaac Newton: delivered at Liverpool and Grantham. E. Law, 1858. HU

C174 [BROUGHAM, H. P.] [Article on Lancaster and Bell, extracted from the Edinburgh Review, no. 37, November 1811, art. 1.] 1811. LEE

C175 BROUGHAM, H. P. (1839) A letter on national education to the Duke of Bedford. Edinburgh, Black, 1839. BR HU

C176 BROUGHAM, H. P. Letter to Lord Lyndhurst, on criminal police and national education. 2nd ed., with a postscript. Ridgway, 1847. LEE

C177 BROUGHAM, H. P. (1818) A letter to Sir Samuel Romilly, M.P., upon the abuse of charities. 4th ed., Longman, 1818. BI; 6th ed., 1818. HU; 8th ed., 1818. LO; 9th ed., 1818. LEE

C178 BROUGHAM, H. P. Appendix to Mr. Brougham's letter [to Sir Samuel Romilly]: containing minutes of evidence taken before the Education Committee. Longman, 1818. LO

C179 BROUGHAM, H. P. Opinions on politics, theology, law, science, education, literature, etc., etc., as exhibited in his parliamentary and legal speeches, and miscellaneous writings. Colburn, 1837. LEI

C180 BROUGHAM, H. P. (1825) Practical observations upon the education of the people, addressed to the working classes and their employers. Longman, 1825. LEI; 15th ed., 1825. HU; 16th ed., 1825. BI; 18th ed., 1825. LEE

C181 BROUGHAM, H. P. (1820) The speech of H. Brougham, Esq., on the education of the poor; spoken in the House of Commons, June 29, 1820. Pamphleteer, vol. XVI, no. 32. HU

C182 BROUGHAM, H. P. (1835) The speech of Henry, Lord Brougham, in the House of Lords, on ... May 21, 1835, on the education of the people. R. Baynes, [etc.], 1835. BI HU LO SH

C183 BROUGHAM, H. P. (1837) Speech in the House of Lords on ... June 29, 1837, on the Education Bill ... to which is annexed a statement of the substance of the bill. Simpkin, Marshall, 1837. LO

C184 BROUGHAM, H. P. (1854) Speeches upon national education, House of Lords, 24th July and 4th August, 1854. Ridgway, 1854. HU

C185 BROUGHAM, H. P. Speeches on social and political subjects ... Griffin, 1857. 2 vols. (The works of ... vols. 9–10.) LEI

C186 BROWN, *Rev.* John, *M.A.* Suggestions on church extension and national education: a letter addressed to the Right Hon. the Lord Wharncliffe ... Leicester, Crossley, 1845. LEE

C187 BROWN UNIVERSITY, *Providence.* Report to the corporation of Brown University on changes in the system of collegiate education ... Providence, G. H. Whitney, 1850. HU

C188 BROWNE, James P. Phrenology, and its application to education, insanity and prison discipline. Bickers, 1869. LEI

C189 BROWNLOW, John. The history and design of the Foundling Hospital, with a memoir of the founder. Warr, pr., 1858. LEI

C190 BROWNLOW, John. The history and objects of the Foundling Hospital, with a memoir of the founder. Jacques, 1865. BR

C191 BRUCE, Henry Austin, 1st baron Aberdare, 1815–1895. (1866) National education: an address delivered to the National Association for the Promotion of Social Science at Manchester, October 6, 1866. Ridgway, 1866. BI

C192 BRUCE, H. A. (1867) Speech on the second reading of the Education of the poor bill, July 10, 1867. Ridgway, 1867. NE

C193 BRUN, Jean-Baptiste. Mémoire sur cette question proposée par l'Institut National. L'émulation est-elle un bon moyen d'éducation?... Paris, Bernard, 1801. BI

C194 BRUNETIERE TALLIEN, C. de, comtesse. An essay on female education ... with a memoir of the the authoress, translated by Lord Brougham. Authoress, [1840?]. [Includes the French text.] LO

C195 BUCKLER, John Chessell, 1770–1851. (1827) Sixty views of endowed grammar schools from original drawings, with letter-press descriptions. Hurst, 1827. BR HU SH

C196 BUCKMASTER, John Charles. (1862) The education question in Parliament; being a digest of proceedings from 1816 to the publication of the Revised code. Chapman & Hall, [1862]. HU

C197 BUCKMASTER, J. C. Local government in Battersea: the substance of an address... A. Chapman, pr., 1867. HU

C198 BUCKMASTER, J. C. On the nature and amount of aid afforded by the Science and Art Department in promoting a knowledge of elementary science among the industrial classes... Longman, 1863. HU

BULL, Henry, joint ed. See Mure, James and others, eds.

C199 BULLAR, John, fl. 1806–1844. (1806) Thoughts on the subject of education at school: addressed to his friends. Southampton, Baker & Fletcher, 1806. HU

BULOW, Bertha von Marenholtz. See Marenholtz-Bülow, B.

C200 BURDETT-COUTTS, Angela Georgina, baroness, 1814–1906. A summary account of prizes for common things offered and awarded by Miss Burdett-Coutts at the Whitelands Training Institution... Hatchard, 1860. BR

C201 BUREAUD-RIOFREY, Antoine Martin. (1835) Education physique des jeunes filles, ou hygiène de la femme avant le mariage. Paris, Librairie des sciences médicales, 1835. LO

C202 BUREAUD-RIOFREY, A. M. Treatise on physical education; specially adapted to young ladies. 2nd ed., Longman, 1838. LEE

C203 BUREAUD-RIOFREY, Mme. (1836) Private education; or, observations on education. Longman, [etc.], 1836. LO; 2nd ed., Longman, [etc.], 1839. BI

C204 BURGESS, Richard, 1796–1881. (1846) A letter to the Rev. W. F. Hook ... on his plan for the education of the people. 2nd ed., Hatchard, 1846. HU

C205 BURGESS, Richard. National education, by rates or taxes: a letter addressed to ... Sir George Grey ... Seeley, Jackson & Halliday, 1855. LEE

C206 BURNAP, George Washington, 1802–1859. The sphere and duties of woman. A course of lectures. 2nd ed., Baltimore, Murphy, 1847. LEE

C207 BURNIER, L. Histoire littéraire de l'éducation morale et religieuse en France et dans la Suisse Romande. Lausanne, Bridel, 1864. 2 vols. in 1. LO

C208 BUTLER, James, of Handsworth, B'ham· (1828) Outlines of practical education; or, a brief statement of the course of elementary, mathematical, classical, and philosophical studies, pursued by his own pupils. London, Hamilton, Adams; Birmingham, B. Hudson; 1828. LEI

C209 [BUTLER, Josephine Elizabeth], 1828–1906. (1868) Letter to Mr. Bryce on examinations for governesses, etc. [Liverpool, T. Brakell, pr., 1868]. LO

C210 BUTLER, J. E., ed. (1869) Woman's work and woman's culture: a series of essays. Macmillan, 1869. BR ReU

C211 BUTLER, Samuel, 1774–1839. (1820) A letter to Henry Brougham, Esq., M.P., on certain clauses in the Education Bills now before Parliament. Longman, [etc.], 1820. HU LEE

C211a BUTLER, Samuel. A letter to the Rev. Samuel Butler, M.A., by J. H. Monk ... with Mr. Butler's answer. Cambridge, Deighton, [etc.], 1810. LEE

C212 [BUTLER, Samuel]. (1822) A letter to Philograntus [i.e. J. H. Monk], by Eubulus, [pseud.]: being a sequel to Thoughts on the present system of academic education ... Longman, [etc.], 1822. LEI

C213 BUTLER, Samuel. The life and letters of ... By his grandson, Samuel Butler. Murray, 1896. 2 vols. BR HU LEI RE

C214 BUTLER, Samuel. A second letter to Henry Brougham, Esq., M.P., on the pretensions of the Free Grammar School of King Edward VI at Shrewsbury, not to have its establishment affected by the Education Bills now pending in Parliament. Shrewsbury, Eddowes, 1821. LEE

C215 [BUTLER, Samuel]. (1822) Thoughts on the present system of academic education in the university of Cambridge. By Eubulus, [pseud.]. Longman, [etc.], 1822. LEI

C216 BUTT, Isaac, 1813–1879. The liberty of teaching vindicated; reflections and proposals on the subject of Irish national education ... Dublin, Kelly, 1865. BI

C217 BYRON, Anne Isabella Noel, baroness Wentworth, 1792–1860. History of industrial schools. [in Mayne. Life and letters of Anne Isabella, lady Noel Byron. 1929.] LEI

C218 [BYRON, A. I. N.] (1839) What De Fellenberg has done for education. Saunders & Otley, 1839. [With appendix by J. Cropper.] HU SH

C219 CABANIS, Georges, 1757–1808. (1802) Rapports du physique et du moral de l'homme. 2e éd., rev. Paris, Crapart, [etc.], 1805. 2 vols. LEI

Cabinet lawyer, *Author of*. *See* Wade, John

C220 CALCUTTA. Hindu and Hooghly colleges. Scholarship examinations of 1845–1846: containing questions . . . with the replies of the most successful candidates . . . Calcutta, Ridsdale, 1847. HU

C221 CALDWELL, Charles, 1772–1853. (1834) Thoughts on physical education, and the true mode of improving the condition of man; and on the study of the Greek and Latin languages. With notes by Robert Cox. Edinburgh, Black, 1836. LEE

C222 CAMBRIDGE essays, contributed by members of the university, 1855. J. W. Parker, 1855. LEI

Cambridge Senate before Whitgift's statutes. *See* Edelston, Joseph

C223 CAMBRIDGE. University. Cambridge problems: being a collection of the printed questions proposed to the candidates for the degree of Bachelor of Arts at the general examinations from 1801 to 1820 inclusive. Cambridge, Deighton, 1821. LEI

C224 CAMERON, *Mrs.* Lucy Lyttelton, *ed*. The nursery and infants' school magazine. Houlston, 1830–1833. 4 vols. [no more pub.]. LEE; vol. 2, 1831. LEI

C225 CAMPAN, Jeanne Louise Henriette, 1752–1822. (1824) De l'éducation; suivi des Conseils aux jeunes filles, d'un Théâtre pour les jeunes personnes, et de quelques essais de morale. Ouvrage mis en ordre et publié . . . par M. F. Barrière. Paris, Baudouin, 1824. Tomes 1–2. HU; Ed. nouvelle, augmentée. Paris, Baudouin, 1824. 3 vols. LEI; 3e ed., 1826. 2 vols. ReU

C226 CAMPAN, J. L. H. Journal anecdotique, ou conversations receuillies dans ses entretiens, par M. Maigne, suivi d'Extraits de sa correspondance sur l'éducation. Paris, Colburn, 1825. LO

C227 CAMPBELL, Augustus. (1839) A speech on the subject of national education, delivered at a public meeting in Liverpool, 3rd April, 1839. With an appendix as to the influence of education on morals and crime. London, Hatchard; Liverpool, Grapel; [1839]. HU

C228 CAMPBELL, Peter Colin and BLACK, John. (1866) Report on the grammar school of Aberdeen . . . to the Lord Provost, magistrates, and town council of Aberdeen, 29th October, 1866. Aberdeen, Avery, pr., 1866. LEI

C229 CAPO-D'ISTRIA, Joannes, *count*, 1776–1831. Rapport présenté à Sa Majesté l'Empereur Alexandre . . . sur les établissements de M. de Fellenberg à Hofwyl en Octobre 1814. Paris, Paschoud, 1815. LO

C230 CAPPE, Catherine, b. 1744. (1805) Observations on charity schools, female friendly societies, and other subjects . . . York, W. Blanchard, pr., for J. Hatchard, London, 1805. HU

CARITAT DE CONDORCET, Antoine Nicolas de. *See* Condorcet, A. N. de Caritat, *marquis de*

C231 CARLILE, James, 1784–1854. (1838) Defence of the national system of education in Ireland. In reply to the letters of J. C. Colquhoun. 2nd ed., Groombridge, 1838. BI

C232 CARLILE, Thomas. The key of knowledge taken away by the National Board of Education; with strictures on a sermon, entitled 'Education, religion and liberty' . . . by the Rev. William Johnston . . . Belfast, Phillips, 1849. LEE

CARLINGFORD, Samuel Parkinson-Chichester, *baron*. *See* Fortescue, Chichester Samuel Parkinson

C233 CARLISLE, George William Frederick Howard, *7th earl of*, 1802–1864. Lectures and addresses [to Mechanics' Institutes in Yorkshire] in aid of popular education . . . Longman, 1852. NE

C234 CARLISLE, Nicholas, 1771–1847. (1818) A concise description of the endowed grammar schools in England and Wales. Baldwin, Cradock & Joy, 1818. 2 vols. BI HU LEE LEI NE NO RE ReU SH; vol. 1 [only], 1818. BR

C235 CARPENTER, Lant, 1780–1840. (1820) Principles of education, intellectual, moral and physical. Longman, 1820. HU LEE LEI NE

CARPENTER, Lant, *joint author*. *See* Shepherd, William *and others*

C236 CARPENTER, Mary, 1807–1877. (1859) The claims of ragged schools to pecuniary educational aid, from the annual parliamentary grant, as an integral part of the educational movement of the country. London, Partridge; Bristol, Arrowsmith; 1859. HU

C237 CARPENTER, Mary. (1853) Juvenile delinquents: their condition and treatment. Cash, 1853. LEE LEI LI

C238 CARPENTER, Mary. (1851) Reformatory schools, for the children of the perishing and dangerous classes, and for juvenile offenders. Gilpin, 1851. BI HU LEE

C239 CARTER, Robert Brudenell, 1828–1918. The artificial production of stupidity in schools; showing that school exercises may be perverted and injure the child. Kellogg, [1859]. SH

C240 CARTER, R. B. On the artificial production of stupidity in schools. [Reprinted from the *Journal of psychological medicine*, 1861.] LO

CELATUS, *pseud*. *See* Owen, Owen

C241 CENTRAL COMMITTEE OF SCHOOLMASTERS. Returns concerning the Assistant Commissioners of Education and inspected schools in the ten specimen districts. The Committee, [1862]. BI

C242 CENTRAL SOCIETY OF EDUCATION. (1839) The educator: prize essays on the expediency and means of elevating the profession in society. By John Lalor, J. A. Heraud, E. Higginson, J. Simpson, Mrs. G. R. Potter. Taylor & Walton, 1839. HU LEI LO

C243 CENTRAL SOCIETY OF EDUCATION. (1837) First publication. Papers . . . also the results of the statistical enquiries of the society. Editor: B. F. Duppa. Taylor & Walton, 1837. BI HU LEE MA ReU SH

C244 CENTRAL SOCIETY OF EDUCATION. (1838) Second publication. Taylor & Walton, 1838. HU LEI MA ReU

C245 CENTRAL SOCIETY OF EDUCATION. (1839) Third publication. Taylor & Walton, 1839. HU MA ReU

C246 CHADWICK, *Sir* Edwin, 1800–1840. (1862) Copy of two papers submitted to the [Newcastle] commission . . . 1862. *See* E190

C247 CHADWICK, *Sir* Edwin. Educational progress: a memoir of the late Horace Grant, Esq., as a successful experimentalist to determine the receptivity of children in primary education. J. Meldrum, [1860]. BR HU

C248 CHALMERS, Thomas, 1780–1847. Letter to the Royal commissioners for the visitation of colleges in Scotland. Glasgow, Collins, 1832. ReU

C249 CHALMERS, Thomas. Speeches and tracts. Glasgow, Chalmers & Collins, 1822. BI

C250 CHANDLER, Richard, 1738–1810. (1811) The life of William Waynflete, bishop of Winchester . . . White & Cochrane, 1811. HU LEE RE

C251 CHANNING, William Ellery, 1780–1842. (1839) Self culture; an address . . . delivered at Boston, America, September, 1838. Strange, [1839]. BI

C252 CHARITY COMMISSIONERS. Reports. For the reports, abridgments, and collections from the reports, *See* E452–8

C253 CHARTER-HOUSE, its foundation and history; with a brief memoir of the founder, Thomas Sutton, Esq. Sewell, 1849. LEE

C254 CHASE, Drummond Percy, 1820–1902. The rights of 'indigentes' in respect to college foundations. A letter addressed . . . to the Rt. Hon. Sir J. Pakington . . . Oxford, Henry & Parker, 1861. BI

C255 CHATHAM, William Pitt, *earl of*, 1708–1778. (1803) Letters written by the late Earl of Chatham to his nephew Thomas Pitt, Esq., then at Cambridge. Göttingen, Dietrich, 1805. LEE

C256 CHAVANNES, Daniel Alexandre. Exposé de la méthode élémentaire de H. Pestalozzi. Vevey, Loertscher et fils, 1805. OX

Christian schools and scholars. *See* Drane, A. T.
Chronicles of Charterhouse. *See* Roper, W. J. J. D.

C257 CHURCH, Richard. The rise and progress of national education in England, its obstacles, wants and prospects: a letter to Richard Cobden. Chapman, 1852. NO

Church and the education question . . . By a churchman. *See* Palmer, J. H.

C258 CHURCH education considered. No pub., n.d. [*c.* 1843]. LEI

C259 The CHURCH education directory . . . a means of reference to training institutions, to the various sources of aid, and generally to the plans now in operation for promoting church education. National Society, 1853. LEI

C260 CHURCH of Rome under Protestant government; its position in Ireland and Prussia compared. Together with some remarks on the national system of education and tenure of land in the earlier country. Macdonald & Tugwell, 1866. BI

C261 CHURCH OF SCOTLAND. *General assembly*. Reports of the committee for increasing the means of education and religious instruction in Scotland . . . submitted . . . 1829–1836. Edinburgh, [Church of Scotland], 1829–1836. 8 vols. in 1. BI

C262 CHURCH OF SCOTLAND. *General assembly*. Statement by the General Assembly's education committee of deficiencies in the means of education for the poor in certain of the large towns of Scotland. Edinburgh, Stark, 1836. SH

CHURCHMAN, *pseud. See* Palmer, J. H.

C263 The CHURCHMAN'S protest against the National Society. Nisbet, 1840. LEE

C264 CLARKE, Joseph. (1852) Schools and school houses: a series of views, plans, and details, for rural parishes. Masters, 1852. LEE NE

C265 CLARKE, Joseph Butterworth Bulmer. (1846) Remarks on Dr. Hook's letter to the Bishop of St. David's; and on a state provision for the education of the people. Hatchard, 1846. HU

C266 CLARKE, Liscombe. (1818) A letter to H. Brougham, Esq., . . . in reply to the strictures on Winchester College contained in his letter to Sir Samuel Romilly, M.P. Hatchard, 1818. LO

Classical instruction. *See* Hodgson, W. B.

C267 CLAVEL, Charles. Lettres sur l'enseignement des collèges en France. Paris, Guillaumin, 1859. LEI

C268 CLIAS, Peter Henry, [*otherwise* Phokio Heinrich Clias], 1782–1854. (1823) An elementary course of gymnastic exercises; intended to develop and improve the physical powers of man. Sherwood, Jones, 1823. HU; 4th ed., Sherwood, Gilbert & Piper, 1825. ReU

C269 CLODIUS, Christian August Heinrich. De educatione populari disciplinaque publica communi morum ac legum vinculo . . . Berlin, Wolf, 1865. LEE

C270 CLONCURRY, Valentine Browne Lawless, *2nd baron*, 1773–1853. Letter . . . to the . . . Marquis of Downshire, on the conduct of the Kildare-Street Education Society, and the employment of the poor. Dublin, T. Reilly, pr., 1826. HU

C271 CLOSE, Francis, 1797–1882. (1850) The 'Exposition' at Willis's Rooms, being the antigovernment education meeting held on 7 February 1850, with animadversions. Hatchard, 1850. HU

C272 CLOSE, Francis. (1856) A few more words on education bills. Hatchard, 1856. BI HU

C273 CLOSE, Francis. (1852) National education. The secular system, the Manchester bill, and the government, contrasted. Hatchard, 1852. HU

C274 CLOSE, Francis. (1838) National education and Lord Brougham's Bill considered; in a series of nine letters; together with an appendix. Cheltenham, Wight, 1838. BI

C275 COCHIN, Augustin, 1823–1872. An account of the reformatory institution for juvenile offenders at Mettray, in France . . . London, Whittaker; Durham, Andrews; 1853. HU

C276 COCHIN, Jean Denys Marie, 1789–1841. (1833) Manuel des fondateurs et des directeurs des premières écoles de l'enfance, connues sous le nom de salles d'asile. Paris, Hachette, 1833. LEI

C277 COCHIN, J. D. M. Manuel des salles d'asile. 3e ed., Paris, Hachette, 1845. HU

C278 COCKBURN, *Sir* William, 1773–1858. Strictures on clerical education in the university of Cambridge. Hatchard, Longman, [etc.], 1809. LO

C279 COCQUIEL, Charles de. Industrial instruction in England, being a report made to the Belgian government. Translated by Peter Berlyn. Chapman & Hall, 1853. HU

C280 [COLE, *Rev.* Henry]. A manual of practical observations on our public schools, contained in two letters originally written to private friends. 3rd ed., Seeley, Burnside & Seeley, 1847. HU LEE

C281 COLERIDGE, Derwent, 1800–1883. (1861) The education of the people. A letter to the Right Hon. Sir John Coleridge... Rivingtons, 1861. BI LEE

C282 COLERIDGE, Derwent. (1842) A letter on the National society's training-college for schoolmasters, Stanley Grove, Chelsea. Addressed to the Rev. John Sinclair. Parker, 1842. BI

C283 COLERIDGE, Derwent. Speech at Sion College on compulsory education, 12th July 1867. College of St. Mark and St. John, 1963. HU LEI

C284 COLERIDGE, Derwent. (1862) The teachers of the people; a tract for the time: with an introductory address to the Right Hon. Sir John Taylor Coleridge. Rivingtons, 1862. LEE

C285 COLERIDGE, *Sir* John Taylor, 1790–1876. (1860) Public school education: a lecture delivered at the Athenaeum, Tiverton. Murray, 1860. HU; 2nd ed., Murray, 1860. ReU

C286 COLERIDGE, Samuel Taylor, 1772–1834. (1818) A dissertation on the science of method; or, the laws and regulative principles of education. 8th ed., Griffin, [18—]. LEI; 9th ed., Griffin, [18—]. BI

COLFE'S GRAMMAR SCHOOL, Lewisham. *See* Lewisham. Colfe's grammar school

C287 COLLARD, C. P. Coup d'oeil sur l'état de l'instruction publique en France. Paris, Levrault, 1835. LO

C288 COLLE, Francesco Maria. Storia scientifico-letteraria dello studio di Padova. Padua, Minerva, 1824–[5]. ReU

C289 COLLEGE OF PRECEPTORS. Educational times. *See* C415 Educational times

College of St. Mary Winton. *See* Wordsworth, Charles

C290 COLLINGS, Jesse. On the state of education in Birmingham: a paper read at the Social science meeting in Birmingham, October, 1868. Birmingham, Cornish, 1869. LO

COLLINS, John, *joint author. See* Lovett, William & Collins, John

C291 COLLINS, Robert Nelson. The teacher's companion: designed to exhibit the principles of sunday school instruction and discipline... Houlston & Stoneman, 1842. LEI; 1843. HU

C292 [COLLINS, William Lucas], 1817–1887. The public schools: Winchester – Westminster – Shrewsbury – Harrow – Rugby. Notes of their history and traditions. By the author of 'Etoniana'. Edinburgh & London, Blackwood, 1867. HU

C293 COLLINSON, Edward. Education; considered in its importance, and general influence on society. Hamilton, Adams, 1844. LEE

C294 COLQUHOUN, John Campbell, 1803–1870. The system of national education in Ireland: its principle and practice. Cheltenham, Wm. Wight, 1838. HU

C295 COMBE, Andrew, 1797–1847. On the introduction of religion into common schools. Edinburgh, Maclachlan & Stewart, [*c.* 1849]. BI

C296 COMBE, Andrew. (1834) Principles of physiology applied to . . . the improvement of physical and mental education. 3rd ed., 1835. ReU; 13th ed., Edinburgh, Maclachlan, Stewart, [etc.], 1847. LEI

C297 COMBE, George, 1788–1858. Discussions on education. Cassell, 1893. HU LEI

C298 COMBE, George. Education, its principles and practice as developed by George Combe. Collated and edited by William Jolly. Macmillan, 1879. LEI LO

C299 COMBE, George. (1833) Lectures on popular education; delivered to the Edinburgh Philosophical Association in April and November 1833 . . . 2nd ed., Edinburgh, Maclachlan, 1837. BI; 3rd ed., 1848. NO

C300 COMBE, George. Notes on the new reformation in Germany, and on national education, and the common schools of Massachusetts. 1845. ReU

C301 COMBE, George. (1819) A system of phrenology. 2nd ed., Edinburgh, Anderson; London, Longman; 1825. [1st ed. had title: Essays on phrenology.] LEI

C302 COMBE, George. (1848) What should secular education embrace? Edinburgh, Maclachlan & Stewart, 1848. HU ReU; 2nd ed., 1848. BI

C303 COMMITTEE APPOINTED TO WATCH PROCEEDINGS IN PARLIAMENT IN REFERENCE TO THE GRANTS FOR NATIONAL EDUCATION. Remarks on the minute of the Committee of the Privy Council on Education . . . establishing a revised code of regulations. Seeleys, 1862. BI

C304 CONCISE. (1826) Concise account of Tunbridge school in Kent, and of its founder, governors and masters: to which is subjoined the scheme for its future establishment . . . 2nd ed., Macoman, 1827. BI

C305 CONDORCET, Antoine Nicolas de Caritat, *marquis de*, 1743–1794. (Fr. 1799, this trans. 1813) A sure and easy method of learning to calculate. Translated from a posthumous work . . . By Elias Johnston. 2nd ed., Edinburgh, Blackwood, 1815. NO

C306 CONFERENCE ON REFORMATORIES, 1855. A short account of the conference . . . held March 2nd, 1855 . . . Seeleys, [etc.], [1855]. HU

C307 CONGREGATIONAL BOARD OF EDUCATION. Crosby-Hall lectures on education. Snow, [1848]. BR HU LEE LEI LO MA NE SH

C308 CONGREGATIONAL BOARD OF EDUCATION. (1847) The late struggle for freedom of education: a brief record of the principal facts and incidents in the contest. Snow, [1847]. LEE

C309   CONNEMARA ORPHANS' NURSERY, *Ballyconree*. Records . . . from its commencement, 19th Oct., 1849, to the end of the year 1853. Wonston, Shayler, 1854.   BI

C310   CONSEILS d'un père et d'une mère à leurs enfans sur l'éducation des filles. Paris, Deterville, 1810.   LO

C311   The CONSEQUENCES of a scientific education to the working classes of this country pointed out . . . By a country gentleman. T. Cadell, 1826.   HU

C312   CONSIDERATIONS sur l'instruction publique. Lille, Fallot, 1816.   BI

CONVENTION OF LITERARY AND SCIENTIFIC GENTLEMEN, *New York*, 1830. *See* New York. Convention of literary and scientific gentlemen

C313   COOK, John, 1807–1874. A letter to a member of Parliament on the parochial schools of Scotland. Edinburgh, Blackwood, 1854.   BI

COOPER, Antony Ashley, *7th earl of Shaftesbury*. *See* Shaftesbury, *earl of*

C314   COOPER, Charles Henry, 1808–1866. Annals of Cambridge. Warwick, pr., 1842–1908. 5 vols. [vols. 1–4, 1842–1852].   ReU

C315   COOPER, C. H. and COOPER, Thompson, 1837–1904. Athenae Cantabrigienses. Cambridge, Deighton, Bell, 1858–1911. 3 vols. ReU; Vols. 1–2 [only]. 1858–1861. 2 vols. LEI

C316   [COPLESTON, Edward], 1776–1849. (1810) A reply to the calumnies of the Edinburgh Review against Oxford. Containing an account of studies pursued in that university. Oxford, Author, 1810.   LEE

C317   COPNER, James. (1860) Hints on the education of childhood. Rivingtons, 1860.   HU

C318   COQUILHAT, J. P. Enseignement universel; lettres à Mr. Marc-Antoine Jullien . . . Première lettre: Lecture, écriture, instruction primaire; parallèle de cet enseignement avec celui de Pestalozzi . . . Liège, J. Desoer, 1827.   HU

C319   CORNELIUS, B. An account of M. Jacotot's method of universal instruction. In a letter to E. N., Esq. Taylor, 1830.   HU

C320   [CORNWALLIS, Caroline Frances], 1786–1858. (1851) The philosophy of ragged schools. Pickering, 1851.   BI BR HU LEE LEI LO SH

C321   CORNWALLIS, C. F. Prize essay. *See* C1440 Two prize essays on juvenile delinquency

C322   CORSTON, William, d. 1843? (1840) A brief sketch of the life of Joseph Lancaster, including the introduction of his system of education. Harvey, Darton & Co., [1840].   HU

C323   COUNTRY GENTLEMAN, *pseud.* (1826) The consequences of a scientific education to the working classes of this country pointed out; and the theories of Mr. Brougham on that subject confuted, in a letter to the Marquess of Lansdown. T. Cadell, 1826.   HU

COUNTY MAGISTRATE, *pseud. See* Barclay, Hugh

COUPER, John, *joint author. See* Thomson, Thomas and Couper, John

Course of lessons for infants. *See* Mayo, Elizabeth

C324   COUSIN, Victor, 1792–1867. (Fr. 1826, Eng. 1834) Elements of psychology . . . Translated from the French . . . by C. S. Henry. 3rd ed., N.Y., Dayton & Saxton, 1842.   LEI

C325   COUSIN, Victor. (Fr. 1837, Eng. 1838) On the state of education in Holland, as regards schools for the working classes and for the poor . . . Translated . . . by Leonard Horner. Murray, 1838.   BI LEI LO SH

C326   COUSIN, Victor. (Fr. 1831, Eng. 1834) Report on the state of public instruction in Prussia . . . Translated by Sarah Austin. E. Wilson, 1834. HU LEI LI; 2nd ed., E. Wilson, 1836.   LO SH

COUTTS, Angela Georgina Burdett. *See* Burdett-Coutts, A. G., *baroness*.

C327   COX, George Valentine, 1786–1875. Recollections of Oxford. Macmillan, 1868.   ReU

C328   CRAIG, Edward. Sound and extensive education, the right, the privilege and the blessing of a people; a lecture delivered before the Northampton Association for the Diffusion of Religious and Useful Knowledge. Hatchard, 1834.   BI

C329   CRAIK, George Lillie, 1798–1866. The pursuit of knowledge under difficulties. Illustrated by female examples. Cox, 1847.   LEI

C330   CRAMER, Friedrich, 1802–1857. Geschichte der Erziehung und des Unterrichts in den Niederländern während des Mittelalters. Stralsund, Löfflersche Buchhandlung, 1843.   LO

C331   CREASY, *Sir* Edward Shepherd, 1812–1878. Some account of the foundation of Eton College, and of the past and present condition of the school. Longman, 1848.   HU LEE

C332   CROFTON, Walter. (1861) The immunity of 'habitual criminals': with a proposition for reducing their number . . . Bell & Daldy, [1861]. HU

C333   CROPPER, James, 1773–1840. Some account of an agricultural school for orphans. *See* C218 Byron, Anne Isabella Noel

Crosby Hall lectures on education. *See* Congregational board of education

C334   CROWTHER, Jonathan, 1794–1856. A defence of the Wesleyan Theological Institution and of the proceedings of the Institution committee and the Conference relative thereto, in reply to the 'Remarks' of Dr. Warren . . . 3rd ed., Mason, 1834.   MA

C335   CRUIKSHANK, George, 1792–1878. (1870) A few remarks on the system of general education as proposed by the National Education League; with a second edition of A Slice of bread and butter, upon the same subject. Tweedie, 1870.   BI

C336   CRYER, Willson. (1843) A lecture on the origin and reception of several important discoveries, delivered to the members of the Bradford Mechanics' Institute . . . January 2nd, 1843. Whittaker, 1843.   LEE

CUCURRON-SICARD, Roch Amboise. *See* Sicard, R. A.

C337   CUNNINGHAM, F. M. An address on education, delivered to the members of the Hampshire Church School Society, at the annual meeting . . . 1st June, 1860. Winchester, Jacob & Johnson, [1860?].   HU

C338 [CUNNINGHAM, Richenda, 'Mrs. Francis Cunningham'], *ed. and trans.*? (Eng. 1829) Memoirs of John Frederic Oberlin, pastor of Waldbach in the Ban de la Roche; compiled from authentic sources, chiefly in French and German. Holdsworth & Ball, 1829. HU LEI LI ReU; 2nd ed., Holdsworth & Ball, 1830. LEE

Curia Oxoniensis. *See* Walker, John

C339 CUTHBERTSON, D. (1833) Addresses delivered at the annual distributions of prizes, to the pupils of the Glasgow grammar school, from 1828 to 1833, inclusive. Glasgow U.P., 1833. LEI

C340 CUVIER, Georges L. C. F. D., *baron*, 1769–1832, and NOEL, Jean-Francois M., 1755–1841. Report on the establishments for public instruction in Holland. [*In* Cousin, V, On the state of education in Holland.] *See* C325 Cousin, V.

C341 DALBY, William, *vicar of Warminster*. (1834) The real question at issue between the opponents and the supporters of a bill now before the House of Commons, and entitled, 'A bill to remove certain disabilities which prevent some classes of His Majesty's subjects from resorting to the universities of England, and proceeding to degrees therein'. London, Rivington; Oxford, Parker, [etc.]; 1834. LEI

C342 DALE, Thomas, 1797–1870. (1828) An introductory lecture delivered in the University of London . . . 1828. Taylor, 1828. LEI

C343 DALLAWAY, R. C. Observations on the most important subject of education; containing many useful hints to mothers, but chiefly intended for private governesses. 2nd ed., Greenwich, Delahoy, 1818. BI LO

C344 DANIELL, John Frederic, 1790–1845. A letter on the study of natural philosophy as a part of clerical education; contributed to the British magazine, Feb. 1844. Corrected by C. A. Swainson. Rivingtons, 1857. BR HU

C345 DAUBENY, Charles Giles Bridle, 1795–1867. (1848) Brief remarks on the correlation of the natural sciences. Drawn up with reference to the scheme for the extension and better management of the studies of the university [of Oxford] . . . Oxford, Vincent, 1848. HU LEI

C346 DAUBENY, C. G. B. Can physical science obtain a home in an English university? An inquiry, suggested by some remarks contained in a late number of the Quarterly Review. Oxford, Vincent, 1853. HU

C347 DAUBENY, C. G. B. On the importance of the study of chemistry. [*in* Royal Institution. Lectures on education. 1854.] *See* C1252

DAVENPORT-HILL, Florence. *See* Hill, Florence Davenport

C348 DAVIDSON, Ellis A. Drawing for elementary schools; being a manual of method of teaching drawing, specially adapted for the use of masters of national and parochial schools. Published under the sanction of the Science and Art Department of the Committee of Council on Education. Chapman & Hall, 1857. HU

C349 DAVIDSON, E. A. (1870) The happy nursery: a book for mothers, governesses and nurses, containing games, amusements and employments for boys and girls. Cassell, Petter & Galpin, [1870?]. NE

C350 DAVIES, Emily, 1830–1921. (1866) The higher education of women. Strahan, 1866. MA

C351 DAVIES, George. (1840) The history and mystery of the Scarborough Lancasterian schools, first established in 1810 . . . Scarborough, Theakstone, 1840. HU LEE

C352 DAWES, Richard, 1793–1867. (1847) Hints on an improved and self-paying system of national education, suggested from the working of a village school in Hampshire; with observations, from personal inspection, on the Irish national schools. 2nd ed., Groombridge, 1847. ReU; 3rd ed., Groombridge, [1848]. HU LEE

C353 DAWES, Richard. (1849) Observations on the working of the government scheme of education, and on school inspection . . . Groombridge, 1849. BR ReU; 2nd ed., Groombridge, 1849. HU LEE

C354 DAWES, Richard. (1850) Remarks occasioned by the present crusade against the educational plans of the Committee of Council on Education. Groombridge, 1850. HU LEE

C355 DAWES, Richard. (1847) Suggestive hints towards improving secular instruction . . . 6th ed., enl., Groombridge, 1853. HU SH

DE BRUNETIERE TALLIEN, C. *See* Brunetière Tallien, C. de

C356 DEFOE, Daniel, 1661?–1731. (1719–1725) The life and adventures of Mr. Duncan Campbell . . . The dumb philosopher; and Everybody's business is nobody's business. Tegg, 1841. 3 vols. in 1. LEE

C357 DE LASPÉE, Henry. Calisthenics; or, the elements of bodily culture, on Pestalozzian principles . . . Darton, [*c*. 1860]. LEI

C357a DELBRUCK, Jules. Les récréations instructives . . . Paris, Hachette, 1862. LO

DE METZ, Frédéric Auguste. *See* Metz, F. A. de

C358 DEMOGEOT, Jacques Claude, 1808–1894, and MONTUCCI, Heinrich. (1868) De l'enseignement secondaire en Angleterre. Paris, 1868. *See* E837

C359 DE MORGAN, Augustus, 1806–1871. (1830) Remarks on elementary education in science. An introductory lecture . . . Taylor, 1830. BI LEE

C360 DENISON, Edward, 1801–1854. A review of the state of the question respecting the admission of dissenters to the universities. Cochran, 1835. LEI

C361 DENISON, George Anthony, 1805–1896. Church education. The present state of the management clause question, with a proposal for meeting and counteracting the evil effects and tendencies of the system of the Committee of Council on Education . . . Rivington, 1849. LEE

C362 DENISON, G. A. (1849) The Church of England and the Committee of Council on Education . . . A letter . . . to . . . Richard, Lord Bishop of Bath and Wells. Rivington, 1849. LEE RE; 2nd ed., Rivington, 1849. BR

DERRY, John, *bp. of Clonfert, joint author. See* Leahy, Patrick and Derry, John

DE SAUSSURE, Albertine Adrienne Necker. *See* Necker de Saussure, A. A.

C363 DETROSIER, Rowland, 1800?–1834. (1831) An address to the new Mechanics' Institution, Manchester, 1831, on the necessity of an extension of moral and political instruction among the working classes. W. Strange, 1831. BR

C364 DEVAUREIX, F. De l'éducation, religieuse, morale, intellectuelle et physique, d'après l'étude de soi-même. Lettres à M. V. Jacotot sur l'Institution Guillard [de Lyon]. Paris, L. Janet, 1842. HU

C365 DE VÉRICOUR, Raymond. Introductory lectures on education and literature. Dublin, Hodges & Smith, 1851. SH

C366 DE WAHL, Anne. Practical hints on the moral, mental, and physical training of girls at school. Parker, 1847. HU

C367 DIBDIN, Thomas Frognall, 1776–1847, ed. and trans. Treatise on the education of daughters, by Fénelon: translated from the French and adapted to English readers ... Cheltenham, Ruff, 1805. LEE

C368 DIESTERWEG, Friedrich Adolf Wilhelm, 1790–1866, ed. (1834) Wegweiser zur Bildung für deutsche Lehrer. 3 Aufl. 1, 2, 4, 5, 6, and 8. Lieferungen. Essen, Bädeker, 1844–1845. 2 vols. LEI

C369 DINNIS, James? (1843) An analytical digest of the education clauses of the Factories Bill ... with observations and objections, to which are added, Practical suggestions to the opponents of the bill. J. Dinnis, 1843. HU LEI

D'ISTRIA, Joannes, count of Capo-. See Capo-d'Istria, J.

C370 DIXON, George. Speech ... on moving his amendment on the second reading of the Elementary Education Bill in the House of Commons, Monday, March 14, 1870. Buck, 1870. BI

D'OLIVET, Mme. Fabre. See Fabre d'Olivet, Mme.

Domestic portraiture. See Fry, Thomas

C371 DORSET SOCIETY FOR PROMOTING THE EDUCATION OF THE POOR. Account of the proceedings of the Dorset society for promoting the education of the poor in the principles of the Established Church. 1813. ReU

C372 DOWNMAN, Hugh, 1740–1809. (1774–1776) Infancy, or, the management of children: a didactic poem in six books. 7th ed., Exeter, Trewman; London, Cadell & Davies; 1809. LEI

C373 [DRANE, Augusta Theodosia], 1823–1894. (1867) Christian schools and scholars, or, sketches of education from the Christian era to the Council of Trent. By the author of 'The three chancellors'. Longmans, [etc.], 1867. 2 vols. SH; 2nd ed., Burns & Oates, 1881. [Published under the author's name.] LEE

C374 DRYDEN, Sir Henry Edward Leigh, d. 1899. Letters on education, etc. Northampton, Adkins, 1847. LEI

C375 DUBOIS-BERGERON, P. Des nouvelles écoles à la Lancaster, comparées avec l'enseignement des Frères des écoles chrétiennes ... 2e éd., rev., corr. and augm., Paris, Le Clere, 1816. HU; 3e éd., Paris, Le Clere, 1817. LEI

C376 DUFF, Sir Mountstuart Elphinstone Grant, 1829–1906. (1867) Inaugural address delivered to the University of Aberdeen on his installation as Rector, 1867. Edinburgh, Edmonston & Douglas, 1867. BR

C377 DUFTON, John. National education, what it is, and what it should be. Parker, 1847. HU LEE ReU SH

C378 DUFTON, John. The prison and the school: a letter to Lord John Russell, M.P. Parker, 1848. HU

C379 DUNCAN, Henry, 1774–1846. (1821) The cottage fireside; or, the parish schoolmaster: a moral tale ... 4th ed., Edinburgh, Waugh & Innes, 1821. LEI

C380 DUNCAN, Jonathan, 1799–1865. A lecture on education, delivered ... at the Guernsey Mechanics' Institution. [No place], Brouard, 1835. BI

C381 DUNCAN, Peter Martin, 1821–1891, and MILLARD, William. (1866) A manual for the classification, training, and education of the feeble-minded, imbecile, and idiotic. Longmans, 1866. LEI

C382 DUNN, Henry. (1843) The bill or the alternative. A letter to ... Sir James Graham ... [on the Factories bill]. Ward & Co., 1843. LEI

C383 DUNN, Henry. (1848) Calm thoughts on the recent minutes of the Committee of Council on Education, and on their supposed bearing upon the interests of civil freedom and Protestant nonconformity. Houlston & Stoneman, [1848]. LEE

C384 DUNN, Henry. National education, the question of questions, being an apology for the Bible in schools for the nation. With remarks on centralization and the voluntary societies, and brief notes on Lord Brougham's bill. Thos. Ward, 1838. BI HU LEE

C385 DUNN, Henry. (1837) Principles of teaching; or, the normal school manual. 7th ed., rev. and enl. Sunday school union, [etc.], [c. 184–?]. LEI; 9th ed., n.d. HU; 11th ed., [185–?]. BI; 15th ed., [185–?]. LEI [First ed. had title: Popular education; or, the normal school manual.]

C386 DUPANLOUP, Félix Antoine Philibert, 1802–1878. Lettres aux hommes du monde sur les études qui leur conviennent. Paris, Donniol, 1867. LEI

C387 DUPANLOUP, F. A. P. (1867–1868) Lettres sur l'éducation des filles et sur les études qui conviennent aux femmes dans le monde. Paris, Gervais, 1879. LEI

DUPAS, Mathilde Larive-. See Larive-Dupas, Mathilde

C388 DUPPA, Baldwin Francis. The education of the peasantry in England; what it is, and what it ought to be. With a somewhat detailed account of the establishment of M. de Fellenberg, at Hofwyl, in Switzerland. Knight, 1834. HU ReU

C389 DUPPA, B. F., ed. Central society of education. First publication. 1837. See C243

C390 DURIVAU, —. Examen raisonné de l'enseignement dit universel, qui a pris naissance dans le Royaume du Pays-Bas. Brussels, M. Hayez, 1827. HU

C391 Du Thon, *Mme.* Adèle. (1823) Lettres à Isabelle; ou, quelques réflexions sur l'éducation et la societé. Murray, 1823. LEI

C392 Dyer, George, 1755–1841. History of the university and colleges of Cambridge. 1814. 2 vols. ReU

C393 East Lancashire Union. First report of the East Lancashire union of institutions having evening schools, from October 1856 to June 1858. With appendices. Manchester, Cave & Sever, pr., 1858. HU; [5th] report . . . with a paper on the East Lancashire Union by U. J. Kay-Shuttleworth. Manchester, Cave & Sever, 1866. BI

C394 Eclectic review, for March 1840. [Essays on education.] LO

C395 [Edelston, Joseph]. Cambridge Senate before Whitgift's statutes and the University Bill of 1855. Cambridge, Metcalfe & Palmer, 1855. BI

C396 Edgeworth, Richard Lovell, 1744–1817. (1809) Essays on professional education. Johnson, 1809. LEI LO NO SH

C397 Edgeworth, R. L. (1820) Memoirs, begun by himself and concluded by his daughter, Maria Edgeworth. Hunter, 1820. 2 vols. HU LEE SH; 2nd ed., Hunter, [etc.], 1821. 2 vols. LEI LO RE ReU

C398 Edgeworth, R. L. A selection from his Memoirs. Edited by Beatrix L. Tollemache. Rivington, [etc.], 1896. LO

C399 Edgeworth, R. L., and Edgeworth, Maria, 1767–1849. (1798) Practical education. 2nd ed., Johnson, 1801. 3 vols. BI DU HU LEI LO OX; with title: Essays on practical education. 3rd ed., Johnson, 1811. 2 vols. LEE RE; New ed., R. Hunter, [etc.], 1815. 2 vols. NE ReU SO; R. Hunter, 1822. 3 vols. SH

C400 Edinburgh. Institution for the education of deaf and dumb children. Report for the year 1816–1817. BR; Feb. 24, 1817 [&] May, 1818. 2 vols. in 1. BI; 1824. BI

C401 Edinburgh. Meeting of citizens. Report of meeting of the citizens of Edinburgh on the Lord Advocate's education bills. Edinburgh, The Scotsman, [1856]. BI

C402 Edinburgh. Public meeting of the friends of national education, 1854. Report of the proceedings at the public meeting . . . in the Music Hall, Edinburgh, January 25, 1854. Black, 1854. HU

C403 Edinburgh. Public meeting on ragged schools, 1847. Popery and the Bible: a letter to Lord Murray, suggested by the proceedings at the public meeting held on July 2, 1847, regarding the use of the Scriptures in ragged schools. Edinburgh, J. Johnstone, 1847. HU

C404 Edinburgh. do. Report of a discussion regarding ragged schools . . . held in the Music Hall, Edinburgh . . . 1847. Edinburgh, Elder, 1847. HU LEI

C405 Edinburgh. Subscribers and friends of the Catholic schools. Report of proceedings at the annual general meeting of the subscribers and friends of the Catholic schools of Edinburgh, held on 29th December 1851. [Edinburgh, 1852?] LEI

C406 Edinburgh. United industrial school. The United industrial school of Edinburgh; a sketch of its origin, progress, and practical influence. *With* Report of annual meeting, 1851, *and* 4th annual report of the committee. Edinburgh, Black, 1851. HU

C407 Edinburgh Academy. Report by the directors to the proprietors . . . on the pronunciation of Latin. Edinburgh, Muirhead, 1827. LO

C408 Edinburgh Academy. Statement by the directors . . . explanatory of the scheme of that institution, December, 1823. Edinburgh, Hutchison, 1824. BI

C409 Edinburgh Infant School Society. Report [no. 1]. Edinburgh, 1832. BI

C410 Edinburgh Ragged Schools. Eight months' experience of the Edinburgh original ragged or industrial schools, Castle Hill and Ramsay Lane; conducted on the principles advocated by the Rev. Thomas Guthrie. Reported by the Committee of management. Edinburgh, Elder, 1848. HU

C411 [Edinburgh Review]. [Review articles, given in chronological order]:

Oct. 1809: Review by Sydney Smith, of 'Essays on professional education', by R. L. Edgeworth. LEE

1810: Review by Sydney Smith of 'Advice to young ladies on the improvement of the mind'. LEE

Aug. 1810: Review of 'Remarks on the system of education in public schools'. LEE

Nov. 1810: [Article on Lancaster and Bell, and Sir Thomas Bernard's 'The new school'.] HU LEE

Nov. 1811: Reviews by Henry Brougham of books on the educational systems of Lancaster and Bell. HU LEE LEI

Dec. 1816: Review of 'Statements respecting the East India College', by T. R. Malthus. LEE

Sept. 1818: Review of the speech of Henry Brougham in the House of Commons, May 8, 1818, on the education of the poor, and charitable abuses. HU LEE

[Jan. ?] 1819: Review of two works on education. LEE

Mar. 1819: Education Committee, and abuse of charities. [Reviews of pamphlets by Brougham and others.] HU LEE

Oct. 1819: Review of various publications by and about M. de Fellenberg, of Hofwyl School. LEE

May 1820: Education of the poor in France. [Reviews of French publications on 'l'enseignement mutuel'.] HU

Mar. 1821: Article on Brougham's Bill for the education of the poor. LEE

Mar. 1821: Reviews of several books on education, etc. LEE

May 1823: Review of 'Observations relative to infant schools', by Thomas Pole. LEE

Apr. 1853: Review of Kay-Shuttleworth's 'Public education as affected by the Minutes of the Committee of Council'. HU

July 1853: Review of reports on popular education in the U.S. HU

July 1861: Government education. [Reviews of the Newcastle Commission report, Nassau Senior on popular education, and M. Arnold on popular education in France.] HU

C412 EDUCATION AID SOCIETY OF MANCHESTER. (1866) Education of the manual-labour class . . . a paper contributed . . . to the National association for the promotion of social science . . . 1866. Manchester, Cave & Sever, 1866. LO

Education and training considered as a subject for a state legislation. *See* Hawksley, Thomas

C413 EDUCATION of the masses. Can it be accomplished? A question addressed to the Lords and Commons of the British Parliament. Oakey, [1856]. BI

C414 EDUCATIONAL outlines, and other letters on practical duties. To which is added a journal of a summer's excursion made by the author and her pupils. By a lady. Groombridge, 1810. LEE

C415 EDUCATIONAL times and journal of the College of preceptors. Vols. 20–23. 1867/8–1870/1. LEI

C416 EDWARDS, Henry. Elementary education; the importance of its extension in our own country. With a sketch of the state of elementary education on the continent. Longman, 1844. LEE ReU

C417 EDWARDS, Samuel Valentine. Suggestions respecting the orphan children now in workhouse schools and in workhouses . . . Dalton & Lucy, 1863. BI

ELLIOT-MURRAY-KYNYNMOND, William Hugh, 3rd *earl of Minto. See* Minto, *earl of*

C418 ELLIS, *Mrs.* Sarah, *formerly* Stickney, d. 1872. The daughters of England. Fisher, 1842. LO; [184–]. [Inscription dated 1844.] LEI

C419 ELLIS, *Mrs.* Sarah. Prevention better than cure: or the moral wants of the world we live in. Fisher, 1847. BR

C420 [ELLIS, *Mrs.* Sarah]. The wives of England, their relative duties, domestic influence and social obligations. Fisher, 1846. LO

C421 ELLIS, *Mrs.* Sarah. (1838) The women of England, their social duties, and domestic habits. Fisher, 1839. LO; 14th ed., Fisher, n.d. LEI

C422 ELLIS, William, 1800–1881. (1859) An address to teachers on the importance of imparting a knowledge of the principles of social science to children . . . delivered at the South Kensington Museum . . . October 1859. H.M.S.O., 1859. LO

C423 ELLIS, William. (1851) Education as a means of preventing destitution; with exemplifications from the teaching . . . at the Birkbeck schools . . . Smith, Elder, 1851. BI HU LEE

C424 ELY, John. (1835) Academic counsels: an address to the students of Airedale College, delivered at the anniversary meeting . . . 1835. Leeds, Knight, 1835. LEE

C425 ELY, John. A letter in rejoinder to, and 'Appendix' to, 'The strictures' of the Rev. George Aycliffe Poole, M.A., on 'An address delivered on occasion of laying the first stone of East Parade Chapel, Leeds . . . 1839, by the Rev. John Ely'. Jackson & Walford, 1840. LEE

C426 EMERY, Thomas. Educational economy; or, state education vindicated from the objections of the votaries of voluntaryism. A. Hall, 1849. HU

C427 ENDOWED schools, their uses and short-comings, with a table showing the number of endowed schools and their scholars in every county in England. Emily Faithful, pr., 1862. LEE

C428 ENGLAND. *High court of chancery.* Attorney-General *v.* the Governors . . . of the free grammar-school . . . in Wimborne Minster . . . Scheme for the administration of the charity . . . approved by the report of N. W. Senior. E. G. Atkinson, pr., 1848. ReU

England's educational crisis. *See* Humphreys, Edward Rupert

C429 ENGLISH journal of education. Vols. 1–4, 1843–1846. BI; vols. 2 *and* 4, 1844 *and* 1846. NE

Essai sur l'éducation de l'enfance. *See* Larive-Dupas, Mathilde

C430 ESSAI sur le livre de M. Jacotot intitulé: Enseignement universel, etc., etc. Par l'éditeur du sommaire des leçons publiques de M. Jacotot. Louvain, Imprimerie de l'Université, 1823. HU

Essay on mechanics' institutes. *See* Arrowsmith, J. H.

Etoniana, *author of. See* Collins, Wm. Lucas

EUBULUS, *pseud. See* Butler, Samuel

C431 EUSEBIUS, *pseud.* The actual state of clerical education examined, and a remedy for its defects proposed, in a letter to the Right Hon. the Earl of Liverpool. Rivington, 1826. LO

C432 EVANS, James Cook. (1843) Letter to Sir James Graham, bart., on the education clauses of the Factory bill, with an appendix containing Lord John Russell's resolutions, with remarks thereon. Ward & Co., 1843. LEI

C433 EVERETT, Joseph David, 1831–1904. The philosophy of teaching: or, psychology in its relation to intellectual culture; being an essay read before the Literary and philosophical society of the University of Glasgow. Griffin, 1858. HU

C434 EXETER DIOCESAN BOARD OF EDUCATION. Report . . . adopted at a public meeting held in Exeter, January 10, 1839. Exeter, Pollard, 1839. LO; 29th report. Exeter, Pollard, 1869. BI

C435 EXETER DIOCESAN BOARD OF EDUCATION. Report of the Committee of management on the 'Revised code'; adopted at a special meeting held January 28th, 1862. Exeter, Pollard, 1862. HU

C436 EXPERIMENTAL education, by the author of 'A Sponsor's gift'. Hatchard, [etc.], 1843. SH

C437 FABRE D'OLIVET, *Mme.* —. (1820) Conseils à mon amie sur l'éducation physique et morale des enfans. Paris, Delaunay, [etc.], 1820. LEI

C438 FARADAY, Michael, 1791–1867. Observations on mental education. [*in* Royal Institution. Lectures on education. 1854.] *See* C1252

C439 FARNHAM, J. J. (1854) The intellectual, moral and religious training of pupil teachers. 2nd ed., Wesley, 1854. LEE

C440 FARRAR, Frederic William, 1831–1903. (1867) A lecture delivered at the Royal Institution on Fri., Feb. 8th, 1867. Macmillan, 1867. ReU

C441 FARRAR, F. W., *ed.* (1867) Essays on a liberal education. Macmillan, 1867. BI LEE LO NE RE; 2nd ed., Macmillan, 1868. BR HU LEI LO ReU

FATHER's guide. *See* Gilbert, Richard

C442 FEARON, Henry Bradshaw. (1856) The importance of teaching common things: a lecture delivered before the Loughborough literary and philosophical society, April 15, 1856. Rivington, 1856. BI HU LEE

C443 FEARON, H. B. (1859) Mental vigour: its attainment impeded by errors in education. A paper read before the Leicester literary and philosophical society, December 13, 1858. Rivington, 1859. BR

C444 FELLENBERG, Philip Emanuel von, 1771–1844. Lettre sur la colonie d'enfants indigents, établie à deux lieues d'Hofwyl. [No pub.], 1830. HU

C445 FELTON, John. An appeal to the British public, in favour of an important national improvement in commerce and education. A plan for abolishing fractions, and reducing calculations in commerce and mensuration . . . Whittaker, 1841. LO

C446 FENELON, François de Salignac de la Mothe-, 1651–1715. (Fr. 1687) Treatise on the education of daughters. Translated from the French and adapted to English readers . . . by the Rev. T. F. Dibdin. Cheltenham, Ruff, 1805. LEE

C447 FENELON, F. de S. de la M.- On the education of daughters. W. Darton, 1812. SH

C448 FICHTE, Johann Gottlieb, 1762–1814. The educational theory of J. G. Fichte: a critical account, together with translations, by G. H. Turnbull. Liverpool U.P., 1926. BR HU LEI LO RE SH

C449 FICHTE, J. G. (Lecture, 1805) On the nature of the scholar, and its manifestations. Translated from the German, with a memoir of the author, by William Smith. J. Chapman, 1854. LEI LO

C450 FICHTE, J. G. (1807–1808) Reden an die deutsche Nation. Neue Aufl. Leipzig, Herbig, 1824. LEI

C451 FIRST book for the instruction of students in the King's College. [Satire.] 2nd ed., Steill, [1828]. SH

C452 FIRST LINES. (1811) The first lines of a system of education according to philosophical principles. T. & E. T. Hookham, 1811. HU

C453 FISHER, Osmond, 1818–1914. A digest of the correspondence on the management clauses between the committee of the National Society and the Committee of the Privy Council on Education: with the clauses in an appendix. Rivington, 1849. BR

C454 FITCH, Sir Joshua Girling, 1824–1903. (1861) Public education. Why is a new code wanted? 2nd ed., Bell & Daldy, 1861. BI
FITZMAURICE, Henry Petty, 3rd marquis of Lansdowne. See Lansdowne, marquis of

C455 FLEAY, Frederick Gard. Hints on teaching. Longman, 1864. BR

C456 FLETCHER, Joseph, 1813–1852. Education: national, voluntary, and free. Ridgway, 1851. BI

C457 FLETCHER, Joseph. The farm-school system of the continent and its applicability to the preventive and reformatory education of pauper and criminal children in England and Wales. Harrison, 1852. BI HU

C458 [FLETCHER, William]. National education: an address to the nation on the education of the children of the poor, as illustrative of the system of instruction pursued in the Christian-Union school, Lower Toynton, Lincolnshire. By the Vicar of Harwell, Berks. Oxford, J. Vincent; London, G. Bell; 1848. HU

C459 FORMBY, Henry. State rationalism in education . . . an examination into the actual working and results of the system of the Board of Commissioners of national education in Ireland. [2nd ed.], Dublin, Duffy; London, Burns & Lambert; 1854. BI HU

C460 FORMBY, Henry. State rationalism in education: second series. A digest of the reasons on which certain members of the clergy and religious orders are unable to accept the Privy-Council education grants . . . Levey, Robson & Franklyn, pr., 1857. HU

C461 FORTESCUE, Chichester Samuel Parkinson, aft. Parkinson-Chichester, baron Carlingford, 1823–1898. National education, Ireland: letter to the Commissioners of national education, Ireland, on the organisation and government of training and model schools. Together with the answer of the Commissioners, and other statements and documents referring thereto. Belfast, Mayne, 1867. LEE NE

C462 FORTESCUE, Hugh, 3rd earl Fortescue, 1818–1905. (1864) Public schools for the middle classes. Longmans, 1864. BR LEE

C463 FOSTER, James. Charges against the Charity Commissioners, in the matter of the Royal Free Grammar School at Giggleswick, submitted to the consideration of the members of both Houses of Parliament. Bradbury & Evans, 1864. LEE

C464 FOSTER, John, 1770–1843. (1820) An essay of the evils of popular ignorance. Revised expressly for the Society [for the promotion of popular instruction]. Bristol, Wright, 1839. LEI LO

C465 FOWLER, Orson Squire, 1809–1887. Memory and intellectual improvement applied to self-education and juvenile instruction. 25th ed., N.Y., Fowler & Wells, 1847 [sic]. LO

C466 FOX, Henry Watson, 1817–1848. The claims of India . . . extracted from the letters of a missionary in that country. Durham, F. Humble, 1844. BR

C467 FOX, Joseph, 1766?–1816. (1808) A comparative view of the plans of education as detailed in the publications of Dr. Bell and Mr. Lancaster. Author, [1808]. LEE LO; 2nd ed., with remarks on Dr. Bell's 'Madras school', [etc.], Darton & Harvey, 1809. HU NE ReU

C468 [FOX, Joseph]. (1811) A vindication of Mr. Lancaster's system of education from the aspersions of Professor Marsh . . . etc. By a member of the Royal Institution. 2nd. ed., Longman, 1812. HU ReU

C469 FOX, William Johnson, 1786–1864. (Lectures 1817) Lectures addressed chiefly to the working classes. Published from the reporter's notes. Vol. 2 [only]. C. Fox, 1845. LEI

C470 Fox, W. J. (1843) On the educational clauses in the Bill now before the House of Commons 'for regulating the employment of children and young persons in factories, and for the better education of children in factory districts'. 2nd ed., C. Fox, 1843. HU

C471 FRANCE. *Imperial council of state.* A system of education for the infant King of Rome, and other French princes of the blood. Drawn up by the Imperial Council of State... under the personal superintendence of the Emperor Napoleon. [Text in English and French.] Lackington, [etc.], 1820. HU LO

C472 FRANK, Arnee. Brief remarks upon an important subject: or, a parent's thoughts on the means of obtaining a guarded and religious education for youth at schools. By a member of the Society [of Friends]. Bristol, Albion Press, 1820. LEE

C473 FRANK, Elizabeth, *ed.* Memoirs of the life and writings of Lindley Murray in a series of letters, written by himself, With a preface, and a continuation of the memoirs, by Elizabeth Frank. York, T. Wilson for Longman, [etc.], 1826. LEI

Frank Fairlegh. *See* Smedley, Francis Edward

C474 FRANKLIN, Benjamin, 1706–1790. (1751) Sketch of an English school. For the consideration of the trustees of the Philadelphia Academy. [*In his* Works. J. Walker, [etc.], 1819.] LO

C475 FRASER, James, 1818–1885. (1868) National education. A sermon, preached in the Church of St. Edmund, Salisbury, October 25th, 1868... Rivingtons, [1868]. HU

C476 FRASER, James. (1861) The Revised code of the Committee of Council on Education, its principles, tendencies, and details, considered in a letter to the Lord Bishop of Salisbury... Bell & Daldy, 1861. HU

C477 FRASER, William, 1817–1879. (1868) Memoir of the life of David Stow; founder of the training system of education. Nisbet, 1868. LEE LEI LI ReU

C478 FRASER, William. The state of our educational enterprises: a report of an examination into the working, results and tendencies of the chief public educational experiments in Great Britain and Ireland. Glasgow, [etc.], 1858. NE

C479 FRASER, William, *of Edinburgh.* On the utility and practicability of elementary instruction in the natural sciences during youth. [No pub.], 1832. BI

C480 FREND, William, 1757–1841. A plan of universal education. B. Fellowes, 1832. HU

C481 FRIEDLANDER, Michel. De l'éducation physique de l'homme. Paris, Treuttel & Würtz, 1815. LEE

C482 FRIENDS' EDUCATIONAL SOCIETY. Reports and essays published from 1837 to 1845. York, Linney, 1846. LEE

C482a FRIENDS' EDUCATIONAL SOCIETY. Proceedings. 1855. *See* C1344

C483 FROEBEL, Friedrich, 1782–1852. Ausgewählte Schriften; hrsg. von Erika Hoffman. Godesberg, Küpper, 1951. 2 vols. [Band 1: Kleine Schriften und Briefe, 1809–1851. Band 2: Die Menschenerziehung.] HU

C484 FROEBEL, Friedrich. Chief writings on education, rendered into English by S. S. F. Fletcher and J. Welton. E. Arnold, 1912. BR HU LEI LO NE NO RE SH SO

C485 FROEBEL, Friedrich. (1827) Autobiography. Translated and annotated by Emilie Michaelis and H. Keatley Moore. 4th ed., Sonnenschein, 1892. HU LEI; 8th ed., 1901. SH; 1903. LO; 1908. BR; 12th ed., Allen & Unwin, 1915. LEE LEI RE SO

C486 FROEBEL, Friedrich. (1826) The education of man. Translated from the German and annotated by W. N. Hailmann. Appleton, [E. Arnold], 1887 [and various reprints]. BR HU LEI LO NE RE SH SO

C487 FROEBEL, Friedrich. do. The student's Froebel, adapted from 'Die Erziehung der Menschheit', by H. W. Herford. Isbister, 1894. HU RE; Pitman, 1905–1916. 2 vols. LO; Vol. 2 [only]. LEI

C488 FROEBEL, Friedrich. [Letters.] Briefwechsel mit Kindern. Hrsg. von Erika Hoffman. Berlin, Metzner, 1940. LO

C489 FROEBEL, Friedrich. do. Extracts from letters. Edited by E. R. Murray. Froebel Soc. and Junior Schools Ass., 1936. HU SO

C490 FROEBEL, Friedrich. (1838–1852, collected 1887) Letters on the kindergarten. Translated from the German edition of 1887 by Emilie Michaelis and H. Keatley Moore. Sonnenschein, 1891. HU LO

C491 FROEBEL, Friedrich. (1843) Mother-play and nursery songs... Translated from the German. Boston, Lee & Shepard; N.Y., Dillingham; [1878]. HU

C492 FROEBEL, Friedrich. Mother's songs, games and stories; rendered into English by Frances and Emily Lord. Rev. ed., W. Rice, 1888 [and various reprints]. BR CA HU LEI LO NE NO SH SO

C493 FROEBEL, Friedrich. The mottoes and commentaries of Friedrich Froebel's Mother play... rendered into English verse by Henrietta R. Eliot; prose commentaries translated and accompanied with an introduction... by Susan E. Blow. N.Y., Appleton, 1895 [and various reprints]. BR LO NE SH

C494 FROEBEL, Friedrich. (1837–1840, collected 1861) Pedagogics of the kindergarten, or... ideas concerning the play and playthings of the child. Translated by Josephine Jarvis. E. Arnold, 1897. LO; N.Y., Appleton, 1909. HU RE

C495 FROEBEL, Friedrich. Education by development: the second part of the Pedagogics of the kindergarten. Translated by Josephine Jarvis. N.Y., Appleton, 1899 [and various reprints]. BR NE RE

C496 FROEBEL, Friedrich. [Pedagogics of the kindergarten.] Theorie des Spiels. Langensalza, Beltz, 1947. 3 vols. LEI SO

C497 FRY, Caroline, *aft.* Mrs. Wilson, 1787–1846. (1830) The listener. 7th ed., J. Nisbet, 1836. 2 vols. LEI; 9th ed., J. Nisbet, 1840. 2 vols. LO

C498 FRY, Caroline. (1833) Scripture principles of education. 2nd ed., Nisbet, 1833. BI; 4th ed., Nisbet, 1839. OX

C499 [FRY, Thomas]. (1833) Domestic portraiture; or the successful application of religious principles in the education of a family, exemplified in the memoirs of three of the deceased children of the Rev. Legh Richmond. N.Y., J. Leavitt, 1833. LEI

C500 FULLER, Thomas, 1608–1661. (1655) The history of the University of Cambridge, and of Waltham Abbey... With notes by J. Nichols. Tegg, 1840. BI

C501 FULLER, Thomas. The history of the University of Cambridge... to the year 1634. Edited by... Marmaduke Prickett and Thomas Wright. Cambridge, Deighton & Stevenson, 1840. LEE
Funeral sermon occasioned by the death of the Rev. Dr. Priestley. *See* Priestley, T.

C502 FURNIVALL, Frederick James, 1825–1910. (1867) Education in early England: some notes used as forewords to a collection of treatises on 'Manners and meals in olden time', for the Early English Text Society. Trübner, 1867. LEE LO

C503 [GABB, James Ashe]. (1832) A brief memoir of James Davies, master of the National School, on Devauden-Hill, Monmouthshire. By a clergyman. 4th ed., Rivington, [etc.], 1833. LEI; 5th ed., Rivington, [etc.], 1834. LO

C504 GAINSFORD, Robert John. Reformatory schools: why and how they should be established and maintained. London, Cash; Sheffield, Leader; [*c.* 1856]. HU

C505 GALL, James. A practical enquiry into the philosophy of education. Edinburgh, Gall, 1840. HU SH

C506 GALLOWAY, Randolph Stewart, 9*th earl of*, 1800-1873. (1854) Observations on the abuse and reform of the monitorial system of Harrow school, with letters and remarks. Hatchard, 1854. LEI

C507 GARBETT, James. 1802–1879. Dr. Pusey and the university of Oxford. A letter to the Vice-Chancellor... Hatchard, 1843. BI

C508 GARBETT, James. (1844) The sense, the mind and the spirit. A sermon preached at the cathedral of Chichester for the national schools, May 31, 1844. Hatchard, 1844. BI

C509 GARBETT, James. University reform: a letter to the... Warden of Wadham College, Oxford. London, Hatchard; Oxford, Vincent; 1853. LEE

C510 GARFIT, Arthur. The conscience clause, and the extension of education in the neglected districts... Rivingtons, 1868. HU

C511 GARFIT, Arthur. Some points of the education question practically considered, with reference to the report of the Commissioners and the new minute, with a brief outline of the rise and progress of popular education in England. Longman, 1862. SH

C512 GASC, J. P. Education rationnelle. Pétition addressée à la Chambre des Députés. Paris, Paulin, 1833. LO

C513 GASKELL, James Milnes, b. 1810. An Eton boy: being the letters of James Milnes Gaskell from Eton and Oxford, 1820–1830. Edited by Charles Milnes Gaskell. Constable, 1938. LEI

C514 GAUME, Jean Joseph. (1851) Le ver rongeur des sociétés modernes; ou, le paganisme dans l'éducation. Paris, Gaume, 1851. LEI

C515 GAUME, J. J. Paganism in education. From the French of 'Le ver rongeur...' Translated by Robert Hill. Dolman, 1852. LEE

C516 GAUTHEY, L. F. F. De l'éducation, ou, principes de pédagogie chrétienne. Paris, Meyruis, 1854–1856. 2 vols. LO

GAWLER, John Bellenden, *aft.* Ker. *See* Ker, J. B.
GENERAL INSTITUTION FOR THE INSTRUCTION OF DEAF AND DUMB CHILDREN, Birmingham. *See* Birmingham. General institution

C517 GENLIS, Stéphanie Félicité du Crest de Saint-Aubain, *comtesse de*, 1746–1830. (1782) Adèle et Théodore; ou, lettres sur l'éducation. Tome 2. 16e éd., Paris, Lecointe & Durey, 1822. LO

C518 GENLIS, *comtesse de*. (1806) Madame de Maintenon... 4e éd., Paris, Maradan, 1813. 2 vols. in 1. LO

C519 [GILBERT, Richard], 1794–1852. (1826) The father's guide in the selection of a school for his sons; being a short account of all the schools in England... By a member of the University of Cambridge. Whittaker, 1826. LEE

C520 GILBERT, Richard. Liber scholasticus; or, an account of the fellowships, scholarships, and exhibitions, at the universities of Oxford and Cambridge... also of such colleges, public schools, endowed grammar schools... as have university advantages attached to them... Rivington, 1829. LEE

C521 GILL, John. (1857) Introductory text-book to school education, method, and school management. New ed., rev. and enl., Longman, 1870. HU; new ed., enl., Longman, 1883. LEI

C522 [GILLY, William Stephen], 1789–1855. Academic errors; or, recollections of youth. By a member of the University of Cambridge. Law, 1817. HU LO

C523 [GILPIN, Joshua]. (1808?) A monument of parental affection to a dear and only son. 6th ed., Wellington, F. Houlston, for J. Hatchard, 1817. LEI

C524 GILPIN, William, 1724–1804. (1791) A sermon preached in the parish church of Boldre, in Hampshire, at the funeral of William Baker, May 18, 1791, to which is added a short account of his life. New ed., Rivington for S.P.C.K., 1825. LEI

C525 GIRARD, Jean Baptiste, [*known as* Le Pére Girard, *and* Le Père Grégoire], 1765–1850. Quelques souvenirs de ma vie, avec des réflexions. [Fribourg, Société fribourgeoise de l'éducation, 1948.] HU

GIRARD COLLEGE FOR ORPHANS, Philadelphia. *See* Bache, A. D.

C526 GLASGOW EDUCATIONAL SOCIETY. (1836) Hints towards the formation of a normal seminary in Glasgow for the professional training of school-masters. Glasgow, Collins, [1836]. SH

C527 GLASSE, Samuel, 1735–1812. (1801?) Six lectures on the Church catechism... 7th ed., Rivington for S.P.C.K., 1824. LEI

C528 GLASSFORD, James, d. 1845. Letter to the Right Honourable the Earl of Roden on the present state of popular education in Ireland. Nisbet, 1829. SH

C529 GOBINET, Charles. (Fr. 1687) The instruction of youth in Christian piety . . . From the French . . . Manchester, Dean, 1803. 2 vols. in 1. LEI

C530 GODDARD, Charles. District committees, and National schools. Two sermons, preached in 1817. Windsor, Knight, pr., 1818. [First sermon incomplete.] HU

C531 GODDARD, Charles. A sermon preached before the South Bucks District Committee of the S.P.C.K., at Burnham, 1820. Rivington, [1820]. HU

C532 GODEFROY, E. N. Essai sur l'éducation populaire. Paris, Charles-Bechet, 1832. LO

C533 GODKIN, James, 1806–1879. (1862) Education in Ireland: its history, institutions, systems, statistics, and progress from the earliest times to the present. London, Saunders, Otley; Dublin, Thom; 1862. BI BR LI SH

C534 GOLIGHTLY, Charles Pourtales, 1807–1885. (1861) A letter to the Rev. Dr. Jeune, vice-chancellor of the University of Oxford, in vindication of the handbill [alleging Romish practices in the Woodard schools] distributed . . . Nov. 22, 1861. Oxford, Slatter & Rose, 1861. HU

C535 GOLIGHTLY, C. P. A second letter . . . Oxford, Slatter & Rose, 1861. HU

C536 GOODACRE, Robert. An impartial view of the new system of education. 2nd ed., Cradock & Joy, [etc.], 1812. ReU

C537 GOODWIN, Harvey, 1818–1891. (1855) Education for working men: an address delivered in the town-hall of Cambridge, October 1855. Cambridge, Deighton & Bell, 1855. HU

C538 GORDON, Robert Augustus. (1850) Observations on village-school education, with suggestions for its improvement: being a paper read at a meeting of the inspectors of the diocese, at Cuddesdon Palace. Oxford, W. Baxter for the Diocesan Board, 1850. BR LEE

C539 GORDON, Thomas. Education in Scotland: its actual amount. 2nd ed., embracing the results of the census. Edinburgh, Paton & Ritchie, 1854. LEI

C540 GORE, Montague, 1800–1864. Lecture on the system of education pursued in the French military schools, delivered . . . at the United Service Institution. Ridgway, 1856. LEE

C541 GOSCHEN, George Joachim, *1st viscount Goschen*, 1831–1907. (1865) Speech . . . on the Oxford University tests abolition bill, June 14th, 1865. Wilson, 1865. BI

C542 GOTTHELF, Jeremias, *pseud.* [i.e. Albert Bitzius], 1797–1857. Weltbild und Gedankenwelt eines Erziehers. Eingeleitet, ausgelesen und aufgebaut von Werner Lenartz. Paderborn, Schöningh, 1954. LEI

C543 GOTTHELF, Jeremias, *pseud.* The joys and sorrows of a schoolmaster. By one of themselves. Allen, [1864]. BI

C544 [GOULBURN, Edward Meyrick], 1818–1897, *ed.* The book of Rugby school: its history and daily life. Rugby, [privately printed], 1856. HU LEE

C545 GOVER, William. Day school education in the borough of Birmingham: our progress, position and needs; a letter to George Dixon, Esq., mayor . . . Simpkin, Marshall, 1867. BI

C546 GOVER, William. [Letter to Lord Lyttelton on the Revised code.] Saltley, Worcester Diocesan training coll., 1862. BI

C547 GRAHAM, Thomas John. On preaching, and on popular education. Simpkin, Marshall, 1850. LEE

C548 GRANT, Alexander Ronald. Remarks on the Revised code. Cambridge & London, Macmillan, 1862. BI HU

C549 GRAY, Joshua. (1836) Thoughts on education; with a particular reference to the grammar school system . . . W. Marchant, pr., 1836. HU

C550 [GREENWOOD, A. B.] National education: some proposals. The essay to which the prize offered by James Clay . . . was awarded. London, Hamilton, Adams; Hull, J. W. Leng; 1868. HU

C551 GREGORY, Robert, 1819–1911. (1865) Do our national schools provide education for all whom they ought to train? A letter to His Grace the Archbishop of Canterbury. Rivingtons, 1865. LEE; 2nd ed., Rivingtons, 1865. BI

C552 GREGSON, John. (1847) The labourer is worthy of his hire; or, elevate the masses. A sermon preached at Sutton Courtney, Berks., May 23rd, 1847. Hatchard, 1847. HU

C553 GREGSON, John. The night school; or, educate the people: a sermon preached at Sutton Courtney, Berks. Hatchard, 1847. HU

C554 GRESLEY, William, 1801–1876. Church-Clavering; or, the schoolmaster. Burns, 1843. LEE LEI

C555 GRIFFITH, George. (1864) The endowed schools of England and Ireland: their past, present, and future. London, Whittaker; Stourbridge, Broomhall; 1864. HU NE

C556 GRIFFITH, George. (1860) The free schools and endowments of Staffordshire and their fulfilment. London, Whittaker; Stafford, Hill & Halden; 1860. BI HU LEI LO ReU SH

C557 GRIFFITH, George. (1852) The free schools of Worcestershire and their fulfilment. Gilpin, 1852. BI

C558 GRIFFITH, George. (1870) Going to markets and grammar schools, being a series of autobiographical records and sketches of forty years in the midland counties, from 1830 to 1870 . . . Freeman, 1870. 2 vols. BR LEE LEI LO

C559 GRIFFITH, George. (1861) History of the free-schools, colleges, hospitals and asylums of Birmingham, and their fulfilment. London, Tweedie; Stafford, Hill & Halden; 1861. BI HU LEI ReU SH

C560 GRIFFITH, George. (1854) The life and adventures of George Wilson, a foundation scholar. Cash, 1854. BI HU

GRIFFITHS, William, *of Tutbury, joint author. See* Adderley, Charles Bowyer and Griffiths, Wm.

C561 GRINFIELD, Edward William, 1785–1864. The crisis of religion: a sermon preached at Laura Chapel, Bathwick, [1811]; containing strictures upon Mr. Lancaster's system of popular education. 2nd ed., Rivington, 1812. HU

C562 GRINFIELD, Edward William. (1825) A reply to Mr. Brougham's 'Practical observations upon the education of the people . . .' Rivington, 1825. HU

C563 GROTE, George, 1794–1871. (1846) Address of . . . [the] president of the City of London Literary and Scientific Institution, at a festival . . . June, 1846, in commemoration of the twenty-first anniversary of the Institution. [The Institution], 1846. BI

C564 GROTE, John, 1813–1866. (1862) A few words on the new educational code and the report of the Education commissioners. Cambridge, Deighton & Bell, 1862. BR HU LEE

C565 GROVES, Edward. Pasilogia: an essay towards the formation of a system of universal language, both written and vocal. Dublin, McGlashan, 1846. LEE

C566 GRUNDTVIG, Nikolai Frederik Severin, 1783–1872. (1832–1840) Grundtvigs Volkshochschule, [mit Einführung von Erich Weniger]. Langensalza, Beltz, [c. 1930?] [Extracts from various works.] LEI

Guardian of education. See Trimmer, Mrs.

C567 GUERIKE, Heinrich Ernst Ferdinand. (Eng. 1837) The life of Augustus Herman Francke . . . founder of the orphan-house in Halle. Translated from the German by Samuel Jackson. Seeley & Burnside, 1837. LEI

C568 GUIZOT, François Pierre Guillaume, 1787–1874. Letter to the primary teachers of France. See C1379 Sullivan, Robert

C569 GUNNING, Henry, 1768–1854. Reminiscences of the university, town and county of Cambridge. Bell, 1855. 2 vols. ReU

C570 GURNEY, J. J. Thoughts on habit and discipline. 3rd ed., 1845. NO

C571 GUTHRIE, Thomas, 1803–1873. Autobiography . . . and memoir by his sons . . . Popular ed., Daldy, Ibsister, 1877. LEI

C572 GUTHRIE, Thomas. (1847) A plea for ragged schools; or, prevention better than cure. 12th ed., Edinburgh, [etc.], [no pub.], 1848. With Supplement to 'A plea . . .', Edinburgh, [etc.], 1847. HU

C573 GUTHRIE, Thomas. Seed-time and harvest of ragged schools; or, a third plea, with new editions of the first and second pleas. Edinburgh, Black, 1860. HU LEE LEI NO SH

C574 GWYNN, T. (1858) The management of boys in school. A paper read at the Vale of Aylesbury Church Schoolmasters' Association, 6th February, 1858. Aylesbury, J. Pickburn, 1858. BI BR

C575 H., S. Memoir of John Sharp, late superintendent of Croydon school. London, Cash; Darlington, Penney; 1857. LEI

C576 [HACKETT, Maria]. (1824) A brief account of cathedral and collegiate schools; with an abstract of their statutes and endowments . . . [No publ.], 1827. HU LEE; [with printed and autograph additions up to 1874.] LO

C577 [HACKETT, Maria.] Correspondence and evidence respecting the ancient collegiate school attached to Saint Paul's cathedral. [No publ.], 1832. LEE

HAEGHEN, Philippe van der, joint author. See Stallaert, Charles & Haeghen, P. van der

C578 HAIGH, Thomas. Advantages to be derived from equalised classes in superior establishments; with suggestions for elementary books . . . Sherwood, Gilbert & Piper, [c. 1810]. HU

C579 HALL, G. J. Sought and saved: a prize essay on ragged schools and kindred institutions. Ragged schools union, 1855. NO

C580 HALL, Robert, 1764–1831. (1803) The sentiments proper to the present crisis: a sermon . . . Author, 1803. LEE

C581 HALL, Robert, fl. 1854. Mettray. A lecture read before the Leeds philosophical and literary society. Cash, 1854. HU

C582 HAMEL, Joseph von, c. 1788–1862. (1818) L'enseignement mutuel; ou, histoire de l'introduction et de la propagation de cette méthode par les soins du docteur Bell, de J. Lancaster et d'autres; description détaillée de son application dans les écoles élémentaires d'Angleterre et de France . . . Traduit de l'allemand. Paris, Colas, 1818. HU

C583 HAMILTON, Elizabeth, 1758–1816. (1808) The cottagers of Glenburnie; a tale for the farmer's ingle-nook. 8th ed., Edinburgh, R. Miller, 1828. HU

C584 HAMILTON, Elizabeth. (1815) Hints addressed to the patrons and directors of schools; principally intended to shew that the benefits derived from the new modes of teaching may be increased by a partial adoption of the plan of Pestalozzi . . . Longman, 1815. HU

C585 HAMILTON, Elizabeth. (1806) Letters, addressed to the daughters of a nobleman, on the formation of religious and moral principle. Cadell & Davies, 1806. 2 vols. LEI

C586 HAMILTON, Elizabeth. (1801) Letters on the elementary principles of education. 2nd ed., 1801. 2 vols. ReU; 3rd ed., Robinson, 1803. 2 vols. BI LEE LEI SH; 5th ed., with additional matter, Wilkie & Robinson, 1810. 2 vols. HU LO; 7th ed., Longman, [etc.], 1824. 2 vols. OX

C587 HAMILTON, Elizabeth. A series of popular essays illustrative of principles essentially connected with the improvement of the understanding, the imagination and the heart. Edinburgh, Manners & Miller, 1813. 2 vols. BI

C588 HAMILTON, Henry Parr, 1794–1880. (1848) The Church and the education question: with reference more especially to the teaching of the catechism to the children of dissenters. A letter to the Lord Bishop of Ripon. 2nd ed., London, Groombridge; Salisbury, Brown; 1855. HU

C589 HAMILTON, H. P. The Privy Council and the National Society: the question concerning the management of Church of England schools stated and examined. J. W. Parker, 1850. HU LEE

C590 HAMILTON, James, 1769–1829. The history, principles, practice and results of the Hamiltonian system for the last twelve years ... with instructions for the use of the books published on this system. Manchester, T. Sowler, pr., 1829. MA

C591 HAMILTON, James, *curate of St. Mary's, Leeds.* Can the Church accept the government plan of education? A letter to the Rev. Dr. Hook. Rivington, 1847. HU

C592 HAMILTON, James Alexander, 1785–1845. An introduction to choral-singing; particularly as adapted to church psalmody ... etc., familiarly explained and illustrated by way of question and answer. Designed for the use of all persons engaged in teaching children and adults to sing in classes on the modern system. D'Almaine, [pref. 1841]. LEI

C593 HAMILTON, Richard Winter, 1794–1848. (1845) The institutions of popular education. An essay: to which the Manchester prize was adjudged. Hamilton, Adams, 1845. LEE LEI LO; 2nd ed., J. Y. Knight, 1846. BR HU ReU

C594 HAMILTON, *Sir* William, 1788–1856. (1852) Discussions on philosophy and literature, education and university reform. Chiefly from the Edinburgh review [1831–1836]; corrected, vindicated, enlarged ... Longman, [etc.], 1852. BR LO; 2nd ed., Longman, [etc.], 1853. LO; 3rd ed., Edinburgh, [etc.]. Blackwood, 1866. HU LEI

HAMPTON, John Somerset Pakington, *baron. See* Pakington, J. S.

C595 HANSON, James. Observations on the education controversy and an examination of the political arguments. Huddersfield, Examiner office, 1852. BR

C596 [HARE, Augustus William], 1792–1834. (1822) A letter to Daniel K. Sandford ... in answer to the strictures of the Edinburgh review on the open colleges of Oxford. By a member of a close college. Oxford, Parker, 1822. LEI

C597 HARE, John Middleton. An analysis and exposure of the new government scheme of education ... Snow, 1847. LEE

C598 HARFORD, John Scandrett, 1785–1866. The life of Thomas Burgess ... late Lord Bishop of Salisbury. Longman, 1840. BR

C599 HARPER, Alfred, *ed.* History of the Cheltenham grammar school. Cheltenham, Free press office, 1851. BR

C600 HARPER, Alfred, *ed.* History of the Cheltenham grammar school from its remodelling under the Chancery deed of 1851, as collected from newspaper reports. Cheltenham, Harper, 1856. BI LO

C601 HARRISON, George. Some remarks relative to the present state of education, in the Society of the people called Quakers. Darton & Harvey, 1802. BI

C602 HARROW GAZETTE. One of our great public schools [Harrow]. [Harrow, Harrow, pr.], 1867. [*From* Harrow gazette, Sept. 2, 1867.] BI

C603 HARROW SCHOOL. Examination papers, [1849–1851]. Harrow, [1852]. LO

C604 [HARROW SCHOOL. MS. lists of pupils, *c.* 1801, *c.* 1810, and *c.* 1815.] HU

C605 HARROW SCHOOL. Prolusiones praemiis anniversariis dignatae et in auditorio recitatae Scholae Harroviensis, VI.Kal.Jul.MDCCCLI. Harrow, J. S. Crossley, [1851]. LEI

C606 HARTFORD. American asylum. 21st report of the directors of the American asylum at Hartford, for the education and instruction of the deaf and dumb. Hartford, 1837. LO

C607 HATFIELD, S., *Miss.* (1803) Letters on the importance of the female sex; with observations on their manners, and on education ... J. Adlard, 1803. LO; 3rd ed., J. Adlard, pr., 1807. LEI

C608 HAUGHTON, Samuel, 1821–1897. University education in Ireland. Williams & Norgate, 1868. LEE

C609 HAUREAU, Jean Barthélémy, 1812–1896. (1850) De la philosophie scolastique. Tome première. Paris, Paguerre, 1850. LO

C610 [HAWKSLEY, Thomas]. (1869) Education and training considered as a subject for state legislation; with suggestions for making a compulsory law efficient and acceptable. By a physician. Re-issue. To which is added, tracts on the charities of London and on self-supporting industrial schools. Churchill, 1869. LEE

C611 [HAWTREY, Stephen Thomas]. A letter, containing an account of St. Mark's School, Windsor, and embodying some suggestions on the subject of education. Windsor, W. Whittington, pr., 1857. HU

C612 HAWTREY, S. T. A narrative essay on a liberal education, chiefly embodied in the account of an attempt to give a liberal education to children of the working classes, [at St. Mark's School, Windsor]. Hamilton, Adams, 1868. LO

C613 HAWTREY, S. T. (1867) Reminiscences of a French Eton. Rickerby, 1867. SH; 2nd ed., Rickerby, 1867. LEE LEI LO

C614 HAY, John Barras, *comp.* Inaugural addresses by Lords Rectors of the University of Glasgow; to which are prefixed an historical sketch and account of the present state of the university. Glasgow, D. Robertson, 1830. BR

C615 HEATHCOTE, Gilbert. An address to the principal farmers, churchwardens, and overseers, of small towns and country villages, on the subject of introducing Dr. Bell's system of instruction into their respective parishes. [Taken from 'Suggestions to the promoters of Dr. Bell's system of instruction', by Frederic Iremonger. 1813.] LO; *see also* C705. Iremonger, F.

C616 HECKER, John. The scientific basis of education, demonstrated by an analysis of the temperaments and of phrenological facts, in connection with mental phenomena and the office of the Holy Spirit in the processes of the mind ... 2nd ed., N.Y., Author, 1868. LEI

C617 HEINROTH, Johann Christian Friedrich August. On education and self-formation, based upon physical, intellectual, moral and religious principles. A. Schloss, 1838. HU

C618 HENLEY, Joseph Warner, 1793–1884. (1855) Speech in the House of Commons on moving that the bill for the better promoting national education be read this day six months. J. Masters, 1855. BR

HENNESSY, *Sir* John Pope. *See* Pope-Hennessy, *Sir* J.

C619 HENRY, Caleb Sprague, 1804–1844, *trans*. Elements of psychology, by Victor Cousin. *See* C324 Cousin, V.

C620 HEPPE, Heinrich. Das Schulwesen des Mittelalters und dessen Reform in sechszehnten Jahrhundert... Marburg, Elwert, 1860. LEI

C621 HERAUD, John Abraham, 1799–1887. Prize essay. *See* C242 Central society of education

C622 HERBART, Johann Friedrich, 1776–1841. Principales oeuvres pédagogiques; traduites et fondues en un seul volume par A. Pinloche. Paris, Alcan, 1894. SO

C623 HERBART, J. F. Vollständige Darstellung der Lehre Herbarts. Langensalza, Greszler, 1887. LO

C624 HERBART, J. F. ABC of sense perception; and minor pedagogical works; translated with introduction, notes and commentary by William J. Eckoff. N.Y., Appleton, 1896. BR

C625 HERBART, J. F. (1806) Allgemeine Pädagogik aus dem Zweck der Erziehung abgeleitet. Göttingen, J. F. Röwer, 1806. LO

C626 HERBART, J. F. do. Mit Vorwort von Herman Nohl. Berlin, Beltz, n.d. SO

C627 HERBART, J. F. do. Herausgegeben von Theodor Fritzsch. Leipzig, Reclam, [1902]. HU

C628 HERBART, J. F. [do.] The science of education: its general principles deduced from its aim... Translated from the German by Henry M. and Emmie Felkin... Sonnenschein, 1892. LEE LO; 2nd ed., Sonnenschein, 1897. BR HU LO NE RE SH; 3rd ed., Sonnenschein, 1904. BI LEI RE

C629 HERBART, J. F. Kurze Encyklopödie der Philosophie aus praktischen Gesichtspunkten. Halle, Schwetschke, 1831. LO

C630 HERBART, J. F. (1816) [Lehrbuch zur Psychologie.] A text-book in psychology: an attempt to found the science of psychology on experience, metaphysics, and mathematics; translated from the original German by Margaret K. Smith. N.Y., Appleton, 1891. LEI SO

C631 HERBART, J. F. Letters and Lectures on education. Translated... and edited with an introduction by Henry M. and Emmie Felkin. Sonnenschein, 1898. HU LO; Sonnenschein, 1901. NE SH; 4th ed., Sonnenschein, 1908. BR LEI RE SO

C632 HERBART, J. F. (1831) [Letters on] the application of psychology to the science of education. Translated and edited... by Beatrice C. Mulliner. Sonnenschein, 1898. HU LEI LO

C633 HERBART, J. F. (1839) Outlines of educational doctrine. Translated by A. F. Lange. Macmillan, 1901. LO RE; N.Y., Macmillan Co., 1909. LEI

C634 HERVEY, *Lord* Arthur Charles, 1808–1894. (1855) A suggestion for supplying the literary, scientific and mechanics' institutes of Great Britain and Ireland with lecturers from the universities. Cambridge, Macmillan; London, Bell & Daldy; 1855. LEI

C635 HEYWOOD, James. Academic reform: university representation. Whitfield, 1860. LO

C636 HIBERNICUS, *pseud*. How is Ireland to be regenerated? or, State education, *versus* ecclesiastical. Omagh, Tyrone constitution office, 1870. HU

C637 HICKSON, William Edward, 1803–1870. (1840) Dutch and German schools. An account of the present state of education in Holland, Belgium, and the German states. With a view to the practical steps which should be taken for improving and extending the means of popular instruction in Great Britain and Ireland. Taylor & Walton, 1840. HU LEI NO

C638 HIGGINSON, Edward, Prize essay. *See* C242 Central society of education

C639 HIGHMORE, Anthony, 1758–1829. Philanthropia Metropolitana; a view of the charitable institutions established in and near London, chiefly during the last twelve years. Longman, [etc.], 1822. NE

C640 HILL, Caroline Southwood. Memoranda of observations and experiments in education. Vizetelly, pr., [1865?] HU

C641 HILL, Florence Davenport. (1868) Children of the state: the training of juvenile paupers. Macmillan, 1868. HU; 2nd ed., rev. and enl. Edited by Fanny Fowke. Macmillan, 1889. CA LEI

C642 HILL, Frederic. (1836) National education: its present state and prospects. Vol. 1 [only]. Knight, 1836. LEE

C643 HILL, Matthew Davenport, 1792–1872. (1860) Charge delivered to the grand jury of [Birmingham] at the Michaelmas quarter sessions, 1860. Bristol, Arrowsmith, pr., 1860. HU

C644 [HILL, M. D.] (1822) Plans for the government and liberal instruction of boys, in large numbers; drawn from experience. Whittaker, 1822. LEE ReU

C645 HILL, M. D. The Recorder of Birmingham: a memoir of... by Rosamund and Florence Davenport Hill, with selections from his correspondence. Macmillan, 1878. HU LEI SH

C646 HILL, M. D. (1863) Reformatory treatment defended; a paper... read at a general meeting of the Society for promoting the amendment of the law... 1863. Newton, The Society, 1863. BI

C647 HILL, Micaiah. Prize essay. *See* C1440 Two prize essays on juvenile delinquency

C648 HILL-TOP SCHOOL, *Birmingham*. Exercises in reading and recitation; performed by the pupils... Birmingham, [The School], 1815. 3 vols. in 1. BI

C649 HINTON, John Howard, 1791–1873. (1852) The case of the Manchester educationists: a review of the evidence taken before a committee of the House of Commons in relation to the state of education in Manchester and Salford. Snow, 1852. HU

Hints for the improvement of early education. *See* Hoare, Louisa

C650 HINTS on district visiting societies; a plan for their formation, and suggestions to visitors, with an appendix. Longman, [etc.], 1836. LEI

C651 HINTS to parents. (1823–1827) Hints to parents, on the cultivation of children in the spirit of Pestalozzi's method. Nos. 1–6 [various eds.]. Harvey & Darton, 1826–1827. HU; 1827. LEE; 1827–1831. LEI; Nos. 1–4, 1824–1825. ReU [1st ed. had title: Hints to mothers.]

Hints towards forming the character of a young princess. *See* More, Hannah

C652 HISTORY and description of the public charities in the town of Frome: containing a copy of the report of the [Charity] Commissioners . . . 1820 . . . notes from Crocker's historical account of the same charities, and an appendix . . . Frome, W. P. Penny, 1833. BR

C653 HISTORY of the Society for promoting female education in the East, established in the year 1834. [Preface by B. W. Noel.] E. Suter, 1847. LEI

C654 HISTORY of the South Leith Sabbath evening school: intended as a practical illustration of the utility and advantages of similar institutions. By the author of 'Advice to the young at the outset of life'. Edinburgh, J. T. Smith, [1827]. HU

C655 [HOARE, Louisa]. (1819) Hints for the improvement of early education and nursery discipline. 2nd ed., Hatchard, 1819. HU LEI; 5th ed., 1820. HU LEE; 7th ed., 1822. ReU; 8th ed., 1824. BI LEE LO; 11th ed., 1831. BI; 12th ed., 1834. BR; 14th ed., 1841. LI; 15th ed., 1846. SH

C656 [HOARE, Louisa]. Essai sur l'éducation de l'enfance. 1837. *See* C782 Larive-Dupas, M.

HOCKERILL. Training institution. *See* Rochester. Diocese. Training institution, Hockerill

C657 HODGSON, J. S. (1839) Considerations on phrenology, in connexion with an intellectual, moral, and religious education. Parker, 1839. LEI

C658 [HODGSON, William Ballantyne], 1815–1880. 'Classical' instruction: its use and abuse. Reprinted from the 'Westminster review' for October 1853. J. Chapman, 1854. HU

C659 HODGSON, W. B. (1864) The education of girls; and the employment of women of the upper classes educationally considered: two lectures. 2nd ed., Trubner, 1869. BI

C660 HODGSON, W. B. On the importance of the study of economic science. [*In* Royal Institution. Lectures on education. 1854.] *See* C1252

C661 HÖLDERLIN, Friedrich, 1770–1843. Briefe zur Erziehung, zusammengestellt von K. Lothar Wolf. [From Hyperion, 1797–1799, and Letters to his brother written 1796–1801.] Marburg, Simons, 1950. LEI

C662 HOLDSWORTH, W. A. (1870) The Elementary education act, 1870, popularly explained: together with the various orders in council issued by the Education Department. Routledge, 1870. LO

C663 HOLE, James. (1860) Light more light: on the present state of education amongst the working classes of Leeds, and how it can best be improved. Longman, 1860. LEE

C664 HOLE, James. (1863) The working classes of Leeds: an essay on the present state of education in Leeds, and the best means of improving it. Simpkin, Marshall, 1863. ReU; 2nd ed., Simpkin, Marshall, 1863. LEE

C665 HOLLAND, Henry Wilkinson. (1870) Proposed national arrangements for primary education. Longmans, [etc.], 1870. HU LEE SH; 3rd ed., Longmans, 1870. LO

C666 HOLTZENDORFF, *baron* Franz von, 1829–1889. The Irish convict system, more especially intermediate prisons. Translated from the German. Dublin, W. B. Kelly, 1860. HU

C667 HOME AND COLONIAL SCHOOL SOCIETY. Manual for infant schools and nurseries. Prepared . . . by Rebecca Sunter . . . under the direction of Miss Mayo . . . The Society, 1856. HU

C667a HOME AND COLONIAL SCHOOL SOCIETY. Pestalozzi and his principles. 2nd ed., The Society, 1864. LO

C668 HOME AND COLONIAL SCHOOL SOCIETY. Quarterly educational magazine. *See* C1181 Quarterly educational magazine

Home education. *See* Taylor, Isaac, 1787–1865

C669 HOME. (1854) A home for the outcast; or, Vagrant orphan asylum (No. 95a, Berwick St., Oxford St.): its origin, progress, and prospects. By a member of the committee. 4th ed., Hatchard, 1854. HU

C670 HOOK, Walter Farquhar, 1798–1875. (1846) On the means of rendering more efficient the education of the people: a letter to the Lord Bishop of St. David's. 4th ed., Murray, 1846. HU; 7th ed., 1846. LEE; 9th ed., 1846. LEE SH; 11th ed., Edinburgh, Black; London, Murray; 1850. LEI

HOPE, Alexander James Beresford. *See* Beresford-Hope, A. J.

C671 HOPLEY, Thomas. Bodily exercise (continued): the third of a series of plain and simple lectures on the education of man. Houlston & Wright, 1858. BR

C672 HOPLEY, Thomas. An introductory lecture on education: being the first of a series of plain and simple lectures on the education of man. 2nd ed., Churchill, 1856. HU

C673 HOPLEY, Thomas. (1854) A lecture on respiration: being the sixth of a series of . . . lectures . . . Churchill, 1854. BR

C674 HORNER, Leonard, 1785–1864, *trans.* (1838) On the state of education in Holland . . . by Victor Cousin. Translated with preliminary observations on the necessity of legislative measures, to extend and improve education among the working classes and the poor in Great Britain. Murray, 1838. BI LEI LO SH

C675 Hort, Fenton John Anthony, 1828-1892. (1862) Thoughts on the Revised code of education, its purpose and probable effects. Cambridge, Macmillan, 1862. BI LEE NE

C678 Hoskins, G. A. What shall we do with our criminals? With an account of the prison of Valencia and the penitentiary of Mettray. Ridgway, 1853. HU

Houghton, Richard Monckton Milnes, *baron. See* Milnes, R. M.

How can the Church educate the people? *See* Mathison, Gilbert Farquhar

C679 How is Ireland to be regenerated? Or, state education *versus* ecclesiastical. By Hibernicus. Omagh, Tyrone constitution office, pr., 1870. HU

Howard, George William Frederick, *7th earl of Carlisle. See* Carlisle, *earl of*

C680 Howitt, William, 1792-1879. Life in Germany; or, scenes, impressions and every-day life of the Germans, including . . . students of the universities. Routledge, 1849. LO

C681 Huber, Victor Aimé, 1800-1869. (Germ. 1838; Eng. 1843) The English universities. An abridged translation, edited by Francis W. Newman. Pickering, 1843. 2 vols. in 3. BI LEI LO SH

C682 Hudson, James William. (1851) The history of adult education, in which is comprised a full and complete history of the mechanics' and literary institutions, athenaeums . . . of Great Britain, Ireland, America, etc., Longmans, [etc.], 1851. HU LO

C683 Hughes, Thomas Smart, 1786-1847. (1827) A sermon preached on . . . April 29, 1826, at Bury Saint Edmund's, on behalf of the charity schools established in that town. Rivington, 1827. ReU

C684 Hughes, William, *F.R.G.S.* (1847) Remarks on geography as a branch of popular education, chiefly with reference to the principles upon which it should be taught in normal schools. 2nd impression. Author, 1851. LEE

C685 Hull Ragged and Industrial Schools. First annual report: together with a report of the proceedings at the first annual meeting of the friends and supporters . . . February 27, 1850. Hull, T. Freebody, pr., 1850. [Photostat copy.] HU

C686 Hullah, John Pyke, 1812-1884. (1841) Wilhem's method of teaching singing, adapted to English use, under the superintendence of the Committee of Council on Education. Revised and reconstructed in 1849. J. W. Parker, 1853. LEI; Parker, 1854. SO

C687 Hulsebos, Gerardus Assisus. Disputatio antiquaria inauguralis de educatione et institutione apud Romanos . . . Utrecht, Kemink, 1867. LO

C688 [Hume, Mary C., *aft.* Hume-Rothery]. (1862) Brief comments on the revised speech of the Rt. Hon. Robert Lowe, M.P., on the Revised code . . . in the House of Commons, February 13, 1862. Hatchard, 1862. BI HU

C689 [Hume, M. C.] Suggestions for a scheme of annual school-grants to be made in a single payment to school managers by the Committee of Council . . . Clowes, 1862. HU

Hume-Rothery, Mary C. *See* Hume, Mary C.

C690 [Humphreys, Edward Rupert]. (1856) England's educational crisis: a letter addressed to Viscount Palmerston, by the head master of an English grammar school. T. Bosworth, 1856. BI HU

Hunter, Agnes Sophia, *aft.* Semple. *See* Semple, A. S.

C691 Husenbeth, Frederick Charles, 1796-1872. The history of Sedgley Park School, Staffordshire. Richardson, 1856. ReU

C692 Hussey, Robert, 1801-1856. A letter to Thomas Dyke Acland . . . on the system of education, to be established in the diocesan schools for the middle classes. Rivington, 1839. HU

C693 Hutchesons School, *Glasgow.* (1867) An account of Hutchesons School since . . . its foundation in 1641 to the present time, submitted for the general information of the patrons . . . Glasgow, Bell & Bain, 1867. LEI

C694 Hutchinson, *Mrs.* E. G. The early education of children, and the effects of home influence on the work of the teacher. Darton, 1854. LEE

C695 Huxley, Thomas Henry, 1825-1895. (1854) On the educational value of the natural history sciences. Van Voorst, 1854. LEE LEI SH

C696 Infant education from two to six years of age. Chambers, 1836. (Chambers's educational course.) ReU

Infant training. *See* Stow, David

C697 Ingham, T. Hastings. (1855) Reformatory schools: report of a speech delivered at the quarter sessions of the peace for the West-Riding, holden at Pontefract, 2nd April, 1855. Skipton, J. Tasker, 1855. HU

C698 Inglis, *Sir* Robert Harry, 1786-1855. Observations on grammar schools. 1840. ReU

C699 Institution for Promoting the British System of Education. (1813) Address of the committee of the Institution . . . Also the report of the finance committee and trustees . . . R. & A. Taylor, 1813. BR

Institution for Promoting the British System of Education. *See also* British and Foreign School Society; Royal Lancasterian Institution

Institution for the Education of Deaf and Dumb Children, *Edinburgh. See* Edinburgh. Institution for the education of deaf and dumb children

C701 Ipswich Dormitory and School of Industry. 2nd annual report, October 20th, 1853. Ipswich, Cowell, 1853. HU

C702 Ireland, John, 1761-1842. A letter to Henry Brougham, Esq., M.P. Murray, 1818. LO

C703 Iremonger, Frederic. (1818) Dr. Bell's system of instruction, broken into short questions and answers for the use of masters and teachers in the National schools . . . Rivington, 1821. LO; New ed., Rivington, 1825. LEI; 2nd ed., Rivington, 1835. RE; new ed., S.P.C.K., 1840. HU

C704 Iremonger, Frederic. (4th ed., 1821) Questions for the different elementary books used in the National schools. 5th ed., Rivington for S.P.C.K., 1826. LEI; new ed., S.P.C.K., 1842. HU

C705 IREMONGER, Frederic. (1813) Suggestions to the promoters of Dr. Bell's system of tuition: with an account of the Hampshire Society for the education of the poor... Winchester, Jacob; London, Longmans; 1813. NO ReU

C706 [IRISH QUARTERLY REVIEW]. Appendix to record. From *Meliora*, for April, 1859. [Account of the work of the Rev. John Clay at Preston prison.] HU

C707 IRISH SABBATH SCHOOL MAGAZINE; or literary and religious intelligencer. Vol. 1, nos. 1–12, Oct. 1832–Sept. 1833. BR

ISTRIA, Joannes Capo d'. *See* Capo d'Istria, J.

C708 ITARD, Jean E. Marie Gaspard [*otherwise* Jean-Marc-Gaspard], 1775–1838. (Fr. 1801; Eng. 1802) An historical account of the discovery and education of a savage man, or of the first developments, physical and moral, of the young savage, caught in the woods near Aveyron, in the year 1798. R. Phillips, 1802. HU

C709 ITARD, J. E. M. G. (1801–1806) The wild boy of Aveyron (Rapports et mémoires sur le sauvage de l'Aveyron). Translated by G. & M. Humphrey... N.Y. and London, Century Co., 1932. LEI

C710 JACKSON, John, 1811–1885. (1849) The gospel the salvation of the lost. A sermon preached in the Philanthropic Society's chapel, St. George's Fields, on Sunday, 28th October, 1849... Reigate, Wm. Allingham, 1849. HU

C711 JACKSON, Samuel, 1787–1861, *trans.* (1837) The life of Augustus Herman Francke... by H. E. F. Guerike. Seeley & Burnside, 1837. LEI

C712 JACOTOT, H. V. Disciplina universalis: Ars medica: anatomia. Louvain, Michel, 1825. HU

C713 JACOTOT, Jean Joseph, 1770–1840. Discours prononcé à l'occasion de l'installation de l'école normale d'enseignement universel pour l'armée. Le 22 octobre 1827. Louvain, H. de Pauw, [1827?]. HU

C714 JACOTOT, J. J. (1823) Manuel de l'enseignement universel, extrait de l'ouvrage du fondateur sur la langue maternelle. Par un maître d'enseignement universel. Louvain, H. de Pauw, 1826. HU

C715 JAMES, George Payne Rainsford, 1799–1860. On the educational institutions of Germany. Saunders & Otley, 1835. LEE

C716 JAMESON, *Mrs.* Anna Brownell, *form.* Murphy, 1794–1860. Characteristics of women, moral, poetical, and historical. Saunders & Otley, 1832. 2 vols. LO

C717 JARDINE, George, 1742–1827. (1818) Outlines of philosophical education, illustrated by the method of teaching the logic class in the University of Glasgow... 2nd ed., enl., Glasgow, Oliver & Boyd, 1825. LEI

C718 JARROLD, Thomas, 1770–1853. (1836) Instinct and reason, philosophically investigated; with a view to ascertain the principles of the science of education. Longman, [etc.], 1736 [i.e. 1836]. LEI

C719 JEX-BLAKE, Sophia, 1840–1912. (1867) A visit to some American schools and colleges. Macmillan, 1867. BI LEE SH

C720 JOHNSON, James. Transactions of the Corporation of the Poor in the city of Bristol: during the period of 126 years... Bristol, P. Rose, 1826. BR

C721 [JOHNSON, W.] Thoughts on education: an address delivered to the friends and supporters of Llandaff-House Academy, Regent Street, Cambridge. London, Simpkin, Marshall; Cambridge, Stevenson; 1830. LEI

C722 JOHNSTON, David, *M.D.* (1827) A general view of the present system of public education in France, and of the laws, regulations, and courses of study in... the Royal University of that kingdom: preceded by a short history of the University of Paris before the Revolution. Edinburgh, Oliver & Boyd, 1827. HU LEI

JONES, Harry Longueville, *joint author*. *See* Wright, Thomas, and Jones, H. L.

C723 [JOWETT, Benjamin], 1817–1893, and [STANLEY, Arthur Penrhyn], 1815–1881. Suggestions for an improvement of the examination statute. Oxford, Macpherson, 1848. HU

JOYCE, Jeremiah, 1763–1816, *joint author*. *See* Shepherd, William *and others*

C724 JOYCE, Patrick Weston, 1827–1914. (1863) A handbook of school management and methods of teaching. 2nd ed., rev. and enl., Dublin, McGlashan & Gill; London, Simpkin, Marshall; 1864. LEI; 3rd ed., Dublin, McGlashan & Gill, 1867. BI

C725 JULLIEN, Marc Antoine, 1775–1848. (1824) Coup d'oeil sur les progrès des connaissances humaines en 1824. Paris, Imprimerie de Rignoux, 1824. LO

C726 JULLIEN, M. A. (1812) Esprit de la méthode d'éducation de Pestalozzi, suivie et pratiquée dans l'institut d'éducation d'Yverdun, en Suisse... Milan, Imprimerie Royale, 1812. BR HU LO ReU

C727 JULLIEN, M. A. Exposé de la méthode d'éducation de Pestalozzi... 2d éd., Paris, Hachette, 1842. [2nd ed. of the above.] BI LO

C728 JULLIEN, M. A. (1821) Esquisse d'un plan de lectures historiques, rapporté spécialement à l'influence des femmes. Paris, Revue Encyclopédique, 1821. LO

C729 JULLIEN, M. A. (1817) Esquisse et vues préliminaires d'un ouvrage sur l'éducation comparée... et séries de questions sur l'éducation... Paris, L. Colas, [etc.], 1817. [Fascimile reprint published by Bureau international d'éducation, Geneva, 1962.] HU LEI

C730 JULLIEN, M. A. do. [Xerographic copy from *Journal d'éducation* [Paris], IIe année, décembre 1817, janvier–février 1818, by University Microfilms, 1961.] BI HU LEE LO

C731 JULLIEN, M. A. Jullien's Plan for comparative education, 1816–1817. [Edited and translated by] Stewart Fraser. N.Y., Columbia Univ. Teachers Coll., 1964. LEI

C732 JULLIEN, M. A. (1808) Essai générale d'éducation physique, morale et intellectuelle, suivi d'un plan d'éducation pratique pour l'enfance, l'adolescence, et la jeunesse. Paris, Firmin Didot, 1808. LO

C733 JULLIEN, M. A. (1808) Essai sur l'emploi du tems . . . destinée spécialement à l'usage des jeunes gens de 15 à 25 ans. 2e éd., Paris, Firmin Didot, 1810. LO

C734 JULLIEN, M. A. (1833) Lettre à la nation anglaise, sur l'union des peuples, et la civilisation comparée, sur l'instrument économique du tems, appelé biomètre, ou montre morale; etc. Londres, Bossange, Barthès & Lowell, 1833. LO

Juvenile delinquency, its causes and cure. *See* Barclay, Hugh

C735 KANT, Immanuel, 1724–1804. (1803) [Ueber Pädagogik.] The educational theory of . . . Translated and edited with an introduction by E. F. Buchner. Philadelphia, Lippincott, 1903. LEE; 1908. LO SH

C736 KANT, Immanuel. [do.] Kant on education. Translated by Annette Churton. Kegan Paul, 1899. BR LEE LEI LO ReU SH SO; Ann Arbor, Michigan U.P., 1960. CA

C737 KAVANAGH, James W. Mixed education: 'the Catholic case' and its Catholic advocate vindicated. [Dublin], Mullany, 1859. SH

KAY, James Phillips, *aft.* Kay-Shuttleworth. *See* Kay-Shuttleworth, *Sir* J. P.

C738 KAY, Joseph, 1821-1878. (1846) The education of the poor in England and Europe. Hatchard, 1846. BI HU LEI ReU

C739 KAY, Joseph. (1850) The social condition and education of the people in England and Europe: shewing the results of the primary schools . . . in foreign countries . . . Longman, [etc.], 1850. 2 vols. HU LEE LEI NE SH; vol. 2 [only]. BI NO; N.Y., Harper, 1863. BR

C740 KAY-SHUTTLEWORTH, *Sir* James Phillips, 1804–1877. The autobiography of . . . Edited [from the MS.] by B. C. Bloomfield. Univ. of London Inst. of ed., 1964. (Education libraries bulletin, supplement 7.) ALL LIBS.

C741 KAY-SHUTTLEWORTH, *Sir* J. P. (1862) Four periods of public education, as reviewed in 1832 – 1839 – 1846 – 1862 . . . Longman, 1862. BR LEI ReU SH SO. [Includes a reprint of his 'The moral and physical condition of the working classes of Manchester in 1832'.]

C742 KAY-SHUTTLEWORTH, *Sir* J. P. (1861) Letter to Earl Granville, K.G., on the Revised code of regulations contained in the Minute of the Committee of Council on Education dated July 29th, 1861. Smith, Elder, 1861. HU LEE NE; [Manchester, Cave & Sever,] 1861. BI

C743 KAY-SHUTTLEWORTH, *Sir* J. P. (1868) Memorandum on popular education. Ridgway, [1868]. HU

C744 KAY-SHUTTLEWORTH, *Sir* J. P. (Written 1841) On the punishment of pauper children in workhouses. [From the MS.] College of S. Mark and S. John, 1961. HU LEI LI LO RE SH

C745 KAY-SHUTTLEWORTH, *Sir* J. P. (1835) Public education as affected by the minutes of the Committee of Privy Council from 1846 to 1852; with suggestions as to future policy. Longman, [etc.], 1853. BI BR HU LEE LEI NE NO RE ReU SH

C746 [KAY-SHUTTLEWORTH, *Sir* J. P.] (1839) Recent measures for the promotion of education in England. Ridgway, 1839. HU; 4th ed., 1839. LEI; 6th ed., 1839. BI BR NE; 8th ed., 1839. SH

C748 [KAY-SHUTTLEWORTH, *Sir* J. P.] (1847) The school in its relations to the state, the church, and the congregation. Being an explanation of the minutes of the Committee of Council on Education, in August and December, 1846. Murray, 1847. BI HU LEE LEI LO NE ReU

C749 KAY-SHUTTLEWORTH, *Sir* J. P. The training of pauper children: a report published by the Poor Law Commissioners in their fourth annual report. Clowes, 1839. LEE

C750 [KEBLE, John], 1792–1866. (1846) Lyra innocentium: thoughts in verse on Christian children, their ways, and their privileges. Oxford, Parker, 1846. LEE; 3rd ed., Oxford, Parker, 1846. LEI

C751 KELLAND, Philip, 1808–1879. (1870) The Scottish school system suited to the people: an introductory lecture to the class of mathematics in the University of Edinburgh, Nov. 2, 1870. Edinburgh, Black, 1870. BR

C752 KELLY, Sophia, *form.* Sherwood, *ed.* (1854) The life of Mrs. Sherwood, chiefly autobiographical, with extracts from Mr. Sherwood's journal; edited by her daughter, Sophia Kelly. Darton, 1854. LEI ReU; Darton, 1857. SH

C753 KENDALL, Henry Edward. (1847) Designs for schools and school-houses, parochial and national. Williams, 1847. LEI

C754 KENNEDY, Benjamin Hall, 1804–1889. Ministerial scheme of national education. [Oxford, 1839.] [Reprint of a letter from the Salopian journal.] HU

C755 [KER, Charles Henry Bellenden], 1785?–1871. A vindication of the enquiry into charitable abuses, with an exposure of the misrepresentations contained in the 'Quarterly Review'. Longman, 1819. HU

C756 KER, John Bellenden, *form.* Gawler. An essay on the archaeology of popular English phrases and nursery rhymes. Southampton, Fletcher, 1834. BR

C757 KILGOUR, Alexander. Mechanics' institutions; what they are, and how they may be made, educationally and politically, more useful. London, Smith, Elder; Edinburgh, Sutherland & Knox; 1853. HU

Kindergarten and humanistic schools: a monthly paper. *See* Ronge, Johann & Bertha.

C758 KING, Benjamin. Poor rates reduced by self-supporting reading, writing and agricultural schools, and by the allotment system under regulations. [Hodson, 1844.] BI

C759 KINGSLEY, Charles, 1819–1875. (1869) An address on education, read before the National association for the promotion of social science, at Bristol . . . 1869. Victoria Pr., 1869. LO

C760 KINKER, J. Rapport sur la méthode de Mr. Jacotot, présenté au Département de l'Intérieur, le 8 septembre 1826. Liège, F. D. Boubers, [1826?]. HU

C761 KINGSTON, William Henry Giles, 1814–1880. (1867) Infant amusements; or, how to make a nursery happy. With practical hints to parents and nurses on the moral and physical training of children. Griffith & Farran, 1867. HU LEI

C762 KNIGHT, Samuel, 1675–1746. (1724) The life of Dr. John Colet, dean of S. Paul's . . . and founder of S. Paul's school . . . 2nd ed., Oxford, Clarendon Pr., 1823. BR RE SH

C763 KNOX, Vicesimus, 1752–1821. (1778–1779) Essays, moral and literary. 16th ed., Mawman, [etc.], 1808. 3 vols. HU

C764 KNOX, Vicesimus. (1820) Remarks on the tendency of certain clauses in a bill now pending in Parliament to degrade grammar schools; with cursory strictures on the national importance of preserving inviolate the classical discipline prescribed by their founders. 2nd ed., corr., 1821. (The Pamphleteer, v. 19.) HU

C765 LACROIX, Sylvestre-François, 1765–1843. (1805) Essais sur l'enseignement en général, et sur celui des mathématiques en particulier. 2e éd., rev. and corr., Paris, Courcier, 1816. LEI

C766 LAGARMITTE, Henri. De l'instruction publique, et des réformes proposées par M. Guizot. [Revue encyclopédique, tome lvii, janvier 1833, p. 1–53.] LO

C767 LALOR, John, 1814–1856. Prize essay. *See* C242 Central society of education

C768 LANCASHIRE PUBLIC SCHOOL ASSOCIATION. National education, not necessarily governmental, sectarian or irreligious; shown in a series of papers read at the meetings . . . Gilpin, 1850. BI

C769 [LANCASTER, Joseph], 1778–1838. (1809) An account of the progress of Joseph Lancaster's plan for the education of poor children and the training of masters for country schools. J. Lancaster, [1809?]. LO

C770 LANCASTER, Joseph. (1810) The British system of education: being a complete epitome of the improvements and inventions practised at the Royal Free Schools, Borough-road, Southwark. Southwark, Author, 1810. BR HU ReU; Author and Longman, 1810. LEE

C771 LANCASTER, Joseph. (1811) Hints and directions for building, fitting up, and arranging school-rooms on the British system of education . . . Author, 1811. HU LEE

C772 LANCASTER, Joseph. (1803) Improvements in education as it respects the industrious classes of the community . . . 2nd ed., 1803. ReU; 3rd ed., with additions. Darton & Harvey, 1805. HU LO NE RE SH; 4th ed., Author, 1806. BI LEE LEI NE NO; 5th ed., Author, 1806. CA; 6th ed., Author, 1806. SO; Abridged ed., Author, 1808. LEI NE RE ReU

C773 LANCASTER, Joseph. The practical parts of Lancaster's 'Improvements' and Bell's 'Experiment'; edited by D. Salmon. C.U.P., 1932. BI LEE LEI LO NE NO ReU SH

C774 LANCASTER, Joseph. (1810) Instructions for forming and conducting a society for the education of the children of the labouring classes of the people. 2nd ed., Author, 1810. LEE

C775 LANCASTER, Joseph. (1805) A letter to John Foster, Esq., Chancellor of the Exchequer for Ireland, on the best means of educating and employing the poor in that country. 1805. ReU

C776 LANCASTER, Joseph. (1816) Oppression and persecution; or, a narrative of a variety of singular facts . . . in the rise, progress, and promulgation of the Royal Lancasterian system of education . . . Bristol, John Evans, 1816. HU

C777 LANCASTER, Joseph. (1811) Report of J. Lancaster's progress from the year 1798, with the report of the finance committee for the year 1810, to which is prefixed an address of the committee for the Royal Lancasterian system . . . Author, 1811. BR ReU

C778 LANCASTER, Joseph. [Review of Lancaster's Outlines of a plan for educating ten thousand poor children.] London, 1806. HU

C779 LANCASTER, Thomas William, 1787–1859. The alliance of education and civil government. Rivington, 1828. ReU

C780 LANSDOWNE, Henry Petty-Fitzmaurice, 3rd marquis of, 1780–1863. (1839) Substance of the Marquess of Lansdowne's speech in the House of Lords, July 5, 1839, on the government plan for promoting national education. Ridgway, 1839. HU SH

C781 LARDNER, Dionysius, 1793–1859. (1828) A discourse on the advantages of natural philosophy and astronomy as part of a general and professional education; being an introductory lecture delivered in the University of London . . . 1828. Taylor, 1828. LEI

C782 [LARIVE-DUPAS, Mathilde]. Essai sur l'éducation de l'enfance. Geneva, Cherbuliez, 1837. [Based on a translation of Louisa Hoare's 'Hints on education'.] LO

LASPÉE, Henry de. *See* De Laspée, H.

C783 LATHAM, Robert Gordon, 1812–1888. (1854) On the importance of the study of language as a branch of education for all classes: a lecture delivered at the Royal Institution of Great Britain . . . 1854. Parker, [1854?] NO; *see also* C1252 Royal Institution

C784 LAURIE, Simon Somerville, 1828–1909. (1867) Primary instruction in relation to education. Addressed to teachers in training. 5th ed., Edinburgh, Thin, 1898. LEI

C785 LAVALLÉE, Théophile. (1853) Histoire de la maison royale de Saint-Cyr, 1686–1793. Paris, Furne, 1853. LEI

C786 LAVALLÉE, Théophile. Madame de Maintenon et la maison royale de Saint-Cyr, 1686–1793. 2e éd., Paris, Plon, 1862. [2nd ed. of above.] BI

C786a LAVALLÉE, Théophile, *ed.* Lettres et entretiens de Mme. de Maintenon. *See* C830 Maintenon, *Mme.* de

C787 LAW MAGAZINE. The Birmingham conferences on the reformation of young criminals. [From the *Law Magazine*, no. CII.] [*c.* 1853.] HU

C788 LAW REVIEW. How should the child-criminal be treated? [From the *Law Review* for May 1853.] HU

LAWLESS, Valentine Browne, 2nd baron Cloncurry. *See* Cloncurry, *baron*

LAYMAN, A., *pseud. See* entries under the titles of the works

C789 LEAHY, Patrick, 1806–1875, and DERRY, John, *bp. of Clonfert.* Statement on the university question, addressed to the Catholic members of Parliament. Dublin, Fowler, 1868. NE

C790 LEE, Edwin, *trans.* The education of mothers of families, by Louis Aimé-Martin . . . Translated from the 3rd Paris edition, with remarks on the prevailing methods of education, and their influence upon health and happiness, by E. Lee. Whittaker, 1842. BI

C791 LEEDS. Free grammar school. (1845) Public examination, June, 1845. Leeds, Slocombe & Simms, 1845. LEE

LE FRANC, Jérôme, *pseud. See* Bellemare, Jean François

C792 LEICESTER LITERARY AND PHILOSOPHICAL SOCIETY. Report of the council presented to the annual general meeting . . . June 1855, and a selection of papers read before the society since its formation [1835]. Leicester, Crossley & Clarke, 1855. LEI

C793 LEIGH, William Henry, *baron.* The reformatory at Mettray: a letter from a visitor to that institution, addressed to a member of the committee of the Warwickshire Reformatory, November, 1855. [Clowes], 1856. BI

C794 LE KEUX, John Henry, 1812–1896, *illus.* (1841–1842) The universities: Le Keux's memorials of Cambridge. A series of views of the colleges, halls and public buildings. With historical and descriptive accounts by Thomas Wright and H. Longueville Jones. Tilt & Bogue, 1841–1842. 2 vols. LEE

C795 [LEMERCIER, Sarah S. A.], *ed.* Popular education in taste: the true resources and their development. A system proposed in extracts from a correspondence. Chapman & Hall, 1852. HU

Lessons on objects. *See* Mayo, Elizabeth

Letter containing an account of St. Mark's School, Windsor. *See* Hawtrey, Stephen T.

C796 LETTER. (1806) A letter respectfully addressed to the . . . archbishops and bishops of the Church of England on Mr. Joseph Lancaster's plan for the education of the lower order in the community. Stockdale, 1806. LO

Letter to Daniel K. Sandford. *See* Hare, Augustus William

Letter to Mr. Bryce on examinations for governesses. *See* Butler, Josephine E.

Letter to Philograntus. *See* Butler, Samuel

C798 LETTER to the Rev. Dr. Goodall, head master of Eton School; on the importance of a religious education. Stockdale, 1803. SH

C799 A LETTER to the Right Hon. Lord Stanley, on national education. By a clergyman of the Established Church. Duncan & Malcolm, 1839. HU LEE

Letters from Cambridge. *See* Appleyard, E. S.

Letters from Hofwyl. *See* Barwell, L. M.

C800 LETTRE à Monsieur Jacotot, inventeur de l'enseignement universel. Louvain, F. Michel, 1824. HU

C801 LEWISHAM. Colfe's grammar school. Bibliothecae Colfanae catalogue. *See* C131 Black, Wm. Henry

C802 LEWISHAM. do. Plan and terms of the Grammar School, Lewisham Hill, [by Dr. Prendergast]. [The School, 1831.] LO

C803 LLOYD, Richard, d. 1834. A letter to a member of Parliament, shewing . . . the serious and dangerous defects of the British and Foreign School, and of Mr. Brougham's bill (now pending) for the general education of the poor. Rivington, 1821. LO

C804 LONDON. Diocesan board of education. 4th [and] 5th reports, July 1844, July 1845. The Board, 1844–1845. LEE

C805 LONDON. Royal universal infirmary for children. Report for the year 1824 . . . to which are added, the rules and regulations, and a list of the directors and governors of the charity. Southwark, J. Robins, pr., 1825. LEI

LONDON. St. Paul's School. *See* St. Paul's School

C806 LONDON. University. *Graduates' committee.* Report to the graduates of the University of London, by their committee; September 1849. Reed & Pardon, [1849]. HU

C807 LONDON INSTITUTION. The charter and bye-laws of the London Institution for the advancement of literature and the diffusion of useful knowledge. The Institution, 1823. LEE

C808 LONDON INSTITUTION. Report of the committee of enquiry of the London Institution . . . The Institution, 1812. LEE

C809 LONGMAN & CO., AND MURRAY, John, *firm.* (1851) On the publication of school books by government at the public expense. A correspondence with the Rt. Hon. Lord John Russell. Longman, & Murray, 1851. HU; Dublin, H.M.S.O., 1851. LEI

C810 LOVETT, William, 1800–1877, and COLLINS, John. (1840) Chartism; a new organization of the people, embracing a plan for the education and improvement of the people, politically and socially . . . 2nd ed., J. Watson, [etc.], 1841. HU

C811 Low, Sampson, 1797–1886. The charities of London. Comprehending the benevolent, education and religious institutions. Their origin and design, progress and present position. S. Low, 1850. LO

C812 LOWE, Robert, *1st visct. Sherbrooke,* 1811–1892. (1868) Middle class education: endowment or free trade? R. J. Bush, 1868. HU

C813 LOWE, Robert. (1867) Primary and classical education: an address delivered before the Philosophical Institution of Edinburgh, November 1867 . . . Revised by the author. Edinburgh, Edmonston & Douglas, 1867. HU LEI

C814 LOWE, Robert. (1861) Speech . . . on moving the education estimate in Committee of supply, July 11, 1861. Ridgway, 1861. HU

C815 LOWE, Robert. (1862) Speech . . . on the Revised code of the regulations of the Committee of the Privy Council on education. In the House of Commons, February 13, 1862. Ridgway, 1862. HU

C816 LUCAS, F. Two lectures on education . . . delivered in the Literary and scientific institution at Staines . . . 1838. Booker & Dolman, 1839. BR

Lucus a non lucendo. *See* Bell, W. B.

Lusus Westmonasterienses. *See* Westminster School

Lyra innocentium. *See* Keble, John

C817 [MACBRIDE, John David], 1778–1868. (1849) An address on national education, delivered in the new school room of the parish of St. Peter-le-Bailey, May 3, 1849, by the principal of Magdalene Hall. Oxford, Vincent; London, Hatchard; 1849. LEI

C818 [McCAUL, Elizabeth Ann, *aft. Mrs*. Finn], *trans*. (1839) The autobiography of Thomas Platter: a schoolmaster of the sixteenth century. Translated from the German by the translator of Lavater's original maxims. Wertheim, 1839. LEE LO

C819 McCLELLAND, James. National elementary education in the United States of America. Faithfull, 1861. BI

C820 McCLELLAND, James. On reformatories for the destitute and the fallen (being . . . a paper read at the statistical section of the British Association). To which is appended Report on agricultural colonies, by M. Demetz. Glasgow, Maclehose, 1856. HU

C821 McEVOY, John. A free inquiry into the Irish education question. Dublin, Webb, 1866. NE

C822 MACGREGOR, John, 1825–1892. (1852) Ragged schools; their rise, progress and results. S. Low, [1852]. LEI

C823 MACKENZIE, *Sir* George Steuart, 1780–1848. General observations on the principles of education: for the use of mechanics' institutions. Edinburgh, Anderson, 1836. LEE

C824 MACKWORTH, Herbert. (1854) Science in the mines: a lecture, delivered in connection with the educational exhibition of the Society of arts, manufactures, and commerce. Routledge, 1854. HU

C825 MACLEOD, Norman, 1812–1872. (1856) The home school; or, hints on home education. Edinburgh, Paton & Ritchie, 1856. HU; 2nd ed., Edinburgh, Paton & Ritchie, 1856. LO

C826 MACNAUGHT, John. Compulsory education in accordance with the principles of the National Education League: [a letter to *The Times*]. [Birmingham, Nat. ed. league, 1870.] BI

C827 MAGEE, William Connor, 1821–1891. A speech delivered by the Right Rev. W. C. Magee, D.D., Lord Bishop of Peterborough, at the Leicester conference of the National Education Union, 27th January, 1870. London, Longmans; Manchester, Nat. Ed. Union; [1870?] LEI

C828 MAGER, Karl, 1810–1858. (1840) Die deutsche Bürgerschule . . . Stuttgart, Sonnenwald, 1840. LEI

C829 MAIGNE, Pierre, *ed*. Journal anecdotique, de Mme. Campan, ou conversations recueillies dans ses entretiens, par M. Maigne . . . Paris, Colburn, 1825. LO

C830 MAINTENON, Françoise d'Aubigné, *marquise de*, 1635–1719. Lettres et entretiens sur l'éducation des filles. Recueillis et publiés pour la première fois par M. Th. Lavallée. Paris, Charpentier, 1861. 2 vols. LO

C831 MAINZER, Joseph, 1801–1851. (1848) Music and education. Longman, 1848. HU

C832 MALTBY, Edward, 1770–1859. (1838) Substance of a speech in the House of Lords, May 7, 1838, on presenting a petition from Manchester and its vicinity, upon the subject of national education. By the Bishop of Durham. Ridgway, 1838. LEE

MANCHESTER. Education aid society. *See* Education aid society of Manchester

C833 MANCHESTER. Mechanics' Institution. Address by Lord Brougham to the members . . . on . . . 21st July, 1835, with a report of the proceedings of the general meeting. Manchester, The Institution, 1835. NE SH

C834 MANCHESTER. Model Secular School. Copy of the correspondence between the committee of the Model Secular School of Manchester and the Committee of Council on Education. 1856 and 1858. *See* E172–3

C835 MANCHESTER. do. Third report. Cave & Sever, 1859. SH

MANCHESTER. National conference on education. *See* National conference on education

C836 MANN, Horace, 1796–1859. (1846) Report of an educational tour. 4th ed., Simpkin, Marshall, 1851. ReU

C837 MANN, Horace. The republic and the school: Horace Mann on the education of free men. Edited by Lawrence A. Cremin. N.Y., Columbia Univ. Teachers Coll., 1957. [Selections from his 1st–12th annual reports to the Massachusetts Board of education, 1837–1848.] LEE LEI NO

C838 MANN, Horace, *barrister*. The resources of popular education in England and Wales: present and future. [From the *Journal* of the Statistical society of London, March, 1862.] HU

C838a MANN, Horace. Education in Great Britain. 1854. *See* E719

C839 MANNING, Henry Edward, 1808–1892. Ireland: a letter to Earl Grey. Longmans, 1868. NE

C840 [MANSFIELD, Robert Blachford]. (1866) School-life at Winchester College; or, the reminiscences of a Winchester junior. With a glossary of words, phrases and customs, peculiar to Winchester College. J. C. Hotten, 1866. LEE; [2nd ed.], J. C. Hotten, 1870. HU LO SH

Manual of practical observations on our public schools. *See* Cole, Henry

C841 MARCEL, Claude. Language as a means of mental culture and international communication; or, manual of the teacher and the learner of languages. Chapman & Hall, 1853. 2 vols. HU

C842 MARENHOLTZ-BÜLOW, Bertha von, *baroness*, 1810–1893. (1868) Child and child-nature. Contributions to the understanding of Fröbel's educational theories. Translated from the 2nd ed. by Alice M. Christie. Sonnenschein, 1879. LEE; 9th ed., Sonnenschein, 1900. LO

C843 [MARENHOLTZ-BÜLOW, Bertha von]. Woman's educational mission: being an explanation of Friedrich Fröbel's system of infant gardens. [Trans. by Elizabeth, countess Krockow von Wickerode.] Darton, 1855. HU LEE LEI ReU

C844 MARKBY, Thomas. Practical essays on education. Strahan, 1868. LEE

C845 MARSH, Herbert, 1757–1839. (1811) The national religion the foundation of national education: a sermon preached in the Cathedral of St. Paul, London, on Thursday, June 13, 1811: being the time of the yearly meeting... Rivington for S.P.C.K., 1811. LEE ReU

C846 MARSH, Herbert. (1811) A vindication of Dr. Bell's system of tuition in a series of letters. Rivington, 1811. HU LO

C847 MARTIN, Henry. (1826) Observations on the importance and advantages of the education of the people; in a letter to James Taylor... B. J. Holdsworth, 1826. [A reply to 'Country Gentleman', q.v.] HU

C848 MARTIN, John. (1862) [Comments on the Revised code.] [No pub.], 1862. BI

C849 MARTIN, John. Thoughts suggested by the suspension of the Revised educational code. Home and colonial training institution, [etc.], [1866?] LEE

MARTIN, Louis Aimé. See Aimé-Martin, Louis

C850 MARTIN, Thomas. An address delivered to the Reigate branch of the Surrey Church of England schoolmasters' and schoolmistresses' association... on... bodily health as an element in popular education... Simpkin & Marshall, [1858]. HU

C851 MARTINEAU, Harriet, 1802–1876. (1859) Endowed schools of Ireland. Reprinted from 'The Daily news'. Smith, Elder, 1859. LO

C852 MARTINEAU, Harriet, (1848) Household education. E. Moxon, 1849. BI HU ReU SH; new ed., Smith, Elder, 1870. LEI NE

C853 MASON, Marian. (1827) On the utility of exercise; or a few observations on the advantages to be derived from its salutary effects, by means of calisthenic exercises... By... a pupil to Captain Clias. T. Clerc Smith, 1827. LEI

C854 MASSEI, Giovanni, conte. (1836) Sulla beneficenza e la istruzione pubblica in Bologna. Lucca, [no pub.], 1836. LEI

C855 [MATHISON, Gilbert Farquhar]. (1844) How can the Church educate the people? The question considered with reference to the incorporation and endowment of colleges for the middle and lower classes of society, in a letter addressed to the Lord Archbishop of Canterbury by a member of the National Society. Rivington, 1844. BI LEE

C856 MAURICE, Frederick Denison, 1805–1872. Administrative reform and its connection with working men's colleges. Cambridge, Macmillan, 1855. LEE

C857 MAURICE, F. D. (1847) The education question in 1847; a letter addressed to the editor of the English journal of education. Bell, [1847]. BR

C858 MAURICE, F. D. (1839) Has the church, or the state, the power to educate the nation? A course of lectures. Rivington, [etc.], 1839. [Cover title: Lectures on national education.] HU LEE ReU SH

C859 MAURICE, F. D. (1855) Learning and working: six lectures delivered... 1854. Macmillan, 1855. SH

C860 MAURICE, F. D. The life of... chiefly told in his own letters. By his son Frederick Maurice. 2nd ed., Macmillan, 1884. 2 vols. LEI SH

C861 MAURICE, F. D. (1855) Plan of a female college, for the help of the rich and of the poor... Cambridge, Macmillan, 1855. HU

C862 MAURICE, F. D. (1866) The representation and education of the people. Strahan, 1866. ReU

C863 [MAURICE, F. D.] (1835) Subscription no bondage, or, the practical advantages afforded by the thirty-nine articles as guides in all branches of academical education. By Rusticus. Oxford, [etc.], Parker, 1835. LEI

C864 MAYO, Charles, 1792–1846. A lecture on the life of Pestalozzi: with other papers. Collected as some explanation of Pestalozzi's principles of education. Home and colonial school soc., 1856. LEI

C865 [MAYO, Charles]. [?] Pestalozzi and his principles. 2nd ed., Home and colonial school soc., 1864. LO

C866 MAYO, Charles. Substance of a lecture on the principles of Pestalozzi delivered at the Royal Institution 1826. Oxford, Munday, pr., [1827?]. LEI; [1829]. LO

C867 MAYO, Charles, ed. (1834) The teacher: or moral influences employed in the instruction of the young, by Jacob Abbott. Revised by the Rev. Charles Mayo. Seeley, [etc.], 1834. LEI NE

C868 MAYO, Charles, and MAYO, Elizabeth. (1837) Practical remarks on infant education, for the use of schools and private families. Seeley & Burnside, for the Home and colonial infant school soc., 1837. LEE LEI SH; 3rd ed., 1841. BI; 4th ed., 1849. ReU

C869 [MAYO, Elizabeth], 1793–1865. (1856?) A course of lessons for infants under the age of four years and a half; forming Part I of 'A manual of instruction for elementary schools and private tuition', in three parts. 4th ed., Home and colonial school soc., 1872. HU

C870 [MAYO, Elizabeth]. (1830) Lessons on objects: as given to children between the ages of six and eight, in a Pestalozzian school, at Cheam, Surrey. 6th ed., Seeley & Burnside, 1837. LO; 8th ed., 1840. HU; 9th ed., 1843. BI LEE NO; 13th ed., 1853. LO

C871 [MAYO, Elizabeth]. (1832) Lessons on shells, as given to children between the ages of eight and ten in a Pestalozzian school, at Cheam, Surrey. Seeley & Burnside, 1832. BI; 2nd ed., 1838. LEI SH; 3rd ed., 1846. LEE

C872 [MAYO, Elizabeth]. Religious instruction, in a graduated series of lessons for young children. By the author of 'Lessons on objects'... [etc.]. Seeley, Burnside & Seeley, 1845. LEI

C873 MAYO, Elizabeth, ed. Manual for infant schools and nurseries. Prepared for the Home and Colonial School Society by Rebecca Sunter ... under the direction of Miss Mayo ... Home and colonial school soc., 1856. HU

C874 MAYOR, John Eyton Bickersteth, 1825–1910, ed. The history of the College of St. John the Evangelist, Cambridge, by Thomas Baker. Edited [from the MS.] by J. E. B. Mayor. C.U.P., 1869. 2 vols. LO ReU

MELGUND, Lord, aft. 3rd earl of Minto. See Minto, 3rd earl of

C875 MELLY, George. 'Adult criminals' and 'industrial sentences'. An address, delivered at the Renshaw Street home mission. Liverpool, Benson & Mallett, 1859. HU

C876 MELLY, George. (1869) The children of Liverpool, and the rival schemes of national education: a speech ... Liverpool ... 1869. Liverpool, Daily Post, pr., 1869. LO

MEMBER FOR KILMARNOCK, pseud. See Simpson, James

MEMBER OF A CLOSE COLLEGE, pseud. See Hare, Augustus William

MEMBER OF THE UNIVERSITY OF CAMBRIDGE, pseud. See Gilly, William Stephen

C877 MEMOIR of John Sharp, later superintendent of Croydon school. [By S. H.] London, Cash; Darlington, Penney; 1857. LEI

C878 MEMOIRS of John Frederic Oberlin, pastor of Waldbach in the Ban de la Roche; compiled from authentic sources, chiefly in French and German. [Translated by Richenda Cunningham.] Holdsworth & Ball, 1829. HU LEI LI ReU; 2nd ed., Holdsworth & Ball, 1830. LEE

C879 MEMORIAL respecting the present state of the College of Glasgow. By the Regius professors of chemistry and materia medica, [i.e. Thomas Thomson and John Couper]. Addressed to the member of Parliament for that city. Johnston, 1835. BI

C880 MENET, John. Mr. Walter's motion [concerning the education grant]; a letter to a friend ... Rivington, 1865. BI

C881 MENET, John. (1867) Practical hints on teaching. With plans of schools. 7th ed., Bell, 1890. LEI

C882 MENET, John. (1862) The Revised code: a letter to a friend, suggested by the pamphlets of the Rev. C. J. Vaughan and the Rev. J. Fraser. Rivington, 1862. BI HU LEE

C883 MENZIES, Allan. Report of twenty-one years' experience of the Dick Bequest for elevating the character and position of the parochial schools and school-masters in the counties of Aberdeen, Banff, and Moray ... Edinburgh & London, Blackwood, 1854. LEE

C884 MÉTHODE d'enseignement universel des langues, des sciences et des arts; ou, manuel d'instructions pour l'enseignement mutuel, naturel, universel et particulier. 2e éd., Paris, Colas, Librairie de la Société pour l'instruction élémentaire, 1828. HU

C885 METROPOLITAN CHURCH UNION. History and present state of the education question: being a collection of documents explanatory of the proceedings of the Committee of Privy Council on Education ... and of the steps taken for the defence of church education. Rivington, 1850. LEE

C886 METTRAY. Colonie agricole et pénitentiaire. [Rapports annuels, 9, 10]. Paris, Claye & Taillefer, 1848–1849. 2 vols. BI; Rapport annuel, [12]. Tours, Ladarèze, 1851. BI

C887 METTRAY. do. Application du système de Mettray aux colonies agricoles d'orphelins et d'enfants trouvés. [Paris, Claye, 1850.] BI

C888 METZ, Frédéric Auguste de, 1796–1873. La Colonie de Mettray. Extrait du Journal des économistes, [1856?]. HU

C889 METZ, F. A. de. Report on agricultural colonies. [In McClelland, James. On reformatories for the destitute ... 1856.] See C820 McClelland, J.

C890 METZ, F. A. de. Report on reformatory farm institutions, read before the International Charitable Conference at Paris. Translation ... by E. B. Wheatley. Hamilton Adams, 1856. BR

C891 MIDDLE-CLASS education. Proposed West of England examinations and prizes. Ridgway, 1857. [From the Journal of the Bath and West of England society.] BI

C892 MIDDLE-CLASS SCHOOLS FUND. Middle-class schools fund, to promote the establishment of middle-class schools, in connexion with the Protestant and Reformed Church of England ... C. A. Macintosh, pr., 1869. HU

C893 MIDLAND COUNTIES HERALD. Notes of a visit to Ruysselede [reformatory]. [Reprinted from the Midland Counties Herald.] Birmingham, Napper & Wright, 1859. HU

C894 MILL, James, 1773–1833. James and John Stuart Mill on education. Edited by F. A. Cavenagh. C.U.P., 1931. BR LEE LEI LO NE NO RE SH SO

C895 MILL, John Stuart, 1806–1873. (1867) Inaugural address, delivered to the University of St. Andrews, Feb. 1st, 1867. Longmans, 1867. SH; 2nd ed., Longmans, 1867. LO; People's ed., Longmans, 1867. HU

C896 MILL, J. S. James and John Stuart Mill on education. Edited by F. A. Cavenagh. C.U.P., 1931. BR LEE LEI LO NE NO RE SH SO

C896a MILL, J. S. Speech at meeting of the National Education League, 1870. See C936

C897 MILL, J. S. (1869) The subjection of women. 2nd ed., Longmans, [etc.], 1869. LO

MILLARD, William, joint author. See Duncan, Peter Martin, and Millard, Wm.

C898 MILLBANK PENITENTIARY. Remarks on the arrangements connected with the schools in the Millbank Penitentiary ... Philanthropic soc., 1825. LO

C899 MILLER, Hugh, 1802–1856. (1854) My schools and schoolmasters; or, the story of my education. Edinburgh, Constable, 1859. LEE; 13th ed., Edinburgh, Nimmo, 1869. LEE; Edinburgh, Nimmo, [etc.], 1889. LO; Edinburgh, Nimmo, [etc.], n.d. LEI

C900 MILLS, Alfred W. Night schools. Houlston & Wright, 1866. BI

C901 MILNES, Richard Monckton, *1st baron Houghton*, 1809–1885. Address on the punishment and reformation of criminals. Reprinted from the Transactions of the National association for the promotion of social science, 1859. HU

C902 MINTO, William Hugh Elliot-Murray-Kynynmond, *3rd earl of*. Remarks on the government scheme of national education as applied to Scotland. Edinburgh, Black; London, Longman; 1848. HU LEI

Modern theme. *See* Owen, Owen

C903 MONK, James Henry, 1784–1856. (1810) A letter to the Rev. Samuel Butler, M.A. . . . with Mr. Butler's answer. Cambridge, Deighton, [etc.], 1810. LEE

C904 MONK, J. H. A vindication of the University of Cambridge from the reflections of Sir James Edward Smith . . . 2nd ed., Murray, 1818. LEE

C905 MONRO, Edward, 1815–1866. (1854) Walter, the schoolmaster. 3rd ed., J. Masters, 1862. HU

C906 [MONTAGU, Basil], 1770–1851. The private tutor: or, thoughts upon the love of excelling and the love of excellence. R. Hunter, 1820. HU

C907 MONTUCCI, Heinrich, and DEMOGEOT, Jacques. (1868) De l'enseignement secondaire en Angleterre et en Ecosse. Paris, 1868. *See* E837

Monument of parental affection. *See* Gilpin, Joshua

C908 MOODY, George, *ed.* English journal of education. *See* C429

C909 [MORE, Hannah], 1743–1833. (1805) Hints towards forming the character of a young princess. Cadell & Davies, 1805. 2 vols. SH; 2nd ed., Cadell & Davies, 1805. 2 vols. HU LEI

C910 MORE, Hannah. (1819) Moral sketches of prevailing opinions and manners, foreign and domestic . . . Cadell & Davies, 1819. LEE

C911 MORE, Hannah. (1799) Strictures on the modern system of female education. 9th ed., Cadell & Davies, 1801. 2 vols. OX; 11th ed., 1811. 2 vols. DU; 12th ed., 1818. 2 vols. LI ReU

MORGAN, Augustus de. *See* De Morgan, Augustus

C912 MORGAN, William. (1853) The Arabs of the city; or a plea for brotherhood with the outcast. Being an address delivered to the Young men's christian association, Birmingham . . . November 29, 1853. Birmingham, Hudson; London, Hamilton, Adams, 1853. HU

C913 MORRICE, David. (1801) The art of teaching . . . examined, methodized, and facilitated; as well as applied to all branches of scholastic education. Lackington, Allen, 1801. LEI

C914 MOSELEY, Henry, 1801–1872. (1855) Report on the Kneller Hall training school. 1855. *See* E169

C915 MOTT, James. Observations on the education of children; and hints to young people, on the duties of civil life. 1819. ReU; York, Wm. Alexander, 1822. LEE

C916 MÜLLER, George, 1805–1898. The diary of George Müller, [1849–1898]: selected extracts by A. Rendle Short. Pickering & Inglis, 1954. LEI

C917 [MULLIS, William]. (1826) Some account of the Blue Coat hospital, and public library, in the college, Manchester, founded by Humphrey Chetham, Esq., in the year 1651. Manchester, Leech & Cheetham, 1826. [Cover title: A concise account of . . .] LEI

MULSO, Hester, *aft. Mrs.* Chapone. *See* Chapone, *Mrs.*

C918 MUNRO, Alexander Fraser. England's mental wants: or, its past and present state of education, and the necessity and advantages of a complete system of secular education for England and Wales. York, Author, 1853. LEE

C919 MURE, James, *and others, eds.* Lusus alteri Westmonasterienses, sive prologi et epilogi ad fabulas in Sti. Petri Collegio actas . . . Curantibus, J. Mure, H. Bull, C. B. Scott. Oxford, [etc.], Parker, [etc.], 1863–1867. 2 vols. LEI

MURPHY, Anna Brownell, *aft. Mrs.* Jameson. *See* Jameson, A. B.

MURRAY, John, *firm, jt. author. See* Longman & Co., and Murray, John

C920 MURRAY, Lindley, 1745–1826. (1826) Memoirs of the life and writings of . . . in a series of letters, written by himself. With a preface, and a continuation of the Memoirs, by Elizabeth Frank. York, T. Wilson for Longman, [etc.], 1826. LEI

C921 MURRAY, Thomas Boyles. The children in St. Paul's. An account of the anniversary of the assembled charity schools of London and Westminster in the cathedral church of St. Paul. [With list of preachers, 1704–1850.] S.P.C.K., 1851. HU

C922 MYERS, Thomas, 1774–1834. (1818) Remarks on a course of education, designed to prepare the youthful mind for a career of honour, patriotism and philanthropy. Author, 1818. LEE; Royal Military Academy, 1818. LO

C923 NAPIER, *Mrs.* Elizabeth. (1834) The nursery governess, [and two other stories]. T. & W. Boone, 1834. BR

C924 NAPOLEON I, *emperor of the French.* A system of education for the infant King of Rome, and other French princes of the blood, drawn up by the Imperial Council of State, with the approbation, and under the personal superintendence, of the Emperor Napoleon. Lackington, [etc.], 1820. [Contains English and French versions.] HU LO

C925 NATIONAL ASSOCIATION FOR THE PROMOTION OF SOCIAL SCIENCE. Sessional papers, 1865/6. LEI

C926 NATIONAL ASSOCIATION FOR THE PROMOTION OF SOCIAL SCIENCE. Transactions. Liverpool meeting, 1858. NE; Edinburgh meeting, 1863. LEI; Sheffield meeting, 1865. NE; Birmingham meeting, 1868. NE; Bristol meeting, 1869. BI NE; Newcastle-upon-Tyne meeting, 1870. LEI

C927 NATIONAL CONFERENCE ON EDUCATION, Manchester, 1868. Report of the National conference on education, held in the Town Hall, Manchester . . . January 15 and 16, 1868. Revised and corrected. Manchester, [no pub.], 1868. LEE

National education. *See* Rushden, G. W.

National education: an address . . . by the vicar of Harwell. *See* Fletcher, Wm.

C928 NATIONAL education: report of the speeches delivered at a dinner given to James Simpson, by the friends of education in Manchester . . . Manchester, Prentice & Cathrall, pr. 1836. HU

National education: some proposals. *See* Greenwood, A. B.

National education and the English language. *See* Pagliardini, Tito

C929 NATIONAL EDUCATION ASSOCIATION OF SCOTLAND. The National education association of Scotland. [1850.] ReU

C930 NATIONAL EDUCATION LEAGUE. [Papers.] 1866–1876. [Bound in 4 vols.] LO

C931 NATIONAL EDUCATION LEAGUE. A brief statement of the object and means of the league. [Birmingham, Nat. ed. league, 1870.] BI

C932 NATIONAL EDUCATION LEAGUE. Educational queries. Birmingham, Nat. ed. league, 1870. [Leaflet no. 86.] BI

C933 NATIONAL EDUCATION LEAGUE. Government Education Bill: amendments proposed . . . [Birmingham, Nat. ed. league, 1870.] BI

C934 NATIONAL EDUCATION LEAGUE. Report of a conference of nonconformist ministers held at Leeds . . . January 18, 1870. Simpkin, Marshall, 1870. BI LEI

C935 NATIONAL EDUCATION LEAGUE. Verbatim report of the proceedings of a deputation to the Rt. Hon. W. E. Gladstone, M.P., the Rt. Hon. Earl de Grey and Ripon, and the Rt. Hon. W. E. Forster, M.P., on . . . March 9, 1870. Birmingham, Nat. ed. league, 1870. BI

C936 NATIONAL EDUCATION LEAGUE. *Meeting, 1870, London.* Speech by J. S. Mill. [Birmingham, Hudson], 1870. BI

C937 NATIONAL EDUCATION UNION. Annual reports, 1st, 1869/70. HU LEI NE

C938 NATIONAL EDUCATION UNION. Authorised report of the great meeting of the friends of religious education . . . London, April 8th, 1870 . . . Also . . . a large conference of schoolmasters on the Education bill, April 9th. Manchester and London, [Nat. ed. union, 1870.] HU

C939 NATIONAL EDUCATION UNION. Elementary education act, 1870: a brief manual. Manchester and London, Nat. ed. union, 1870. HU

C940 NATIONAL EDUCATION UNION. Report of the educational congress held in Manchester, Nov. 3rd and 4th, 1869. Longmans, 1869. ReU

C941 NATIONAL EDUCATION UNION. A verbatim report, with indexes, of the debate in Parliament during the progress of the Elementary education bill, 1870, together with a reprint of the Act . . . Manchester and London, Nat. ed. union, [1870]. BI BR CA HU LEE LEI NE RE

C942 NATIONAL SOCIETY FOR PROMOTING THE EDUCATION OF THE POOR IN THE PRINCIPLES OF THE ESTABLISHED CHURCH. Annual reports, 15th and 16th, Rivington, 1826–1827. HU; 28th, Rivington, 1839. BR

C943 NATIONAL Society for promoting the education of the poor in the principles of the Established Church. Digest of correspondence with the Committee of the Privy Council on Education. 1849. *See* C453 Fisher, O.

C944 NATIONAL Society for promoting the education of the poor in the principles of the Established Church. Diocesan and local boards of education formed during the years 1838–1839 in connection with the National Society . . . [Nat. soc., 1839.] BI

C945 NATIONAL Society for promoting the education of the poor in the principles of the Established Church. Summaries of the returns to the general inquiry made by the National Society into the state and progress of schools for the education of the poor in the principles of the Established Church, during the years 1856–1857 throughout England and Wales. Nat. Soc., 1858. NE

C946 NAVILLE, François Marc Louis, 1784–1846. (1832) De l'éducation publique, considérée dans ses rapports avec le développement des facultés, la marche progressive de la civilisation, et les besoins actuels de la France. 2e éd., rev. and augm., Paris, P. Dufart, 1833. HU

C947 NECKER DE SAUSSURE, Albertine Adrienne, 1766–1841. (1828–1838) L'éducation progressive, ou, étude du cours de la vie. Tome 1, Paris, Sautelet, 1828. Tome 2, Paris, Paulin, 1832. BR; Lausanne, Rouiller, 1834. 2 vols. BI; Brussels, Meline, 1836. 2 vols. LEI; Paris, Paulin, 1836–1838. 3 vols. HU; Paris, Paulin, 1844. 2 vols. LEE LO; Tome 1, 4e éd., tome 2, 6e éd., Paris, Garnier, 1864. LO ReU

C948 NEIGEBAUR, Johann Ferdinand. Das Volks-Schulwesen in den preussischen Staaten. Berlin, E. S. Mittler, 1834. LO

C949 NESBIT'S ACADEMY, Kennington. Report of the general progress of Messrs. Nesbit's pupils for the year 1849 . . . Kennington, Nesbit's Academy, 1849. BI

C950 NETHERLANDS. (1817) Règlement sur l'organisation de l'enseignement supérieur dans les provinces méridionales du royaume des Pays-Bas. Ghent, Houdin, 1817. LEI

C951 NEW YORK. *Convention of literary and scientific gentlemen, 1830.* Journal of the proceedings . . . N.Y., Leavitt & Carvill, 1831. SH

C952 NEWLAND, Henry Garrett, 1804–1860. Remarks addressed to W. H. Bellamy on the state of education in Ireland . . . Dublin, McGlashan, 1849. LEE

C953 NEWMAN, Francis William, 1805–1897, *ed.* (1843) The English universities, by Victor A. Huber. An abridged translation. Pickering, 1843. 2 vols. in 3. BI LEI LO SH

C954 NEWMAN, John Henry, 1801–1890. (1873 in this form) The idea of a university, defined and illustrated . . . Pickering, 1873. SH; Longmans, 1902 [and various reprints]. LEI LO SH

C955 NEWMAN, J. H. Select discourses from The idea of a university. Edited . . . by M. Yardley. C.U.P., 1931. LEE NE NO RE SH

C956 NEWMAN, J. H. (1859) Lectures and essays on university subjects. Longman, 1859. LEE

C957 NEWMAN, J. H. (1852) On the scope and nature of university education. Dent, 1915 [and various reprints]. BR LEE LEI NO RE SH

C958 NEWMAN, J. H. (1856) University sketches, edited . . . by Michael Tierney. Dublin, Browne & Nolan, [1952]. LEE RE SH

C959 NEWMARCH, Charles Henry, 1824–1903. Recollections of Rugby. By an old Rugbaean. Hamilton & Adams, 1848. BI

C960 NEWNHAM, William, 1790–1865. The principles of physical, intellectual, moral, and religious education. Hatchard, 1827. 2 vols. HU LEE

C961 NEWPORT (I.o.W.) Royal Lancasterian school. Report and address of the committee . . . delivered January 15, 1813. Newport, R. Squire, pr., [1813]. HU

C962 NICHOL, John, 1833–1894. (1869) Address on national education delivered in the City Hall, Glasgow, on April 6, 1869. Glasgow, Maclehose, 1869. BI

C963 NICHOL, John Pringle, 1804–1859. Moral training in our common-schools. Suggestions of certain practical methods of increasing its efficiency . . . London & Glasgow, Griffin, 1858. LEE

C964 NICHOLS, James, 1785–1861, ed. The history of the University of Cambridge, by Thomas Fuller. See C500 Fuller, T.

C965 NICOL, James, 1810–1879. On the study of natural history as a branch of general education: an inaugural lecture at Marischal College. Edinburgh, Oliver & Boyd, 1853. BR

C966 NISSEN, L., and others. Theoretisch-praktisches Handbuch für unmittelbare Denkübungen . . . für Lehrer an Volksschulen. Duisberg and Essen, Bädeker & Kürzel, 1812. 3 vols. in 1. LO

C967 NOEL, Jean-François M., 1755–1841. Report on the establishment for public instruction in Holland. 1811. [In Cousin. On the state of education in Holland.] See C325 Cousin, V.

NOEL BYRON, Anne Isabella. See Byron, A. I. Noel

C968 The NON-DESCRIPT. By the students of Macclesfield. Nos. 1–20, Aug. 10–Dec. 1, 1805. [All pub.] Manchester, Wheeler, 1805. LEI

C969 NORRIS, John Pilkington, 1823–1891. Educational reports. Vols. 1–5, 1850–[1867]. [Vol. 1, 1850–1853; vol. 2, 1853–1855; vol. 3, 1855–1856; vol. 4, 1858–1859; vol. 5, 1867.] Longman, [etc.], ReU

C970 NORTH BRITISH REVIEW. Vol. 11 [containing a review of Guthrie's 'A second plea for ragged schools'.] 1849. HU

C971 NORTHEND, Charles. (2nd ed., 1853) The teacher and the parent: a treatise upon common-school education; containing practical suggestions to teachers and parents. 8th ed., enl., N.Y., Barnes & Burr, 1860. HU

C972 NORTHERN ASSOCIATION OF CERTIFICATED CHURCH SCHOOLMASTERS. (1862) An inquiry into the truth of the report of A. F. Foster, Esq., Assistant Commissioner, on the state of popular education in the mining districts of the county of Durham. Durham, G. Walker, 1862. BI NE

C973 NUGÉE, George. The necessity for Christian education to elevate the native character in India. [Sir P. Maitland prize essay, Cambridge.] Rivington, 1846. LO

C974 NUNN, Joseph. Strictures on the reports on education in Manchester, Liverpool, Birmingham, and Leeds, presented to the House of Commons by J. G. Fitch and D. R. Fearon; together with an appendix on the government Education bill and government hindrances to education. Addressed to W. E. Forster. London, Macintosh; Manchester, Powlson; 1870. HU

C975 The NURSERY and infant's school magazine, edited by Mrs. Cameron. Houlston, 1830–1833. 4 vols. [no more pub.]. LEE; vol. 2, 1831. LEI

C976 NYON, —. Manuel pratique, ou précis de la méthode d'enseignement mutuel pour les nouvelles écoles élémentaires; rédigé par M. Nyon [pour la Société d'Enseignement Elémentaire]. Paris, L. Colas, 1816. HU

C977 OAKELEY, Frederick, 1802–1880. The question of university education for English Catholics . . . in a letter to the Bishop of Birmingham. Burns & Lambert, 1864. BR

C978 O'BRIEN, James Thomas, 1792–1874. (1852) The education question; a speech . . . at the annual meeting of the Church education society for Ireland . . . Dublin . . . April 15, 1852. Dublin, Hodges & Smith, 1852. BI

C979 O'BRIEN, J. T. (1860) Some remarks on a pamphlet entitled 'The education question – thoughts on the present crisis', [by J. Napier]. Dublin, Herbert; London, Hamilton, Adams, [etc.]; 1860. BI LEE

C980 OBSERVATIONS. (1821) Observations on Mr. Brougham's Bill 'for better providing the means of education for His Majesty's subjects'. Baldwin, Cradock & Joy, 1821. LEE

OLIVET, Mme. Fabre d'. See Fabre d'Olivet, Mme.

C981 O'MALLEY, Thadeus, 1796–1877. A sketch of the state of popular education in Holland, Prussia, Belgium, and France. 2nd ed., Ridgway, 1840. HU

C982 ON self-supporting schools of industry and mental discipline. Where reading, writing, and arithmetic, etc., are taught and united with the healthy exercise of garden farm culture, as practised at Eastbourne . . . Huddersfield, Kemp, 1844. BI

C983 ORGAN, James P. Hints on the educational, moral, and industrial training of the inmates of our reformatories, prisons, and workhouses. Dublin, Author, 1860. HU

C984 The ORIGIN, nature and object of the new system of education. Murray, 1812. ReU

C985 OSBORN, Rev. W. C. The claims of the poor. Bath, Wood bros., 1850. HU

C986 OSBORN, Rev. W. C. (1849) A lecture on the prevention of crime, delivered . . . in the . . . Town Hall, Ipswich, November 26th, 1849. Ipswich, Robinson Taylor, [1849]. HU

C987 OWEN, Hugh, jnr. (1870) The Elementary education act, 1870 . . . with introduction, notes, and index . . . and an appendix . . . Knight, 1870. LEE

C988 [OWEN, Owen]. (1847) The modern theme: or, education, the people's right and a nation's glory: being the substance of a lecture on the British system. By Celatus. J. Johnstone, 1847. HU

C989 OWEN, Robert, 1771–1858. (1816) An address delivered on 1st January, 1816, on opening the Institution for the formation of character, established at New Lanark. R. & A. Taylor, pr., 1816. HU

C990 OWEN, Robert. (1836–1844) The book of the new moral world, containing the national system of society ... Part 1. Glasgow, Robinson, etc., 1840. LEI

C991 OWEN, Robert. (1857) The life of Robert Owen, by himself. With an introduction by M. Beer. Bell, 1920. LEI SH

C992 OWEN, Robert. A new view of society, and other writings. Dent, 1927 [and reprints]. BI LEI LO SH SO

C993 OWEN, Robert Dale, 1801–1877. (1824) An outline of the system of education at New Lanark. Glasgow, [etc.], Wardlaw & Cunninghame, [etc.], 1824. [On microfilm.] HU; [typescript copy]. LEI

C994 OXFORD. University. The Eldon law scholarship founded at Oxford. 1830. ReU

C995 OXFORD. do. *Board of heads of houses and proctors.* (1853) Report and evidence of the committee appointed ... upon the recommendations of Her Majesty's Commissioners for inquiring into the state of the University of Oxford ... Oxford, O.U.P., 1853. BI

C996 OXFORD. do. *Committee on university extension, 1865.* University extension: [reports of sub-committees]. Macmillan, 1866. NE

C997 PAGE, David Perkins, 1810–1848. (1849) Theory and practice of teaching; or, the motives and methods of good school-keeping. 15th ed., N.Y., Barnes, 1853. HU

C998 PAGE, Thomas. Letter to the Right Hon. Lord Ashley, M.P., on the present defective state of national education and the necessity of government interference. Seeley, 1843. BR SH

C999 PAGET, *Sir* James, 1814–1899. (1854) On the importance of the study of physiology. [*In* Royal Institution. Lectures on education.] *See* C1252

C1000 [PAGLIARDINI, Tito]. National education and the English language. By a foreigner. Manchester, Heywood, 1868. BI

C1001 PAKINGTON, John Somerset, *baron Hampton,* 1799–1880. (1855) General education: speech delivered ... in the House of Commons ... March 16, 1855, on moving for leave to introduce a Bill for the better promotion of national education. Hatchard, 1855. LEE

C1002 [PALMER, John Hinde]. The Church and the education question. Remarks on the Church's opposition to the government plan of national education. By a churchman. Hooper, 1840. LEE

C1003 PARENT, *pseud.* Some remarks on the present studies and management of Eton school. 2nd ed., Ridgway, 1834. SH

C1004 The PARENTS' friend; or, extracts from the principal works on education, from the time of Montaigne to the present day, methodized and arranged. With observations and notes by the editor. J. Johnson, 1802. 2 vols. HU

C1005 The PARENT's great commission; or, essays on subjects connected with the higher part of education. 2nd ed., Longman, [etc.], 1851. LEI

C1006 PARISH schools and the Church of Scotland; or, a few words addressed to members of the legislature on the Lord Advocate's Parochial schools bill. By a member of the General Assembly's Parish schools committee. Edinburgh, Blackwood, 1856. BI

C1007 PARKER, William, *M.R.C.S., of Birkenhead.* The second part of microscopical science under six series of subjects: farmer's friend, lady's companion, engineer's help, medical adviser, government subjects, and Pestalozzian schools. Bath, Peach, 1866. LEE

PARKINSON-CHICHESTER, Samuel, *formerly* Fortescue. *See* FORTESCUE, Chichester S. P.

C1008 PAROZ, Jules. (1869?) Histoire universelle de la pédagogie. 5e éd., Paris, Delagrave, 1883. LO

C1009 PATTISON, Mark, 1813–1884. (1868) Suggestions on academical organization, with especial reference to Oxford. Edinburgh, Edmonston & Douglas, 1868. LEE ReU

C1010 PAYNE, Joseph, 1808–1876. Lectures and papers on education. Edited by his son, Joseph Frank Payne. Longmans, 1883–1892. 2 vols. LEE

C1011 PAYNE, Joseph. Lectures on the science and art of education ... Edited by his son ... Longmans, 1880. BI LEI NO; 2nd ed., 1883. LO RE

C1012 PEACOCK, George, 1791–1858. Observations on the statutes of the University of Cambridge. J. W. Parker, 1841. ReU

C1013 PEARS, Steuart Adolphus, 1815-1875. Mind and body; and, Moral influence. Two lectures on education. Hatchard, 1855. BI

C1014 PEEL, *Sir* Robert, 1788–1850. (1837) Address to the students of the University of Glasgow ... on his inauguration into the office of Lord Rector, January 11, 1837. Murray, 1837. BR

C1015 PELISSIER, Pierre. (1856) L'enseignement primaire des sourd-muets ... avec une iconographie des signes. Paris, Dupont, 1856. LO

C1016 PEMBERTON, Robert. The attributes of the soul from the cradle, and the philosophy of the divine mother; detecting the false basis, or fundamental error, of the schools, and developing the perfect education of man. Saunders & Otley, 1849. HU

C1017 PERCIVAL, John, 1834–1918. On the relation of the universities to school education. [No pub.], [1870?] LEE

C1018 PERRY, James. The Perryian principles and course of education. W. Pople, 1828. LO

C1019 PERRY, Walter Copland, 1814–1911. (1845) German university education; or, the professors and students of Germany ... Longman, [etc.], 1845. ReU; 2nd ed., rev., Longman, [etc.], 1846. LEI; 2nd ed., rev., 1848. BR

C1020 PESTALOZZI, Johann Heinrich, 1747–1827. Werke in acht Banden. Zurich, Erlenbach, 1945. 8 vols. SO

C1021 PESTALOZZI, J. H. Ausgewählte Schriften; hrsg. von W. Flitner. Godesberg, Küpper, 1949. HU

C1022 PESTALOZZI, J. H. Ausgewählte Schriften; hrsg. von F. Mann. Langensalza, Beyer, 1889–1894. 4 vols. LO

C1023 PESTALOZZI, J. H. Ausgewählte Briefe Pestalozzis. [Hrsg. von] H. Stettbacher. Basle, Schwabe, 1945. LEI

C1024 PESTALOZZI, J. H. The education of man: aphorisms. N.Y., Philosophical lib., [1951]. BI HU LEI RE SH SO

C1025 PESTALOZZI, J. H. Educational writings; edited by J. A. Green, with the assistance of F. A. Collie. E. Arnold, 1912. HU SH

C1026 PESTALOZZI, J. H. Grundlehren über Mensch und Erziehung: seine Schriften in Auswahl, hrsg. von H. Schneider. [4. Aufl.] Stuttgart, Kröner, 1949. LEI

C1027 PESTALOZZI, J. H. Pestalozzi; [edited] by L. F. Anderson. N.Y., McGraw-Hill, 1931. HU

C1028 PESTALOZZI, J. H. Pestalozzi und seine Anstalt in Stanz. Berlin, Beltz, n.d. SO

C1029 PESTALOZZI, J. H. Pestalozzis lebendiges Werk. Hrsg. von A. Haller. Basle, Birkhäuser, 1946. 4 vols. LEI

C1030 PESTALOZZI, J. H. Sämtliche Werke. 7. Band: Die Kinderlehre der Wohnstube. Christoph und Else. Bearbeitet von E. Dejung und W. Nigg. Berlin, De Gruyter, 1940. LO

C1031 PESTALOZZI, J. H. (1801) How Gertrude teaches her children... Translated by L. E. Holland and F. C. Turner, and edited... by E. Cooke. Sonnenschein, 1894 [and various reprint dates]. BI BR LEE LEI RE SO; 3rd ed., Allen & Unwin, 1915, rep. 1938. HU LEE NO SH SO

C1032 PESTALOZZI, J. H. Kriminalpädagogik. Berlin, Beltz, n.d. SO

C1033 PESTALOZZI, J. H. (1827) Letters on early education. Addressed to J. P. Greaves, Esq. Translated from the German manuscript with a memoir of Pestalozzi. Sherwood, [etc.], 1827. LEI NE RE ReU; Griffin, 1850. HU LEE LO

C1034 PESTALOZZI, J. H. (1807) [Ueber Körperbildung.] Einleitung auf den Versuch einer Elementargymnastik. Langensalza, Beltz, [194–]. LEI

Pestalozzi and his principles. See Home and colonial school society

PETTY-FITZMAURICE, Henry, 3rd marquis of Lansdowne. See Lansdowne, marquis of

C1035 PHELPS, Mrs. Almira Hart Lincoln, 1793–1884. (1836) The female student; or, lectures to young ladies on female education, for the use of mothers, teachers, and pupils. [2nd ed.], Scott, 1841. BI; 1844. NO

C1036 PHILADELPHIA. Girard college for orphans. Report on education in Europe, to the trustees. By A. D. Bache. Philadelphia, priv. printed, 1839. LEE LEI

C1037 PHILANTHROPIC SOCIETY. An account of the school for the indigent blind in St. George's Fields, Surrey, instituted 1799, containing the present state of the school, with the laws and regulations of the institution, to which is annexed the list of subscribers. Philanthropic Soc., 1812. SH

C1038 PHILANTHROPIC SOCIETY. The Philanthropic farm school, Redhill, Surrey. [Report of the first year's progress, 1849/50, by Sydney Turner.] [1850.] LEI

C1039 PHILANTHROPIC SOCIETY. The Philanthropic farm school, Redhill, Surrey. Report of the residential chaplain for the year ending 31st December 1853. 1854. HU

C1040 PHILANTHROPIC SOCIETY. Report of the anniversary festival of the Philanthropic Society's farm-school, Red Hill, held at the London Tavern, on... April 30th, 1856. Varty, 1856. HU

C1041 PHILANTHROPIC SOCIETY. (1846) Report on the system and arrangements of the Colonie Agricole at Mettray... [by Messrs. Turner & Paynter]. Truscott, 1846. BI; 2nd ed., rev., Hatchard, 1846. LEE

C1042 PHILLIPS, Sir Thomas, 1801–1867. (1850) The life of James Davies, a village schoolmaster. J. W. Parker, 1850. HU

C1043 PHILLIPS, Sir Thomas. (1849) Wales: the language, social condition, moral character, and religious opinions of the people, considered in their relation to education, with some account of the provision made for education in other parts of the kingdom. J. W. Parker, 1849. BR CA HU LEI LO RE

C1044 [PHILLPOTTS], Henry, 1778–1869. (1832) A speech delivered in the House of Lords, March 22nd, 1832, on the new plan of national education in Ireland, by Henry, lord bishop of Exeter. Murray, 1832. LEI

C1045 PHILLPOTTS, Henry. (1836) A speech delivered in the House of Lords... March 15, 1836, in moving for a select committee to inquire into the operation of the Commission for national education in Ireland. Murray, 1836. BI

Philosophy of ragged schools. See Cornwallis, Caroline Frances

C1046 PILBROW, James. Thoughts on the physical education of females and their moral influence. Groombridge, 1840. RE

C1047 PILLANS, James, 1778–1864. (1856) Contributions to the cause of education. Longmans, 1856. HU ReU

C1048 PILLANS, James. (1828) Principles of elementary teaching, chiefly in reference to the parochial schools of Scotland... Edinburgh, Black, 1828. BI; 2nd ed., Edinburgh, Black, 1829. BR SH

C1049 PILLANS, James. (1852) The rationale of discipline as exemplified in the High School of Edinburgh. MacLachlan & Stewart, 1852. SH

C1050 PIROUX, Joseph. Dissertation sur l'éducation des sourds-muets, et prospectus d'une méthode de dactylologie, à l'usage des sourds-muets... Paris, Hachette, 1859. BI

C1051 PITMAN, Sir Isaac, 1813–1897. An appeal to those who can read on behalf of those who cannot read. Bath, [c. 1870]. HU

PITT, William, earl of Chatham. See Chatham, earl of

PLACE, Benjamin, pseud. See Thring, Edward

C1052 A PLAIN and serious address to the parents of poor children, on the subject of schools. S.P.C.K., [c. 1820?]. LEI

C1053 Plain thoughts on the abstract of Mr. Brougham's Education Bill, humbly submitted to the consideration of the British legislature. By a plain Englishman. Rivington, 1821. LO

Plans for the government and liberal instruction of boys. See Hill, M.D.

PLATT, Thomas Joshua, baron, joint author. See Vaughan, Charles John and Platt, T. J.

C1054 PLAYFAIR, Lyon, 1st baron Playfair, 1818–1898. (1870) Address on education; delivered at the Newcastle-upon-Tyne congress of the Social Science Association, September 1870. [No pub.], 1870. LEE

C1055 PLAYFAIR, Lyon. (1852) Industrial instruction on the continent. (Museum of practical geology, Government School of Mines. Introductory lecture of the session 1852–1853.) H.M.S.O., 1852. HU

Ploughing and sowing . . . By a clergyman's daughter. See Simpson, Mary E

C1056 POLE, Thomas, 1753–1829. (1814) History of the origin and progress of adult schools. 1814. ReU

C1057 POLE, Thomas. Observations relative to infant schools. 1823. ReU

C1058 POOLE, John. (1812) The village school improved; or, the new system of education practically explained . . . Oxford, Parker, 1813. LEE

C1059 POPE-HENNESSY, Sir John, 1834–1891. The failure of the Queen's Colleges and of mixed education in Ireland. Bryce, 1859. BI BR

Popery and the Bible. See Edinburgh. Public meeting on ragged schools, 1847

Popular education in taste. See Lemercier, Sarah S. A., ed.

C1060 PORTER, Sarah, 'Mrs. G. R. Porter', 1791–1862. Prize essay. See C242 Central society of education.

C1061 PORTER, John Scott, 1801–1880. Is the 'national' or the 'denominational' system of education the best suited to the circumstances of Ireland? A plea for the united education of the youth of Ireland in national schools . . . With additions and an appendix. London, Simpkin; Belfast, Greer; 1868. HU

C1062 POTTS, Robert, 1808–1885. A brief account of the scholarships and exhibitions open to competition in the University of Cambridge, with specimens of the examination papers. Longmans, 1866. NO

C1063 POUND, William. Remarks upon English education in the nineteenth century. Rivingtons, 1866. LEE

C1064 POWELL, Baden, 1796–1860. State education considered with reference to prevalent misconceptions on religious grounds. London, Parker; Oxford, Talboys; 1840. LEE

C1065 A PRACTICAL treatise on day-schools. By a Schoolmaster. 1816. ReU

Practical view of Christian education in its early stages. See Babington, T.

C1066 PRAEGER, Emil Arnold. Outlines of the elementary principles of anthropological education. Bailliere, 1850. BI

C1067 [PRENDERGAST, Joseph], 1791?–1875. Plan and terms of the Grammar School, Lewisham Hill. [The School, 1831.] LO

C1068 A PREPARATION for Euclid, as used in a Pestalozzian school, at Stanmore, Middlesex. Seeley & Burnside, 1831. HU

C1069 PRESTON, Samuel. School education for the nineteenth century. Simpkin, Marshall, 1846. BR

C1070 PRESTON, Thomas, ed. (1870) The Elementary education act, 1870. With a popular analysis, and appendix of forms, and copious index. 2nd ed., Wm. Amer, 1870. CA LEI

C1171 PRIAULX, Osmond de Beauvoir. National education: its principles and objects exemplified in a plan for a normal school. Bohn, 1842. HU

C1172 PRICKETT, Marmaduke and WRIGHT, Thomas, eds. The history of the University of Cambridge, by Thomas Fuller. See C501 Fuller, T.

C1173 [PRIESTLEY, Timothy], 1734–1814. (1804) A funeral sermon occasioned by the death of the Rev. Dr. Priestley. Author, [1804]. LEE

C1174 PRIESTLEY, Timothy. A funeral sermon occasioned by the death of the late Rev. Joseph Priestley . . . preached at Jewin-Street chapel, London . . . on Sunday, April 29, 1804 . . . A. Hogg, 1804. LEI

C1175 The PRINCIPLES of collegiate education discussed and elucidated, in a description of Gnoll College, Vale of Neath, South Wales . . . Stanford, 1857. LEI

Principles of education. See Sewell. Elizabeth Missing

C1176 PRINSEP, Charles Robert, 1789-1864. Draft of an act for the better establishment of the free grammar school . . . Tonbridge, Kent. 1822. ReU

Private tutor. See Montagu, Basil

PROVIDENCE. Brown University. See Brown University, Providence

Psychological enquiries. See Brodie, Sir B. C.

Public schools . . . By the author of Etoniana. See Collins, William Lucas

C1177 PULSIFER, J. D. Lecture on phonetics; delivered before the Maine State Convention of Teachers at Lewiston, Mass., U. States, 27 November, 1860. Bath, Pitman, [c. 1872]. HU

C1178 PUSEY, Edward Bouverie, 1800–1882. Collegiate and professional teaching and discipline. Parker, 1854. ReU

C1179 PYCROFT, James, 1813–1895. On school education: designed to assist parents in choosing and in co-operating with instructors for their sons. Oxford, H. Slatter, 1843. HU

PYTHIAS, pseud. See Fox, Joseph

C1180 QUAIN, Richard, 1800–1887. On some defects in general education: being the Hunterian oration of the Royal College of Surgeons for 1869. Macmillan, 1870. LEE

C1181 QUARTERLY educational magazine, and record of the Home and Colonial School Society. Vols. 1 and 2. [All pub.] S. Low, 1848–1849. LEE; Vol. 1, 1848. LO

C1182 QUARTERLY journal of education. Vols. 1–10. [All pub.] Society for the diffusion of useful knowledge, 1831–1835. BI ReU; vols. 1–4, 1831–1832. HU; vols. 1–3. SH; vols. 1–2. LEI; vol. 6. LEE NE; vol. 10. NE

C1183 QUARTERLY REVIEW. [Review articles, arranged in chronological order.]

Oct. 1811: Bell and Lancaster's systems of education. BR HU LEI

Dec. 1811: Ensor on national education. HU

Sept. 1812: First annual report of the National Society, 1812. HU

April 1817: [Review of 'Statements respecting the East India College', by T. R. Malthus.] LEI

1819: [Review of 'Church-of-Englandism and its catechism examined', by Jeremy Bentham.] LEI

1820: [Review of Edgeworth's Memoirs.] LEI

1825: Mechanics' institutes and infant schools. HU

1827: State of the universities. HU

1829: Elementary teaching. HU

1831: Memoirs of Oberlin. HU

1855: Reformatory schools. HU

C1184 QUEEN'S COLLEGE, London. Introductory lectures delivered at Queen's College, London. Parker, 1849. BI

C1185 The QUEEN'S colleges and the Queen's university. [Belfast, Cork and Galway.] By a professor. Bell & Daldy, 1859. BI

C1186 QUICK, Robert Herbert, 1831–1891. (1868) Essays on educational reformers. Longmans, 1894. LO; 1902. LO SH; 1904. LEI LO

C1187 RACKHAM, Thomas. Industrial training of pauper children in the Guiltcross Union, Norfolk. Hartnell, 1850. LEI

C1188 RAGGED SCHOOL UNION. 4th annual report. The Union, 1848. HU

C1189 RAGGED SCHOOL UNION. The London ragged schools. The Union, 1847. [Occasional papers, no. 3.] BI

C1190 RAGGED SCHOOL UNION. Ragged school union magazine. Oct. 1849. HU; vol. 5, 1853, with the 9th annual report. LO; vol. 6, 1854, with the 9th annual report. BR; vol. 7, 1855, with the 11th annual report. BR

C1191 RAINHAM, Kent. National schools. Subscribers to the new school house; opened November 9th, 1846. Sittingbourne, Coulter, [1846]. BI

C1192 RAMSAY, John. A letter to the ... Lord Advocate of Scotland on the state of education in the Outer Hebrides in 1862. Glasgow, Gilchrist, 1863. LEE

C1193 RANDOLPH, Edward John. (1862) The good properties of the Revised Code considered, in a letter to the Archbishop of York. Rivingtons, 1862. HU

C1194 RAPET, Jean Jacques. Considérations sur l'éducation. Paris, Plassan, 1831. LO

C1195 RATCLIFF, Charles. (1861) Ragged schools in relation to the government grants for education. The authorized report of the conference held at Birmingham, January 23, 1861. Longman, [1861]. HU NE

C1196 RAUMER, Karl von. Contributions to the history and improvement of the German universities. N.Y., Brownell, 1859. BI

C1197 RAWES, Henry Augustus, 1826–1885. Cui bono? University education: a letter to a Catholic layman. Longman, 1864. HU

C1198 REASONS why the clergy should adopt the government plan of national education. By a presbyter of the Church of England. Ridgway, 1840. LEE

Recent measures for the promotion of education in England. See Kay-Shuttleworth, Sir J. P.

C1199 RECOLLECTIONS of a Blue-Coat boy; or, a view of Christ's Hospital. Swaffham, F. Skill, 1829. LO

C1200 REED, Andrew, jnr., and REED, Sir Charles, 1819–1881. (1863) Memoirs of the life and philanthropic labours of Andrew Reed, D.D., with selections from his journals. Edited by his sons. 2nd ed., Strahan, 1863. LEI

C1201 REFORMATORY AND REFUGE UNION. A classified list of reformatories, refuges, industrial schools, prisoners' aid societies, and penitentiaries in Great Britain and Ireland ... The Union, 1859. HU

C1202 REFORMATORY AND REFUGE UNION. The metropolitan reformatories and refuges. An authentic account of thirty institutions. R. K. Burt, pr., 1856. HU

C1203 REID, Thomas, 1710–1796. (1788) Essay on the active powers of the human mind. Tegg, 1843. LO

C1204 REINER, Charles. Lessons on form; or, an introduction to geometry. As given in a Pestalozzian school, Cheam, Surrey. Taylor & Walton, 1837. HU OX

C1205 REINER, Charles. (1831) Lessons on number, as given in a Pestalozzian school, Cheam, Surrey. The master's manual. 3rd ed., Taylor, 1851. LEE; The scholar's praxis. 2nd ed., Taylor, 1835. HU

Religious instruction in a graduated series of lessons. See Mayo, Elizabeth

C1206 REMARKS on female education; adapted particularly to the regulation of schools. Holdsworth, 1823. BI

C1207 REMARKS on the minute of the Committee of the Privy Council on Education, dated July 29, 1861, establishing a revised code of regulations. Seeley, [etc.], 1862. [Issued by the Committee appointed April 19, 1860, to watch proceedings in Parliament in reference to the grants for national education.] HU

C1208 REMARKS on the plan proposed by the Lord Bishop of Ossory and Ferns, for the settlement of the education question in Ireland. By a manager of a national school. Dublin, Hodges & Smith, 1854. BI

C1209 REMARKS on the Rev. Dr. Vincent's 'Defence of public education'; with an attempt to state fairly the question, whether the religious instruction and moral conduct of the rising generation are sufficiently provided for . . . in our schools and universities . . . By a layman. Hatchard, 1802. HU LO

C1210 REMARKS suggested by proceedings of the late meeting at Lincoln held for the purpose of instituting a system of national education. 1812. ReU

C1211 REMARKS upon Mr. Beverley's letter to the Duke of Gloucester, with a few statements . . . illustrative of the present state of the university of Cambridge; by a member of Trinity College. Cambridge, Hall, 1833. LEI

Remarques sur la méthode de M. Jacotot. *See* Bauclos, Louis de

C1212 RENWICK, T. W. A course of lectures on education, physical, mental and moral. Liverpool, Marples, 1842. LO

Reply to the calumnies of the Edinburgh Review against Oxford. *See* Copleston, E.

C1213 REPORT of the proceedings at the public meeting of the friends of national education in the Music Hall, Edinburgh, January 25, 1854. Black, 1854. HU

C1214 A REVIEW and compendium of the minutes of evidence taken before the Select committee of the House of Lords, appointed . . . 1854, to inquire into the practical working of the system of national education in Ireland . . . with prefatory remarks, explanatory notes, and an appendix. Edited by an advocate of Lord Stanley's plan. London, Groombridge; Dublin, Thom; 1855. LEI

C1215 REVUE de l'éducation nouvelle: journal des mères et des enfants. Paris. 1e & 2e séries, nov. 1848–oct. 1850, 5e & 6e séries, nov. 1852–oct. 1854. LEI

C1216 REVUE ENCYCLOPEDIQUE. [Extract from Tome LVI, novembre 1832]; Education intérieure ou domestique. LO

C1217 REY, Joseph Philippe Etienne. De la méthode Jacotot. Grenoble, Prudhomme, [183–?]. HU LO

C1218 RICARDO, Ralph. Juvenile vagrancy: suggestions for its diminution. Dean, [1850?]. BI

C1219 RICHARD, Henry, 1812–1888. (1870) United secular and separate religious education: speech on moving an amendment on the Education Bill in the House of Commons, June 24th, 1870. Hodder & Stoughton, 1870. BI LO

C1220 RICHSON, Charles, 1806–1874. The agencies and organization required in a national system of education. Longman, 1856. [From the Transactions of the Manchester statistical society, Nov. 15, 1855.] BI

C1221 RICHSON, Charles. (1850) Pauper education: its provisions and defects; with certain objections to its extension, considered in a letter to . . . Sir Geo. Grey. 2nd ed., Rivingtons, 1850. LEE

C1222 RICHSON, Charles. (1861) The Revised Code and the report of the Royal Commissioners on Education in 1861 contrasted in some essential particulars. Manchester, Sowler, 1861. LEE

C1223 RICHTER, Jean Paul Friedrich, 1763–1825. (German 1807?; Eng. 1848) Levana, oder Erziehlehre, von Jean Paul. 2. Aufl. Stuttgart & Tübingen, Cotta, 1814. 3 vols. in 1. LO

C1224 RICHTER, J. P. F. Levana, or, the doctrine of education. Translated from the German. Longman, 1848. BI HU LEE NO; Boston, Ticknor & Fields, 1866. LEI; 1876. ReU; Bell, 1884. RE; Sonnenschein, 1887. HU SH

C1225 RIGG, James Harrison, 1821–1909. (1870) Denominational and national education. Reprinted from the 'London quarterly review', Jan. 1870 . . . Beveridge, pr., [1870]. HU

C1226 RIGG, J. H. (1870) The history and present position of primary education in England and in connexion with Wesleyan Methodism: an address to the students in the Wesleyan Training Institution, Westminster, Feb. 1870. Wesleyan Tr. Coll., [1870]. HU LEE

C1227 RIO, A. F. La petite Chouannerie; ou, histoire d'un collège breton [i.e. Collège de Vannes] sous l'Empire. Londres, Moxon, 1842. LEI

RIOFREY, Antoine Martin Bureaud-. *See* Bureaud-Riofrey, Antoine Martin

RIOFREY, *Mme.* Bureaud-. *See* Bureaud-Riofrey, *Mme.*

C1228 RIVINGTON, Septimus. (1869) The history of Tonbridge School from its foundations in 1553 to the present date. 2nd ed., rev. and enl., Rivingtons, 1898. SH

C1229 ROBERTS, William, 1767–1849. Memoirs of the life of Mrs. Hannah More. Seeley & Burnside, 1836. 2 vols. HU

C1230 ROBERTSON, John. Observations on the social condition of Ireland, and on the Irish national schools. [No pub.], 1855. BI

C1231 ROBERTSON, John, *late of Edinburgh.* A view of the system of education, pursued in the public schools and university of Edinburgh; with remarks on the present state of learning in Scotland. Warren, 1818. BI

C1232 ROBIANO BORSBEEK, Louis François de-Paule Marie Joseph, *comte de*, 1781–1855. Dei sistemi attuali d'educazione del popolo. 2a ed., Milan, Ferrario, 1819. BI

C1233 ROBINS, Sanderson, 1801–1862. (1850) Church schoolmaster. Rivington, 1850. ReU

C1234 ROBINS, Sanderson. (1862) Twenty reasons for accepting the revised educational code. Longman, 1862. HU

C1235 ROBINSON, Edward. A concise view of the universities, and of the state of theological education in Germany. Edinburgh, Clark, 1835. BI

C1236 ROBINSON, Robert. (1863) Teacher's manual of method and organisation adapted to the primary schools of Great Britain, Ireland, and the colonies. 3rd ed., Longmans, 1869. LEI

C1237 ROCHESTER. Diocese. *Training institution, Hockerill. Committee.* The new educational code; memorial . . . to the Rt. Hon. Earl Granville . . . [No pub., 1861.] BI

C1238 RODGERS, James. A practical treatise on infant education; being an entire plan for organizing and conducting infant schools . . . Hatchard, [etc.], [c. 1825?]. LEE

C1239 ROEBUCK, John Arthur, 1801–1879. (1833) The speech of Mr. Roebuck, M.P., on national education. Chappell, 1833. LEI

C1240 ROGERS, James Edwin Thorold, 1823–1890. (1861) Education in Oxford. Smith, Elder, 1861. ReU

C1241 ROLLIN, Charles, 1661–1741. (1726–1731) Traité des études. Nlle. éd., revue par M. Letronne. Paris, Didot, 1845. 3 vols. LEI ReU

C1242 RONGE, Bertha. 'Kinder Garten': an address on infant training. 1854. LO

C1243 RONGE, Johann, and RONGE, Bertha. Kinder Garten and humanistic schools: a monthly paper for promoting a reformed system of education and the harmony between home and school. Nos. 1–3, May–July 1856. Darton. LEI

C1244 RONGE, J., and RONGE, B. (1855) A practical guide to the English kinder-garten... being an exposition of Froebel's system of infant training... 3rd ed., Hodson, 1863. LEI; 3rd ed., Myers, 1865. HU; 4th ed., Myers, 1871. LEE; 14th ed., Myers, 1883. LO; 15th ed., Myers, 1884. CA

C1245 RONGE, J., and RONGE, B. Revised report: addresses by Herr and Madame Ronge, on the kinder garten system of elementary education. Manchester, Fletcher & Tubbs, 1859. LEE

C1246 [ROPER, William John James Duff]. Chronicles of Charterhouse, by a Carthusian. Bell, 1847. [Sometimes attributed to W. J. D. Ryder.] LEE ReU

C1247 ROSENKRANZ, Johann Karl Friedrich, 1805–1879. (Germ. 1848) [Paedagogik als System.] The philosophy of education. Translated from the German by Anna C. Brackett. 2nd ed., N.Y., Appleton, 1886. CA; N.Y., Appleton, 1908. LO

C1248 ROSMINI SERBATI, Antonio, 1797–1855. (1857) The ruling principle of method applied to education. Translated by Mrs. William Grey. Boston, Heath, 1887. LEE LEI

C1249 ROTCH, Benjamin. Suggestions for the prevention of juvenile depravity. Court, 1846. BI

C1250 ROTH, Mathias. (1852) Movements or exercises, according to Ling's system, for the due development and strengthening of the human body in childhood and in youth. Extracted from... 'The prevention and cure of disease by movements', etc. Groombridge, 1852. LEI

C1251 ROUSSEAU, Jean Jacques, 1712–1778. (1762) Emile, ou de l'éducation. Paris, Didot, 1816. 3 vols. LO

C1252 ROYAL INSTITUTION, London. Lectures on education, delivered at the Royal Institution of Great Britain. Parker, 1854. LEI LO; Parker, 1855. HU LO MA RE

C1253 ROYAL LANCASTERIAN INSTITUTION. Reports of the finance committee and trustees... for the years 1810–1812. Longman, 1811–1813. BR; Report for 1812. HU

ROYAL LANCASTERIAN INSTITUTION. See also British and foreign school society; Institution for promoting the British system of education

ROYAL SOCIETY OF ARTS. See Society of arts

ROYAL UNIVERSAL INFIRMARY FOR CHILDREN. See London. Royal universal infirmary.

C1254 RUMFORD, Benjamin Thompson, count von, 1753–1814. Essays on the management of the poor, and industrial occupation for soldiers in barracks... J. Masters, 1851. HU

C1255 RUMFORD, count von. Essays political, economical, and philosophical. Vol. 1, 5th ed., [and] vol. 3, new ed., Cadell & Davies, 1800–1802. LEE

C1256 [RUSHDEN, G. W.] National education. Melbourne, Argus, 1853. LO

C1257 RUSHTON, Edward, 1796–1851. A letter, addressed to the Town Council and select vestry of the borough of Liverpool, upon juvenile crime. Liverpool, Egerton Smith, 1850. HU

C1257a RUSKIN, John, 1819–1900. (1866?) Sesame and lilies. [In his Works; ed. by E. T. Cook and A. Wedderburn. Vol. 18, 1905.] LEI

C1258 RUSSELL, John Scott, 1808–1882. Systematic technical education for the English people. Bradbury, Evans, 1869. HU LEE

RUSTICUS, pseud. See Maurice, F. D.

C1259 [RYDER, W. J. D.] Chronicles of Charterhouse. See C1246

S.H. See H., S.

C1260 SAILLET, Alexandre de. Les écoles royales de France, ou, l'avenir de la jeunesse... Paris, Lehuby, [1843?]. LEI

SAINT-AUBIN, Stéphanie Félicité du Crest de, comtesse de Genlis. See Genlis, Mme.

C1261 ST. JOHN, James Augustus, 1801–1875. (1858) The education of the people. Chapman & Hall, 1858. BI HU ReU

C1262 ST. PAUL'S SCHOOL, London. Prolusiones literariae, praemiis quotannis propositis dignatae, et in D. Pauli schola recitatae comitiis maximiis, A.S.H. MDCCCXL. Gilbert & Rivington, pr., 1840. LEI

C1263 SALISBURY DIOCESAN BOARD OF EDUCATION. (1862) The Revised code: memorial to the Committee of Council... Salisbury, Brown, 1862. BI

C1264 SALISBURY DIOCESAN BOARD OF EDUCATION. A short account of the Salisbury diocesan board of education. Compiled by the secretary. Salisbury, Bennett, 1865. BI

SALTLEY TRAINING COLLEGE. See Worcester. Diocese. Training college, Saltley

C1265 SALZMANN, Christian Gotthilf, 1744–1811. (1806) Plan zur Erziehung der Erzieher. Hamburg, Hauswedell, 1946. LEI

C1266 SANDFORD, Sir Daniel Keyte, 1798–1838. (1822) A letter to the Reverend Peter Elmsley, A.M., in answer to the appeal made to Professor Sandford, as umpire between the University of Oxford and the Edinburgh Review. Oxford, Munday & Slatter, [etc.], 1822. LEI

C1267 SANDFORD, Elizabeth, 'Mrs. John Sandford', Female improvement. Longman, 1836. 2 vols. HU

C1268 SANDFORD, John, 1801–1873. (1845) Parochialia; or, church, school, and parish. The church system, and services, practically considered. Longman, 1845. BR

SAUSSURE, Albertine Adrienne Necker de. See Necker de Saussure, A. A.

C1269 SAUVESTRE, Charles. On the knee of the Church. Female training in Romish convents and schools. Wm. Macintosh, 1869. LO

C1270 SCHAIBLE, Charles H. The theory and practice of teaching modern languages in schools. Trübner, 1863. LO

C1271 SCHEME for the regulation and management of the school and charities in the township of Hartwith, as ordered by the Board of Charity Commissioners...16 November 1866. Ripon, [no pub.], 1866. LEE

C1272 SCHILLER, Friedrich v., 1759–1805. (Written 1795) Ueber die aesthetische Erziehung des Menschen. [And translation.] See B929

C1273 SCHIMMELPENNINCK, Mrs. Mary Anne, 1778–1856. (1829) Select memoirs of Port Royal... 5th ed., Longman, 1858. 3 vols. BI

C1274 SCHLEIERMACHER, Friedrich Ernst Daniel, 1768–1834. Uber die Bildung zur Persönlichkeit und Gemeinschaft: ausgewählte Abschnitte aus Schleiermachers Schriften. Hrsg. von H. Seiler. Bielefeld and Leipzig, Velhagen & Klasing, 1928. LEI

C1275 The SCHOOL and the teacher, for the use of masters, mistresses, and pupil teachers in elementary schools. Conducted by Church schoolmasters. Vols. 4–5, 1857–1858. LEI

School in its relation to the state. See Kay-Shuttleworth, Sir J. P.

School-life at Winchester College. See Mansfield, R. B.

C1276 SCHOOLMASTER, pseud. A practical treatise on day-schools. 1816. ReU

C1277 The SCHOOLMASTER, a weekly essay... Vols. 1–2, 1829–1830. LEI

Schoolmaster: essays on practical education. See Society for the diffusion of useful knowledge.

C1278 A SCHOOLMASTER's difficulties, abroad and at home. Longman, 1853. LEI

C1279 SCHOOLS for all in preference to schools for Churchmen only. 1812. ReU

C1280 SCHUBERT, Gotthilf Heinrich v., 1780–1860. Memoirs of John Frederic Oberlin. Translated by Mrs. Sydney Williams. [In Memoirs of Felix Neff, John F. Oberlin and Bernhard Overberg.] See C1518

SCOTT, Charles Broderick, joint ed. See Mure, James, and others, eds.

C1281 SCOTT, John. (1862) The working classes entitled to a good education: an address to the students in the Wesleyan training institution, Westminster, January 30th, 1862. Mason, 1862. BI

Scriptural education in Ireland. See Whately, Richard

C1282 SEDGWICK, Adam, 1785–1873. (1833) A discourse on the studies of the University [in Cambridge]. Cambridge, Pitt, pr., 1833. NO ReU; 2nd ed., Cambridge, Deighton, 1834. LEE LO; 4th ed., Cambridge, Deighton; London, Parker; 1835. LEI; 5th ed. with additions and a preliminary discourse. Parker, [etc.], 1850. LEE LEI

C1283 SEEBOHM, Frederic, 1833–1912. (1870) How can compulsory education be made to work in England? Longmans, 1870. LEI

C1284 SEELEY, Sir John Robert, 1834–1895. Lectures and essays. Macmillan, 1870. LEE

C1285 SEGUIN, Edouard, 1812–1880. (1866) Idiocy; and its treatment by the physiological method. N.Y., Columbia univ. Teachers coll., 1907. LEI NO

C1286 SEMPLE, Agnes Sophia, formerly Hunter. Thoughts on education; in two parts: the first on general education, and the second part on that of females. Murray, 1812. LEE

C1287 SENIOR, Nassau William, 1790–1864. (1861) Suggestions on popular education. Murray, 1861. BR ReU SH

SERBATI, Antonio Rosmini. See Rosmini Serbato, A.

C1288 A SERIOUS address on the great importance of Sunday schools, with a copious appendix. Published for the benefit of [Canterbury] Union Chapel Sunday School. Canterbury, Blake, [etc.], [1807]. LEE

C1289 [SEWELL, Elizabeth Missing], 1815–1906. (1865) Principles of education, drawn from nature, and applied to female education in the upper classes. By the author of 'Amy Herbert'. Longmans, 1865. 2 vols. HU NE

C1290 SHAFTESBURY, Antony Ashley Cooper, 7th earl of, 1801–1885. (1839) Speech of Lord Ashley, in the House of Commons, June 14, 1839; on Lord Stanley's motion... to revoke the appointment of the Committee of Privy Council on Education. [Private circ.], 1839. HU

C1291 SHEFFIELD. Mechanics' institution and mechanics' library. Report of the proceedings of the soirée held...in honour of Sir Arnold James Knight...July 5, 1843. Sheffield, The Institution, 1843. BI

C1292 SHEPHERD, William, 1768–1847, and others. (1815) Systematic education; or, elementary instruction in the various departments of literature and science, with practical rules for studying each branch of useful knowledge. By Rev. W. Shepherd, Rev. J. Joyce, Rev. L. Carpenter. Longman, 1815. 2 vols. BI; vol. 1 [only]. LEE; 2nd ed., Longman, 1817. 2 vols. LEI NoU ReU

SHERBROOKE, Robert Lowe, 1st visct. See Lowe, R.

C1293 SHERIDAN, Thomas, 1719–1788. (1775) Lectures on the art of reading in two parts. Part 1: The art of reading prose; Part 2: The art of reading verse. 6th ed., Mawman, [etc.], 1805. SH

C1294 SHERWOOD, Mrs. Mary Martha, 1775–1851. (1854) The life of Mrs. Sherwood, chiefly autobiographical, with extracts from Mr. Sherwood's journal; edited by her daughter, Sophia Kelly. Darton, 1854. LEI ReU; Darton, 1857. SH

C1295 SHINTON, William Edward. Lectures on an improved system of teaching the art of writing ...to which are added, practical hints to young penmen. Longman, 1823. HU

C1296 SHIRREFF, Emily Anne Eliza, 1814–1897. (1858) Intellectual education: and its influence on the character and happiness of women. Parker, 1858. BR HU LEE SH

C1297 SHORT, Thomas Vowler, 1790–1872. (1822) A letter addressed to the . . . Dean of Christ Church, on the state of the public examinations in the University of Oxford. Oxford, Parker, 1822. LEI

C1298 A SHORT account of the Blue Coat charity school, Birmingham. 1832. ReU

C1299 SHREWSBURY SCHOOL. Sabrinae corolla in hortulis regiae scholae Salopiensis contexuerunt tres viri floribus legendis. Bell, 1850. LEI

SHUTTLEWORTH, Sir James Phillips Kay-. See Kay-Shuttleworth, Sir J. P.

C1301 SICARD, Roch-Ambroise, 1742–1822. (1800) Cours d'instruction d'un sourd-muet de naissance, pour servir à l'éducation des sourds-muets. Paris, Le Clere, An VIII [1801]. LO

C1302 SICARD, Roch-Ambroise. Cours d'instruction d'un sourd-muet de naissance, et qui peut être utile à l'éducation de ceux qui entendent et qui parlent . . . 2e éd., Paris, Le Clere, 1803. BI NoU

SILLERY, marquise de. See Genlis, comtesse de

C1303 SIMON, Jules, 1814–1896. (1865) L'école. Paris, Lacroix, [etc.], 1865. LO

C1304 [SIMPSON, James], 1781–1853. (1837) Anti-national education, or the spirit of sectarianism morally tested by means of certain speeches and letters from the member for Kilmarnock. Edinburgh, Black, 1837. LEE; With an appendix. Edinburgh, Black, 1838. BI

C1305 SIMPSON, James. (1834) Necessity of popular education, as a national object; with hints on the treatment of criminals . . . Edinburgh, Black, 1834. HU ReU SH

C1306 SIMPSON, James. do. 2nd ed.: The philosophy of education, with its practical application to a system and plan of popular education as a national object. Edinburgh, Black, 1836. BI HU LEE ReU SH

C1307 SIMPSON, James. (1850) The normal school as it ought to be; its principles, objects and organization. Edinburgh, Neill, 1850. BI

C1308 SIMPSON, James. Prize essay. See C242 Central society of education

C1309 [SIMPSON, Mary E.] (1861) Ploughing and sowing; or, annals of an evening school in a Yorkshire village [i.e. Carnaby], and the work that grew out of it. From letters and private notes. By a clergyman's daughter. Edited by the Rev. F. Digby Legard. 2nd ed., enl., Mozley, 1861. HU

C1310 SINCLAIR, Catherine, 1800–1864. (1836) Modern accomplishments, or, the march of intellect. Edinburgh, Waugh & Innes; London, Nisbet; 1836. LEI

C1311 SINCLAIR, John, 1797–1875. Letter to a member of Parliament on national education. Rivington, 1842. LEE

C1312 SINCLAIR, John. (3rd ed., 1862) Remarks on school rates in England and America. 4th ed., National Society's depository, 1867. BI

C1313 SINCLAIR, John. Remarks on the common school system of the United States, in a letter to the Rt. Hon. Earl Granville . . . [National Society], 1857. BI

C1314 SKEATS, Herbert S. (1861) Popular education in England: being an abstract of the report of the Royal commissioners on education . . . Bradbury & Evans, 1861. LEI

Sketches from Cambridge. By a don. See Stephen, Sir Leslie

C1315 SLACK, Samuel. Considerations on the nature and tendency of classical literature. With remarks on the discipline at present pursued in the free grammar school of King Charles II at Bradford in the county of York. Slack, 1822. BI

C1316 SLEIGHT, William. (1848) A voice from the dumb: a memoir of John William Lashford, late a pupil in the Brighton and Sussex Institution for the Deaf and Dumb. [2nd ed.], London, Hamilton, Adams; Brighton, Johnson; 1849. LEE

C1317 [SMEDLEY, Francis Edward], 1818–1864. (1850) Frank Fairlegh; or, scenes from the life of a private pupil. Hall, Virtue, 1850. LO

C1318 SMILES, Samuel, 1812–1904. (1838) Physical education; or, the nurture and management of children; founded on the study of their nature and constitution. Edinburgh, Oliver & Boyd, 1838. LEE; another ed. Edited, with additions, by Sir Hugh Beevor. W. Scott, 1905. LEI

C1319 SMILES, Samuel. (1859) Self-help, with illustrations of conduct and perseverance. Murray, 1936 reprint. LEI

C1320 SMITH, Benjamin Frederick. (1861) A letter to the Lord Archbishop of Canterbury, on the Revised Code, with a special report on its financial bearing on the diocese of Canterbury. Cox & Wyman, 1861. BI LEE

C1321 SMITH, Goldwin, 1823–1910. (1861) Lectures on the study of history, delivered in Oxford, 1859–1861. 2nd ed., Oxford, Parker, 1865. LO

C1322 SMITH, Goldwin. A plea for the abolition of tests in the University of Oxford. Oxford, Wheeler & Day, 1864. LO

C1323 SMITH, James, rector of Islandmagee. National education in Ireland: a letter addressed to the Lord Bishop of Cashell, in the 'Dublin Evening Post' of 22 April, 1845. HU

C1324 [SMITH, Rev. Richard Henry]. Twigs for nests; or, notes on nursery nurture. By the author of 'The expositions of the cartoons of Raphael', etc. Nisbet, 1866. LEI

C1325 SMITH, Sydney, 1771–1854. Selections from the writings of . . . Longman, 1855. [Includes reviews, from the Edinburgh Review, of educational books.] LEI

C1326 SMITH, Sydney. [Review of Broadhurst's] Advice to young ladies on the improvement of the mind. [Extracted from the Edinburgh Review, 1810.] LEE

C1327 SMITH, Sydney. [Review of Edgeworth's] Essays on professional education. [Extracted from the Edinburgh Review, Oct. 1809.] LEE

C1328 SMITH, William, 1816–1896, ed. and trans. (1845) On the nature of the scholar, and its manifestations, by J. G. Fichte. Translated from the German, with a memoir of the author. Chapman, 1845. LEI LO

C1329 SMYTH, Richard, 1826–1878. (1861) Philanthropy, proselytism and crime: a review of the Irish reformatory system; with a glance at the reformatories of Great Britain, and at Mr. Maguire's Industrial schools bill. Londonderry, Hamilton, [etc.], 1861. LEI

C1330 SOCIÉTÉ D'AGRICULTURE, ARTS ET COMMERCE DU DOUBS. Projet de souscription pour l'instruction gratuite des enfans du pauvre. Besançon, Mourgeon, [1814]. HU

C1331 SOCIÉTÉ POUR L'INSTRUCTION ÉLÉMENTAIRE. Méthode d'enseignement universel des langues, des sciences et des arts; ou, manuel d'instructions pour l'enseignement mutuel, naturel, universel et particulier. 2e éd., Paris, Colas, 1828. HU

C1332 SOCIETY FOR BETTERING THE CONDITION OF THE POOR. Reports. Vols. 1–2, 4–5, Bulmer, 1798–1808. LEI; vols. 1–4, Bulmer, 1798–1805. BI; see also C114–116 Bernard, Sir T.

C1333 SOCIETY FOR PROMOTING CHRISTIAN KNOWLEDGE. An account of the society... Rivington, 1805. BI

C1334 SOCIETY FOR PROMOTING THE AMENDMENT OF THE LAW. The treatment of criminal children. Spottiswoode, [c. 1853]. HU

C1335 SOCIETY FOR PROMOTING THE EDUCATION OF THE POOR IN IRELAND. [Reply to] an address to the London Hibernian Society. [Dublin, Bentham & Hardy, 1825.] BI

C1336 SOCIETY FOR PROMOTING THE EDUCATION OF THE POOR IN IRELAND. Reports, 1–16. Dublin, Bentham & Hardy, [etc.], 1813–1828. BI

C1337 SOCIETY FOR THE DIFFUSION OF USEFUL KNOWLEDGE. Quarterly journal of education. See C1182 Quarterly journal of education

C1338 SOCIETY FOR THE DIFFUSION OF USEFUL KNOWLEDGE. (1836) The Schoolmaster: essays on practical education, selected from the works of Ascham, Milton, Locke, and Butler; from the Quarterly journal of education; and from lectures delivered before the American institute of instruction. Knight, 1836. 2 vols. HU LEE LEI

C1339 SOCIETY FOR THE EDUCATION OF THE POOR IN THE HIGHLANDS. Moral statistics of the Highlands and Islands of Scotland. To which is prefixed a Report on the past and present state of education in these districts. Inverness, The Society, 1826. LO

SOCIETY FOR THE ENCOURAGEMENT OF ARTS, ETC. See Society of arts

C1340 SOCIETY FOR THE PROMOTION OF POPULAR INSTRUCTION. Memoirs of Felix Neff, John F. Oberlin, and Bernhard Overberg. Translated from the German, by Mrs. Sydney Williams. Bristol, Wright & Albright for the Society, 1840. LEI

C1341 SOCIETY OF ARTS, MANUFACTURES AND COMMERCE. (1854) Lectures in connection with the educational exhibition of the Society... Routledge, 1854. BR LO; 2nd ed., Routledge, 1855. HU

C1342 SOCIETY OF ARTS, MANUFACTURES AND COMMERCE. Middle class instruction, and class instruction in mechanics' institutions, considered in two reports of the Society... Longman, 1857. HU

C1343 SOCIETY OF ARTS, MANUFACTURES AND COMMERCE. The report of the committee appointed by the Council of the Society... to inquire into the subject of industrial instruction, with the evidence... [Chairman and reporter: James Booth.] Longman, 1853. LEI

C1344 SOCIETY OF FRIENDS. Sketch of the history of education in the Society of Friends, with a review of the proceedings of the Friends' educational society, and other papers. York, Simpson, 1855. BI

Some account of the Blue Coat hospital... in the college, Manchester. See Mullis, W.

Some account of the life and writings of Mrs. Trimmer. See Trimmer, Mrs. S.

C1345 SOME remarks. (1834) Some remarks on the present studies and management of Eton school, by a parent. 2nd ed., Ridgway, 1834. SH

C1346 SOPWITH, Thomas, 1803–1879. (1853) Education: its present state and future advancement; being the substance of a lecture. Newcastle-upon-Tyne, Author, 1853. HU

C1347 SOPWITH, Thomas. Education in village schools: an address delivered at the opening of a new school at Thropton, in Northumberland, on the 30th September, 1867. London, Willis & Sotheran; Newcastle-upon-Tyne, T. P. Barkas; 1868. NE

C1348 SOUTHEY, Robert, 1774–1843, and SOUTHEY, Charles Cuthbert. (1844) The life of the Rev. Andrew Bell: comprising the history of the rise and progress of the system of moral tuition. London, Murray; Edinburgh, Blackwood; 1844. 3 vols. [Vols. 1–2 by Robert Southey; vol. 3 by Charles Cuthbert Southey.] LEE LEI ReU

C1349 SPENCER, Herbert, 1820–1903. On education. Edited by F. A. Cavenagh. C.U.P., 1932. LEI NE NO SH

C1350 SPENCER, Herbert. (Articles 1854–1859, book 1861) Education: intellectual, moral, and physical. G. Manwaring, 1861. HU; Williams & Norgate, [1861]. BI LO ReU; Williams & Norgate, various reprint dates. LEI LO NO SH; Watts, 1929. SH

C1351 SPENCER, Herbert. Essays on education, etc. [Introduction by Charles W. Eliot.] Dent, various reprint dates of 1911 ed. CA LEE LEI NE SH

C1352 SPENCER, Herbert. (1855) The principles of psychology. Longman, 1855. BI; 3rd ed., Williams & Norgate, 1881. 2 vols. LEI; 1890. 2 vols. SH

C1353 SPENCER, Thomas, 1796–1853. Remarks on national education; Observations on the school return for the diocese of Bath and Wells; [and other pamphlets]. Green, 1840–1842. LO

C1354 SPROAT, Gilbert Malcolm. Education of the rural poor, with a full discussion of the principles and requirements of remedial legislation thereon. R. J. Bush, 1870. BR

C1355 SPURZHEIM, Johann Caspar [*otherwise* Johann Christoph], 1776–1832. (1821) A view of the elementary principles of education, founded on the study of the nature of man. Edinburgh, Constable, 1821. LO; 2nd ed., Treuttel, Würtz & Richter, 1828. BI; 4th American edition, revised from the 3rd London ed., Boston, Marsh, [etc.], 1835. LEI

C1356 STAACK, Johann. Briefe über den segenreichen Einfluss der Schullehrer-Conferenzen auf das Schul- und kirchliche Leben, und auf das staatsbürgerliche Wohl. Altona, Hammerich, 1832. LO

C1357 STACE, —, '*Mrs.* Henry Stace'. A voice to mothers. Nisbet, 1859. RE

C1358 STALLAERT, Charles, and HAEGHEN, Philippe van der. De l'instruction publique au moyen âge. (VIIIe au XVIe siècle.) Brussels, [no pub.], 1850. LEE

C1359 STANHOPE, Edward, 1840–1893. [A letter on education.] *See* C19 Akroyd, E.

C1360 STANLEY, Arthur Penrhyn, 1815–1881. (1844) The life and correspondence of Thomas Arnold, D.D. Fellowes, 1844. 2 vols. HU; 2nd ed., Fellowes, 1844. 2 vols. BR SO; 4th ed., Fellowes, 1845. 2 vols. BR; 7th ed., Fellowes, 1852. LO; 8th ed., Fellowes, 1858. 2 vols. BI; 6th ed., Murray, 1846. ReU; 11th ed., Murray, 1880. 2 vols. SH; Teachers' ed., Murray, 1901 [and reprints]. CA LO NO; 2nd ed., Ward, Lock, 1890. LEI; Ward Lock, n.d. LO

STANLEY, Arthur Penrhyn, *joint author*. *See* Jowett, Benjamin and Stanley, A. P.

C1361 STAUNTON, Howard, 1810–1874. (1865) The great schools of England: an account of the foundation, endowment, and discipline of the chief seminaries of learning in England ... Sampson Low, 1865. HU LI NE NO RE ReU SH; New ed., rev. and corr., with an appendix containing notices of the endowed grammar schools of England and Wales. Strahan, 1869. LEI

C1362 STEINBERG, *Mme.* —. Lecture on female education. Paris, Author, 1855. LEE

C1363 [STEPHEN, *Sir* Leslie], 1832–1904. Sketches from Cambridge, by a don. Macmillan, 1865. [Reprinted from Pall Mall gazette.] BI; *another ed.* with a foreword by G. M. Trevelyan. O.U.P., 1932, repr. 1936. LEI

C1364 STEVEN, William. (1845) History of George Heriot's Hospital, with a memoir of the founder, and an account of the Heriot foundation schools. 3rd ed. ... by Frederick W. Bedford. Edinburgh, Bell & Bradfute, 1872. LEE

C1365 STEVENS, C. A. Copy of a letter to the vice-president of the Committee of Council on Education ... [H.M.S.O.], 1868. *See* E479

C1366 STEWART, John, *curate of Sporle*. The Killarney poor scholar. 1830. ReU

STEWART, Randolph, *9th earl of Galloway*. *See* Galloway, *earl of*

STICKNEY, Sarah, *aft.* Mrs. Ellis. *See* Ellis, *Mrs.* S.

C1367 STONHOUSE, *Sir* James, 1716–1795. (1774) The religious instruction of children recommended. 10th ed., Rivington, 1824. LEI

C1368 STOUGHTON, John. (1851) Philip Doddridge: his life and labours. A centenary memorial. Jackson & Walford, 1851. LEI

C1369 STOW, David, 1793–1864. Bible training for Sabbath schools. Blackie, 1846. ReU

C1370 [STOW, David]. (1833) Infant training; a dialogue, explanatory of the system adopted in the Model Infant School, Glasgow. By a director. Glasgow, Collins, [1833]. [Later called 'Granny and Leezy'.] BI

C1371 STOW, David. (1834) Moral training. 5th ed., Blackie, 1841. ReU

C1372 STOW, David. (1836) The training system adopted in the model schools of the Glasgow Educational Society: a manual for infant and juvenile schools, which includes a system of moral training suited to the condition of large towns. Glasgow, McPhun, 1836. LEE NE; 8th ed., Longman, 1850. BR HU LI NO; 10th ed., enl., Longman, 1854. LEI ReU

C1373 STOW, David. [The training system.] Factory statistics. Blackie, 1846. [From Training system. 7th ed.] BI

C1374 STOW, David. [The training system.] The use of monitors. With separation of the sexes. [Blackie, 1846.] [From Training system. 7th ed.] BI

C1375 STOWELL, Hugh, 1799–1865. A second letter to the inhabitants of Manchester, on the proposed system of national education, containing strictures on Mr. Cobden's letter, and on the recent meeting in the Theatre Royal. Manchester, J. Pratt, [1837]. HU

C1376 STRICTURES on the publications of the Central Society of Education. Ward, 1837. LEE

C1377 STYLES, John. (1812) A sermon, preached at Salter's Hall, February 23, 1812, for the benefit of the Royal Lancasterian Institution ... Gale & Curtis, 1812. HU

Subscription no bondage. *See* Maurice, F. D.

Suggestions for a scheme of annual school-grants. *See* Hume, Mary C.

Suggestions for an improvement of the examination statute. *See* Jowett, B., and Stanley, A. P.

C1378 SUGGESTIONS for examinations of women, particularly of teachers ... Manchester, Havill, 1868. BR

C1379 SULLIVAN, Robert, 1800–1868. Lectures and letters on popular education, including a translation of M. Guizot's celebrated letter to the primary teachers of France. Dublin, Wm. Curry, 1842. LO

C1380 SULLIVAN, William K. (1866) University education in Ireland: a letter to Sir John Dalberg Acton, Bart. 2nd ed., Dublin, Kelly; London, Ridgway; 1866. NE

C1381 SUNDAY SCHOOL SOCIETY. Plan of a society established in London, A.D. 1785, for the support and encouragement of Sunday schools throughout the British dominions; with a list of subscribers, and extracts of letters ... Bermondsey, printed at the Manufactory for the employment of the deaf and dumb, 1812. HU

C1382 SUNDAY SCHOOL SOCIETY FOR IRELAND. Hints for conducting Sunday schools; useful also for day schools, and families. 2nd ed., enl., Dublin, M. Goodwin, pr., 1821. HU

C1383 SUNDAY school teachers' magazine and journal of education. N.S. vols. 14–15, 1843; 3rd series, vol. 1, 1844, vols. 3–5, 1846–1848. R. Davis. ReU

C1384 SUNDAY SCHOOL UNION. Annual report, 1838. LEE

C1385 SUNDAY SCHOOL UNION. Report of the meetings for the celebration of the sunday school jubilee, Sept. 14, 1831. The Union, 1831. RE

C1386 SUNDAY SCHOOL UNION. The union magazine for sunday school teachers. Vols. XVI–XIX, 1859–1862. LEI

C1387 SUNTER, Rebecca. The Home and Colonial School Society's manual, for infant schools and nurseries. Prepared at the desire of the committee by Miss Rebecca Sunter, late mistress of the Model Infant School, under the direction of Miss Mayo... Home and Colonial School Soc., 1856. HU

C1388 SYMONS, Jelinger Cookson, 1809–1860. School economy: a practical book on the best modes of establishing and teaching schools, and of making them thoroughly useful to the working classes by means of moral and industrial training. Parker, 1852. LEE ReU

C1389 TAINSH, Edward Campbell. Prize essay. On the best means of making the schoolmaster's function more efficient than it has hitherto been in preventing misery and crime. With report of a discussion on the essay at the fourth annual meeting of the United Association of Schoolmasters of Great Britain... 1857. Edinburgh, Constable; London, Hamilton, Adams; 1858. LEI

C1390 TAIT'S MAGAZINE. State education versus national education. Reprinted, by permission, from the November number of Tait's Magazine. Manchester, Love & Barton, pr., 1837. HU

TALLIEN, C. de Brunetière. See Brunetière Tallien, C. de

C1391 TANDEL, Charles Antoine. Plan d'une université pour la Belgique; accompagné de réflexions sur la surveillance en matière d'instruction publique et sur l'usage de la langue maternelle. Brussels, Demanet, 1831. BI

C1392 TARTT, W. M. On subjects connected with crime and punishment. [Read before the British Association at Leeds, 1858.] From the Journal of the Statistical society of London, March 1859. HU

C1393 TATE, Thomas, 1807–1888. (1854) The philosophy of education; or, the principles and practice of teaching. In five parts. Longman, 1854. LEE

C1394 TATE, Thomas. (1845) Treatise on the first principles of arithmetic after the method of Pestalozzi... designed for the use of teachers and monitors in elementary schools. 7th ed., Longman, 1849. NO

C1395 TAYLOR, Mrs. Ann, 1757–1830. (1818?) Reciprocal duties of parents and children. 3rd ed., Taylor & Hessey, 1819. LEE LEI

C1396 [TAYLOR, Isaac], of Stanford Rivers, 1787–1865. (1838) Home education, by the author of 'Natural history of enthusiasm'. Jackson & Walford, 1838. BI BR LEE LO SH; 5th ed., rev., Bohn, 1851. HU LEI LO OX ReU

C1397 TAYLOR, Jane, 1783–1824. (1825) Memoirs, correspondence, and poetical remains. New ed., Holdsworth & Ball, 1831. LEE

C1398 TAYLOR, John, 1694–1761. (1752) The value of a child; or, motives to the good education of children; in a letter to a daughter. 2nd ed., Hunter, 1816. BI

C1399 TAYLOR, John Orville, 1807–1890. (1834) The district school. N.Y., Harper, 1834. LEI

C1400 TAYLOR, William Benjamin Sarsfield, 1781–1850. History of the University of Dublin, founded by Queen Elizabeth... Cadell, 1845. SH

C1401 TAYLOR, William Cooke, 1800–1849. Notes of a visit to the model schools in Dublin, and reflections on the state of the education question in Ireland suggested by that visit. Dublin, Hodges & Smith, 1847. BI SH

C1402 The TEACHER taught; or, the Sunday school instructor furnished with materials for his work, in a series of questions... By the author of 'The mine explored'. [Part 1]. 3rd ed., enl., Nisbet, 1841. HU

C1403 The TEACHER'S visitor; edited by William Carus Wilson. Vols. 6 and 7, 1847. Seeley, [etc.], HU

C1404 The TECHNICAL educator: an encyclopedia of technical education. Cassell, [etc.], [1870]. 2 vols. LO

TERRINGTON, Thomas John, joint author. See Wilderspin, Samuel and Terrington, T. J.

C1405 THIRLWALL, Connop, 1797–1875. (1850) The advantages of literary and scientific institutions for all classes: a lecture delivered at the Town Hall, Carmarthen, on Dec. 11th 1849. London, Longman; Carmarthen, Spurrell: 1850. LEI

C1406 THIRLWALL, Connop. (1846) 'Charity shall cover the multitude of sins.' A sermon preached in the chapel of the Philanthropic Society, St. George's Fields, on Sunday, May 17, 1846. J. Samuel, pr., [1846]. HU

THOMPSON, Benjamin, count von Rumford. See Rumford, Benjamin Thompson, count von

C1407 THOMPSON, D'Arcy Wentworth, 1829–1892. (1864) Daydreams of a schoolmaster. Edinburgh, Edmonston & Douglas, 1864. ReU; 2nd ed., 1864. BR LEE; Isbister, [1898]. LO; Harrap, [pref. 1913]. LEI

C1408 THOMPSON, D'A. W. Wayside thoughts. Nimmo, 1868. ReU

C1409 THOMSON, Alexander, Punishment and prevention. Nisbet, 1857. HU

C1409a [THOMSON, Thomas], 1773–1852, and [COUPER, John]. Memorial respecting the present state of the College of Glasgow. By the Regius professors of chemistry and materia medica. Addressed to the member of Parliament for that city. Johnston, 1835. BI

THON, Adèle du. See Du Thon, A.

Thoughts on education. See Johnson, W.

Thoughts on the present system of academic education. See Butler, Samuel

C1410 THOUGHTS upon domestic or private education. Longman, 1806. HU

C1411 THRING, Edward, 1821–1887. (1864) Education and school. 2nd ed., Macmillan, 1867. BI HU LEE LEI RE ReU

C1412 THRING, Edward. Three letters and axioms on education. Uppingham, Hawthorn, 1858. BI

C1413 THRING, Edward. Truth in schools. Uppingham, Hawthorn, 1860. LO

C1414 TIMBS, John, 1801–1875. (1858) School days of eminent men. Kent, 1858. [Pt. 1: Sketches of the progress of education in England ... Pt. 2: Early lives of celebrated authors, etc.] BR LEE; 2nd ed., rev., Lockwood, 1862. HU LEI LO

C1415 TODD, James Henthorn, 1805–1869. Remarks on some statements ... on academical education in Ireland. Dublin, Hodges & Smith, 1844. SH

C1416 TODD, John, 1800–1873. Sunday school teacher. Sunday school union, 1848. ReU

C1417 TOOKE, William, 1744–1820, trans. Sermons on education ... from the German of G. J. Zollikofer. Longman, 1806. 2 vols. BI

C1418 TOWNSEND, John. (1828) Memoirs of the Rev. John Townsend, founder of the asylum for the deaf and dumb and of the Congregational school. Courthope, 1828. LO

C1419 TOWNSEND, William Charles, 1803–1850. (1826) The paean of Oxford, a poem, to which is prefixed a reply to the charges adduced against the university in recent numbers of the Edinburgh and Westminster reviews. Longman, 1826. LO

C1420 TRENCH, Frederick Fitzwilliam. Observations on the system of the Church Education Society, as applicable to Ireland ... Dublin, Hodges & Smith, 1852. BI

C1421 TRENCH, William le Poer. Reasons for refusing to co-operate with the Board of National Education restated, and addressed to the clergy. Dublin, Hodges & Smith, 1847. LO

C1422 TREVELYAN, Sir Charles Edward, 1807–1886. (1838) On the education of the people of India. Longman, [etc.], 1838. ReU

C1423 TRIMMER, Mrs. Sarah, 1741–1810. (1805) A comparative view of the new plan of education promulgated by Mr. Joseph Lancaster ... Rivington, 1805. BI ReU

C1424 TRIMMER, Mrs. Sarah. Essay on Christian education. [In the Guardian of education.] See C1425

C1425 TRIMMER, Mrs. Sarah. The Guardian of education. Conducted by Mrs. Trimmer. Vols. 1–5, May 1802–Sept. 1806. Hatchard. BI LEI ReU; vols. 1–3, 1802–1804. HU

C1426 TRIMMER, Mrs. Sarah. (1787) The oeconomy of charity; or, an address to ladies concerning Sunday-Schools ... Johnson, & Rivington, 1801. 2 vols. ReU SH

C1427 TRIMMER, Mrs. Sarah. (1814) Some account of the life and writings of Mrs. Trimmer, with original letters, and meditations and prayers, selected from her Journal. Rivington, [etc.], 1814. 2 vols. LEI SH; 2nd ed., Rivington, 1816. 2 vols. BR HU LEE; 3rd ed., Rivington, 1825. BR ReU

C1428 TRINITY College, Dublin. [Dublin, 1870.] NE

C1429 TROLLOPE, William, 1798–1863. (1834) A history of the royal foundation of Christ's Hospital; with an account of the plan of education, the internal economy of the institution, and memoirs of eminent Blues ... Pickering, 1834. LEE LI RE ReU SH

C1430 TRUSLER, John, 1735–1820. (1790?) The progress of man and society. [1810?]. NoU

C1431 TUCKER, Henry Tippetts. A lecture on lectures, delivered before the members of the Pitminster, Corfe, Trull, and Angersleigh Agricultural Society, November 1855. HU

C1432 TUCKFIELD, —, 'Mrs. Hippisley Tuckfield'. Education for the people, embracing: I. Pastoral teaching; II. Village teaching; III. The teacher's text book; IV. Instruction of the deaf and dumb. Taylor & Walton, 1839. BI BR HU

C1433 TURLEY, Edward Astbury. First lines of education: a course of four lectures, delivered to the Literary and Scientific Institution, Worcester ... Worcester, The Institution, 1839. LEE

C1434 [TURNER, Sydney], 1814–1879. (1850) The Philanthropic farm school, Redhill, Surrey. [Report of the first year's progress, 1849/50.] [1850]. LEI

C1435 TURNER, Sydney. (1849) 'Pray for us.' A farewell sermon, preached in the Philanthropic Society's Chapel, St. George's Fields, on Sunday, April 16th, 1849. Reigate, Wm. Allingham, 1849. HU

C1436 TURNER, Sydney, and PAYNTER, —. (1846) Mettray: report on the system and arrangements of 'La Colonie Agricole', at Mettray. Presented to the committee of the Philanthropic Society, St. George's Fields, 19th August, 1846. Truscott, 1846. BI; 2nd ed., rev., Hatchard, 1846. LEE

C1437 TURNER, William, 1761–1859. (1813–1815) The Warrington Academy. Part I: Historical account of the Warrington Academy. Part II: Historical account of students educated in the Warrington Academy. Reprinted from articles originally published in the Monthly Repository, vols. VIII, IX and X, 1813–1815. Edited by G. A. Carter. Warrington, Library and Museum committee, 1957. LEI NE SH

Twice-revised code. Reprinted from Fraser's magazine. See Arnold, Matthew

Twigs for nests. See Smith, Richard Henry

C1438 TWINING, Thomas, 1806–1895. Science for the people: a memorandum on various means for propagating scientific and practical knowledge among the working classes, and for thus promoting their physical, technical and social improvement ... Goodman, 1870. BR

C1439 TWISLETON, Edward Turner Boyd, 1809–1874, ed. Evidence as to the religious working of the common schools in the state of Massachusetts ... 3rd ed., Ridgway, 1855. [Originally presented to the Committee of the House of Commons on the Manchester and Salford Education bill.] HU

C1440 Two prize essays on juvenile delinquency. Smith, Elder, 1853. [1. Juvenile delinquency, by Micaiah Hill. 2. On the treatment of the dangerous and perishing classes of society, by C. F. Cornwallis.] BI

C1441 TYLOR, Alfred, 1824–1884. Education and manufactures. No. 4. Longmans, 1863. BR

C1442 TYNDALL, John, 1820–1893. (1854) On the importance of physics as a branch of education for all classes: a lecture delivered at the Royal Institution of Great Britain. Parker, 1854. BR; *see also* C1252 Royal Institution

C1443 ULLATHORNE, William Bernard, 1806–1889. Notes on the education question. Richardson, 1857. HU

C1444 The UNION magazine for Sunday school teachers. Vols. XVI–XIX, 1859–1862. Sunday school union. LEI

C1445 UNWIN, William Jordan. (1856) Education the work of the people: a letter to Lord John Russell on the resolutions for establishing a system of national education, submitted to Parliament, March 6, 1856. Ward, [1856]. BI HU

C1446 UNWIN, W. J. (1862) The primary school. First part: School management. [No more pub.] Longmans, 1862. LEE; Longmans, [1863?]. LEI

C1447 UNWIN, W. J., *ed.* Prussian primary education, its organization and results. Ward, 1857. BI LEE

C1447a VALLET DE VIRIVILLE, Auguste de. Histoire de l'instruction publique en Europe et principalement en France, depuis le christianisme jusqu'à nos jours ... Paris, Administration du Moyen Age et de la Renaissance, 1849. LO

C1448 VAUGHAN, Charles John, 1816–1897. (1854) A letter to the Viscount Palmerston, M.P., ... on the monitorial system of Harrow school. Murray, 1854. LEI

C1449 VAUGHAN, C. J. (1861) The Revised code of the Committee of Council on Education dispassionately considered. An address to the clergy of the Deanery of Doncaster. 3rd ed., Cambridge and London, Macmillan, 1862. HU

C1450 VAUGHAN, C. J., and PLATT, Thomas Joshua, *baron.* (1854) Correspondence between the Rev. Dr. Vaughan and the Hon. Baron Platt; on the occasion of Baron Platt's removing his son from the school [i.e. Harrow]. Salisbury, Beeton, pr., [1854]. HU

C1451 VAUGHAN, Henry Halford, 1811–1885. (1854) Oxford reform and Oxford professors; a reply to certain objections urged against the report of the Queen's Commissioners. Parker, 1854. LEE

C1452 VAUGHAN, Herbert, *cardinal,* 1832–1903. (1868) Popular education in England: the conscience clause, the rating clause, and the secular current. Longmans, 1868. [Reprinted in a revised form from the Dublin review, Jan. 1868.] BR

C1453 VAUGHAN, William. (1828) A vocabulary arranged for the instruction of the deaf and dumb ... London, Newman; Manchester, Robinson; 1828. LEI

VÉRICOUR, Raymond de. *See* De Véricour, R.

VICTORIA INFANT SCHOOL, *Barnard Castle. See* Barnard Castle. Victoria infant school

C1454 VINCENT, William, 1739–1815. (1801) A defence of public education, addressed to the ... Lord Bishop of Meath. Cadell & Davies, 1801. HU LO; 2nd ed., Cadell & Davies, 1802. LEI; 3rd ed., Cadell & Davies, 1802. BI LEE NE SH

Vindication of Mr. Lancaster's system of education. *See* Fox, Joseph

Vindication of the enquiry into charitable abuses. *See* Ker, C. H. B.

C1455 VINET, Alexandre Rodolphe, 1797–1847. L'éducation, la famille et la société. Paris, 1855. HU

C1456 VIREY, Julian Joseph, 1775–1840. (1802) De l'éducation publique et privée des Français. Paris, Deterville, An X–1802. LO

VIRIVILLE, Auguste Vallet de. *See* Vallet de Viriville, A.

Von deutschen Hochschulen allerlei. *See* Bekker, E. I.

VON RAUMER, Karl. *See* Raumer, Karl von

C1457 WADDINGTON, George, 1793–1869. (1848) Sentiments proper to the present time: an inaugural address ... delivered at the opening of the new building of the Gateshead Mechanics' Institute, April, 1848. Gateshead, W. Douglas, pr., [1848]. HU

C1458 [WADE, John], 1788–1875. An account of public charities in England and Wales, abridged from the reports of His Majesty's Commissioners on charitable foundations, with notes and comments. By the editor of 'The cabinet lawyer'. Simpkin & Marshall, 1828. LEI

WAHL, Anne de. *See* De Wahl, Anne

C1459 WAINEWRIGHT, Latham. The literary and scientific pursuits which are encouraged and enforced in the University of Cambridge, briefly described and vindicated. Hatchard, 1815. LEE

C1460 WAKEFIELD. Prison. [Statistical tables relating to Wakefield Prison, *c.* 1860.] HU

WAKEFIELD. West Riding proprietary school. *See* West Riding proprietary school

C1461 WALCOTT, Mackenzie Edward Charles, 1821–1880. William of Wykeham and his colleges. Winchester, D. Nutt, 1852. BI HU LEE ReU

C1462 [WALDO, Peter]. Admonitions for Sunday schools; written for a particular parish, and now published for general use. By a layman. New ed., Rivington, 1808. LEI; new ed., Rivington, 1825. LEI

C1463 WALKER, Donald. (1834) British manly exercises: in which rowing and sailing are now first described; and riding and driving ... walking, running, leaping ... etc. T. Hurst, 1834. LEI

C1464 WALKER, Donald. (1836) Exercises for ladies; calculated to preserve and improve beauty ... founded on physiological principles. 2nd ed., Hurst, 1837. LEI

C1465 WALKER, Donald. (1837) Games and sports; being an appendix to 'Manly exercises' and 'Exercises for ladies'; containing the various indoor games and sports; the out-of-door games and sports, those of the seasons, etc. ... New ed., J. Thomas, 1840. LEI

C1466 [WALKER, John], 1770–1831. (2nd ed. 1822) Curia Oxoniensis. 3rd ed., 1825. ReU

C1467 WALPOLE, Spencer Horatio, 1806–1898. (1856) Speech delivered in the House of Commons, June 17, 1856, on the national system of education in Ireland. Rivingtons, 1856. BI HU

C1468 WALTER, John, 1818–1894. Education. Correspondence relative to the resolutions to be moved on the subject of the educational grant, on Tuesday, May 5, by John Walter. Spottiswoode, 1863. LEE

C1469 [WARD, Paul]. Reminiscences of Cheltenham College, by an old Cheltonian. Bemrose, 1868. LO

C1470 WARNER, Richard, 1763–1857. An address to the children of the Bath and Bath-Forum Free School for the education of poor boys, on the system of Dr. Bell. Bath, W. Meyler, 1812. BR

C1471 WARREN, —, Mrs. How I managed my children, from infancy to marriage. Houlston & Wright, 1865. LEE

C1472 WATKINS, Rev. Frederick. A letter to His Grace the Archbishop of York [i.e. C. T. Longley], on the state of education in the church schools, of Yorkshire. London, Bell & Daldy; Leeds, T. Harrison; 1860. [Photostat copy.] HU

C1473 WATKINS, Frederick Nelson. Ship reformatories. 1858. HU

C1474 WATSON, Joseph, 1765?–1829. (1809–1810) Instruction of the deaf and dumb; or, a view of the means by which they are taught to speak and understand a language... With a vocabulary. Darton & Harvey, 1809–1810. 2 vols. BI

C1475 WATSON, William Henry. (1853?) The Sunday School Union: its history and work. With a memorial sketch of the author by W. H. Groser. S.S.U., & Nelson, 1869. LEE

C1476 WATTS, Isaac, 1674–1748. (1741–1751) The improvement of the mind; or, a supplement to the art of logic... to which is added a Discourse on the education of children and youth. Rivington, [etc.], 1801. BR; Rivington, 1804. LEI; New ed., Maxwell & Wilson, 1809. BI; Rivington, 1811. RE; Hemming & Tallis, 1814. SH; New ed., Cox, 1815. 2 vols. HU; J. Bumpus, [etc.], 1821. OX; Dove, 1826. LEE

C1477 WEBSTER, —, 'Mrs. Alfred Webster'. Dancing, as a means of physical education; with remarks on deformities, and their prevention and cure. London, Bogue; Bath, Simms; 1851. LEI

C1478 The WEEKLY offertory; its parochial utility proved... A system proposed for insuring useful, tolerant and religious education to all the children of the working classes, till twelve and fourteen years of age, without aid from the public funds... By a parish priest of the diocese of Rochester. London, H. Batty; Hertford, A. C. Windeyer; 1847. HU

C1479 WEETON, Ellen, b. 1776. Miss Weeton: journal of a governess, 1807–1825. Edited by E. Hall. O.U.P., 1936–1939. 2 vols. LEI

C1480 WERDINSKY, Adolph de, count. Letter to the proprietary of grammar schools in England, on the imperative necessity of a reform in the system of educating their youth. Hatchard, 1838. HU

C1481 WESLEY, John, 1703–1791. Works, [edited by Thomas Jackson]. Vol. 13. 4th ed., Mason, 1841. [Includes: A short account of the school in Kingswood – A plain account of Kingswood school – Remarks on the state of Kingswood school – A thought on the manner of educating children – etc.] HU

C1482 WESLEYAN EDUCATION COMMITTEE. (1861) Letter of the... committee... to the Rt. Hon. the Earl Granville, K.G., on the Revised educational code. [Chairman: J. Scott.] Wesleyan training college, 1861. BI

C1483 WEST, Mrs. Jane, 1758–1852. (1806) Letters to a young lady, in which the duties and character of women are considered... 2nd ed., Longman, 1806. 3 vols. LEI

C1484 WEST-RIDING PROPRIETARY SCHOOL, Wakefield. The proceedings at the opening of the ... school, August 6th, 1834; to which are added the rules and regulations adopted by the directors, for its government... London, Longman; Wakefield, Nichols; 1834. LEE

C1485 WESTMINSTER AND FOREIGN QUARTERLY REVIEW. Of a liberal education in general... Reprinted from the... review for July 1848. [Discussion of Whewell's book of that title.] Waterlow, 1848. HU

C1486 WESTMINSTER SCHOOL. Lusus alteri Westmonasterienses, sive prologi et epilogi ad fabulas in Sti. Petri Collegio actas... Curantibus J. Mure, H. Bull, C. B. Scott. Oxford, [etc.], Parker, [etc.], 1863–1867. 2 vols. LEI

C1487 WEYLAND, John, 1774–1854. A letter to a country gentleman on the education of the lower orders, and on the best means of attaining all that is practicable or desirable of that important object. Hatchard, 1808. LEE SH

C1488 WEYMOUTH, Richard Francis, 1822–1902. Inaugural address read at the public re-opening of Mill Hill school, 1869. 5th ed., Longmans, 1879. HU

What De Fellenberg has done for education. See Byron, A. I. N.

C1489 WHATELY, Richard, 1787–1863. Charges, and other tracts. Parker, 1836. [Includes tract on 'National education in Ireland'.] RE

C1490 WHATELY, Richard. Scriptural education in Ireland: memorials of the dean and chapter of St. Patrick's, Dublin, and of the clergy of the diocese of Derry, to His Grace the Archbishop of Dublin [i.e. R. Whately], with His Grace's replies... Fellowes, 1832. BR

C1491 WHATTON, William Robert, 1790–1835. History of Manchester [grammar] school. 1828. ReU

C1492 WHEELHOUSE, William St. James. Reformatory schools: an address to the justices of the West Riding of Yorkshire, embodying a plan for the establishment of reformatory schools. Leeds, M. Beecroft, pr., 1856. BR HU

C1493 WHEWELL, William, 1794–1866. (1847) The Christian's duty towards transgressors. A sermon preached in the chapel of the Philanthropic Society, St. George's Fields, on Sunday, May 16, 1847 . . . J. Samuel, pr., [1847]. HU

C1494 WHEWELL, William. (1845) Of a liberal education in general; and with particular reference to the leading studies of the University of Cambridge. Cambridge, Parker, 1845. NO; London, Parker, 1845. HU LEI SH

C1495 WHEWELL, William. (1854) On the influence of the history of science upon intellectual education: a lecture delivered at the Royal Institution of Great Britain . . . 1854. Parker, [1854?]. LO NO; see also C1252 Royal Institution

C1496 WHEWELL, William. (1837) On the principles of English university education. Parker, 1837. BI LI LO ReU SH

C1497 WHEWELL, William. do. 2nd ed., including additional thoughts on the study of mathematics. Parker, 1838. BI LEI NE

C1498 WHEWELL, William. (1855) Remarks on the proposed reform of the University of Cambridge, May 31, 1855. [Cambridge, Metcalfe & Palmer, 1855.] BI

C1499 WHEWELL, William. (1835) Thoughts on the study of mathematics, as a part of liberal education. 2nd ed., to which is added a letter to the editor of the 'Edinburgh Review' . . . Cambridge, Deighton; London, Parker, 1836. HU SH

C1500 WHITMAN, Walt, 1819–1892. (1845–1848) Walt Whitman looks at the schools; [edited by] F. B. Freedman. N.Y., King's crown ,pr., 1950. [Extracts from contributions to Brooklyn *Evening Star* and *Daily Eagle*.] HU RE

C1501 WHITMORE, William Wolryche. A memoir relating to the industrial school at Quatt, addressed to the rate-payers of the South-East Shropshire District School. Bridgnorth, Edkins, pr., [1849]. HU

C1502 WHYTEHEAD, Thomas, 1815–1843. (1841) College life; letters to an undergraduate. 2nd ed., Masters, 1841. BI

C1503 WIEBÉ, Edward. (1869) The paradise of childhood: a complete manual for the kindergarten. 3rd ed., Sonnenschein, and Allen, n.d. RE; Golden jubilee edition; edited by Milton Bradley . . . Springfield, Mass., Milton Bradley, 1923. HU

C1504 WIESE, Leopold. (Germ. 1850; Eng. 1854) Deutsche Briefe über englische Erziehung. I. 1850. 3 Aufl., Berlin, Wiegandt & Grieben, 1877. LEI

C1505 WIESE, Leopold. German letters on English education. [Pt. 1.] Translated by W. D. Arnold. Longman, 1854. LEI

C1506 WIGHAM, John. [Letter] to John Shank More, professor of the law of Scotland in the University of Edinburgh. [On juvenile delinquency.] Edinburgh, H. Armour, pr., 1851. HU

C1507 WILBERFORCE, Robert Isaac, 1802–1857. A letter to the most noble the Marquis of Lansdowne on the establishment of a board of national education. Murray, 1839. BI

C1508 WILDERSPIN, Samuel, 1792?–1866. (1832) Early discipline illustrated; or, the infant system progressing and successful. 1832. ReU; 2nd ed., Simpkin & Marshall, 1834. BI; 2nd ed., Westley & Davis, [etc.], 1834. LEE; 3rd ed., Hodson, 1840. LO

C1509 WILDERSPIN, Samuel. do. 6th ed., with title: The infant system, for developing the intellectual and moral powers of all children, from one to seven years of age. Simpkin & Marshall, 1843. HU; 7th ed., 1849. ReU; 8th ed., Hodson, 1852. NO ReU

C1510 WILDERSPIN, Samuel. (1823) On the importance of educating the infant children of the poor; showing how 300 children, from eighteen months to seven years of age, may be managed by one master or mistress; containing also an account of the Spitalfields infant school. Goyder, 1823. LEI; 2nd ed., with considerable additions. Goyder, 1824. HU

C1511 WILDERSPIN, Samuel. do. 3rd ed., with title: Infant education; or, remarks on the importance of educating the infant poor. Simpkin & Marshall, 1825. HU ReU; 4th ed., Simpkin & Marshall, 1829. OX

C1512 WILDERSPIN, Samuel. A system of the education of the young, applied to all the faculties . . . Hodson, 1840. BI

C1513 WILDERSPIN, Samuel, and TERRINGTON, Thomas John. Manual for religious and moral instruction of young children in nursery and infant schools. Hamilton, Adams, 1845. ReU

C1514 WILKINSON, John. Popular education: the National Society; the two Manchester schemes; the Committee of Privy Council. A letter to the Rt. Rev. Edward Denison, Lord Bishop of Salisbury. Longman, 1852. BI HU

C1515 WILKS, Mark, of Paris. The Ban de la Roche, and its benefactor, M. Jean Frédéric Oberlin, Lutheran pastor at Waldbach, in the Department of the Vosges. Westley, 1820. LEE

C1516 WILLIAMS, H. R. (1850) The dens of London and the poor of Spitalfields: a plea for ragged schools. [No pub.], [1850]. HU

C1517 [WILLIAMS, Jane], 1806–1865. (1848) Artegall; or, remarks on the reports of the Commissioners of enquiry into the state of education in Wales. Longman, 1848. LEI

C1518 WILLIAMS, —, 'Mrs. Sydney Williams', ed. and tr. (1840) Memoirs of Felix Neff, John F. Oberlin, and Bernhard Overberg. Translated from the German. Bristol, Wright & Albright, for the Society for the promotion of popular instruction, 1840. LEI

C1519 WILLIAMS, William Mattieu, 1820–1892. Who should teach Christianity to children? the schoolmasters or the clergy? A letter to the Rev. William Henry Gray. Edinburgh, MacLachlan & Stewart, 1853. LEE

C1520 WILLM, Joseph. (Fr. 1843) The education of the people: a practical treatise on the means of extending its sphere and improving its character. With a preliminary dissertation on some points connected with the present position of education in this country, by J. P. Nichol. Glasgow, 1847. HU; 2nd ed., J. Nichol, 1850. ReU

C1521 WILMOT, John James Tall. A few words on education. 4th ed., Macintosh, [etc.], 1863. HU

C1522 WILMSEN, Friedrich Philipp, 1770–1831. (1818) Die Unterrichts-Kunst. Ein Wegweiser für unkundige zunächst für angehende Lehrer in Elementarschulen. Berlin, Amelang, 1818. LO

WILSON, Mrs. Caroline, formerly Fry. See Fry, C.

C1523 WILSON, Harry Bristow, 1774–1853. The history of Merchant-Taylors' School from its foundation to the present time. 1812–1814. 2 vols. ReU; Rivington, [etc.], 1814. BR SH

C1524 [WILSON, John Iliffe]. (1820?) A brief history of Christ's Hospital, with a list of the governors. 4th ed., Effingham Willson, [c. 1828]. LEI

C1525 WILSON, Joseph, of the Inner Temple. Memorabilia Cantabrigiae: or, An account of the different colleges in Cambridge ... E. Harding, 1803. LO

C1526 WILSON, Thomas, 1663–1755. (1724) The true Christian method of educating children: a sermon ... 11th ed., Rivington for S.P.C.K., 1824. LEI

C1527 WILSON, William, B.D. Advice to the instructors of infants' schools on the commencement of their duties in such an institution. 2nd ed., Suter, [183–?]. NO

C1528 WILSON, William, B.D. (1825) The system of infants' schools. G. Wilson, 1825. HU; 2nd ed., G. Wilson, 1825. LEE; 3rd ed., G. Wilson, 1826. LEE

C1529 WILSON, William Carus, 1791–1859, ed. The teacher's visitor. Vols. 6–7. Seeley, 1847. HU

C1530 WINSTANLEY, David. A schoolmaster's notebook, being an account of a nineteenth-century experiment in social welfare. Edited by E. and T. Kelly. Manchester, Chetham Soc., 1957. CA HU NE

C1531 WITTWOR, L. O. Notes relating to education. Edinburgh, Constable, 1851. HU

C1532 WOLLSTONECRAFT, Mary, afterwards Godwin, 1759–1797. (1792) A vindication of the rights of woman ... With a biographical sketch of the author. N.Y., Blanchard, 1856. LO

Women's educational mission. See Marenholtz-Bülow, Bertha

C1533 WOOD, John. (1828) Account of the Edinburgh Sessional School, and the other parochial institutions for education established in that city in the year 1812. With strictures on education in general. 3rd ed., with additions. Edinburgh, J. Wardlaw, 1830. LEI; 4th ed., Edinburgh, J. Wardlaw, 1833. HU LO SH

C1534 WOODBRIDGE, William C. Sketches of Hofwyl, and the institutions of M. de Fellenberg ... in a series of letters to a friend. [In Letters from Hofwyl, by Mrs. Barwell.] See C82 Barwell, L.

C1535 WOODBRIDGE, Suffolk. Charities. Scheme for the management and regulation of the charity of Seckford hospital, and the grammar school, at Woodbridge ... Directed by the high court of Chancery ... 1861. Roworth, 1861. LEI

C1536 WOOLER, William M. Physiology of education: comprising a compendious cyclopaedia of mental, moral, and social facts. Simpkin, Marshall, [1859]. LEE

C1537 WORBOISE, Emma Jane, 1825–1887. (1859) The life of Thomas Arnold. Hamilton, Adams, 1861. LEE; Isbister, 1885. LO

C1538 WORCESTER. Diocese. Training college, Saltley. Committee of governors. Report ... containing suggestions on the Revised code so far as it bears directly on training colleges ... Birmingham, Hall, 1862. BI

C1539 [WORDSWORTH, Charles], 1806–1892. The College of St. Mary Winton, near Winchester. Oxford and London, Parker, 1848. LO

C1540 WORDSWORTH, Christopher, 1807–1885. (1845) Diary in France, mainly on topics concerning education and the Church. 2nd ed., Rivington, 1846. LO

C1541 WORDSWORTH, Christopher. Discourses on public education. Rivington, 1844. NO

C1542 WÖRLEIN, J. W. Pädagogische Wissenschaftskunde: ein enzyklopädisch-historisch, litterarisch-kritisches Lehrbuch des pädagogischen Studiums. Erlangen, Palm & Enke, 1826. 3 vols. LO

C1543 WORSLEY, Henry. Juvenile depravity: £100 prize essay. Gilpin, 1849. BI

C1544 WOTHERSPOON, James. (1839) Speech ... on the subject of education, at the Radical soirée held at Kirkaldy ... January 1839. [Kirkaldy, Fife Herald, 1839.] LEI

C1545 [WRIGHT, J. M. F.] (1827) Alma mater; or, seven years at the University of Cambridge; by a Trinity-man. Black, 1827. 2 vols. in 1. BR

C1546 WRIGHT, Thomas, 1810–1877, and JONES, Harry Longueville, 1806–1870. The universities: Le Keux's memorials of Cambridge: a series of views ... with historical and descriptive accounts by T. Wright and H. L. Jones. Tilt & Bogue, 1841–1842. 2 vols. LEE

WRIGHT, Thomas, joint ed. See Prickett, Marmaduke and Wright, T.

C1547 WRIGLEY, Thomas. (1857) A plan by which the education of the people may be secured, without state interference, or compulsory rating, and in strict accordance with the principles of civil and religious liberty. Simpkin & Marshall, 1857. HU LEE

C1548 WYKE-HOUSE SCHOOL, *Brentford.* Annual examination of the scholars ... June 16th–18th, 1828. [Brentford, The School], 1828. BI

C1549 WYSE, *Sir* Thomas, 1791–1861. Education reform; or, the necessity of a national system of education. Longman, 1836. BI

C1550 YATES, James, 1789–1871. (1826) Thoughts on the advancement of academical education in England. Baldwin, Cradock & Joy, 1826. SH; 2nd ed., Baldwin, Cradock & Joy, 1827. ReU

C1551 YORKSHIRE CATHOLIC REFORMATORY SCHOOL. 3rd annual report ... Read ... 18th January 1860. Richardson, 1860. BI

C1552 YORKSHIRE SCHOOL FOR THE BLIND. 1st report of the committee ... York, Wilson, 1837. LEE

C1553 ZELLER, Carl August, 1774–1846. Der Schulmeisterschule, oder, Anleitung für Schullehrer zur geschicktern Verwaltung ihres Amtes. Königsberg, Nicolovius, 1817. LO

C1554 ZINCKE, Foster Barham. A speech on the National Education League, delivered at a public meeting at Ipswich, Nov. 16th, 1869. Birmingham, Nat. ed. league, [1870?]. BI

C1555 ZOLLIKOFER, Georg Joachim, 1730–1788. Sermons on education, on reflection ... From the German ... Translated by W. Tooke. Longman, 1806. 2 vols. BI

Textbooks and children's books published, or first published, 1801-1870

A.L.O.E., *pseud. See* Tucker, Charlotte Maria

D1 ABBOTT, Jacob, 1803–1879. The child at home. [Edited] by J. S. C. Abbott. [Part 1]. Seeley, 1834. LEI

D2 ABBOTT, Jacob. Everyday duty, illustrated by sketches of childish character and conduct. Allan Bell, 1837. ReU

D3 [ABBOTT, Jacob]. Rollo at school. New ed., rev. by the author. Boston, Phillips, Sampson & Co., [*c.* 1855]. LEI

D4 ABBOTT, John Stevens Cabot, 1805–1877, *ed.* The child at home, [by Jacob Abbott]. *See* D1

D5 ABÉCÉDAIRE des petits enfans, ou les difficultés de la lecture sont graduées de manière à les rendre moins sensibles . . . 2e éd., rev., Milan, Sonzogno, 1843. LEI

Account of the chief truths of the Christian religion. *See* A Catechetical instruction

Accidence; or, first rudiments of English grammar. *See* Devis, E.

Ackermann's juvenile forgetmenot. *See* Juvenile forgetmenot

D6 ACKWORTH SCHOOL. Arithmetical tables of money, weights, measures, etc. Used in Ackworth School and recommended for the use of schools in general. W. Darton, [182–]. HU

ADAIR, James, *pseud. See* Phillips, *Sir* Richard

D7 ADAM, Alexander. (1830?) The rudiments of correct reading; consisting of rules and examples adapted to the capacity of children. Edinburgh, Oliver & Boyd, 1856. HU

D8 ADAMS, Henry Cadwallader, 1817–1899. (1851) A new Greek delectus, adapted to the arrangement of the Rev. C. Wordsworth's grammar. With a lexicon and appendix. 3rd ed., corr. and enl., D. Nutt, 1855. LEI

D9 ADAMS, H. C. (1861) Schoolboy honour: a tale of Halminster College. New ed., Routledge, 1863. LEI

D10 ADAMS, John, 1750?–1814. (1802) A new history of Great Britain; from the invasion of Julius Caesar, to the present time . . . On a plan nearly similar to that of Dr. Henry. 6th ed., corrected and continued . . . G. B. Whittaker, [etc.], [182–]. HU

D11 ADAMS, John, *teacher of mathematics at Edmonton.* The young lady's and gentleman's atlas. 1805. NoU

Adelaide; or, the intrepid daughter. *See* Hofland, B.

D12 The ADVANTAGES of education elucidated, in the history of the Wingfield family. 1819. NoU

Adventures of old Mother Hubbard. *See* Mother Hubbard

D13 AESOP. The beauties of Aesop, and other fabulists; being a collection of fables, selected from Aesop, Dodsley, Gay, etc., for the use of schools . . . Adorned with cuts by T. Bewick. 3rd ed., J. Richardson, 1822. HU

D14 AESOP. The fables of Aesop, and others; for the improvement of youth, with instructive applications. Joseph Smith, [*c.* 1830?]. 2 vols. LEI

Affectionate advice to apprentices. *See* Watkins, Henry George

D15 AGRICULTURAL class book; or how best to cultivate a small farm and garden: together with hints on domestic economy. Published by direction of the Commissioners of national education in Ireland. Dublin, Thom, 1853. LEI

D16 AHN, Johann Franz, 1796–1865. A first Italian reading book. With a vocabulary of the words, and copious notes, by A. H. Monteith. Allmann, 1873. LEI

D17 AHN, J. F. A new, practical and easy method of learning the German language. First and second courses in one volume. Leipzig, Brockhaus; London, Cassell; 1864. 2 vols. in 1. LEI

D18 AHN, J. F. A new, practical and easy method of learning the Italian language. First and second course. [By Giuseppe Marchetti?]. Trübner, [etc.], 1863. LEI

Aids to [mental] development. *See* Maurice, Mary Atkinson

D19 AIKIN, John, 1747–1822. (1804) Letters to a young lady on a course of English poetry. Johnson, 1804. NoU; 2nd ed., Johnson, 1807. LEI

D20 [AIKIN, John]. (1802) The arts of life: I, Of providing food. II, Of providing cloathing. III, Of providing shelter . . . By the author of 'Evenings at home'. Johnson, 1802. LEI

D21 [AIKIN, John, and BARBAULD, Anna Letitia] (1792–1796) Evenings at home; or, the juvenile budget opened . . . 5th ed., Johnson, 1805. 5 vols. OX; 13th ed., 1823. 6 vols. NoU; 18th ed., revised by A. Aikin and Miss Aikin. Longmans, 1858. BI; Edinburgh, Nimmo, [1868]. LEI; Kendrick, n.d. [*c.* 1840?]. NE

D22 AIKIN, Lucy, 1781–1864. (1811) Juvenile correspondence, or, letters designed as examples of the epistolary style, for children of both sexes. Johnson, 1811. LEI

D23 AIKIN, Lucy, *comp.* (1801) Poetry for children: consisting of short pieces to be committed to memory. 1801. NoU; 7th ed., Longman, 1818. LEE; new ed., with additions and corrections, Longman, 1824. HU; new ed., considerably improved, Longman, [1825]. LEI

D24 AIKIN, Lucy, *ed.* Evenings at home. 18th ed., 1858. *See* D21

D25 AIKIN, Lucy, *ed.* A legacy for young ladies, by Mrs. Barbauld. 1826. *See* D72

D26 AIKIN, Lucy, *trans.* Travels of Rolando, [by L. F. Jauffret]. 1852. *See* D718

D27 [AIKIN, Lucy]? Sandford and Merton [by T. Day] in words of one syllable, by Mary Godolphin [i.e. Lucy Aikin?]. Cassell, [etc.], [1868]. LEI

Alchemist. *See* Robson, Mary

D28 ALDERSON, James. (1793) Orthographical exercises: in a series of moral letters... 14th ed., rev. and corr. by Rev. Thomas Smith. Law & Whittaker, [etc.], 1818. LEI

D29 [ALDRICH, Henry], 1647–1710. (1691) Artis logicae rudimenta. With illustrative observations on each section [by John Hill]. 4th ed., Oxford, Parker; London, Rivington; 1828. LEI

D30 [ALER, Paul], 1656–1727. (1687) Gradus ad Parnassum... 1802. NoU

D31 ALEXANDER, *Mrs.* Cecil Frances, *form.* Humphreys, 1818–1895. (1848) Hymns for little children. 56th ed., J. Masters, 1878. LEI

D32 ALICIA and her aunt; or, think before you speak. A tale for young persons. Newman, 1822. LEE

D33 [ALLAN, Louisa]. (2nd ed., 1814) The decoy; or, an agreeable method of teaching children the elementary parts of English grammar by conversations and familiar examples. 5th ed., Harvey & Darton, 1823. LEE

D34 ALLBUT, J. Elements of useful knowledge in geography, history, and other sciences. 7th ed. 1805. NoU

D35 ALLEN, Alexander, 1814–1842, and CORNWELL, James. (1841) An English school grammar, with very copious exercises... 13th ed., Simpkin, Marshall, 1848. HU; 18th ed., Simpkin, Marshall, 1851. HU [1st ed. had title: A new English grammar.]

D36 ALLISON, M. A. The guide to English history and biography. [Revised by] E. C. Brewer. *See* D145 Brewer, E. C.

D37 [ALPHABET, illustrated with engravings of animals]. 1801. NoU

D38 AMBROSE. (1796) Ambrose and Eleanor... Translated by Lucy Peacock. 3rd ed., Baldwin, Cradock & Joy, 1807. [Free and abridged translation of 'Fanfan et Lolotte'.] ReU

D39 ANDERSEN, Hans Christian, 1805–1875. Tales for the young. A new translation. Warne, [1847]. LEE

D40 ANDERSON, Robert. Geography for junior classes. Nelson, 1859. HU

Anna Ross. *See* Kennedy, Grace

ANSTICE, Joseph, *joint compiler.* *See* Keble, John, and Anstice, Joseph, *comps.*

D41 ANTHOLOGIA; sive Epigrammatum Graecorum delectus. In usum Scholae Regiae Westmonasteriensis. Oxford, Collingwood for G. Ginger, 1825. HU

D42 The ANTI-SPELLING book; a new system of teaching children to read without spelling. Bull & Churton, 1833. HU LEE

D43 [APPLETON, George S.] (1849) Mother Goose in hieroglyphics. [Facsimile reprint of 1849 ed.] Gollancz, 1963. LEI

D44 ARGUS, Arabella, *pseud.* (1815) The adventures of a donkey. W. Darton, 1823. LEI ReU; Darton & Clark, [c. 1840?]. NE

D45 ARGUS, Arabella. (1821?) Ostentation and liberality: a tale. Darton, [18–]. 2 vols. in 1. LEE [Possibly appeared in an undated ed. before 1821.]

D46 [The ARITHMETICAL grammar. Abridged ed.] Otley, Walker, [c. 1840?]. [t.p. wanting.] LEI

D47 ARITHMETICAL tables for the use of schools on the National system. 1857. NoU

D48 ARNOLD, Thomas, 1795–1842, *ed.* (1831?) M. Tullii Ciceronis Verrinarum libri septem... Orations on the impeachment of C. Verres... with a marginal summary by Thomas Arnold... For the use of Rugby School. 3rd ed., Rugby, Crossley; London, Whittaker, [etc.]; 1847. LEI

D49 ARNOLD, Thomas Kerchever, 1800–1853. (1839) Henry's first Latin book. 19th ed., Rivington, 1866. BI; 27th ed., Rivington, 1886. CA

D50 ARNOLD, T. K. (1839) A practical introduction to Latin prose composition. New ed., edited and revised by George Granville Bradley. Longmans, 1897. LEI

D51 ARNOLD, T. K., *ed.* Eclogae Ovidianae; being the fifth part of the Lateinisches Elementarbuch, by Professors Jacobs and Doering. Edited by Thomas Kerchever Arnold. 10th ed., Rivington, 1860. LEI

D52 ARROWSMITH, Aaron, 1750–1823. A compendium of ancient and modern geography for the use of Eton School. 1831. NoU

D53 ARROWSMITH, Samuel. The Bible atlas with ancient and modern names, being a delineation of the geography and chronological arrangement of the history of the Holy Bible... London, Author; Oxford, Fellowes, [etc.]; [etc.]; 1835. NO

Artis logicae rudimenta. *See* Aldrich, Henry

Arts of life. *See* Aikin, John

D54 ASPIN, Jehoshaphat. (1832) Ancient customs, sports, and pastimes, of the English, explained from authentic sources, in a familiar manner. J. Harris, 1832. LEI; *with* The British story briefly told. *See* D151

D55 The ASSEMBLED alphabet; or, acceptance of A's invitation. Being a sequel to the 'Invited alphabet'. By R. R. Darton, 1809. NoU

Assistant of education. *See* Fry, Caroline

D56 [ATKINS, Sarah], *aft. Mrs.* Wilson. (1822) Fruits of enterprize exhibited in the travels of Belzoni in Egypt and Nubia... By the author of 'The India cabinet'. 2nd ed., 1822. NoU

D57 [ATKINS, Sarah]. (1821–1823) Grove Cottage, and The India cabinet opened. By the author of 'Fruits of enterprise'. New ed., Harris, 1838. LEI

ATTHILL, *Mrs.* Caroline A., *form.* Halsted. *See* Halsted, C. A.

D58 AUNT Annie's tales. Jarrold, n.d. [1867?]. ReU

D59 AUNT Ann's gift; or, moral emblems in prose and verse. Newman, n.d. NoU

Aunt Effie's rhymes for little children. *See* Hawkshaw, Ann

AUNT FRIENDLY, *pseud. See* Baker, Sarah S.

D60 AUNT JUDY'S MAGAZINE. Aunt Judy's Christmas volume for young people. Edited by Mrs. Alfred Gatty. Bell & Daldy, 1868. LEI

AUNT MARY, *pseud. See* Robson, Mary

D61 AUNT SOPHY, *pseud.* Little Susan: a tale in easy words, for children under six years of age. Hooper, 1842. LEE

AUNT SUSAN, *pseud. See* Prentiss, Elizabeth

D62 AUSTIN, Sarah, 1793–1867, *trans.* (Eng. 1834) The story without an end. From the German of Carové. New improved ed., Effingham Wilson, [c. 1840?]. LEI

D63 AUSWAHL vorzüglicher Gedichte zur angenehmen und nützlichen Unterhaltung für die Jugend. Neuhaldensleben, Eyraud, [c. 1840]. LEI

B64 B., W. (1807) The elephant's ball, and grande fête champêtre. A facsimile reproduction of the edition of 1807 with an introduction by Charles Welsh. Griffith & Farran, [etc.], 1883. LEI NO

Babes in the wood. *See* Children in the wood

D65 BABILLARD. (182–?) Le Babillard; an amusing introduction to the French language. By a French lady. 3rd ed., Grant & Griffith, n.d. [2nd ed. 1834]. ReU

D66 BAGATELLE. (1800?) La Bagatelle; intended to introduce children of three or four years old to some knowledge of the French language. New ed., 1831. 2 vols. in 1. NoU

D67 BAGLEY, George, *teacher of mathematics.* (1805?) The young mathematician's assistant; or, schoolmaster's guide. Being a short and comprehensive system of arithmetic. Shrewsbury, 1805. NoU

D68 BAKER, *Mrs.* Sarah Schoonmaker, *form.* Tuthill, 1824–1906. Charlie Clement; or, the boy friend. By Aunt Friendly [i.e. Mrs. Baker]. Warne, 1868. HU

BALDWIN, Edward, *pseud. See* Godwin, William

D69 [BALLANTYNE, Robert Michael], 1825–1894. (1857) The butterfly's ball and the grasshopper's feast, [by William Roscoe]. With prose version by Comus, author of 'Three little kittens' . . . etc. [i.e. R. M. Ballantyne]. Nelson, 1857. LEI

D70 BANKS, William. The English master; or, student's guide to reasoning and composition; exhibiting an analytical view of the English language, of the human mind, and of the principles of fine writing. Longman, [etc.], 1823. HU

D71 [BARBAULD, Anna Letitia], 1743–1825. (1780–1781) Hymns in prose for children, by the author of *Lessons for children.* 19th ed., enl., Baldwin, [etc.], 1818. LEI; new improved ed., [1872?]. NoU

D72 BARBAULD, A. L. (1826) A legacy for young ladies, consisting of miscellaneous pieces in prose and verse. Edited by Lucy Aikin. 1826. NoU

D73 [BARBAULD, A. L.] (1778) Lessons for children, in four parts. Parts 1 and 2. J. Johnson, 1812. NE; Parts 1–4. Baldwin, Cradock & Joy, [etc.], 1818–1820. 4 vols. LEI; Baldwin, Cradock & Joy, 1821–1825. 4 vols. ReU; Edinburgh, Nelson, 1840. LO; new ed., Longman, [etc.], 1851. HU

D73a [BARBAULD, A. L.]. Leçons pour des enfans depuis l'âge de deux ans jusqu'à cinq ans. Ouvrage en quatre parties. Traduit . . . par M. Pasquier. Darton, 1816. BI

D74 [BARBAULD, A. L.]. Instructive lessons for children. By the author of Hymns in prose. [c. 180–?] (Nursery library). NoU

D75 [BARBAULD, A. L.]. More instructive lessons for children . . . [c. 180–?] (Nursery library). NoU

BARBAULD, A. L., *joint author. See* Aikin, John, and Barbauld, A. L.

D76 BARBER, *Miss.* Reduction. [MS. exercises in arithmetic.] 1827. NoU

D77 BARBIERI, Giuseppe Filippo. (Grammaire 1819) Le nouveau maîtré italien, abrégé de la Grammaire des grammaires italiennes . . . divisé par leçons, avec des thèmes . . . Paris, Rey & Gravier, 1824. LEI

D78 BARCLAY, John, *fl.* 1826. The elements of natural and experimental philosophy . . . for the use of schools and private education. 1826. NoU

D79 BARDI, G., *conte.* Elementary lessons for children. Originally composed in Italian. Harvey & Darton, 1830. LEI NoU

D80 BARFF, Frederick S. (1869) An introduction to scientific chemistry; designed for schools and candidates for university matriculation examinations. Groombridge, 1881. LEI

D81 [BARNARD, *Sir* John], 1685–1764. (1740) A present for an apprentice; or, a sure guide to gain both esteem and estate . . . Layton, 1852. LEI

BARNSTAPLE. Bray's Academy. *See* Bray's Academy, Barnstaple.

BARROW, *Rev.* S., *pseud. See* Phillips, *Sir* Richard

D82 BARTON, Bernard, 1784–1849, *ed.* Fisher's juvenile scrap-book, 1838. *See* D466 Fisher

D83 BARWELL, *Mrs.* Louise Mary, 1800–1885. (1833) Little lessons for little learners, in words of one syllable. Westley & Davis, 1833. LEI

Basket of flowers. *See* Schmid, J. C. v.

D84 BASSLE, Gustave Adolphe. Système mnémonique: ou art d'aider le mémoire. Divisé en six leçons, et suivie de la chronologie de l'histoire ancienne et moderne, et autres branches de l'éducation, mnémonisées. Londres, Jennings, 1841. LEE

D85 BATTLEDORES. Bowden's indestructible battledore. Gainsborough, [18–?]. NoU

D86 BATTLEDORES. New battledore. Birmingham, [c. 1830?]. NoU

D87 BATTLEDORES. New battledore. Nos. 1–8. Derby, [18–?]. NoU

D88 BATTLEDORES. New royal battledore. Kettering, [18–?]. NoU

D89 BAYLEY, Catherine. Vacation evenings; or, conversations between a governess, with the addition of a visitor from Eton: being a series of original poems, tales and essays ... tending to incite emulation, and inculcate moral truth. Longmans, [etc.], 1809. 3 vols. in 1. LEI

D90 BEALE, Dorothea, 1831–1906. (1858) The student's text book of English and general history, from B.C. 100 to the present time ... New ed., Bell, 1882. CA

D91 BEARD, John Relly, 1800–1876. (1859) Self-culture: a practical answer to the questions 'What to learn?' 'How to learn?' 'When to learn?' ... forming a complete guide to self-instruction. 3rd ed., Manchester, [etc.], Heywood; London, Simpkin, Marshall; [187–?]. LEI

D92 BEASLEY, M., *of Stourbridge*. (1812, with title: Orthographical instructions) Dictation exercises, with suitable orthographical instructions, for the use of schools. 5th ed., 1825. NoU

BEAUMONT, Jeanne Marie Le Prince de. *See* Le Prince de Beaumont, J. M.

Beauties of Aesop, and other fabulists. *See* D13 Aesop

Beauties of history. *See* Stretch, L. M.

D93 BEAUTY AND THE BEAST. The history of Beauty and the Beast. Derby, Thos. Richardson, [18–]. ReU [Originally written by Mme. Le Prince de Beaumont.]

Beauty and the beast. *See also* Corner, Julia; Lamb, Charles

D94 BEDFORD, James Gower. Questions for junior classes. Compiled for the use of schools. 5th ed. Whittaker, 1838. HU

D95 BEE. (1795) The Bee, a selection of poetry from approved authors. 6th ed., Darton & Harvey, 1811. NoU

D96 BEETON, Samuel Orchard, 1831–1877, *ed.* Beeton's annual. *See* D98

D97 BEETON, S. O., *ed.* Boy's own magazine. *See* D139

D98 BEETON'S annual: a book for the young. Edited by S. O. Beeton and the Rev. J. G. Wood. Warne, 1866. LEI

D99 BELL, Catherine Douglas, d. 1861. (1859) The children's mirror; or, which is my likeness? Nelson, 1859. LEI

D100 BELL, J. H. Information for young persons, on some of the most interesting subjects ... 2nd ed., Leeds, Hobson, 1829. LEE

BELSON, Mary, *aft.* Mrs. Elliott. *See* Elliott, M.

D101 BEMMELEN, J. van. Leçons faciles & instructives, destinées à être traduites en hollandais ou en anglais ... 2e éd. corr. Leyden, Honkoop, [c. 1800?]. [Inscription dated 1802.] LEI

D102 [BENSON, Edward White], *fl.* 1824. (1824) Education at home; or, a father's instructions: consisting of miscellaneous pieces for the instruction and amusement of young persons, from ten to twelve years of age. Baldwin, Cradock & Joy, 1824. LEI NoU

D103 [BERQUIN, Arnaud], 1749–1791. (1782–1783) The children's friend. New ed., 1804. 4 vols. NoU

D104 [BERQUIN, Arnaud]. (1792) The looking-glass for the mind ... chiefly translated from L'ami des enfans. With 74 cuts ... by J. Bewick. 9th ed., 1803. NoU ReU; 10th ed., J. Harris, [etc.], 1806. NE; 23rd ed., 1862. ReU

D105 BERQUIN, Arnaud. (1796) The blossoms of morality ... 8th ed., Harris, [etc.], 1828. BI

D106 BERQUIN, Arnaud, *trans.* (1791) Le petit Grandisson. Traduction libre du hollandais. 3e éd., Londres, Vernor & Hood, 1801. LEI

D107 BERTHA. (1830) Bertha's visit to her uncle in England. Murray, 1831. 3 vols. [Ascribed to Jane Marcet.] ReU

D108 BETTS, John, *firm.* A companion to Betts' portable globe and diagrams. Betts, [185–?]. NoU

BEVAN, Favell Lee, *aft.* Mrs. Mortimer. *See* Mortimer, F. L.

D109 BIBLE. A curious hieroglyphick Bible. 20th ed., 1812. ReU

D110 BIBLE. The modern hieroglyphical Bible. [18–]. ReU

D111 BIBLE. *Old Testament. Psalms.* 104th psalm. [Folding card with lithographs and text, in cover. Illus. by S. M. Farington.] [1860]. NoU

D112 A BIBLE geography, by a lady. 3rd ed., 1820. NoU

D113 BIDLAKE, John Purdue. (1856) Physical geography for children. 3rd ed., 1857. NoU

D114 BIGLAND, John, 1750–1832. Letters on English history; for the use of schools. Longman, [etc.], 1817. OX

D115 [BILBY, Thomas]. (1828) A course of lessons, together with the tunes, to which they are usually sung in infant schools; and also a copious collection of hymns and moral songs, suitable for infant instruction ... 2nd ed., Rivington, 1830. HU

D116 BILLARD, Elisabeth. Pauline; ou, la vertueuse orpheline. Londres, Bowdery & Kerby, 1823. LEI

D117 BILTON, Charles. (1866) Repetition and reading book, for pupil teachers and the upper classes of schools ... New ed., Longmans, [etc.], [187–]. HU

D118 BINGLEY, William, 1774–1823. (1817) ... Practical introduction to botany ... 2nd ed. ... adapted to the use of students, by John Frost. Baldwin, Cradock & Joy, 1827. LEI

D119 BIRD, John, *lecturer on astronomy*. (1824) The juvenile observatory: a course of astronomical lectures for the instruction of youth. Eton, E. Williams, 1824. NoU

D120 BIRKIN, William. Mangnall's historical and miscellaneous questions . . . Revised by William Birkin. Richardson, 1844. SH

BLAIR, *Rev.* David, *pseud. See* Phillips, *Sir* Richard

D120a BLAIR, Hugh, 1718–1800. (Lectures, 1783) An abridgment of Lectures on rhetoric. For the use of schools. Brattleborough, Holbrook & Fessenden, 1824. HU

D121 BLAIR, Robert, 1699–1746. The poems of Thomas Gray and Robert Blair, arranged for the use of young people. E. Lacey, [183–?]. NE

D122 BLANCHARD, Pierre. L'Esope des enfans. Londres, N. Hailes, 1828. LEI

D123 [BLANCHARD, Pierre]? Leçons pour les enfans de 3 à 5 ans, composés de phrases à lire, et de petites historiettes . . . 4e éd., Paris, P. Blanchard, 1822. [Possibly by the publisher.] LEI

D124 BLANCHARD, Pierre. (1805?) Le nouveau La Bruyère; ou, les enfans bien élevés. Ouvrage classique, divisé en trois parties: 1. La morale; 2. La vertu; 3. La civilité. Londres, Didier & Tebbett, 1805. 2 vols. LEI

Blind child. *See* Pinchard, *Mrs.*

D125 BOBBIO, G., *comp.* Antologia greca, compilata ad uso dei ginnasi e licei italiani . . . 2a ed. Bolognese . . . Bologna, Maraggiani, 1865. 2 vols. in 1. LEI

D126 BOHNY, Nicholas. The new picture book; being pictorial lessons of form, comparison, and number, for children under seven years of age . . . 3rd ed., Edinburgh, Edmonston & Douglas, 1866. LEI

BONIFACE, Joseph Xavier. *See* Saintine, J. X. B., *pseud.*

D127 BONNYCASTLE, John, 1750?–1821. (1782) An introduction to algebra . . . 12th ed., J. Nunn, Longman, [etc.], 1822. LEI; new ed., enlarged . . . by E. C. Tyson. 1833. NoU

D128 BONNYCASTLE, John. (1786) An introduction to astronomy, in a series of letters from a preceptor to his pupils. 7th ed. 1816. NoU

D129 BONNYCASTLE, John. (1782) An introduction to mensuration and practical geometry . . . 11th ed., corr., Rivington, [etc.], 1816. LEI; 13th ed., corr., Rivington, [etc.], 1823. HU

D130 BOOK OF TRADES. (1804–1805) The Book of trades, or library of the useful arts. Part II. 4th ed. R. Phillips, 1811. LEI

D131 BOOK OF TRADES. The Book of trades; or, circle of the useful arts. 6th ed., Glasgow, 1841. NoU

D132 [BORTHWICK, Jane L.]. The illustrated book of songs for children. Edited by H.L.L., author of 'Hymns from the land of Luther' [i.e. J. L. Borthwick]. Nelson, [pref. 1863]. LEI

D133 BOS, Lambert, 1670–1717. (Latin 1714?) The antiquities of Greece. A new edition. For the use of a school at Kensington. Cadell & Davies, 1805. LEI

BOSWELL, Roger, *pseud. See* Reid, Hugo

D134 BOUILLY, Jean Nicolas, 1763–1842. (1811? Paris; 1813 London) Conseils à ma fille; ou, nouveaux contes. 2e éd., Paris, Rosa Rel, 1812. LO; Londres, Colburn, [etc.], 1813. LEI

D135 BOUILLY, J. N. (1809) Contes à ma fille. Nlle. éd., rev., Londres, Dulau, [etc.], 1863. LEI

D136 BOUILLY, J. N. Les encouragements de la jeunesse. Paris, Deville, [etc.], 1815. LEE

D137 BOURN, Thomas, 1771–1832, *ed.* [Works by William Butler.] *See* Butler, W.

D138 BOWRING, *Sir* John, 1792–1872. Minor morals for young people, illustrated in tales and travels. 1834–1839. 3 vols. ReU

Boys and their rulers. *See* Ward, E.

Boys' own book. *See* Clarke, William

D139 BOY'S OWN MAGAZINE. The boy's own volume of fact, fiction, history and adventure, Christmas, 1865. Edited by the publisher. Beeton, 1865. LEI

Boys' penny magazine. Annual volume. *See* Boy's yearly book

D140 BOY'S WEEK-DAY BOOK. (1833) The boy's week-day book. R.T.S., 1834. LEE

D141 BOY'S yearly book for [1865]. [Annual volume of the Boy's penny magazine.] S.O. Beeton, 1865. LEE LEI

D142 BRADLEY, John. Elements of geography, for the use of schools, etc. Liverpool, J. Lang, pr., 1812. LEE

D143 BRADLEY, William Windham. Lessons in Latin prose: consisting of rules and exercises . . . 2nd ed., Longman, 1864. LEE

D144 BRAY'S ACADEMY, *Barnstaple*. [Two copybooks, completed by William Coham Turner in 1836 and 1838.] HU

D145 BREWER, Ebenezer Cobham, 1810–1897. (6th rev. ed., 1847) The guide to English history and biography. [Originally by M. A. Allison.] 58th ed., Jarrold, 1883. OX

D146 BREWER, E. C. (1864?) My first book of science. 8th ed., [187–?]. NoU

D147 BREWER, E. C. (1st series, 1864) The young tutor (second series): an elementary course of general knowledge. [186–?]. NoU

D148 BRIDGE, Bewick, 1767–1833. A treatise on the elements of algebra. 5th ed., Cadell, 1821. BI

D149 BRITISH heroism. 1801. NoU

D150 BRITISH STORY. (1832) The British story briefly told, from early times to the present period . . . Harris, 1832. (The little library, vol. 10.) LEI

D151 BRITISH STORY. The British history briefly told, and A description of the ancient customs, sports, and pastimes of the English, [by J. Aspin]. Harris, [1840]. NoU

D152 The BRITISH youth's vade mecum, being a brief history of the constitutional establishments of the British Empire. 1806. NoU

D153 BROOK-SMITH, John. (1860) Arithmetic in theory and practice. [6th ed.] Macmillan, 1881, repr. 1895. CA; repr. 1898. HU

D154 BUCKLE, J. [MS. arithmetic book, dated Oct. 29th, 1806.] LEI

D155 [BUDDEN, Maria E.], *form.* Halsey, 1780?–1832. (1822) Claudine; or, humility the basis of all virtues . . . By M.E.B. 5th ed., Harris, [c. 1828]. ReU

D156 [BUDDEN, M. E.]. (1814) A key to knowledge; or, things in common use. Simply and shortly explained – in a series of dialogues. Written by a mother, author of 'Always happy' . . . etc. Harris, 1814. NoU; 3rd ed., revised by the author, Harris, 1820. LEI; 9th ed., Harris, 1833. NoU; 12th ed., with additions, Grant & Griffiths, 1848. LEE

D157 [BUDDEN, M. E.]. (182–) True stories from English history, chronologically arranged, from the invasion of the Romans, to the death of George III. By a mother, author of 'True stories from ancient history', etc. 2nd ed., enl., Harris, [1828?]. LEI

D158 [BUNBURY, Selina]. (1826) The pastor's tales. By the author of 'Early recollections'. Edinburgh, Wm. Oliphant, [1826]. HU

D159 The BUNCH of primroses. Published under the direction of the Committee of general literature and education. S.P.C.K., 1846. HU

D160 BUNYAN, John, 1628–1688. Pilgrim's progress in words of one syllable, by Samuel Phillips Day. Cassell, [1869?]. LEI

D161 BUQUET, C. P. A grammatical collection of phrases and idioms, systematically arranged so as to impart a progressive knowledge of the . . . French language, for the use of the Edinburgh Academy, schools and students. 2nd ed., Edinburgh, Author, & Oliver & Boyd, 1839. NE

D162 BUREAU. (1805) Le Bureau typographique; livre élémentaire à l'usage des enfans. Orné de 24 jolis tableaux d'arts & métiers . . . Londres, Didier & Tebbett, 1808. LEI

Burford Cottage. *See* Kendall, E. A.

D163 BURGESS, John Cart, 1798–1863. Useful hints on drawing and painting; intended to facilitate the improvement of young persons. Privately printed, 1818. NoU

D164 BURN, Robert Scott. (1868) The handbook of object teaching, consisting of essays descriptive of the sciences, machines, and industrial processes . . . Edinburgh & London, Fullarton, [1868]. LEI

D165 BURRITT, Elihu, 1810–1879. Old Burchell's pocket for the children. Cassell, [etc.], [1868]. NE

D166 [BUSBY, Richard], 1606–1695. (1688) Rudimentum grammaticae Latinae metricum, in usum scholae regiae Westmonasteriensis. 1810. NoU

D167 BUTLER, Charles. An easy introduction to the mathematics . . . Adapted to the use of schools, junior students at the universities, and private learners . . . Oxford, Bartlett & Newman, pr., 1814. 2 vols. HU

D168 BUTLER, John Olding. (1826) The geography of the globe . . . With alterations and additions by J. Rowbotham. 8th ed., Simpkin, Marshall, 1850. LEI

D169 BUTLER, Samuel, 1774–1839. (1822) An atlas of ancient geography. Longman, [c. 1835]. SO; Longman, [c. 1848?]. LEI

D170 BUTLER, Samuel. An atlas of modern geography. New ed., re-engraved, with corrections . . . Edited by the author's son. Longman, 1854. LEI

D171 BUTLER, William, *writing-master*, d. 1822. (2nd ed., 1795) Arithmetical questions, on a new plan: intended to answer the double purpose of arithmetical instruction and miscellaneous information . . . designed for the use of young ladies. 5th ed., S. Couchman, 1811. OX; 10th ed., edited by Thomas Bourn. Printed for the proprietors, 1829. HU

D172 BUTLER, William. (1799) Chronological, biographical, historical and miscellaneous exercises, on a new plan: designed for the daily use of young ladies. 7th ed., enl. Printed for the proprietor, and sold by J. Harris, [etc.], 1823. HU

D173 BUTLER, William. (1798) Exercises on the globe and maps . . . designed for the use of young ladies. 6th ed. Printed for the author, 1814. OX; 12th ed., with an appendix by Thomas Bourn. Printed for the editor, 1831. LEI

D174 BUTLER, William. (1813) Geographical exercises on the New Testament . . . Designed for the use of young ladies . . . 3rd ed., enlarged by . . . Thomas Bourn. Printed for the editor, and sold by J. Harris, [etc.], 1825. LEI

D175 BUTLER, William. Outline maps to his Geographical and biographical exercises, for the use of young ladies. 1811. NoU

BUTT, Lucy Lyttelton, *aft.* Mrs. Cameron. *See* Cameron, L. L.

BUTT, Mary Martha, *aft.* Mrs. Sherwood. *See* Sherwood, M. M.

D176 BUTTER, Henry, b. 1794? (1830) The etymological spelling book and expositor . . . 21st ed., 1836. NoU; 66th ed., Simpkin, 1843. HU; 206th ed., Simpkin, Marshall, 1856. LEI; 298th ed., Simpkin & Marshall, 1868. BR; 421st ed., Simpkin, Marshall, [1883?]. LEI

D177 C., M. John and Henry; or, the disobedient child. By M.C., a sincere friend of youth. Harvey & Darton, 1842. LEI

C.P.H. *See* H., C.P.

D178 A CABINET of natural history . . . with engravings on wood by T. Bewick. Alnwick, 1809. NoU

D179 [CADEAU pour les bons enfants.] No place, [c. 1800?] NoU

D180 CALLCOTT, John Wall, 1766–1821. (1806) Dr. Calcott's [*sic*] Grammar of music . . . 12th ed., carefully revised by Henry Aspinall West. Davidson, [c. 1860?]. LEI

D181 CALLCOTT, Maria, *lady*, 1785–1842. (1835) Little Arthur's history of England. New ed., Murray, 1859. LEI; 1864. NoU; The century edition. Murray, 1936. LEI; [Further revised.] Murray, 1962. SO

D182 CALVERT's lithographic drawing book. Nos. 6, 7, 10, 13. [18–?]. NoU

D183 CAMERON, *Mrs.* Lucy Lyttelton, *form.* Butt, 1781–1858. The buried treasure. Houlston, [18–]. ReU

D184 CAMERON, *Mrs.* L. L. (1823) Cleanliness next to godliness. Houlston, [18–]. ReU

D185 CAMERON, *Mrs.* L. L. The collier's family. Houlston, [18–]. ReU

D186 CAMERON, *Mrs.* L. L. Content and discontent. Houlston, [1830?]. ReU

D187 CAMERON, *Mrs.* L. L. (1824?) The cradle. J. Nisbet, 1829. ReU

D188 [CAMERON, *Mrs.* L. L.]. The evening visit, by the author of Margaret Whyte. W. Whittemore, 1824. ReU

D189 CAMERON, *Mrs.* L. L. The footman. Houlston, [18–]. ReU

D190 CAMERON, *Mrs.* L. L. (1827) The fruits of education. 2nd ed., Houlston, 1834. ReU

D191 CAMERON, *Mrs.* L. L. The housemaid. Houlston, [18–]. ReU

D192 CAMERON, *Mrs.* L. L. The kitchenmaid. Houlston, [18–]. ReU

D193 CAMERON, *Mrs.* L. L. (1821) Memoirs of Emma and her nurse; or, the history of Lady Harewood. 11th ed., Houlston, [184–?]. ReU; 14th ed., Houlston & Stoneman, 1846. LEI

D194 CAMERON, *Mrs.* L. L. The nurserymaid's diary. Wightman & Cramp, [18–]. ReU [Also assigned to Mrs. Sherwood.]

D195 CAMERON, *Mrs.* L. L. The Oakengates wake. J. Nisbet, 1829. 2 pts. ReU

D196 CAMERON, *Mrs.* L. L. The pink tippet. Wightman & Cramp, [18–]. 4 pts. in 2. ReU

D197 CAMERON, *Mrs.* L. L. The singing-gallery. Houlston, [1823?]. ReU

D198 CAMERON, *Mrs.* L. L. The three flower-pots. Houlston & Stoneman, 1847. ReU

D199 CAMERON, *Mrs.* L. L. The two death-beds. Houlston, [1823?]. ReU

D200 CAMERON, *Mrs.* L. L. Vain wishes. Houlston, [18–]. ReU

D201 CAMERON, *Mrs.* L. L. (1824?) The village nurse. J. Nisbet, 1829. ReU

D202 CAMERON, *Mrs.* L. L. The young mother. Wm. Whittemore, 1823. ReU

D203 CAMPAN, Jeanne Louise Henrietta, 1752–1822. (1824) De l'éducation; suivi des Conseils aux jeunes filles, d'Un Théâtre pour les jeunes personnes... *See* C225

D204 CAMPE, Joachim Heinrich, 1764–1818. (Germ. 1779; Fr. 1779) Le nouveau Robinson pour servir à l'amusement et à l'instruction des enfans. Traduction revue et corrigée d'après la dernière édition de l'original allemand, enrichie de notes allemandes et d'un vocabulaire complet par J. B. Engelmann. 4e éd., Frankfurt on Main, F. Wilmans, 1814. LEI

D205 CAMPION'S juvenile lithographic drawing book. [18–?]. NoU

D206 CAREY, George G. A complete system of theoretical and mercantile arithmetic... Compiled for the use of the students at the Commercial Institution, Woodford. James Swan for J. M. Richardson, 1817. HU

D207 CAREY, John, 1756–1826. A clue for young Latinists, and non-Latinists, to trace the original forms and signification of nouns and verbs... Longman, 1821. HU

D208 CAREY, John. (1809) Practical English prosody and versification, etc. New ed., Baldwin, Cradock & Joy, 1816. LO

D209 CAROVÉ, Friedrich Wilhelm, 1789–1852. (Eng. 1834) The story without an end. From the German of Carové by Sarah Austin... New impr. ed., Effingham Wilson, [c. 1840?]. LEI

D210 CARPENTER, Thomas. (1796) The scholar's spelling assistant; wherein the words are arranged on an improved plan... Intended for the use of schools and private tuition. New ed., Longman, [etc.], 1833. LEI; new ed., 1839. NoU

D211 CARROLL, Lewis, *pseud.* [i.e. Charles Lutwidge Dodgson], 1832–1898. (1865) Alice's adventures in Wonderland. Macmillan, 1869. NE

D212 CASPARI, Karl Heinrich. (Germ. 1851?) The schoolmaster and his son. A story of the Thirty years' war. From the German. J. Morgan, [1864?]. LEI

D213 CASSELL, John, 1817–1865, *ed.* The child's educator; or, familiar lessons on natural history, human physiology and health, geography... language (English and French), arithmetic... and miscellanies. Edited and conducted by John Cassell. W. Kent, [1856]. HU

D214 CASSELL, *publisher.* The popular educator. [Edited by R. Wallace.] Cassell, 1852–1855. 6 vols. in 3. SH; Vols. 1–2. 1852–1853. LEE

D215 CASSELL, *publisher.* Cassell's educational course. The English language... by W. C. Fowler. Kent, [1857]. BI

D216 CATECHETICAL. (Pre-1780) A catechetical instruction: being an account of the chief truths of the Christian religion explained to the meanest capacity... New ed., Rivington for S.P.C.K., 1821. [Formerly had title: An account of the chief truths...] LEI

D217 A CATECHISM of ancient general biography. Principally designed for the use of schools. By a lady. Houlston, 1833. LEE

D218 A CATECHISM of chemistry; containing a concentrated and simple view of its elementary principles; adapted to those commencing the study of that science. By an amateur. Edinburgh, Oliver & Boyd, 1820. LEI

D219 A CATECHISM of drawing and perspective. [By W. Pinnock?]. Edinburgh, [1821]. NoU

D220 A CATECHISM of Indian history for junior classes. Calcutta, Bishop's College Pr., 1869. LO

D221 CATO. (1816?) Cato; or, interesting adventures of a dog; interspersed with real anecdotes. By a lady, author of 'The infant's friend', etc., etc. 4th ed., J. Harris, [183–?]. LEI

D222 CHAMBERLAIN, Eliza. Chamberlain's young scholar's new English dictionary. 1846. NoU

D223 CHAMBERS, Richard, *F.L.S.* (1835) The geographical and biographical compendium, containing concise memoirs of illustrous persons; a gazetteer of remarkable places; and forming not only a useful class book... but a key to the author's Geographical questions and exercises. New ed., rev. and enl., Sherwood, Gilbert & Piper, [etc.], 1838. LEI

D224 CHAMBERS, William, 1800–1883. (1857) Youth's companion and counsellor. New ed., Chambers, 1880. LEI

D225 CHAMBERS, W., and CHAMBERS, Robert, 1802–1871, *eds.* (1833–1835) Chamber's information for the people. New impr. ed. Part 1, nos. 1–4. Edinburgh, Chambers, [*c.* 1840?]. LEI

D226 CHAMBERS, *publishing firm.* Chambers's educational course:

(*a*) Arithmetic: theoretical and practical, with exercises for competitive examinations. Chambers, 1877. LEI

(*b*) Chambers's scientific reader. Chambers, [*c.* 1870]. HU

(*c*) Chambers's spelling book, by Rev. James Currie. Chambers, [1866]. BI

(*d*) Exemplary and instructive biography. For the study of youth. Edinburgh, Chambers, [etc.], 1836. LEI

(*e*) Exercises in etymology, by William Graham. [2nd ed.], Chambers, [1855]. BI; new. rev. ed., Chambers, 1870. LEI

(*f*) Rudiments of knowledge. Edinburgh, Chambers, 1848. HU

D227 CHAPBOOKS. *Glasgow.* [Collection of 7 chapbooks published by J. Lumsden & Son. Glasgow, 181–?] NoU

D228 CHAPBOOKS. *Otley.* [Collection of 16 chapbooks, published by Yorkshire J.S. Publishing & Stationery Co., Otley, *c.* 1840.] NoU

D229 CHAPBOOKS. *York.* [Collection of 33 chapbooks, published by J. Kendrew, York, 18–.] NoU

D230 CHAPONE, *Mrs.* Hester, 1727–1801. (1773) Letters on the improvement of the mind. Addressed to a lady. A. K. Newman, 1811. HU; J. Sharpe, 1829. LEI; 8th ed., Walter, & Dilly, 1848. SH

D231 CHAPPELL, J., *publisher.* [Writing-book, used by R. T. Stuchbery, 1842.] HU

D232 [CHARLESWORTH, Maria Louisa], 1819–1880. (1854) Ministering children: a tale dedicated to childhood. By the author of 'Visits to the poor',... etc. Seeley, Jackson & Halliday, 1856. HU; 1876. LEI

D233 CHARLESWORTH, M. L. (1867) Ministering children: a sequel. Seeley, Jackson & Halliday, 1873. LEI; 1876. HU

D234 CHART of the kings and queens of England from William I to George, prince of Wales, Regent. [No place], [181–?]. NoU; another copy, with names omitted. NoU

D235 CHEMISTRY and chemical analysis... Forming the third volume of Natural philosophy for the use of schools. Printed and published by direction of the Commissioners of National Education, Ireland. Dublin, Thom, [etc.], 1861. LEI

D236 CHERPILLOUD, J. (1817) The book of versions; or, guide to French translation; for the use of schools... New ed., J. Souter, [182–?]. LEI

D236a CHERPILLOUD, J., *ed.* Elisabeth, ou, les exilés de Sibérie. *See* D312 Cottin, S.

D237 CHESTERFIELD, Philip Dormer Stanhope, *4th earl of,* 1694–1773. The accomplished gentleman; or, principles of politeness, and of knowing the world. Dublin, Richardson & Son, [1847?]. [Abridgment of the Letters, by John Trusler.] HU

D238 CHESTERFIELD, *earl of.* The elements of a polite education; carefully selected from the Letters to his son. Edited by G. Gregory. Dublin, Wm. Porter, pr., 1802. LEI

Chick-seed without chick-weed. *See* Leathley, *Mrs.*

D239 CHILD, Lydia Mary, *form.* Francis, 1802–1880. (*c.* 1831) The girl's own book. 6th ed., Tegg, [etc.], 1833. LEI

D240 CHILD, L. M. Stories for holiday evenings ... [18–?]. NoU

D241 The CHILD and the hermit; or, a sequel to The story without an end, [by F. W. Carové]. By C.M. Darton & Clark, for the author, [*c.* 1840]. LEE

D242 CHILDREN IN THE WOOD. The children in the wood; in prose and verse. Mozley, [18–]. NoU

D243 CHILDREN IN THE WOOD. The babes in the wood. In prose and verse. Illustrated with ten coloured plates. New ed., Bickers & son, 1863. LEI

D244 The CHILDREN's friend. By the Rev. W. Carus Wilson. Vol. 2, 1825; vols. 12–13, 1835–1836. Kirkby Lonsdale, Foster. LEI

D245 The CHILDREN's picture-book of English history; illustrated with fifty engravings. Bell & Daldy, 1859. HU

D246 CHILDREN's. (1860) The children's picture fable-book, containing 160 fables. With 60 illustrations by Harrison Weir. Routledge, [187–?]. LEI

D247 CHILDS, George. Childs's drawing book of objects; studies from still-life... [18–?]. NoU

D248 CHILDS, George. The easy drawing book. Part 7. [18–?]. NoU

Child's Christian year. *See* Keble, John, and Anstice, Joseph, *comps.*

D249 The CHILD's companion; or, Sunday scholar's reward. Vols. 1, 4–5, 8. R.T.S., 1824–1830. LEI; The Child's companion, and juvenile instructor. New series. R.T.S., 1850. NE; 1854, 1857. LEI NoU; 1860. LEI; 1861–1862. NO; 1863. LEE

D250 CHILD's. (Pre-1780) The Child's first book. Part. 1. New ed., Rivington for S.P.C.K., 1820. LEI; Part 2. New ed., Rivington for S.P.C.K., 1820. LEI

D251 The CHILD's friend; or, reading and spelling made completely easy... Recommended for the use of schools and private families. Wellington & Iron Bridge, Houlston & son, [180–?]. HU

Child's guide to knowledge. *See* Ward, *Mrs.* R.

D252 The CHILD'S own magazine, for 1864, 1865. Sunday school union. 2 vols. LEI

D253 The CHILD'S second book, being a sequel to the first . . . by J.F., schoolmaster. Penrith, —, 1806. NoU

D254 CHOIX de lectures historiques propres à exercer et enricher les facultés de l'âme. Dijon, Douillier, [18–]. ReU

D255 The CHRISTIAN atonement. R.T.S., [1830?]. (R.T.S. tract, 1st series, No. 130.) ReU

D256 CICERO, Marcus Tullius. Verrinarum libri septem . . . Orations on the impeachment of C. Verres . . . with . . . a marginal summary by Thomas Arnold . . . For the use of Rugby School. 3rd ed., Rugby, Crossley; London, Whittaker, [etc.]; 1847. LEI

D257 CLARK, John, fl. 1845. (1840) Second book of drawing. Edinburgh, Chambers, 1845 rep. HU

D258 [CLARK, Samuel], 1810–1875. ? (1856?) The balloon travels of Robert Merry and his young friends over various countries in Europe, by Peter Parley [pseud., i.e. Samuel Clark?]. [18–]. NE

D259 [CLARK, Samuel]. The first catechism of Bible history. By the Rev. T. Wilson [pseud., i.e. Samuel Clark]. New ed., [c. 1850?]. NoU

D260 [CLARK, Samuel]. The little geologist, or first book of geology. By the Rev. T. Wilson. Darton & Clark, [c. 1840]. LEI

D261 [CLARK, Samuel]. Peter Parley's Wonders of art, ancient and modern. Darton & Clark, [1841]. HU

D262 [CLARK, Samuel]. (1837?) Peter Parley's Wonders of the earth, sea and sky. Edited by [actually written by] the Rev. T. Wilson. New ed., with additions, Darton, [c. 1840?]. LEE

D263 [CLARK, Samuel]. Third lessons on natural philosophy for children. By the Rev. T. Wilson. Darton & Hodge, [184–?]. ReU

D264 [CLARK, Samuel], ed. (c. 1840) Peter Parley's Tales about Europe, [by S. G. Goodrich]. Edited by the Rev. T. Wilson. 6th ed., Darton, [c. 1850?]. LEE

CLARK, Rev. T., pseud. See Galt, John

D265 [CLARKE, R. F.]. A system of arithmetic, with the principles of logarithms; compiled for Merchant Taylors' School. Smith, Elder, 1833. HU

D266 [CLARKE, William], 1800–1838. (1828) The boy's own book: a complete encyclopaedia of sports and pastimes; athletic, scientific, and re-creative. 4th ed., 1829. NoU; new ed., rev. and enl., Crosby Lockwood, 1880. LEI

Classical English letter-writer. See Frank, Elizabeth

Claudine. See Budden, Maria E.

D267 CLOWES, John, 1743–1831. The parables . . . explained in the way of question and answer. For the use of young people. Manchester, 1815–1817. NoU

D268 CLOWES, John. Religious instruction for youth, on a variety of serious and important subjects, discussed principally in short dialogues between a father and his son. Manchester, Nanfan & Davis, [1812]. 2 vols. HU

D269 CLOWES, John, trans. (1797) Pious reflections, for every day in the month, [by Fénelon]. 1823. NoU

D270 COBBETT, William, 1762–1835. (Dated 1829, actually 1830) Advice to young men and (incidentally) to young women in the middle and higher ranks of life . . . (From the edition of 1829). Frowde, 1906. LEE; P. Davies, 1926. LEI

D271 COBBETT, William. (1824) A French grammar; or, plain instructions for the learning of French. 6th ed., Author, 1835. LEE

D272 COBBETT, William. (1818) A grammar of the English language, in a series of letters . . . 2nd ed., Author, 1819. NoU; 3rd ed., Author, 1819. LEI; 4th ed., W. Benbow, 1820. HU; Anne Cobbett, 1836. LEE; Anne Cobbett, 1838. HU

D273 COBBIN, Ingram, 1777–1851. Elements of geography, on a new plan, rendered plain and amusing . . . designed for preparatory schools. 5th ed., Westley & Davis, 1836. LEI

Cobwebs to catch flies. See Fenn, E.

D274 COCK ROBIN. The death and burial of Cock Robin. Hodgson, [1835?]. NoU

D275 COCKLE, Mrs. Mary, pseud. (1808) The fishes grand gala. A companion to the 'Peacock at home'. Chapple, 1808. 2 vols. ReU

D276 COLART, —. Histoire de France, méthodique et comparée, avec texte, tableaux synoptiques et 75 gravures sur acier, employée pour l'éducation des Enfants de France, et de S.M.T.F. Par M. Colart, leur instituteur . . . 2e éd., Paris, Ch. Gosselin, 1836. LEI

D277 [COLBURN, Warren], 1793–1833. (1821) Intellectual arithmetic, upon the inductive method of instruction, with a key . . . By a teacher of youth. 7th ed., J. S. Hodson, 1840. LEI

D278 [COLE, Sir Henry], 1808–1882, ed. Faery tales and ballads. The sisters. Golden Locks. Grumble and Cheery, and the Eagle's verdict. The ballads of Chevy Chase and Sir Hornbook . . . Edited by Felix Summerly, [pseud., i.e. Sir Henry Cole]. J. Cundall, 1846. (The home treasury.) LEI

D279 COLENSO, John William, 1814–1883. (1843) Arithmetic; designed for the use of schools. [2nd ed.], [Longman, c. 1850]. [Lacks t.p.] BI; new ed., Longman, 1862. HU

D280 COLENSO, J. W. (1841?) The elements of algebra; designed for the use of schools. 4th ed., Cambridge, Deighton, 1844. BI; Part 1. 15th ed., Longman, [etc.], 1860. LEI

D281 COLERIDGE, Henry Nelson, 1798–1843. (1830) Introductions to the study of the Greek classic poets. Designed principally for the use of young persons at school and college. Part 1. Containing: I. General introduction. II. Homer. [no more pub.]. 2nd ed., Murray, 1834. LEI; 3rd ed., Murray, 1846. HU

D282 COLLECTANEA Latina: sive, Excerpta ex Eutropii Historia Romana; ex libro Sex. Aur. Victoris De viris illustribus urbis Romae . . . [etc.]. In usum tyronum ingenuis artibus operam dantium. Edinburgh, Black, 1834. HU

D283 COLLECTION of original fables, moral and instructive . . . Ryle, [c. 1850?]. NoU

D284 COLLETT, John, *master of the academy, Evesham.* Sacred dramas: intended chiefly for young persons. To which is added, An elegy . . . Evesham, Author, 1805. LEI

D285 [COLLIER, John Payne], 1789–1883. (1828) Punch and Judy. With 24 illustrations . . . by George Cruikshank . . . Accompanied by the dialogue of the puppet-show, an account of its origin, and of puppet plays in England. 6th ed., Bell & Daldy, 1873. LEI

D286 COLLIER, William Francis, b. 1830. History of the British Empire. Nelson, 1863. LEI

D287 COMIC alphabet. No place, [18–?]. NoU

COMMITTEE OF GENERAL LITERATURE AND EDUCATION of the S.P.C.K. *See* Society for promoting Christian knowledge

Companion to the Bible. *See* Timpson, T.

D288 A COMPENDIUM of simple arithmetic . . . J. Wallis, 1871. NoU

D289 COMPENDIUM of zoology, being a description of more than three hundred animals . . . [Ed. by A. D. M'Quin.] New ed., rev. and corr., Baldwin, Cradock & Joy, 1818. [Originally edited by Thomas Boreman with title 'A description of more than 300 animals'. 'Recomposed' by A. D. M'Quin in 1812.] LEI

D290 CONSTRUCTION. (1729?) The construction of the Latin verse-grammar. For the use of the lower forms in Westminster school. 1810. NoU

D291 The CONTENTED villager. R.T.S., [18–]. [Pre-1840] ReU

D292 CONVERSATIONS. (c. 1810?) Conversations d'une mère avec sa fille . . . ou, dialogues composés pour la maison d'éducation de Madame Campan, près de Paris: et arrangés par Madame D—— à l'usage des demoiselles anglaises. 3e éd., Londres, G. & W. B. Whittaker, 1820. [French and Italian.] LEI; 12e éd., Londres, Whittaker, 1845. HU
Conversations introducing poetry. *See* Smith, Charlotte

D293 CONVERSATIONS of Angelina and her doll. Interspersed with interesting stories. [Edinburgh, 18–?]. NoU
Conversations on botany/chemistry/natural philosophy/political economy. *See* Marcet, Jane

D294 CONVERSATIONS on geology, comprising a familiar explanation of the Huttonian and Wernerian systems, the Mosaic geology . . . Maunder, 1828. NoU

D295 CONVERSATIONS on poetry: intended for the amusement and instruction of children. By the author of the 'Buxton diamonds', etc. Darton, [1824?]. LEI

D296 CONYBEARE, William John, 1815–1857. (2nd ed., 1845) School chronology; or, the great dates of history. 12th ed., Longman, 1862. HU

D297 COOKE, Thomas. (1771?) The universal letter-writer; or, new art of polite correspondence . . . with a plain and easy grammar of the English language . . . Derby, H. Mozley, [c. 1838]. LEI

D298 COOPER, *Rev. Mr., pseud.?* (1761) A new history of England, from the earliest period to the present time, on a plan recommended by the Earl of Chesterfield. By the Rev. Mr. Cooper. 15th ed., Harris, 1809. NoU; History of England . . . 21st ed. . . . brought down to . . . 1829. J. Harris, [etc.], 1830. LEI

D299 CORNER, Julia, 1798–1875. (1854) Beauty and the beast. An entertainment for young people . . . Embellished by Alfred Crowquill. Dean, 1854. (Little plays for little actors.) LEI

D300 CORNER, Julia. (185–) The first history of England that should be placed in the hands of a child. [3rd ed.?], T. Dean & son, [c. 1856?]. LEI

D301 CORNER, Julia, do., *with title* Every child's history of England. New ed., Dean, [1870]. NoU

D302 CORNER, Julia. The history of England: from the earliest period to the present time. Adapted to youth, schools, and families. New ed. . . . Dean & son, [1861]. LEI

D303 CORNER, Julia. The history of Ireland: from the earliest period to the present time. Adapted for youth, schools, and families. New ed., enl., Dean & son, [c. 1846?]. LEI

D304 CORNER, Julia. The history of Poland and Russia from the earliest period to the present time, adapted for youth, schools, and families. Dean, [1841]. NoU

D305 CORNER, Julia. (184–?) The play grammar; or, the elements of grammar explained in easy games. 9th ed., Dean, [185–?]. NoU; 12th ed., enl., Dean & son, [c. 1858?]. LEI; 15th ed., Dean, [c. 1860?]. LEE

D306 CORNER, Julia. (1848) The village school. With the history, and what became of some of the scholars. T. Dean, [c. 1850]. LEE

D307 CORNER, Julia. (1854) Whittington and his cat. An entertainment for young people . . . Embellished by Alfred Crowquill. Dean, 1854. (Little plays for little actors.) LEI

D308 CORNWELL, James, 1812–1902. (1847) A school geography. 12th ed., Simpkin, Marshall, [etc.], [c. 1850?]. LEI

D309 CORNWELL, James, and FITCH, *Sir* Joshua Girling. (1855) The science of arithmetic: a systematic course of numerical reasoning and computation . . . 9th ed., Simpkin, Marshall, [etc.], 1864. HU
CORNWELL, James, *joint author.* *See* Allen, Alexander, and Cornwell, James

D310 COSTUMES. (1831?) Costumes; or, a short sketch of the manners, and customs, of the principal foreign inhabitants of the globe . . . [1850?] NoU

D311 COTTIN, Sophie [*otherwise* Marie], *formerly* Risteau, 1773–1807. (1806) Elisabeth; ou, les exilés de Sibérie. Londres, Deconchy, 1808. LEI

D312 COTTIN, Sophie, do. To which are added . . . explanations of difficult words, phrases, and idiomatical expressions, to assist in a correct translation . . . For the use of schools. By J. Cherpilloud. S. Leigh, 1817. HU
Course of lessons, together with the tunes. *See* Bilby, Thomas
Cowslip. *See* Turner, Elizabeth

D313 COXE, Edward, *ed.* Goldsmith's History of England, abridged by himself . . . to which is added, a . . . continuation to the present year . . . By E. Coxe. 15th ed., Derby, Mozley, 1845. NoU

D314 COXE, Edward, *ed.* Dr. Goldsmith's History of Rome, abridged for the use of schools; divided into sections, with numerous examining questions . . . By Edward Coxe. Mozley, [182–]. HU; Derby, Mozley, [184–?]. NoU

D314a CRABB, George, 1778–1851. The preceptor and his pupils; or, Dialogues, examinations and exercises on grammar in general and the English grammar in particular. For the use of schools and private students. T. Boosey, 1807. HU

D315 [CRESPIGNY, Mary Champion]. Letters of advice from a mother to her son. Cadell & Davies, 1803. LEI

D316 The CRIES of York. Part 1 [only, of 2]. York, Kendrew, [18–]. NoU

D317 CROCKER, Abraham. (3rd ed., 1814) The elements of land surveying designed principally for the use of schools and students. 4th ed., [1817?]. NoU

D318 CROCUS. (1816 or 1824?) The crocus, containing original poems for young people. By J.E.M. New ed., Birmingham, Cornish, 1899. LEI

D319 CROMBIE, Alexander, 1762–1840. Gymnasium; sive, Symbola critica. Johnson, 1812. 2 vols. [Handbook to Latin prose composition.] HU

D320 CROSBY, T., *ed.* (1799?) The tutor's assistant: being a compendium of arithmetic, by F. Walkingame. New ed., corrected, and every question worked anew, by T. Crosby. York, T. Wilson, 1840. HU; Crosby's new ed. with considerable additions. York, Wilson, 1841. LEE

D321 CROSSLEY, John Thomas. Crossley's comprehensive class book. History – physics – natural history – geography – and miscellanies. Hamilton, Adams, [etc.], [*c.* 1850?]. LEI

CROWQUILL, Alfred, *pseud. See* Forrester, C. R., and Forrester, A. H.

D322 CRUCHLEY, George Frederick. Cruchley's new and improved school atlas. Cruchley, [1842?]. NoU

D323 CUMYNG, *Mrs.* —, *trans.* Juvenile biography . . . By Mr. Josse. Dulau, [etc.], [1801?]. LEI

D324 CRUIKSHANK, George, 1792–1878, *ed. and illus.* (1854) Cinderella and the glass slipper. Bogue, [1854]. LEI

D325 CURRIE, *Rev.* James. Chambers's spelling book; with numerous exercises for dictation. Chambers, [1866]. (Chambers's educational course.) BI

D326 CURTIS, John Charles. (1864?) Outlines of English history, arranged in chronological order. 4th ed., Simpkin, Marshall, 1867. HU

D327 CURWEN, John, 1816–1880. (1858) The standard course of lessons and exercises in the tonic sol-fa method of teaching music . . . with additional exercises. 3rd ed., rewritten, 1872. Tonic sol-fa agency, 1876. LEI

D328 CURWEN, John, *ed.* An elementary sacred course of lessons and exercises on the tonic-sol-fa method of teaching to sing. Tonic sol-fa agency, [1867?]. LEI

Daisy. *See* Turner, Elizabeth

D329 DALE, Thomas, 1797–1870, *ed.* (1836) The student's guide . . . By John Todd. Revised by the Rev. Thomas Dale. 2nd ed., Seeley, 1837. LEI

Dame Wiggins of Lee. *See* Sharpe, *Mrs.*

D330 DARTON, William, *publisher.* Six studies of animals. Darton, 1822. NoU

D331 DAVIDSOHN, Moritz. Moral and religious guide, based on the principle of universal brotherhood, especially intended for Jewish schools and families . . . Houlston & Stoneman, 1855. LEI

D332 DAVYS, George, 1780–1864. A plain and short history of England, for children: in letters from a father to his son, with a set of questions at the end of each letter. 7th ed., Rivington, 1845. LEE

D333 DAY, Samuel Phillips. (1869) Bunyan's Pilgrim's progress in words of one syllable. Cassell, [1869?]. LEI

D334 DAY, Thomas, 1748–1789. (1783–1789) The history of Sandford and Merton. 11th ed., J. Stockdale, 1802. NE; 1803. NoU; 9th ed., Stockdale, 1812. 3 vols. LEI; Whittingham & Arliss, 1816. 3 vols. OX; 1818. 2 vols. ReU; Edinburgh, Gall & Inglis, n.d. NO; Nelson, 1887. LEE

Deaf and dumb. *See* Sandham, Elizabeth

Decoy. *See* Allan, Louisa

DE FIVAS, Victor. *See* Fivas, Victor de

D335 [DEFOE, Daniel], 1660–1731. (1715–1718) The family instructor. Vols. 1–2. Byfield, [etc.], 1809. 2 vols. in 1. LEE

D336 DEFOE, Daniel. (1719) The history of Robinson Crusoe. Mozley, [18–]. NoU

D337 DE MORGAN, Augustus, 1806–1871. The connexion of number and magnitude; an attempt to explain the fifth book of Euclid. Taylor & Walton, 1836. HU

D338 DE MORGAN, Augustus. (1832–1842 in parts) The differential and integral calculus . . . Also, Elementary illustrations of the differential and integral calculus. Baldwin & Cradock, 1842. LEI

D339 DE MORGAN, Augustus. (1830) The elements of arithmetic. J. Taylor, 1830. LO; 4th ed., Taylor & Walton, 1840. LEI; [5th ed., repr.], Taylor, Walton & Maberley, 1853. SH; do., Walton & Maberly, 1857. HU LO

D340 DE MORGAN, Augustus. (1837) Elements of trigonometry, and trigonometrical analysis . . . Taylor & Walton, 1837. HU

D341 [DE MORGAN, Augustus]. (Pref. 1831) Mathematics, I. Baldwin & Cradock, 1836. 3 vols. in 1. [Contents: Study and difficulties of mathematics – Arithmetic and algebra – Examples of the processes of arithmetic and algebra.] LEI

DE PORQUET, Louis Philippe R. Fenwick. *See* Fenwick de Porquet, L. P. R.

D342 DESPREZ, A. V. The unique, a tabular view of the French language. 6th ed., Hooper, [1840?]. LEI

D343 DEVIS, Ellen [*or* Ellin]. (1775) The accidence; or, first rudiments of English grammar. Designed for the use of young ladies. 15th ed., C. Law, 1814. LEI

D344 DIBDIN, Charles, 1745–1814. Music epitomized: a school book; in which the whole science of music is clearly explained . . . 9th ed., with considerable additions . . . and a new classification, by J. Jousse. Goulding, D'Almaine, Potter & co., [182–]. [Consists of 'Questions in Mr. Dibdin's lectures', 1804, with answers.] HU

D345 DICKENS, Charles, 1812–1870. (1851–1853) A child's history of England. Chapman & Hall, n.d. LEE

D346 DICKES, William. Household pictures for home and school. Jarrold, [*c*. 1860]. LEI

D347 DICKINSON, *Miss* M., *of Twickenham*. (1807) French and English dialogues, written for the use of the Countess of Sefton's children. 3rd ed., Dulau, 1816. LEI

D348 DICKSEE, J. R. The school perspective: being a progressive course of instruction in linear perspective . . . Specially designed for the use of schools. Simpkin, Marshall, (pref. 1859). LEI

D349 DIURNAL readings; being lessons for every day in the year . . . 1812. NoU

D350 DODDRIDGE, Philip, 1702–1751. (1743) The principles of the Christian religion, expressed in plain and easy verse, and divided into short lessons, for the use of children and youth. A. Wilson, 1811. HU

DODGSON, Charles Lutwidge. *See* Carroll, Lewis, *pseud.*

DOERING, Friedrich Wilhelm, 1756–1837, *jt. author*. *See* Jacobs, F. C. W., and Doering, F. W.

Dog of knowledge. *See* Memoirs of Bob the spotted terrier

DOMINA, *pseud*. *See* Kent, Anna

D352 DONALDSON, John William, 1811–1861. (1848) A complete Greek grammar, for the use of students. 3rd ed., enl., Cambridge, Deighton, Bell; London, Bell & Daldy; 1862. LEI

D353 DONALDSON, J. W. (1852) A complete Latin grammar for the use of students. 2nd ed., enl., Cambridge, Deighton, Bell; London, Bell & Daldy; 1860. LEI

D354 [DORSET, *Mrs.* Catherine Ann], *formerly* Turner, 1750?–1817? (1807) The peacock 'at home': a sequel to The Butterfly's ball. Written by a lady. J. Harris, 1807. ReU; 27th ed., 1815. NoU; facsimile reproduction, with an introduction by C. Welsh. Griffith & Farran, 1883. LEI NO NoU

D355 [DORSET, *Mrs.* C. A.]. (1807) The lion's masquerade: a sequel to 'The peacock "at home".' Written by a lady. A facsimile reproduction of the edition of 1807, with an introduction by C. Welsh. Griffith & Farran, 1883. LEI NO NoU

D356 DOUBLET, V. (Pref. 1839) Rhétorique des demoiselles . . . Nlle. éd., Tours, A. Mame, 1868. LEI

D357 DOUGALL, John, 1760–1822. The young man's best companion and guide to useful knowledge. Bungay, T. Kinnersley, 1815. LEI

D358 DOUGHTY, *Mrs.* Sarah P. Grateful Annie; or, the new skates, etc. Wakefield, Wm. Nicholson & sons, [*c*. 1850?]. ReU

D359 DOUIN, *Mme.* —. The French primer; containing a copious vocabulary of familiar words . . . Souter, 1822. LEE

D360 DOVE, Elizabeth Ann. Tales for my pupils; or, an attempt to correct juvenile errors. Author, 1822. LEE

D361 DRAPER, Bourne Hall. (1831) Bible illustrations; or, a description of manners and customs . . . explanatory of the Holy Scriptures. 2nd ed., Harris, 1833. (The little library.) LEI

D362 DRAPER, B. H. Stories of the animal world, arranged so as to form a systematic introduction to zoology. [18–]. NoU

Drawing for young children. *See* Grant, Horace

D363 DRAWING lessons in perspective, for the use of schools and beginners. [18–?]. NoU

D364 DRESSER, Christopher. The rudiments of botany, structural and physiological . . . J. S. Virtue, 1859. HU

D365 DRUMMOND, James Lawson, 1783–1853. (1831) Letters to a young naturalist on the study of nature and natural theology. Longman, [etc.], 1831. LEI

Ducks and green peas. *See* Lund, John

DU FRESNOY, Nicholas Lenglet. *See* Lenglet du Fresnoy, Nicholas

D366 DULCKEN, H. W. A picture history of England, from the invasion of Julius Caesar to the present time; written for the use of the young. Routledge, [1866]. HU

D367 DUN, Andrew, *ed*. The rudiments of the Latin tongue, by Thomas Ruddiman. Corrected and revised by Andrew Dun. Aberdeen, J. Chalmers for A. Brown, 1803. LEI

D368 DYCHE, Thomas, *fl*. 1707–1719. (1707) A guide to the English tongue. In two parts. To which is added an appendix . . . Corr., enl. and impr. Gainsborough, H. Mozley, 1811. HU

D369 DYMOND, Edith. Eight evenings at school. Harvey & Darton, 1825. LEI

D370 DYMOND, Henry. Instructive narratives for young persons, members of the Society of Friends. Harvey & Darton, 1825. LEI

D371 EARNSHAW, Christopher. The grammatical remembrancer: a short but comprehensive English grammar for the use of young students in general. To which are added, Geographical pronunciation . . . and Lingua technica . . . Huddersfield, Author, 1817. LEE

D372 An EASY grammar of writing; or, penmanship analysed. In two parts . . . Particularly recommended to schools, apprentices, and young persons, of both sexes, who wish for any knowledge of business. By the Master of the Farnham Commercial Academy. Alton, W. Pinnock, 1810. HU

D373 EASY. (1833) Easy lessons on money matters; for the use of young people. Published under the direction of the Society for Promoting Christian Knowledge. Parker, 1833. LO

D374 EDGAR, John George, 1834–1864. The boyhood of great men: intended as an example to youth. 3rd ed., D. Bogue, 1854. HU

D375 EDGEWORTH, Maria, 1767–1849. Works. Baldwin & Cradock, 1832. 18 vols. LO

D376 EDGEWORTH, Maria. Belinda. 2nd ed., J. Johnson, 1802. ReU

D377 EDGEWORTH, Maria. (Vols. 1–2, 1780?; earliest extant, 1801) Early lessons. 4 unbound parts. 1809. NoU; 7th ed., R. Hunter, 1820. 2 vols. BR; 8th ed. Vols. 1 and 2. 1822. NoU; Vol. 1, 8th ed., vol. 2, 9th ed., Hunter, 1822–1824. SO; Vols.1–2, 9th ed., vols. 3–4, 5th ed., Hunter, 1824. LEI; Vol. 1, 10th ed., Hunter, 1827, vol. 3, 5th ed., Hunter, 1824. LO; Vol. 2, 16th ed., vol. 3, 10th ed., Longman, 1845. NO; Routledge, n.d. OX; Routledge, [c. 1870]. SH; Routledge, [c. 1890]. 3 vols. in 1. HU

D378 EDGEWORTH, Maria. (1822) Frank; a sequel to *Frank* in *Early lessons*. 2nd ed., R. Hunter [&] Baldwin, Cradock & Joy, 1825. 3 vols. LEI; 3rd ed., Baldwin & Cradock, 1833. ReU

D379 EDGEWORTH, Maria. (1825) Harry and Lucy concluded; being the last part of Early lessons. Hunter, [etc.], 1825. 4 vols. BI LEI

D379a EDGEWORTH, Maria. Les jeunes industriels, faisant suite à L'Education familière. Traduit par Mmes. L. Sw.-Belloc et Ad. Montgolfier. 2nd éd., Paris, Renouard, n.d. 8 vols. LO

D380 EDGEWORTH, Maria. (1801) Moral tales for young people. Johnson, 1802. 3 vols. LEI; 2nd ed., 1806. 3 vols. NoU; 6th ed., vols. 2 and 3, 1813. NoU; 7th ed., 1816. 3 vols. NoU; Simpkin, Marshall, 1853. BR; Routledge, 1893. SO; Blackie, [c. 1900?]. LEE

D381 EDGEWORTH, Maria. [Moral tales]. The good French governess, Angelina, and The Prussian vase. London and Edinburgh, Chambers, 1873. LO

D382 EDGEWORTH, Maria. (1821) Rosamond: a sequel to 'Early lessons'. Vol. 1. R. Hunter, [&] Baldwin, Cradock & Joy, 1821. NE; 5th ed., 1850. 2 vols. NoU

D383 EDGEWORTH, Maria. (1848) Orlandino. Chambers, 1874. NoU

D384 EDGEWORTH, Maria. (1804) Popular tales. Vol. 1 [only]. 2nd ed., 1805. NoU

D385 EDGEWORTH, Maria. (1795–1796?) The parent's assistant; or, stories for children. 4th ed., J. Johnson, 1804. 6 vols. HU; new ed., 1834. 3 vols. NoU; new ed. in one volume, Longman, [etc.], 1855. LEI; new ed., Macmillan, 1897. LEE

D386 EDGEWORTH, Maria. Rosamond: a series of tales. Routledge, 1856. [Collected tales from 'Early lessons'.] LEI

D387 EDGEWORTH, Maria. Simple Susan. Longman, 1846. 2 vols. LEI; new ed., Routledge, 1858. HU [From 'The Parent's assistant'.]

D388 EDGEWORTH, Richard Lovell, 1747–1817, and EDGEWORTH, Maria. (1816) Readings on poetry. Hunter, 1816. LEI; 2nd ed., 1816. NoU

Education at home. *See* Benson, Edward White

Elegantiae Latinae. *See* Valpy, Edward

D389 ELEMENTS. (1833) The Elements of botany: for families and schools. 3rd ed., enl. Parker, for the Committee of general literature and education of the S.P.C.K., 1837. LEI LO; 10th ed., by Thomas Moore. Longmans, 1865. HU

D390 ELEMENTS. (1837) Elements of practical knowledge; or, the young enquirer answered: etc. 2nd ed., J. van Voorst, 1841. LO

D391 ELEPHANT'S. (1807) The Elephant's ball and grande fête champêtre, by W.B. Facsimile reproduction of the edition of 1807, with introduction by C. Welsh. Griffith & Farran, 1883. LEI NO

D392 ELLIOTT, James William, 1833–1915, *comp.* (1870) National nursery rhymes and nursery songs. Set to original music by J. W. Elliott... Routledge, [etc.], [1870]. SO

D393 ELLIOTT, Mary, *formerly* Belson. (1812) The orphan boy; or, a journey to Bath. To which is added, The orphan girl, founded on facts. By Mary Belson. New ed., 1818. NoU

D394 ELLIOTT, Mary. (1819) Peggy and her mammy. Darton, 1819. LEE

D395 ELLIOTT, Mary. (1820) Rural employments; or, a peep into village concerns. W. Darton, 1820. NoU

D396 ELLIOTT, Mary. (1822) The sunflower; or, poetical truths for young minds... W. Darton, 1822. NoU

D397 ELLIOTT, Mary. William's secret. Darton, 1819. LEE

D398 ELLIS, William, *of King's Coll., Aberdeen.* (1782) A collection of English exercises; translated from the writings of Cicero, for school-boys to re-translate into Latin... 6th ed., rev. and corr., Rivington, [etc.], 1813. HU

D399 ELMSLEY, Peter, 1773–1823, *ed.* (1821) ... [Greek script]. Bacchae [of Euripides]. In usum studiosae juventutis... Oxford, Clarendon Pr., 1821. LEI

D400 ELRINGTON, Thomas, 1760–1835, *ed.* (1788) Euclid's Elements of geometry, translated from the Latin of T. Elrington... New ed., Cambridge, [etc.], Deighton, [etc.], 1856. LEI

D401 ENFIELD, William, 1741–1797. (1774) The speaker; or, miscellaneous pieces, selected from the best English writers... To which are prefixed two essays: I. On elocution; II. On reading works of taste. Stereotype ed., A. Wilson for J. Johnson, [etc.], 1808. LEI; new ed., 1810. NoU; 2nd ed., Gainsborough, Mozley, 1812. BI

D402 The ENGLISH primer, or, child's first book ... Banbury, Rusher, [18–?]. NoU

D403 The ENGLISH spelling book improved: containing ... a variety of tables of spelling, instructive lessons, and entertaining stories... To which are added, a correct set of improved arithmetical tables ... a concise English grammar... etc. 2nd ed., Banbury, J. G. Rusher, (pref. 1830). LEI

D404 ENTICK, John, 1703?–1773. (1764) [A new spelling-dictionary. A. Wilson's stereotype office, 180–]. [Lacks t.p.]. HU; Entick's spelling dictionary of the English language... abridged... by T. Ash. 1813. NoU

D405 An EPITOME of ancient geography; with historical notes, and questions for examinations. For the use of schools. By a Friend of youth. Newbury, S. Maunder for W. Pinnock, [c. 1840]. [Possibly by Samuel Maunder.] HU

D406 ETON COLLEGE. [Collection of MS. Latin verses, with masters' corrections. c. 1824–1828.] 2 vols. LEI

Eton Latin grammar. See Introduction to the Latin tongue

D407 EUCLID. The elements of Euclid; containing the first six, and the eleventh and twelfth books, chiefly from the text of Dr. Simson. Edited by Jackson Muspratt Williams. London, C. Tilt; Cambridge, T. Stevenson; 1829. OX

D408 EUCLID. Elements of geometry, translated from the Latin of Thomas Elrington . . . to which is added a compendium of algebra, also a compendium of trigonometry . . . New ed., Cambridge, [etc.], Deighton, [etc.], 1856. LEI

D409 EUCLID. Elements of geometry, the first six books, and the portions of the eleventh and twelfth books read at Cambridge . . . designed for the use of the junior classes in public and private schools. By Robert Potts. Longman, 1866. CA

D410 EURIPIDES. . . . Bacchae. In usum studiosae juventutis recensuit et illustravit Petrus Elmsley. Oxford, Clarendon Pr., 1821. LEI

D411 EUROPEAN travellers: an instructive game. E. Wallis, n.d. [between 1818 and 1840?]. LEI

D412 EVANS, John, 1767–1827. (1804) Juvenile pieces, designed for the youth of both sexes . . . with an Essay on education. 6th ed., enl. and corr. . . . Baldwin, Cradock & Joy, 1818. HU

D413 EVANS, John, d. 1832. The progress of human life: Shakspeare's seven ages of man illustrated by a series of extracts . . . for . . . schools and families . . . to the improvement of the rising generation. [With] a brief memoir of Shakspeare. Chiswick, Whittingham, 1820. NoU

D414 EVANS, R. M. The story of Joan of Arc. Wm. Smith, 1841. HU

Evenings at home. See Aikin, John, and Barbauld, A. L.

D415 EVERGREEN tales for the young. With illustrations by T. Gilks. Dean & son, [c. 1860?]. [Originally published in parts as 'Little child's pictorial keepsake'.] LEI

D416 EVES, Charles, and EVES, Georgiana. The derivative spelling book. 10th thousand. Simpkin, [etc.], 1852. HU

D417 The EVIDENCE and effects of the Gospel. Liverpool, R.T.S., [18–]. ReU

D418 The EVIL of irresolution. Edinburgh, R.T.S., 1814. ReU

D419 EWING, Thomas, of Edinburgh. (2nd ed., 1816) Principles of elocution . . . also numerous extracts in prose and poetry . . . 8th ed., impr., Edinburgh, Oliver & Boyd; London, Whittaker; 1826. LEI

D420 EWING, Thomas. (1816) A system of geography; or, a new and easy plan from the latest and best authorities . . . For the use of schools and private students. 22nd ed., Edinburgh, Oliver & Boyd, 1871. HU

D420a EXEMPLA minora; or, new English examples, to be rendered into Latin . . . for the use of the lower forms. [By Joseph Pote, edited by T. Morell?] New ed., Eton, E. Williams, 1817. LO; new ed., York, 1821. NoU; new ed., Eton, 1831. NoU

D420b EXEMPLA moralia; or, third book of new English examples, to be rendered into Latin . . . New ed., rev., Eton, E. Williams, 1815. HU

D421 EXEMPLARY and instructive biography. For the study of youth. Edinburgh, W. & R. Chambers, [etc.], 1836. (Chambers's educational course.) LEI

D422 EXERCISES in false spelling . . . By a Friend to youth. 2nd ed., Newbury, [18–]. NoU

D423 EXERCISES. (1744?) Exercises, instructive and entertaining, in false English; written with a view to perfect youth in their mother tongue . . . 7th ed. [sic], Leeds, 1802. NoU

D424 EXPERIMENTS illustrative of chemical science; systematically arranged . . . by the author of the Elements of chemical science. Glasgow, McPhun, 1826. LEE

D425 F., J., schoolmaster. The child's second book, being a sequel to the first . . . Penrith, 1806. NoU

D426 FABLES for the nursery, original and select. Harris, 1825. ReU

Fairy Know-a-bit. See Tucker, Charlotte Maria

Family instructor. See Defoe, Daniel

D427 The FAMILY tutor, and school companion. [Vol. 1], nos. 7, 9–11, Apr.–June 1851; vol. 2, nos. 13–21, July–Nov. 1851; vol. 3, nos. 25–27, and 30, Jan.–Mar. 1852. LEI

Fanfan et Lolotte. See Ambrose and Eleanor

D428 FARNELL, William Keeling. Farnell's new copy-book series, 2: Simple formations, with prefixes and affixes. [18–?]. NoU

D428a FARNHAM. Commercial academy. An easy grammar of writing . . . By the Master of the Farnham Commercial Academy. Alton, W. Pinnock, 1810. HU

D429 FARRAR, Frederic William, 1831–1903. (1858) Eric; or, little by little: a tale of Roslyn School. Black, 1898. NE

D430 FARRAR, F. W. (2nd ed., 1866) Greek grammar rules. Drawn up for the use of Harrow School. 23rd impr., Longmans, [18–]. LEI

D431 FARRAR, F. W. (1862) St. Winifred's; or, the world of school. Edinburgh, Black, 1863. LEE

D432 FARTHER. (1776) Farther English examples; or, book of cautions for children, in rendering English into Latin . . . New ed., impr., Eton, E. Williams, 1818. HU

D433 FASQUELLE, Jean Louis, 1808–1862. Cassell's lessons in French; containing a complete view of the idioms of the French language, in a series of easy and progressive lessons . . . Part 1. Cassell, Petter & Galpin, [1853]. [Reprinted from the 'Popular educator'.] HU

D434 A FATHER'S advice to his son at school. 1807. NoU

D435 FAVOURITE pleasure books for young people . . . 1859. NoU

D436 FELLER, Friedrich Ernst. Dizionario italiano-tedesco e tedesco-italiano. Leipzig, Teubner, 1859. BR

D437 FEMALE. (1811) The Female instructor; or, young woman's friend and companion... Fisher, 1832. LEI

D438 FENELON, François de Salignac de la Mothe-, 1651–1715. Pious reflections for every day in the month; together with A father's advice to his son ... Chelsea, 1823. [Translated from Fénelon's 'Manuel de piété' by John Clowes.] NoU

D438a [FENN, Eleanor], lady, 1743–1813. (1783?) Cobwebs to catch flies; or, dialogues in short sentences. Adapted for children from the age of three to eight years. New ed., Baldwin & Cradock, [etc.], 1829. 2 vols. LEI; new ed., Baldwin & Cradock, 1833. 2 vols. in 1. ReU; Second series, new ed., Lockwood, [1867]. LEI

D439 [FENN, Eleanor]. Easy reading, adapted to the capacities of children, from five to seven years old ... Being a companion to ... the 'Little vocabulary ...' By Mrs. Lovechild, [pseud., i.e. Lady Fenn.] 1814. NoU

D440 [FENN, Eleanor]. Little tales for the nursery. Amusing and instructive. By Solomon Lovechild [i.e. Lady Fenn]. 3rd ed., Dean, [1855?]. LEE

D441 [FENN, Eleanor]. Mrs. Lovechild's book of two hundred and sixteen cuts, designed to teach children the names of things. Harvey & Darton, 1824. ReU

D442 [FENN, Eleanor]. (c. 1790) The mother's grammar, being a continuation of The Child's grammar... J. Marshall, [c. 1800]. NoU

D443 [FENN, Eleanor]. (c. 1785) Sketches of little boys and girls, by Solomon Lovechild. Dean & son, [1852]. LEI

D444 [FENN, Eleanor], comp. The family miscellany, in prose and verse; designed to supply lessons for children of various ages. Selected by Mrs. Lovechild, as a sequel to 'Infants' friend'. J. Harris, & Darton & Harvey, 1805. LEI

D445 FENN, John. The school-master's legacy and family monitor; adapted to every age and station in life, inculcating the practice of religion and morality... Woodbridge, Author, 1843. BR

D446 FENNING, Daniel, fl. 1754–1775. (1754) The British youth's instructor; or, a new and easy guide to practical arithmetic... 1806. NoU; 13th ed., carefully revised and corrected by... Thomas Smith. Johnson, 1866. BR

D447 FENNING, Daniel. (1754?) A new and easy guide to the use of globes, and the rudiments of geography... 9th ed., corr. and impr. by the editor. Johnson, [etc.], 1809. LEI

D448 FENNING, Daniel. (1756) The universal spelling-book; or, a new and easy guide to the English language... York, 1805. NoU; Stereotype ed., York, Wilson, [1820]. LEE; Derby, Mozley, 1837. LEI

D449 FENNING, Daniel. Wogan's improved universal spelling book ... New ed., Dublin, Richardson, [1841?]. HU; London, Richardson, [1846?]. LEE

D450 FENNING, Daniel. (1758?) The young algebraist's companion; or, a new and easy guide to algebra ... designed for the use of schools ... A new 2nd ed. To which are added two supplements by John Hellens [and] the late William Davis. W. Baynes, & Anne Davis, 1808. HU

D451 FENWICK, Eliza. The class book. See D1045 Phillips, Sir Richard

D452 FENWICK DE PORQUET, Louis Philippe R. (1844?) Corrigé, ou partie française du Trésor de l'écolier français; with grammatical annotations... New ed., Simpkin, Marshall, [187–?]. LEI

D453 FENWICK DE PORQUET, L. P. R. De Porquet's Italian grammar ... for the use of English pupils ... 2nd ed. Simpkin, Marshall for the author, 1851. LEI

D454 FENWICK DE PORQUET, L. P. R. (1825) Modern Parisian phraseology: ou, choix de phrases diverses. 28th ed., Simpkin, Marshall, 1864. HU

FERN, Fanny, pseud. See Parton, Sarah Payson

D455 Les FÊTES d'enfants: scènes et dialogues. Avec une préface de M. l'abbé Bautain ... 2e éd., Paris, Hachette, 1864. [Author's preface signed S.E.J.] LEI

D456 FIBEL für evangelische Volksschulen. Erster Theil. Neue verm. Ausg. Stuttgart, Hallberger, 1870. LEI

D457 [FIELD, William], 1768–1851. (1798) An introduction to the use of globes, with questions for examination annexed. Designed principally for the use of schools. 2nd ed., Warwick, Sharpe, pr.; London, J. Johnson; 1801. HU

D458 The FINCHLEY manuals of industry ... prepared for the use of the National and industrial schools of the Holy Trinity, Finchley. J. Masters, 1852. 4 vols. in 1. [I. Cooking. II. Gardening. III. Household work. IV. Plain needlework.] LEI

D459 FIRESIDE amusements. Edinburgh, W. & R. Chambers, 1850. LEI

D460 FIRST book of arithmetic for the use of schools. Published by direction of the Commissioners of national education in Ireland. Revised and corrected. Dublin, A. Thom, 1857. LEI

D461 FIRST lessons in geography, in question and answers. By a lady. [Rev. ed.], Ward, 1854. NoU

D462 The FIRST missionary in England, intended for the instruction of youth. By C.P.H. Gossling & Egley. NE

D463 FIRST steps in general knowledge. Published under the direction of the Committee of General Literature and Education. Part 2: The surface of the earth. S.P.C.K., 1847. HU; Part 4: The vegetable kingdom. S.P.C.K., 1856. LEE

D464 FIRST steps to astronomy and geography. Hatchard, 1828. LEI

D465 FISCHEL, Moritz Mark. (1855) German reading book on an entirely new principle; a story by Franz Hoffmann, literally translated with copious notes ... and an elementary German grammar. D. Nutt, 1855. LEI

FISHER, Anne, aft. Mrs. Slack. See Slack, A.

D466 FISHER'S juvenile scrap-book, 1838. By Agnes Strickland and Bernard Barton. Fisher, [1837?]. LEI

D467 FITTON, Elizabeth, and FITTON, Sarah Margaret. Conversations on botany. *See* D878 Marcet, Jane

D468 FITZHARDING, J. W., *ed.* The juvenile gleaner: a keepsake for the young. [2nd year's issue.] Lacey, [1833?]. LEI

D469 FIVAS, Victor de. (*c.* 1840) Clef des thèmes de 'La nouvelle grammaire des grammaires françaises'. Londres, Lockwood, [1873?]. HU

D470 FIVAS, Victor de. (*c.* 1840) New grammar of French grammars: comprising the substance of all the most approved French grammars extant . . . with numerous exercises . . . 16th ed., Simpkin, Marshall, 1857. LO; 45th ed., rev. and enl., Crosby Lockwood, 1882. LEI

D471 FIVE hundred questions and exercises on Goldsmith's British geography. Longman, Hurst & Rees, [183–?]. NoU

D472 FLEMING, Marjory, 1803–1811. The complete Marjory Fleming: her journals, letters and verses; transcribed and edited by F. Sidgwick . . . Sidgwick & Jackson, 1934. LEI; 1935. ReU

D473 [FLETCHER, Ann, *and others*]. (1796–1798?) The study of history rendered easy, by a plan founded on experience. Vol. 1, England; vol. 2, Rome; vol. 3, France. Authors, 1798–1801. 3 vols. HU

D474 FLETCHER, William, *master of Woodbridge grammar school and vicar of Stone.* Lessons of wisdom for the young; or, spring mornings and evenings. J. Harris, (dedic. 1827). LEI

D475 FLETCHER, William. (1828) The little grammarian; in a series of instructive tales, forming an easy guide to the parts of speech, and rules of syntax. 2nd ed., J. Harris, 1833. HU LEI

FLEURY, Jules Raymond Lamé. *See* Lamé Fleury, Jules Raymond

D476 FLORIAN, Jean Pierre Claris de, 1755–1794. Select fables . . . Translated from the French . . . by the author of 'A cup of sweets' . . . [i.e. Elizabeth Sandham]. J. Harris, 1806. ReU

D477 FLORILEGIUM. (1814?) Florilegium poeticum, in usum Scholae Wintoniensis, [by George Whitaker]. Winchester, Robbins & Wheeler, 1840. HU

D478 FOERSTER, F. F. Moritz. (1858) A new, practical, and easy method of learning the Spanish language, after the system of F. Ahn. First course. 13th ed., Allman & son, 1880. HU; 20th ed., Allman, [*c.* 1899?]. LEI

D479 FOOD. (1818) Food for the young, adapted to the mental capacities of children of tender years. By a mother. W. Darton, jun., 1818. NoU

D480 FORBES, Duncan, 1798–1868. A grammar of the Persian language. Selection of easy extracts for easy reading, together with a copious vocabulary. 2nd ed., Allen & co., Madden & co., 1844. LO

D481 [FORRESTER, Charles Robert], 1803–1850, and [FORRESTER, Alfred Henry], 1804–1872. (1842) The pictorial grammar, by Alfred Crowquill, [pseud. Text by C. R. Forrester, illustrations by A. H. Forrester]. Harvey & Darton, [1842]. LEI NoU

D482 FORSTER, Josiah. Some reflections on the importance of a religious life, offered to the younger members of the Society of Friends. Darton & Harvey, 1834. LEI

D483 FORSYTH, J. S. The first lines of botany, or primer to the Linnaean system; being a simplified introduction to a knowledge of the vegetable kingdom . . . James Bulcock, 1827. HU

D484 FOSTER, Edward Ward. Chart of the history of England, from B.C. 1100 to A.D. 1857. 20th ed., [185–?]. NoU

D485 FOSTER, E. W. Charta sacro-sanctae scripturae . . . a chronological analysis of the Bible . . . shewing the rise and progress of Christianity. Revised issue. 1856. NoU

D486 FOSTER, E. W. A chronological chart of the ancient and modern history of the British Empire . . . 16th ed., [185–]. NoU

D487 FOSTER, Vere Henry Lewis, 1819–1900. Copy book no. 10. Dublin, [*c.* 1870]. NoU; *another issue*, London, [*c.* 1870]. NoU

D488 FOWLER, William Chauncey, 1793–1881. The English language, in its elements and forms: with a history of its origin and development . . . With additions by the editors. Kent, [1857]. (John Cassell's educational course.) BI

D489 [FOX, Sara, *formerly* Hustler]. Catch who can; or, hide and seek. Original double acrostics. By Sphinx. Longmans, 1869. HU

D490 [FRANK, Elizabeth]. (1811) Classical English letter writer; or, epistolary selections; designed to improve young persons in the art of letter-writing, and in the principles of virtue and piety . . . By the author of 'Lessons for young persons in humble life'. York, T. Wilson for Longman, London, 1814. HU

D491 [FRANK, Elizabeth]. (1810) True stories; or, interesting anecdotes of young persons: designed through the medium of example, to inculcate principles of virtue and piety. By the author of 'Lessons for young persons in humble life'. 2nd ed., York, T. Wilson, for Longman [etc.], 1812. LEI

D492 FRANKLY, Onesiphorus. The adventures and conversations of a morning. W. & T. Darton, 1810. NoU ReU

FRASER TYTLER, Alexander/Ann. *See* Tytler, Alexander/Ann Fraser

D493 FRÉDÉRIC, J. B. (1858) A first French grammar, in French and English . . . intended as an aid in using Dr. Ahn's celebrated First French course, for the use of schools and junior pupils. 12th ed., Allman, 1883. HU

D494 FREEMAN, Philip, 1818–1875. (1864) Guessing stories; or, the wonderful things seen by the man with the extra pair of eyes. A book for young people. 4th ed., Bell, 1878. OX

D495 [FRENCH, Sarah]. Letters to a young lady. Boston; Crosby, Nichols; 1855. LO

D496 FRENCH. (1833) The French history briefly told, from early times to the present period . . . Harris, 1833. (The little library.) LEI NoU

FRESNOY, Nicholas Lenglet du. *See* Lenglet du Fresnoy, Nicholas

D497 FRIEND TO YOUTH, *pseud.* [possibly Samuel Maunder]. An epitome of ancient geography; with historical notes, and questions for examination. For the use of schools. Newbury, S. Maunder for W. Pinnock, [*c.* 1840]. HU

D498 FRIEND TO YOUTH. Exercises in false spelling . . . 2nd ed., Newbury, [18–?]. NoU

FRIEND TO YOUTH, *pseud. See also* Pinnock, William

Friendly instructor. *See* Harrison, Elizabeth

D499 FROST, John, 1803–1840, *ed.* Bingley's practical introduction to botany . . . 2nd ed. . . . adapted to the use of students, by John Frost. Baldwin, Cradock & Joy, 1827. LEI

Fruits of enterprize. *See* Atkins, *Mrs.* Sarah

D500 FRY, Caroline, *aft. Mrs.* Wilson, 1787–1846. The assistant of education: religious and literary. Intended for the use of young persons. Vols. 1–9. Baker & Fletcher, 1823–1827. BI LEE; vols. 1–4. 1823–1825. NoU

D501 FRYER, Thomas, and FRYER, Thomas William. (5th ed., 1836) The united new and much admired system of arithmetic and mental calculation, of Dr. Willcolkes and Messrs. T. and T. W. Fryer . . . 7th ed., enl. and rev., Derby, H. Mozley, pr.; London, Longmans; 1840. HU

G——, A. M. D. *See* Loriquet, Jean Nicolas

GAILER, J. E. *See* Gayler, J. E.

D502 GALL, James, *the elder.* (1830?) Key to the book for teaching children to read; with an introductory essay on the fundamental principles of education. 2nd ed., Edinburgh, James Gall, 1832. HU

D503 [GALT, John], 1779–1839. The national reader; consisting of easy lessons in history, geography, biography, natural history, mythology, etc. . . . by the Rev. T. Clark, [pseud.] [182–?]. NoU

D504 GAPING. The Gaping, wide-mouthed, waddling frog: a new and entertaining game of questions and commands . . . 1823. Field & Tuer, 1887. LEI

D505 GARDEN. (1831) The Garden; or, familiar instructions for the laying out and management of a flower garden. J. Harris, 1831. (The little library, vol. 6.) LEI

D506 GARDINER, William, 1766–1825. (1823) The shepherd's boy of Snowdon Hill; containing the adventures of David Jones, in various parts of Asia . . . D. Mackay, [etc.], [1823]. LEI

D507 GARLAND, Anne. Help for infant minds. Huddersfield, Brook, 1830. LEE

D508 The GARLAND, or thirteen extracts with coloured vignettes for rewards. [183–]. ReU

D509 Die GARTENLAUBE: illustrirtes Familienblatt, 1866. Leipzig, E. Keil. LO

D510 GARWOOD, John. A short introduction to history, as an exercise for the memory of young persons; suggested by Coglan's system of mnemonics. Lowestoft, Gowing, 1814. HU

D511 GASC, Ferdinand E. A. (1858) The first French book: being a new, practical and easy method of learning the elements of the French language. Bell, 1885. HU

D512 GASC, F. E. A. Materials for French prose composition; or, selections from the best English prose writers, to be turned into French . . . New ed., Bell & Daldy, 1869. LEI

D513 GASTRELL, Francis, 1662–1725. (Christian institutes, 1707) The faith and duty of a Christian . . . chiefly selected from the Christian institutes of Bishop Gastrell, designed for the use of young people. New ed., enl. [Edited by Basil Woodd.] Rivington for S.P.C.K., 1825. LEI

D514 A GATHERED blossom; or, a brief memoir of Elizabeth R—. Birmingham, J. Groom, 1846. HU

D515 GATTY, Margaret, '*Mrs.* Alfred Gatty', 1807–1873. (1855–1871) Parables from nature. [First series]. Bell & Daldy, 1855. LO; do., with a memoir by her daughter, J. H. Ewing . . . First series. Bell, 1891. LEI; First [&] second series. Bell, 1885–1886. 2 vols. in 1. LEI

D516 GATTY, Margaret, *ed.* Aunt Judy's Christmas volume for young people. Bell & Daldy, 1868. LEI

D517 GAULTIER, Camille, *abbé*, 1746?–1818. (Fr. 1789?) Complete course of geography by means of instructive games. New ed., Harris, 1817. LEI

D518 GAULTIER, Camille. (1800–1801) A method of making abridgements . . . 1800–[01]. 2 parts in 1. NoU

D519 GAYLER, J. E. (3rd ed., 1835) Neuer Orbis pictus für die Jugend; oder, Schauplatz der Natur, der Kunst und des Menschenlebens . . . nach der früheren Anlage des Comenius bearbeitet und eingerichtet von J. E. Gailer. [5. Aufl.] Reutlingen, J. C. Mäcken, jun., 1842. OX

D520 GENERAL reading, for schools of mutual instruction. Part 1. Miscellaneous. Wellington (Salop) & London, Houlston, 1828. HU

D521 GENLIS, Stéphanie Félicité du Crest de Saint-Aubin, *comtesse de*, 1746–1830. (1810) Arabesques mythologiques, ou les attributs de toutes les divinités de la fable; en 54 planches gravées d'après les dessins coloriés de Madame de Genlis . . . Ouvrage fait pour servir à l'éducation de la jeunesse . . . Paris, Ch. Barrois, 1810. LEI

D522 GENLIS, *comtesse de.* (1799) La Bruyère the less; or, characters and manners of the children of the present age. Dublin, Stockdale 1801. LO

D523 GENLIS, *comtesse de.* (1780) Théâtre d'éducation. Nlle. éd., Paris, Lecointe, 1829. 3 vols. HU; do., do., Tome 5. LO

D524 [GENLIS, *comtesse de*]. (Fr. 1784; Eng. 1785) Les veillées du château, ou cours de morale à l'usage des enfans. Par l'auteur d'Adèle et Theodore. London, Robinson, [etc.], 1814. 4 vols. LO

D525 GENLIS, *comtesse de.* Tales of the castle . . . translated into English by Thomas Holcroft. 8th ed., 1806. 5 vols. NoU

D526 GEOGRAPHICAL. (1802) A Geographical companion to Mrs. Trimmer's scripture, antient and English abridged histories . . . in three parts. By a lady. B. Tabart, 1802. 3 pts. in 1 vol. NoU

D527 GEOGRAPHY and astronomy familiarized, for youth of both sexes. 1801. NoU

D528 GEOGRAPHY. (2nd ed., 1794) Geography and history selected by a lady for the use of her own children. [By E.R.] 7th ed., enl., C. Law, [etc.], 1808. LEI; 10th ed., Law & Whittaker, 1815. LO

D529 GIBSON, Gilbert Maxwell. (1851) Le petit fablier; d'après un plan absolument neuf... Enrichi de notes étymologiques et d'un vocabulaire. Edinburgh, Oliver & Boyd, 1856. HU

D530 GILES, John Allen, 1808–1884. (1846) First lessons in Roman history, for the use of beginners. London, E. Stanford for C. H. Law, Eastbourne, 1871. HU

D531 [GILPIN, William], 1724–1804. (1798) [Moral contrasts]. A memoir of Naimbanna, a young African prince. Published under the general direction of the Committee of general literature and education. S.P.C.K., 1843. LEI

D532 [GLEIG, George Robert], 1796–1888. (1850?) A school history of England... Abridged from 'The family history of England'. Published under the direction of the Committee of general literature and education appointed by the Society for promoting Christian knowledge. 4th ed., Parker, 1853. HU

D533 GOAKMAN, Benjamin Rhodes, ed. The religious and moral selector, in prose and verse... 2nd ed., Editor, 1813. LEI

D534 GODOLPHIN, Mary [i.e. Lucy Aikin?] Sandford and Merton [by Thomas Day, retold] in words of one syllable by Mary Godolphin. Cassell, [1868]. LEI

D535 [GODWIN, William], 1756–1836. (1805) Fables ancient and modern. Adapted for the use of children. By Edward Baldwin, [pseud.]. 10th ed., M. J. Godwin, 1824. LEI

D536 [GODWIN, William]. (1806) The history of England for the use of schools and young persons. By Edward Baldwin. New ed., Hodgkins, 1807. LEI

D537 [GODWIN, William]. (1809) History of Rome: from the building of the city to the ruins of the republic... For the use of schools and young persons. By Edward Baldwin. 2nd ed., M. J. Godwin, 1811. HU

GOLDSMITH, Rev. J., pseud. See Phillips, Sir Richard

D538 [GOLDSMITH, Oliver], 1728–1774. (1764) An history of England in a series of letters from a nobleman to his son. New ed., continued to the peace of 1802... Vol. 1 [only]. Rivington, [etc.], 1807. LEI

D539 GOLDSMITH, Oliver. Pinnock's improved edition of Dr. Goldsmith's abridgment of the history of England... and a continuation to the year 1819... 14th ed., Pinnock & Maunder, 1819. HU; do. do. With a continuation to the reign of George the Fourth. 17th ed., 1821. NoU; Whittaker's improved edition of Pinnock's Goldsmith's History of England... by W. C. Taylor, continued by W. H. Pinnock. 43rd ed., Whittaker, 1854. LO; do. do. New rev. ed., Whittaker, 1865. LEI

D540 GOLDSMITH, Oliver. The history of England, from the earliest times to the death of George the Second. With a continuation to... 1825 by J. Watkins. Fisher, 1832. LEI

D541 Goldsmith's History of England, abridged by himself; to which is added, a... continuation to the present year... By E. Coxe. 15th ed., Derby, Mozley, 1845. NoU

D542 GOLDSMITH, Oliver. (1774) History of Greece, abridged, for the use of schools. New ed. Sold by the booksellers, 1804. HU; another ed., Winchester, Pinnock, 1812. LEE; Pinnock's improved edition of Dr. Goldsmith's History of Greece... Revised... By W. C. Taylor. 13th ed., Whittaker, 1838. BI

D543 GOLDSMITH, Oliver. (1769, abridged ed. 1772) Dr. Goldsmith's Roman history, abridged by himself for the use of schools. A new and correct ed. Derby, Mozley, 1817. LEE; Dr. Goldsmith's History of Rome, abridged for the use of schools; divided into sections, with numerous examining questions... By Edward Coxe. London, J. & C. Mozley, [182–]. HU; do. do. Derby, Mozley, [184–?]. NoU

D544 GOLDSMITH, Oliver? (1762) A pretty book of pictures for little masters and misses, or Tommy Trip's history of beasts and birds... Written by Oliver Goldsmith for John Newbery... 15th ed. Embellished with... engravings on wood from the original blocks engraved by Thomas Bewick... in 1779. Edwin Pearson, 1867. LEI

D545 GOODACRE, Robert. A treatise on bookkeeping, adapted to the use of schools... To which is added a familiar dissertation on the various bills and notes, used in commerce as substitutes for cash. 1811. NoU

D546 GOODFELLOW, Robin, pseud. The rocking-horse. J. Souter, 1819. ReU

D547 [GOODRICH, Samuel Griswold], 1793–1860. Geography for beginners... By Peter Parley, [pseud.]. N.Y., Huntington & Savage, 1847. NO

D548 GOODRICH, S. G. Peter Parley's first school reader. Halifax, 1864. NoU

D549 [GOODRICH, S. G.]. (1828) Parley's Tales about Europe. Edited by the Rev. T. Wilson [i.e. S. Clark]. 6th ed., Darton, [c. 184–]. LEE

D550 [GOODRICH, S. G.]. Tales about Greece. By Peter Parley. [Edited and altered by George Mogridge]. Tegg, 1837. LEI

D551 [GOODRICH, S. G.]. Tales of animals. Comprising quadrupeds, birds, fishes, reptiles, and insects. By Peter Parley. 3rd ed., Tegg, 1834. LEI

D552 [GOODRICH, S. G.]. (1837) Universal history, on the basis of geography. By Peter Parley. Tegg, 1838. BI

D553 [GOODRICH, S. G.]. What to do, and how to do it; or, morals and manners taught by examples, by Peter Parley. [Illustrated by Samuel Williams]. Darton & co., [184–?]. LEI

D554 GOODY. (1765) The history of Goody Two Shoes. 1806. NoU

Gradus ad Parnassum. See Aler, P.

GRAHAM, Mrs. Maria, aft. Lady Callcott. See Callcott, Maria

D555 GRAHAM, William, teacher of elocution. (1836) Exercises on etymology. [2nd ed.], Chambers, [1855]. (Chambers's educational course.) BI; new rev. ed., Chambers, 1870. LEI

D556 GRANDINEAU, F. (1832) Le petit précepteur; or, first steps to French conversation. For the use of young beginners. 2nd ed., 1837. NoU; 59th ed., Hodder & Stoughton, 1892. LEI

D557 GRANDINEAU, F. Il piccolo precettore; or, first steps to Italian conversation. Being a translation from Le Petit précepteur . . . with additional exercises. New ed., rev., Hodder & Stoughton, 1877. LEI

D558 GRANDMAMMA Easy's Alderman's feast: a new alphabet. Dean, [c. 1850]. LEI

D559 GRANDPA BEN, pseud. The history of a ship. Darton & Clark, [1838]. ReU

D560 [GRANT, Horace]. (1838) Drawing for young children, containing 150 drawing copies, and numerous exercises. By the author of 'Arithmetic for young children'. Knight, for the Society for the diffusion of useful knowledge, 1838. LEI; Knight; 1840. LEE

D561 GRANT, James. (1863) Dick Rodney; or, the adventures of an Eton boy . . . Routledge, 1863. LEI

D562 GRAY, Asa, 1810–1888. First lessons in botany and vegetable physiology . . . to which is added a copious glossary . . . of botanical terms. N.Y., Ivison & Phinney, 1859. HU

D563 GRAY, Thomas, 1716–1771. The poems of Thomas Gray and Robert Blair, arranged for the use of young people. Edward Lacey, [183–?]. NE

D564 GREENWOOD, James, d. 1737. (1711) The London vocabulary, English and Latin . . . R. Baldwin, 1802. ReU; 25th ed., revised . . . by N. Howard. 1814. NoU; New ed., revised . . . by N. Howard. 1836. NoU

D565 GREENWOOD, James, fl. 1860–1870. (1861 in parts) Wild sports of the world: a boy's book of natural history and adventure. Beeton, 1862. LEE LEI

D566 GREGORY, George, 1754–1808, ed. (1800) The elements of a polite education, carefully selected from the Letters of the late Rt. Hon. Philip Dormer Stanhope, Earl of Chesterfield, to his son. Dublin, Wm. Porter, pr., 1802. LEI

D567 GREGORY, Olinthus Gilbert, 1774–1841. Mathematics for practical men; being a commonplace book of principles, theorems, rules and tables . . . with their most useful applications . . . Baldwin, Cradock & Joy, 1825. HU

D568 GREIG, John, 1759–1819. (1805) An introduction to the use of globes, for the young of both sexes; particularly designed for schools and private teachers . . . 2nd ed., corr. and enl., B. Crosby, & W. Kent, 1810. HU LEE

D569 GREIG, John. (2nd ed., 1800) The young ladies' new guide to arithmetic; being a short and useful selection . . . chiefly on domestic affairs . . . for the use of ladies' schools and private teachers. New ed., Baldwin, Cradock & Joy, 1816. RE

D570 GREY, Richard, 1694–1771. (1730) Memoria technica; or, a new method of artificial memory . . . To which are subjoined Lowe's Mnemonics delineated . . . New ed., Oxford, Vincent, 1819. BI

D571 [GRIERSON, Miss —]. The visit; or, Mama and the children. Edinburgh, Wm. Oliphant, [etc.], 1824. ReU

D572 GROS, C. New elements of conversation, French and English. 7th ed., Dulau, 1832. LO

D573 GROS, C., ed. The elements of French conversation, with familiar and easy dialogues . . . by J. B. Perrin. 18th ed., revised and corrected by C. Gros. Law & Whittaker, [etc.], 1815. LEI; 26th ed., Longmans, 1833. LO

D574 GROS, C., ed. Fables amusantes, de J. B. Perrin, suivies d'une table générale et particulière des mots . . . 16e édition, revue et corrigée par C. Gros . . . Londres, Law & Whittaker, [etc.], 1817. LEI

Grove Cottage. See Atkins, Sarah

Guide to English literature. See Ward, —

GUIZOT, Henriette, aft. Mme. de Witt. See Witt, H. de

D575 GUIZOT, Pauline, 1773–1827. (1821) L'écolier; ou, Raoul et Victor. 7e éd., Paris, Didier, 1847. 2 vols. LEI

D576 GUIZOT, Pauline. (1812) Les enfants; contes à l'usage de la jeunesse. 3e éd., Paris, Klosterman, & Delaunay, [182–?]. 2 vols. LEI; 8e éd., Paris, Didier, 1851. 2 vols. BR

D577 GUTHRIE, William, 1708–1770. (1770) A new geographical, historical and commercial grammar; and present state of the several kingdoms of the world . . . 21st ed., Johnson, [etc.], 1808. LEI

D578 GUTHRIE, William, (1785?) An atlas to Guthrie's Geographical grammar. 1804. NoU

D579 GUY, John. Geography for children. 20th ed., 1848. NoU

D580 GUY, Joseph, the elder. Guy's new British spelling book; or, an easy introduction to spelling and reading, in seven parts . . . 2nd ed., Cradock & Joy, 1810. HU

D581 GUY, Joseph, the elder. (2nd ed., 1811) Guy's school geography, on a new and easy plan . . . 26th ed, rev., enl. and corr., Cradock, [etc.], 1860. LEI

D582 GUY, Joseph, junior. Guy's English school grammar, in which practical illustration is . . . blended with theory . . . Adapted throughout to the use of schools and private teachers. 5th ed., enl., Baldwin, Cradock & Joy, 1819. HU

D583 GUY, Joseph, junior. Guy's new exercises in orthography; containing selections from the most admired authors, in prose and verse. Baldwin, Cradock & Joy, 1818. LEI

D584 H., C.P. The first missionary in England, intended for the instruction of youth. Gossling & Egley, 1828. NE

H.L.L., pseud. See Borthwick, Jane L.

D585 [HACK, Maria, form. Barton], 1777–1844. (1820) Stories of animals, intended for children between five and seven years old. Harvey & Darton, 1820. LEE

D586 HACK, Maria. (1818) Winter evenings; or, tales of travellers. Darton, Harvey & Darton, 1818. 4 vols. LEI

D587 HALE, *Sir* Matthew, 1609–1676. (Written *c.* 1673) The counsels of a father, in four letters . . . to his children. To which is added, The practical life of a true Christian . . . 3rd ed., Taylor & Hessey, 1821. BI

D588 HALL, Anna Maria, 'Mrs. S. C. Hall', 1800–1881. (1830) Chronicles of a school room, by Mrs. S. C. Hall. Westley & Davis, 1830. HU

D589 HALL, A. M. Fanny's fancies, by Mrs. S. C. Hall. Groombridge, [*c.* 1860?]. LEI

D590 HALL, A. M., *ed.* The juvenile forget me not. A Christmas and New Year's gift, or birthday present, for the year 1830. Edited by Mrs. S. C. Hall. N. Hailes, [etc.]. LEI; 1833. Ackermann. LEI ReU

D591 HALL, *Mrs.* Clara, *ed.* The juvenile mirror: (not to flatter) but to show young people how to avoid errors, follies and vices. Edward Lacey, [etc.], [183–?]. ReU

D592 HALL, John Paxton, and HALL, Thomas, *eds.* (1850?) First French course, and France and the French . . . New ed., Bateman, 1856. HU; new ed., Bateman, 1877. LEI

HALL, *Mrs.* S. C. *See* Hall, Anna Maria

D593 HALLIWELL [*aft.* Halliwell-Phillipps], James Orchard, 1820–1889, *ed.* (1842) The nursery rhymes of England. Collected chiefly from oral tradition. 6th ed., J. R. Smith, [1855]. LEI

D594 HALSTED, Caroline Amelia, *aft. Mrs.* Atthill, d. 1851. (1835) The little botanist; or, steps to the attainment of botanical knowledge. Harris, 1835. 2 vols. LEI

D595 HAMEL, Nicolas. Grammatical exercises upon the French language, compared with the English . . . New [7th] ed., Longman, 1824. LEE

D596 HAMILTON, James, 1769–1829. (1824) The Gospel of St. John, adapted to the Hamiltonian system. Glasgow, Author, 1824. LO; 5th ed., *with title:* The Gospel of St. John, in Latin; with an interlinear and analytical translation, on the principles of the Hamiltonian system. To which are prefixed, a preface, explanatory of the principles of that system . . . J. Souter, 1833. HU

D597 HAMILTON, James. (1825) Perrin's Fables; adapted to the Hamiltonian system, by a literal, and analytical translation. Boosey, 1825. BI; 4th ed. For the use of schools. Souter, for the author's widow, 1834. LEE

D598 [HAMILTON, Joseph]. (14th ed., 1801) Johnson's dictionary of the English language in miniature; to which are added, an alphabetical account of the heathen deities . . . and a copious English grammar. New ed., rev. and corr., Joseph Smith, 1827. HU

D599 HANDBOOKS for home improvement, comprising How to write; How to talk; How to behave; How to do business. (Complete in one volume.) N.Y., Fowler & Wells, [185–?]. BR

D600 HANWAY, Jonas, 1712–1786. (Abridgment 1786) Domestic happiness promoted; in a series of discourses from a father to his daughter, on occasion of her going into service . . . Being for the most part adapted also to the use of Sunday schools. Abridged from 'Virtue in humble life'. New ed., Rivington, 1811. HU

D601 HAPPY stories for happy hearts; by the author of 'Spring flowers and summer blossoms'. New ed., Dean, [1863]. NE

HARCOURT, Henry, *pseud. See* Williams, Charles

D602 HARDCASTLE, Lucy. An introduction to the elements of the Linnaean system of botany, for young persons. Derby, 1830. NoU

D603 HARDCASTLE, William. Catechism of astronomy, and the use of globes, containing . . . (648) questions . . . With numerous problems for solution by pupils. 4th ed., Relfe, [185–?]. LEI

D604 HARDING, William. (1823) Taylor improved. Universal stenography, or a new and practical system of short hand writing . . . For the use of schools . . . New [10th] ed., enl. and impr. Simpkin & Marshall, [pref. 1830]. LEI

D605 HARFORD, Mary. The winter scene, to amuse and instruct the rising generation. 1818. NoU

D606 HARRIS, Bartholomew, *firm.* Excellentia copy book. [18–?]. NoU; do., no. 8, small hand. [18–?]. NoU

D607 HARRIS, Bartholomew. Historical copy book. [18–?]. NoU

D608 HARRIS, Bartholomew. The Times copy book. [18–?]. NoU; do. [smaller hand]. [18–?]. NoU

D609 HARRIS's first book; or, reading made completely easy. Otley, Yorkshire J.S. Publishing & stationery co., [*c.* 1870?]. LEE

D610 [HARRISON, *Mrs.* Elizabeth], *fl.* 1724–1756. (2nd ed., 1741) The friendly instructor; or, a companion for young ladies and gentlemen . . . in two parts. With a preface by Philip Doddridge. New ed., rev. and corr. Houlston, 1836. LEE

D611 HARRISON, *Mrs.* Elizabeth. Familiar dialogues between children, originally written by Mrs. Harrison; and recommended by Dr. Doddridge. Now first abridged and adapted to the use of schools. Otley, Walker, 1815. LEI

D612 HARTON, Marian. MS. notebook, 1868–1873. [Contains answers to a series of questions, religious, historical and miscellaneous, in connection with a course known by the initials I.C.S.] HU

D613 [HAWKS, Francis Lister], 1798–1866. (1833?) Uncle Philip's conversations with children about the habits and mechanical employments of inferior animals. New ed., Tegg, 1835. LEI

D614 [HAWKSHAW, Ann, *lady*], 1812–1885. Aunt Effie's rhymes for little children. With 24 illustrations by H. K. Browne. 1864. NoU

D615 HAYTER, Charles, 1761–1835. (1813) An introduction to perspective, practical geometry, drawing and painting . . . in a series of dialogues between the author's children, and letters addressed to his pupils . . . 6th ed., Bagster, 1845. LEI

D616 HEDGE, Mary Ann [*or* Marianne]. Letters on profane history, addressed to a beloved godchild. 2nd ed., Baldwin, Cradock & Joy, 1822. HU

D617 [HEDGE, M. A.]. (1824) The orphan sailor boy; or, young Arctic voyager. By the author of 'Affection's gift', 'Samboe', etc. Harvey & Darton, 1824. LEI

Helen of the glen. *See* Pollok, Robert

D618 HENDRY, Elizabeth Anne. (1824) The history of Greece, in easy lessons: adapted for children from six to ten years of age. Harvey & Darton, 1824. NoU

D619 HENRY. (1827) Henry and his tutor. Harvey & Darton, [c. 1828?]. [Also has title: Interesting walks of Henry and his tutor.] LEI

D620 HENSLOW, John Stevens, 1796–1861. Illustrations to be employed in practical lessons on botany, adapted to beginners of all classes. Prepared for the South Kensington Museum. Chapman & Hall, 1858. HU [imperfect copy]

D621 HENSLOW, J. S. (1868) Lessons in elementary botany, by Daniel Oliver; the part of systematic botany based upon material left in manuscript by the late Professor Henslow. New ed., Macmillan, 1886. HU

D622 [HEY, Wilhelm], 1789–1854. The child's picture and verse book: commonly called Otto Speckter's Fable book. With the original German and with French. Translated into English by Mary Howitt. Longman, 1844. LEI

Hieroglyphical Bible. See Bible

D623 HILEY, Alfred. (1868) Recapitulatory examples in arithmetic for the use of candidates for the Oxford and Cambridge local examinations. 14th ed. Longmans, 1891. CA

D624 [HILL, John], ed. Artis logicae rudimenta, [by Henry Aldrich]. With illustrative observations on each section. 4th ed., Oxford, Parker; London, Rivington; 1828. LEI

Histoire ancienne des Egyptiens . . . par A.M.D.G.—— See Loriquet, J. N.

Histoire romaine . . . par A.M.D.G.—— See Loriquet, J. N.

D625 HISTORIC anecdotes: France. Colburn & Bentley, 1830. LEI

Historical and miscellaneous questions. See Mangnall, Richmal

Historical charades. See Maitland, Julia Charlotte

D626 HISTORY. (1810?) The history and adventures of little Henry, exemplified in a series of figures. 3rd ed., Fuller, 1810. NoU

History of Beauty and the beast. See Beauty and the beast

D627 A HISTORY of England for young persons . . . S.P.C.K., [c. 1856?]. LEI

History of England in a series of letters from a nobleman to his son. See Goldsmith, Oliver

D628 The HISTORY of insects. R.T.S., 1839. NO

D629 The HISTORY of Jeannot and Colin. Derby, [18–?]. NoU

D630 HISTORY. (1810) The history of little Fanny, exemplified in a series of figures. Fuller, 1810. NoU ReU

D631 HISTORY. (1798?) The history of Martin and James; or, the reward of industry. Designed for the improvement of children. Harvey & Darton, 1833. LEI

D632 The HISTORY of Mr. S— and David Thompson. Glasgow, R.T.S., 1814. ReU

D633 A HISTORY of my pet animals, during a year's residence in the country; in a series of letters, addressed to my niece Selina. By E.W. 2nd ed., rev. and corr., Darton, [c. 1830]. LEE

History of Robin Hood. See Robin Hood

D634 The HISTORY of Susan Ward. Liverpool, R.T.S., n.d. [pre-1840]. ReU

D635 HISTORY of tame and domesticated animals. R. Dutton, 1806. ReU

D636 HISTORY. (1791?) The History of the Davenant family . . . By H.S. Vol. 1 [only]. [18–]. NoU

D637 HISTORY of the dog; containing a variety of interesting anecdotes . . . including the fact from which the melo-drama of the Forest of Bondy is taken. Derby, Mozley, [c. 1810]. LEE

History of the seven champions of Christendom. See Johnson, Richard

D638 The HISTORY of Tommy Playlove and Jacky Lovebook . . . Glasgow, 1819. NoU

D639 HOARE, G. R. The young traveller; or, adventures of Etienne in search of his father. A tale for youth. 2nd ed., Harris, 1825. LEE

D640 [HODGKIN, John]. A sketch of the Greek accidence, arranged in a manner convenient for transcription . . . Simpkin & Marshall, 1824. HU

D641 HODGKIN, Jonathan B. Three MS. copybooks, c. 1856–1859. HU

D642 HODSON, Thomas. (1800) The accomplished tutor; or, complete system of liberal education . . . 3rd ed. Vol. 1 [only, of 2]. H. D. Symonds, [etc.], 1836. LEI

D643 [HOFLAND, Mrs. Barbara, form. Mrs. Hoole], 1770–1843. (1823) Adelaide; or, the intrepid daughter: a tale . . . By the author of 'Theodore', 'Son of a genius', etc. Harris, 1823. LEI ReU

D644 HOFLAND, Mrs. Barbara. (1816) The affectionate brothers. New ed., A. K. Newman, 1829. ReU

D645 HOFLAND, Mrs. Barbara. Africa described, in its ancient and present state. Longman, [etc.], 1828. ReU

D646 HOFLAND, Mrs. Barbara. (1825) Alfred Campbell; or, travels of a young pilgrim in Egypt and the Holy Land. A. K. Newman, [1840]. ReU; new ed., with additions. A. K. Newman, 1841. LEI

D647 HOFLAND, Mrs. Barbara. (3rd ed., 1819) The Barbadoes girl: a tale for young people. New ed., A. K. Newman, [184–]. HU

D648 HOFLAND, Mrs. Barbara. The daughter-in-law. New ed., [1829?]. ReU

D649 HOFLAND, Mrs. Barbara. (1823) The daughter of a genius: a tale for youth. Harris, 1823. ReU

D650 HOFLAND, Mrs. Barbara. Decision, a tale. New ed., A. K. Newman, 1834. ReU

D651 HOFLAND, Mrs. Barbara. Ellen, the teacher. Harris, 1819. ReU

D652 HOFLAND, Mrs. Barbara. Farewell tales. A. K. Newman, 1840. ReU

D653 HOFLAND, *Mrs.* Barbara. (1817) The good grandmother and her offspring, a tale. 2nd ed., with additions. A. K. Newman, 1828. ReU

D654 HOFLAND, *Mrs.* Barbara. History of an officer's widow and her young family. 1814. ReU

D655 HOFLAND, *Mrs.* Barbara. Reflection, a tale. 1826. ReU

D656 HOFLAND, *Mrs.* Barbara. Rich boys and poor boys, and other tales. (1833?). ReU

D657 HOFLAND, *Mrs.* Barbara. The sisters, a domestic tale. A. K. Newman, 1814. ReU; 1828. ReU

D658 HOFLAND, *Mrs.* Barbara. (1812) The son of a genius, a tale for youth. New ed., 1818. ReU; new ed., Harris, 1821. LEE; new ed., rev. and enl., Harris, 1827. LEI

D659 HOFLAND, *Mrs.* Barbara. The young cadet. Harris, [1827?]. ReU

D660 HOFLAND, *Mrs.* Barbara. (1828?) The young Crusoe, or the shipwrecked boy. 1829. ReU

D661 HOFLAND, *Mrs.* Barbara. (1826) The young pilgrim, or Alfred Campbell's return to the East... Harris, 1826. ReU

D663 HOLDEN, Hubert Ashton, 1822–1896, *ed.* (1852) Foliorum centuriae; being select passages for translation into Latin and Greek prose. [4th ed.]. Bell, 1901. HU

D664 The HOLIDAY present for youth: being interesting sketches and pictures... R. Yorke Clerke, [1849?]. LEE

D665 HOLLAND, Thomas, and HOLLAND, John, 1766–1826. (3rd ed., 1798) Exercises for the memory and understanding... 4th ed., Bolton, T. Garner for the editor, 1805. LEI

D666 HOLMES, Jane Elizabeth. The beautiful temple, and other tales. Wm. Darton & son, [c. 1830?]. ReU

D667 HOME & COLONIAL SCHOOL SOCIETY. Selection of hymns and poetry, for the use of infant and juvenile schools and families. In five parts. 6th ed., Groombridge, 1857. NO

HOMESPUN, *Mrs.* Prudentia, *pseud. See* West, Jane

D668 HOOD, Thomas, 1835–1874. (1865) Jingles and jokes for the little folks. Cassell, [1865]. LEI

HOOLE, *Mrs.* Barbara, *formerly Mrs.* Hofland. *See* Hofland, B.

D669 HOPKINS, Henry. (1845) Exercises in orthography, on an improved plan... New ed., with extensive additions. Simpkin, Marshall, [185–]. HU

D670 HORT, William Jillard. The new pantheon, or an introduction to the mythology of the ancients. For the use of young persons... New ed., Longmans, [1854]. LEE

D671 HORT, W. J. An epitome of the history of England; adapted to domestic and to school education. Longman, 1822. BI

D672 HORT, W. J. An introduction to the study of chronology and ancient history: in question and answer. 1833. NoU

D673 HOWARD, N., *ed.* The London vocabulary, by James Greenwood. *See* D564 Greenwood, J.

D674 HOWE's primer; or, the child's first book. Derby, Bemrose, [c. 1820]. HU

D675 HOWITT, J. Howitt's first book for children; arranged to suit the capacity of the youngest child. Newman, 1850. LEE

D676 HOWITT, Mary, 1799–1888. Hope on, hope ever. Thos. Tegg, [1840]. ReU

D677 HOWITT, Mary. (1834) Sketches of natural history. Effingham Wilson, [1834?]. ReU

D678 HOWITT, Mary. The two apprentices. 1865. NoU

D679 HOWITT, Mary, *ed.* The dial of love: a Christmas book for the young. Darton, 1853. [Afterwards called 'The birthday gift'.] LEI

D680 HOWITT, Mary, *trans.* (1844) The child's picture and verse book, [by Wilhelm Hey]; commonly called Otto Speckter's Fable book. With the original German and with French. Translated into English by Mary Howitt. Longman, 1844. LEI

D681 HOWITT, William, 1792–1879. (1854) A boy's adventures in the wilds of Australia; or, Herbert's note-book. Hall, Virtue & co., 1854. LEI

D682 HOWITT, William. (1839) The boy's country book: being the real life of a country boy, written by himself... Edited by William Howitt. 2nd ed., Longman, 1841. LEE; 3rd ed., Longman, 1847. LEI

HUGHES, Mary, *formerly* Robson. *See* Robson, Mary

D683 [HUGHES, Thomas], 1822–1896. (1857) School days at Rugby, by an old boy. 4th ed. Boston, Ticknor & Fields, 1858. MA

D684 [HUGHES, Thomas]. (1861) Tom Brown at Oxford, by the author of 'Tom Brown's schooldays'. Macmillan, 1892. LEI

HUGHS, Mary, *formerly* Robson. *See* Robson, Mary

D685 HUISH, Robert. Pretty little tales for pretty little children; or, our Grandmama's clock. New ed., Allman, [c. 1850]. LEE

D686 The HUMBLE reformer. 2nd ed., W. Kent, [1808?]. ReU

D687 HUME, David, 1711–1776. The student's Hume: a history of England from the earliest time to the revolution of 1688. Based on the History of David Hume. Incorporating the corrections and researches of recent historians, and continued down to the year 1858. Murray, 1862. NO

HUMPHREY, *Old, pseud. See* Mogridge, George

D688 HUNT, L. H. A syntax of the English language; with new and copious examples, from some of our best authors in verse and prose... [At head of title:] For the use of the higher classes in schools, as well as for the enquiring amongst other classes. Saffron Walden, G. Youngman, [1823?]. HU

D689 HUNTER, *Rev.* John. Elements of plane trigonometry: with numerous problems... Longman, 1863. (Gleig's school series.) HU

D690 HUTCHINSON, James. (c. 1853) Arithmetic simplified, for the use of schools and private families. In two parts. Part second. 10th ed., Wright, Simpkin, 1857. HU

D691 HUTTON, Charles, 1737–1823. (1770?; 3rd ed., 1796) The compendious measurer, being a brief, yet comprehensive treatise on mensuration and practical geometry. 5th ed., 1803. NoU

D692 HYDE, Anna M. (1859?) English history condensed and simplified for children. N.Y., J. Miller, 1863. LEI

Hymns for infant minds. See Taylor, Ann, and Taylor, Jane

Hymns in prose for children. See Barbauld, A. L.

D693 The ILLUSTRATED ABC, or the child's first step to learning. Sudbury,—, [18–?]. NoU

D694 The ILLUSTRATED London spelling book. Illustrated London news, 1849. LEE; new ed., [185–?]. NoU

D695 ILLUSTRATED reading book. [185–?]. NoU

D696 An IMPORTANT discovery; or, temper is everything. R.T.S., n.d. [pre-1840]. ReU

D697 IMPROVING tales, containing The Storm . . . [etc.]. A. K. Newman, 1817. ReU

D698 IN. (1825) In school and out of school; or, the history of William and John . . . By one who knows both. Dean & Munday, 1828. LEI

D699 INFANT. (1815?) The infant minstrel; or, poetry for young minds. By various female writers. 4th ed. Harvey & Darton, 1829. ReU

D700 The INFANT-SCHOOL children. Published under the direction of the Committee of general literature and education. S.P.C.K., [c. 1860?]. NoU

D701 INNES's British Minerva primer, or London first book for children. [18–?]. NoU

D702 INSECTS. (1833?) Insects and their habitations. A book for children. Published under the direction of the Committee of general literature and education of the Society for the promotion of christian knowledge. J. W. Parker, 1836. LEI

D703 INSTRUCTIVE conversation cards, consisting of geographical delineations of 32 principal places in England. W. & T. Darton, [c. 1810?]. LEI

Instructive lessons for children. See Barbauld, A. L.

Instructive picture book. See Yonge, C. M.

Intellectual arithmetic, upon the inductive method. See Colburn, Warren

Interesting walks of Henry and his tutor. See Henry and his tutor

D704 INTRODUCTION. (1758) An introduction to the Latin tongue, for the use of youth. New ed., Eton, 1802. NoU; new ed., York, Wilson, 1803. [With additional imprint, Eton, 1768.] LEE; new ed., Eton, E. P. Williams, 1850. [Cover title: Eton Latin grammar.] HU

Introduction to the use of globes. See Field, William

D705 INVITED. (1808) The invited alphabet, or address of A to B, containing his friendly proposal for the amusement and instruction of good children . . . By R.R. Darton, 1809. NoU

D706 IRELAND. *Commissioners of national education.*

(*a*) Agricultural classbook. 1853. *See* D15

(*b*) Chemistry and chemical analysis. 1861. *See* D235

(*c*) First book of arithmetic. 1857. *See* D460

(*d*) Second book of lessons. 1855. *See* D1191

(*e*) Selections from the British poets. 1858. *See* D1199

(*f*) Third book of lessons. 1862. *See* D1337

(*g*) Treatise on mensuration. 1850. *See* D1358a

D707 IRVING, C., *LL.D.* A catechism of botany: containing a description of the most familiar and interesting plants . . . with an appendix, on the formation of an herbarium. Longman, [etc.], [1821]. LEE

D708 IRVING, David, 1778–1860. (1801) The elements of English composition. 11th ed., Edinburgh, Wm. Whyte, 1841. HU

D709 [J., S.E.]. Les fêtes d'enfants: scènes et dialogues. Avec une préface de M. l'abbé Bautain . . . 2e éd., Paris, Hachette, 1864. LEI

J.E.M. *See* M., J.E.

J.F. *See* F., J.

D710 JACKSON, John. (1821) Rational amusement for winter evenings; or, a collection of above 200 curious and interesting puzzles and paradoxes relating to arithmetic, geometry, geography, etc. . . . Longman, [etc.], 1821. LEI

D711 JACOBS, Friedrich Christian Wilhelm, 1764–1847, and DOERING, Friedrich Wilhelm. Eclogae Ovidianae; being the fifth part of the Lateinisches Elementarbuch, by Professors Jacobs and Doering. Edited by Thomas Kerchever Arnold. 10th ed., Rivingtons, 1860. LEI

D712 JAMES, John Angell, 1785–1859. (1824) The Christian father's present to his children. 3rd ed., F. Westley, 1825. LEI

D713 JAMESON, Anna Brownwell, *formerly* Murphy, 1794–1860. (*c.* 1815?) A first, or mother's dictionary for children; containing upwards of three thousand eight hundred words which occur most frequently in books and conversation . . . The whole adapted to the capacities of younger pupils. W. Darton, [*c.* 1815?]. HU; 2nd ed., 1824. ReU; 4th ed., Darton, [18–]. LO

D714 [JAMIESON, *Mrs.* Frances, *formerly* Thurtle]. The young travellers; or, a visit to the grandmother. Containing . . . a sketch of the elements of zoology, botany, mineralogy, and other branches of natural history. By a lady. 2nd ed., Godwin, 1816. LEI

D715 JAMIESON, P. Juvenile library, or school class book, consisting of reading lessons in those branches of knowledge most necessary to be known. [18–?]. NoU

D716 JANEWAY, James, 1636?–1674. (1671) A token for children; being an account of the conversion, holy and exemplary lives, and joyful deaths, of several young children. Westley, 1825. LEI

D717 JAUFFRET, Louis François, 1770–1850? Education pratique d'Adolphe et de Gustave; ou, recueil des leçons données par L. F. Jauffret à ses enfans . . . [No pub.], 1806. BI

D718 [JAUFFRET, L. F.]. (Eng. 1804) Travels of Rolando; or, a tour round the world; translated by Miss Aikin. Newly corrected and revised by Cecil Hartley. Routledge, 1852. LEI

D719 JENSCH, H., *ed. and trans.* The learner's first book. Nach dem . . . Werke J. Tibbins für Deutsche bearbeitet. Arnsberg, Ritter, 1845. LEI
Jessica's first prayer. *See* Stretton, Hesba, *pseud.*

D720 JOHN and Henry; or, the disobedient child. By M. C., a sincere friend of youth. Harvey & Darton, 1842. LEI

D721 JOHN Williams, the sailor boy. Houlston, n.d. [pre-1840]. ReU

D722 JOHNS, Bennett George, *fl.* 1845–1851. The first reading book. Darton, 1851. LEI

D723 JOHNS, Charles Alexander, 1811–1874, *ed.* (1848?) Gardening for children. 3rd ed., [18–]. NoU

D724 JOHNSON, Lorenzo D. Memoria technica; or, the art of abbreviating . . . also rules for memorizing . . . Adapted to the use of schools. 3rd ed., rev. and impr., Boston; Gould, Kendall & Lincoln; 1847. LEE

D725 [JOHNSON, Richard], 1573–1659? (*c.* 1597) History of the seven champions of Christendom. W. S. Fortey, [18–]. ReU
JOHNSON, Richard, 1734–1793. *See* Cooper, *Rev. Mr., pseud.*? [probably a pseudonym of Richard Johnson]

D726 JOHNSON, Samuel, 1709–1784. (1755) Comprehensive Johnson's dictionary: an enlarged edition of Johnson's Dictionary . . . 1851. NoU

D727 JOHNSON, Samuel. Johnson's dictionary of the English language in miniature . . . [Edited by the Rev. Joseph Hamilton.] New ed., rev. and corr., Joseph Smith, 1827. HU

D728 [JOHNSTONE, Christian Isobel], 1781–1857. (1831) The public buildings of the city of London described. By the author of 'Public buildings of Westminster described'. J. Harris, 1831. (The little library.) LEI

D729 [JOHNSTONE, C. I.]. (1827) Scenes of industry, displayed in the bee-hive and the ant-hill. [1827?] ReU; 2nd ed., J. Harris, 1830. LEI

D730 JONES, John, 1766?–1827. A grammar of the Greek tongue, on a new and improved plan. Longman, [etc.], 1804. LEE

D731 JONES, Stephen, 1763–1827. (1790) A general pronouncing and explanatory dictionary of the English language, for the use of schools, foreigners, etc., on the plan of Mr. Sheridan. New ed., corr. [At head of title: Sheridan improved.] Longman, [etc.], 1813. HU; stereotyped ed., Longman, [etc.], 1824. LEI

D732 JOSSE, Augustin Louis, 1763–1841. (Eng. 1801) Juvenile biography; or lives of celebrated children . . . Translated by Mrs. Cumyng. Dulau, [etc.], [1801?]. LEI

D733 A JOURNEY in the Highlands. In two parts. 2nd ed., 1815. ReU

D734 JOUSSE, J., 1760–1837. Catechism of music. D'Almaine, [183–?]. LEI

D735 JOUSSE, J. A catechism of thorough-bass and harmony . . . adapted to the capacity of young students. 2nd ed., D'Almaine, [183–?]. LEI

D736 JOUSSE, J., *ed.* Music epitomized. *See* D344 Dibdin, Charles

D737 JOUSSE, J. Pocket dictionary of three thousand Italian, German, French and English musical terms . . . with three supplements . . . 6th ed., D'Almaine, [183–?]. LEI

D738 JOYCE, Jeremiah, 1763–1816. Dialogues in chemistry. 1809. 2 vols. NoU

D739 JOYCE, Jeremiah. Letters on natural and experimental philosophy, addressed to a youth settling in the metropolis. 2nd ed., 1821. NoU

D740 JOYCE, Jeremiah. (1800–1805) Scientific dialogues intended for the instruction and entertainment of young people, in which the first principles of natural and experimental philosophy are fully explained. New ed., Johnson, 1809. 6 vols. NoU; *another issue*, vols. 1–3, and 6. 1815. NoU; new ed., Baldwin, Cradock & Joy, 1821–1825. 6 vols. LO; new ed., complete in one vol., Scott, [etc.], 1840. LEI; new ed., containing the recent additions to science, by C. V. Walker. 1846. NoU

D741 JOYCE, Jeremiah. (1808) A system of practical arithmetic, applicable to the present state of trade, and money transactions . . . For the use of schools. R. Phillips, 1810. BR; 4th ed., R. Phillips, 1812. OX; new ed., rev. and corr., Allman, 1856. HU

D742 JULIA Wentworth; or the fatal effects of folly and disobedience. [18–]. NoU

D743 JULIUS. (1801?) Julius, or the deaf and dumb orphan; a tale for youth of both sexes: founded on the popular play of Deaf and dumb, [by J. N. Bouilly]. 3rd ed., J. Harris, 1806. LEI [On the work of the Abbé de l'Epée.]

D744 JUMEL, Jean Charles. Galerie des jeunes personnes, ou les qualités du coeur et de l'esprit, présentées dans des exemples de vertus, pour servir à l'éducation de la jeunesse. Paris, Alexis Eymery, 1813. LEI
Juvenile drama. *See* Sandham, Elizabeth

D745 The JUVENILE forget-me not. A Christmas and New Year's gift, or birthday present for the year 1830. Edited by Mrs. S. C. Hall. N. Hailes, [etc.], [1830]. LEI; Ackermann's Juvenile forget-menot. A Christmas, New Year's, and birth-day present, for youth of both sexes, 1832. Edited by Frederic Shoberl. Ackermann, 1832. LEI; The Juvenile forget me not . . . for the year 1833. Edited by Mrs. S. C. Hall. Ackermann, 1833. LEI ReU

D746 The JUVENILE gleaner: a keepsake for the young, edited by J. W. Fitzharding. [2nd year's issue.] Lacey, [1833?]. LEI

D747 [JUVENILE incidents]. [No place of pub.] [18–?]. NoU

D748 The JUVENILE keepsake, a present for all seasons. London, E. Lacey; Liverpool, H. Lacey; [1830?]. LEI

D749 The JUVENILE miscellany; or, friend of youth. Vol. 1, Jan.–June, 1819; vols. 4–8, July 1820–Dec. 1822. LEI

D750 The JUVENILE miscellany of amusement and instruction. Smith, Elder, 1842. LEE

D751 The JUVENILE missionary magazine. Vol. 1, nos. 1–2, June–July 1844; vol. 4, no. 42, Nov. 1847; vol. 5, no. 52, Sept. 1848; vol. 13, no. 141, Feb. 1856. LEI

D752 The JUVENILE musical instructor; being an easy guide to the attainment of a knowledge of the first principles of music. By a Professor. T. Garlick and W. Horn, [c. 1820]. HU

D753 JUVENILE. (1801) The Juvenile Plutarch: containing accounts of the lives of celebrated children, and of the infancy of persons who have been illustrious for their virtues or talents. 4th ed., Darton, 1820. BR

D754 The JUVENILE protrectress. With, Kate of Rosemount. To which is added, The casket, and other tales ... Johnson, [c. 1850]. LEE

D755 JUVENILE. (1838) The juvenile rambler; or, sketches and anecdotes of the people of various countries ... J. Harris, 1838. ReU

D756 KAY, R. The new preceptor; or, young lady's and gentleman's true instructor in the rudiments of the English tongue ... Newcastle, 1801. NoU

D757 [KEBLE, John, 1792–1866, and ANSTICE, Joseph], comps. (1841) The child's Christian year: hymns for every Sunday and holy-day, compiled for the use of parochial schools. 2nd ed., Oxford, Parker, 1842. LO; [3rd ed.], Oxford, Parker, 1849. LEE; 4th ed., Oxford, Parker, 1859. LEE

Keeper's travels in search of his master. See Kendall, E. A.

D758 KEITH, Thomas, 1759–1824. (1798) The complete measurer; or, the whole art of measuring: being a plain and comprehensive treatise on practical geometry and mensuration. For the use of schools ... Enlarged by Samuel Maynard. New ed., Longman, [etc.], 1839. [A revision of Wm. Hawney's Complete measurer (1717).] LEI

D759 KEITH, Thomas. (1788) The complete practical arithmetician: containing several new and useful improvements. Adapted to the use of schools and private tuition. 5th ed., Rider & Weed, for J. Walker, [etc.], 1811. HU

D760 KEITH, Thomas. (1804) A new treatise on the use of globes; or, a philosophical view of the earth and heavens ... New ed., enlarged and improved by G. N. Wright. Tegg, 1857. LEI; also A key to Keith's Treatise on the globes ... By C. Vines. S. Brooke, for the author, 1820. LEI

KELLY, Sophia, formerly Sherwood, b. 1815, joint author. See Sherwood, M. M., and Kelly, S.

D761 KELTY, Mary Ann, 1789–1873. (1840) Mamma and Mary discoursing upon good and evil. In six dialogues. 2nd ed., Harvey & Darton, [184–]. LEI

D762 [KENDALL, Edward Augustus], 1776–1842. (1835) Burford Cottage, and its robin-red-breast. T. Tegg, 1835. ReU

D763 [KENDALL, E. A.]. (1798) Keeper's travels in search of his master. 14th ed., 1826. ReU; Grant & Griffith, 1850. [In Animal histories.] LEI

D764 [KENNEDY, Benjamin Hall], 1804–1889. (1866) The public school Latin primer ... Longmans, 1889. LEI

D765 [KENNEDY, Grace], 1782–1823. (1823) Anna Ross; a story for children. By the author of 'The decision'; ... etc. Edinburgh, W. Oliphant, 1824. [1st ed. had title: Anna Ross, the orphan of Waterloo.] LEI

D766 KENNETT, White, 1660–1728. (1710) The Christian scholar; in rules and directions for children and youth, sent to English schools. Especially designed for the poor boys taught and clothed by charity. 22nd ed., Rivington for S.P.C.K., 1823. LEI

D767 [KENT, Anna]. York House; or, conversations in a ladies' school ... J. Dennett, for Williams & son, 1813. HU; 2nd ed., 1829. NoU

D768 KENT, Anna. Sequel to York House; or, friendship's memorial ... 1818. NoU

D769 KETT, Henry, 1761–1825. (1802) Elements of general knowledge ... designed chiefly for the junior students in the universities, and the higher classes in schools. Oxford, O.U.P., 1802. 2 vols. LEI; 2nd ed., 1802. 2 vols. NoU

Key to knowledge. See Budden, Maria E.

D770 [KILNER, Dorothy], 1755–1836. (1799) The rational brutes; or, talking animals. By M. Pelham, [pseud.]. Harris, 1816. LEI

D771 [KILNER, Dorothy]. (c. 1785?) The village school. New ed., J. Harris, [etc.], 1828. [Defective copy.] LEI; new ed., 1831. ReU

D772 [KILNER, Mary Jane], b. 1753. (c. 1783?) Memoirs of a peg top, by S.S. [pseud.]. New ed., Harris, 1828. LEI

D773 KIND words for boys and girls. Year 1867. NE

D774 KINGSLEY, Charles, 1819–1875. (1855) Glaucus; or, the wonders of the shore. Macmillan, 1886. LEI

D775 KINGSLEY, Charles. (1870) Madam How and Lady Why; or, first lessons in earth lore for children. Bell & Daldy, 1870. NO; 2nd ed., Macmillan, 1889. LEI

D776 KINGSLEY, Charles. (1863) The water-babies: a fairy tale for a land-baby. Macmillan, 1891. LEE

D777 KINGSTON, William Henry Giles, 1814–1880. (1858) Fred Markham in Russia; or, the boy travellers in the land of the Czar. Griffith & Farran, 1858. LEI

D778 KINGSTON, W. H. G. Mountain Moggy; or, the stoning of the witch. A tale for the young. S.P.C.K., [1866]. LEI

D779 KINGSTON, W. H. G. (1859) Round the world: a tale for boys. Nelson, 1859. LEI

D780 KNIGHT, Anne, compiler. School-room lyrics. New ed., Simpkin, [1859?]. HU

D781 KNIGHT, Charles, 1791–1873. (1854) Once upon a time. Murray, 1854. 2 vols. LEI

D782 KNIGHT'S penny magazine. Vols. 1–2, 1846. LEI

D783 KNOTT, Robert Rowe. (1839–1842, pts. 1–3) The new aid to memory. Part the third: adapted to scripture history . . . 2nd ed., Whittaker, 1843. LEE

D784 [KNOX, Vicesimus], 1752–1821, *compiler*. (1791?) The poetical epitome; or, Elegant extracts abridged from the larger volume, for the improvement of scholars at classical and other schools, in the art of speaking, reading, thinking, composing, and in the conduct of life. J. Johnson, [etc.], 1807. [Incomplete.] HU

L., H.L., *pseud. See* Borthwick, Jane E.

Ladder to learning. *See* Trimmer, *Mrs.* Sarah

LADY, pseud. *See under titles of works*

LADY OF ENGLAND, *pseud. See* Tucker, Charlotte Maria

D785 LAMB, Charles, 1775–1834. (1808) The adventures of Ulysses. New ed., M. J. Godwin, 1819. NoU

D786 LAMB, Charles. (1811) Beauty and the beast. With an introduction by Andrew Lang. [1887]. NoU; Rodale Pr., 1955. [With reproductions of the original engravings.] LEI

D787 LAMB, Charles. (1805) The king and queen of hearts: an 1805 book for children . . . Now re-issued in facsimile, with an introduction by E. V. Lucas. [Facsimile of 1809 ed.] Methuen, 1902. LEI

D788 LAMB, Charles. (1811) Prince Dorus . . . Introduction by Andrew W. Tuer. Leadenhall Pr., 1890/1891. [Facsimile of 1811 ed.] NoU

D789 [LAMB, Charles, and LAMB, Mary Ann], 1764–1847. (1809) Mrs. Leicester's school; or, the history of several young ladies, related by themselves. 2nd ed., M. J. Godwin, 1809. BR; 4th ed., M. J. Godwin, 1814. ReU; 5th ed., M. J. Godwin, 1817. LEI; 10th ed., 1827. NoU; 11th ed., rev. and impr., Baldwin & Cradock, 1836. NE

D790 LAMB, Charles, and LAMB, Mary Ann. Mrs. Leicester's school, and other writings in prose and verse. With introduction and notes by Alfred Ainger. Macmillan, 1908. LO

D791 LAMB, Charles, and LAMB, Mary Ann. Poetry for children; to which are added Prince Dorus, and some uncollected poems by Charles Lamb. Chatto & Windus, 1878. BR

D792 LAMB, Charles, and LAMB, Mary Ann. (1807) Tales from Shakespeare. 4th ed., 1822. 2 vols. NoU; new ed. To which are now added, scenes illustrating each tale. C. Knight, 1844. 2 vols. LEI

D793 LAMÉ FLEURY, Jules Raymond. (New ed., 1844) L'histoire de France racontée à la jeunesse. Première partie: Depuis les origines jusqu'à l'avènement des Valois. Nlle. éd. revue et corrigée. Paris, Borrani, 1885. LEI

D794 [LANCELOT, Claude], 1615?–1695. (Fr. 1644) A new method of learning with facility the Latin tongue . . . Translated from the French of the Messieurs de Port Royal, and improved, by T. Nugent. New ed., rev. and corr., F. Wingrave, 1803. 2 vols. LEI; Wingrave & Collingwood, 1816. 2 vols. LO

D795 LANDELLS, Ebenezer, 1808–1860, and LANDELLS, Alice. (1860) The girl's own toy-maker and book of recreation. 2nd ed. Griffith & Farran, 1860. NE; 4th ed., Griffith & Farran, 1863. LEI

D796 LANGFORD, R., *ed*. A treatise on arithmetic, by Francis Walkingame . . . Revised by R. Langford. 1824. NoU

LANGLET DU FRESNOY, Nicholas. *See* Lenglet du Fresnoy, N.

D797 LANGLEY, E. Langley's new engrossing copies. [18–?]. NoU

D798 LARDNER, Dionysius, 1793–1859. An analytical treatise on plane and spherical trigonometry, and the analysis of angular sections. 2nd ed., Taylor, 1828. BI

D799 LARDNER, Dionysius. (1855–1856) Common things explained. First [and] Second series . . . From the 'Museum of science and art'. Crosby Lockwood, [1874?]. LEI

D800 [LAS CASES, Marin Joseph Emmanuel Auguste Dieudonné de, *marquis de la Caussade*], 1766–1842. [A genealogical, chronological, historical and geographical atlas . . .] By Mr. Le Sage. 20 nos. in 1 vol. [Lacks nos. 5, 10.] [1801]. NoU

D801 LATHAM, Robert Gordon, 1812–1888. (1843) An elementary English grammar, for the use of schools. 18th thousand, rev. and enl. Walton & Maberley, 1860. HU

D802 LAYCOCK, John. A touchstone to try the French scholar on the difficulties of that prevailing language. Leeds, 1825. NoU

D803 [LEA, T.]. Sunday enjoyments; or, religion made pleasant to children. Hatchard, 1824. LO

D804 [LEATHLEY, Mrs. —]. (185-) Chick-seed without chick-weed; being very easy and entertaining lessons for little children. Darton & co., [185–?]. LEI

D805 LE BRETON, Philip, 1779–1864. Elémens de la grammaire françoise. A grammar of the French language, compiled from the best authorities, on a new plan . . . Law & Whittaker, 1815. LEI

D806 LEÇONS pour les enfans de 3 à 5 ans, composés de phrases à lire, et de petites historiettes . . . 4e éd. Paris, P. Blanchard, 1822. [Possibly by the publisher.] LEI

D807 LECOUTZ DE LEVIZAC, Jean Pons Victor. (1797) A theoretical and practical grammar of the French tongue: in which the present usage in every part of syntax is displayed. 3rd ed., Dulau, 1806. LEE; [Revised] by J. H. Sievrac. 20th ed., Dulau, 1835. LO

D808 LEE, Richard Nelson, 1806–1872. (1850) The life of a fairy. Illustrated by Alfred Crowquill. Darling, [1850]. LEI

D809 LE FEBVRE, J. E., *trans*. Visite d'une semaine. Ouvrage traduit de l'anglois de Lucie Peacock. 2e éd., Londres, Law & Whittaker, 1817. LEI

D810 The LEISURE hour: a family journal of instruction and recreation. Nos. 888–939, Jan. 2– Dec. 25, 1869. R.T.S. LEI

D811 LENGLET DU FRESNOY, Nicholas, 1674–1755. An abridgment of ancient geography. 2nd ed., 1829. NoU

D812 LENGLET DU FRESNOY, Nicholas. (Fr. 1736; Eng. 1744) Geography for children; or, a short and easy method of teaching and learning geography . . . Translated from the French. 22nd ed., Johnson, 1806. BI; 31st ed., Rivington, 1829. NoU

D813 LENNIE, William, 1779–1852. (1810?) The principles of English grammar . . . 54th ed., Edinburgh, Oliver & Boyd; London, Simpkin; 1863. HU; 69th ed., with the author's latest improvements . . . Edinburgh & London, 1871. HU

D814 LENNIE, William. A key to Lennie's Principles of English grammar, containing an enlarged account of the author's method of teaching grammar . . . 6th ed., with some additions. Edinburgh, Author, 1824. LEI

D815 LE PRINCE DE BEAUMONT, Jeanne-Marie, 1711–1780. (c. 1759) Le magasin des adolescents. Edition stéréotype. Paris, Laurens, 1822. 2 vols. LEE

D816 LE PRINCE DE BEAUMONT, Jeanne-Marie. (1757) Le magasin des enfans. Tomes 1–4. Metz, Lamort, 1821. LEE

LE SAGE, Mr., pseud. See Las Cases, M. J. E. A. D. de

Lessons for children. See Barbauld, A. L.

D817 LESSONS intended for introduction into schools and cottages; consisting of descriptive hymns selected from A Manual of sacred poetry, for the use of public and private charities. 2nd ed., Birmingham, Smith, 1823. BI

D818 LESSONS on industrial education, for the use of female schools. By a lady. Longman, [etc.], 1849. LO

D819 LETTERS from a nobleman to his son, during the period of his education at Eton and Oxford. R. Phillips, 1810. 2 vols. BI HU LEI

Letters of advice from a mother to her son. See Crespigny, Mary Champion

D820 LETTERS. (1825) Letters on entomology, intended for the amusement and instruction of young persons . . . Whittaker, 1825. LEI NoU

Letters to a young lady. See French, Sarah

LEVIZAC, Jean Pons Victor Lecoutz de. See Lecoutz de Levizac, J. P. V.

D821 LIFE and death of a monkey; or, the village of Alton: a tale for young persons. By a lady. E. Lloyd, 1814. LEI

D822 [LILY, William], 1468?–1522. A short introduction of grammar generally to be used . . . [Revised by John Ward]. London, 'printed for W. Lily and John Ward', [c. 1800]. [Printed by Edward Baines, Leeds.] LEI

D823 LINDLEY, John, 1799–1865. School botany; or, an explanation of the characters and differences of the principal natural classes and their orders . . . For the use of students preparing for their matriculation examination in the University of London. Longman, 1839. HU

D824 LINDLEY, John. School botany, descriptive botany, and vegetable physiology; or, the rudiments of botanical science. New ed., Bradbury & Evans, 1862. HU

Line upon line. See Mortimer, Mrs. Favell Lee

Lion's masquerade. See Dorset, Mrs. Catherine Ann

D825 The LITTLE child's picture magazine, in easy words. Edited by Joseph Foulkes Winks. Vol. 6, 1859. London, Simpkin, Marshall; Leicester, Winks; 1859. LEI

D826 LITTLE. (1830) The little enquirer; or, instructive conversations for children from five to six years of age. Harvey & Darton, 1830. LEE LEI LO

Little ferns for Fanny's little friends. See Parton, Sarah Payson

D827 LITTLE. (185–) Little Mary's picture book of English history. Ward, Lock & Tyler, [187–?]. LEI

D828 LITTLE. (185–) Little Mary's primer. Ward, Lock & Tyler, [187–?]. LEI

D829 LITTLE. (185–) Little Mary's reading book. [18–?]. NoU

D830 LITTLE. (185–) Little Mary's spelling book. Ward, Lock & Tyler, [187–?]. LEI

D831 LITTLE Pinky, the miner's orphan. Wertheim, Macintosh & Hunt, [184–]. HU

D832 LITTLE. (182–?) The little reader; a progressive step to knowledge. 3rd ed., Harris, 1838. LO

D833 LITTLE. (Pre-1830) Little Sophy. 3rd ed., Derby, H. Mozley & son, [18–]. ReU

D834 LITTLE Susan: a tale in easy words, for children under six years of age. By Aunt Sophy. Hooper, 1842. LEE

Little Susy series. See Prentiss, Elizabeth

D835 [LLOYD, Charles], 1766–1829. Travels at home, and voyages by the fire-side; for the instruction and entertainment of young persons. Vol. 5: America. Longman, 1815. LEI

D836 LONDON. (1812?) London: a descriptive poem. By a well known Cockney. Darton, 1812. NoU

D837 LONDON SCHOOL SOCIETY. Rhymes, prose readings, and mental exercises for the training school. Groombridge, [184–?]. LEI

D838 [LORIQUET, Jean Nicolas]. Histoire ancienne des Egyptiens, des Babyloniens, des Assyriens . . . [etc.] à l'usage des maisons d'éducation. Par A.M.D.G——, [pseud.]. Lyons, Rusand, [182–?]. [Inscription dated 1831.] LEI

D839 LORIQUET, J. N. Histoire romaine, depuis la fondation de Rome, jusqu'à la fin de L'Empire d'Occident; à l'usage des maisons d'éducation: par A.M.D.G——. Lyons, Rusand, [182–?]. [Inscription dated 1831.] LEI

D840 LOUDON, Mrs. Jane, 1807–1858. The entertaining naturalist: being popular descriptions, tales, and anecdotes of more than 500 animals . . . of which a knowledge is indispensable in polite education . . . New ed., rev. and enl. [by J.W.L.]. Bohn, 1850. LEI

D841 LOUDON, *Mrs.* Jane. The year-book of natural history, for young persons. Murray, 1842. HU

D843 LOUDON, John Claudius, 1783–1843. Self-instruction for young gardeners, foresters, bailiffs ... in arithmetic and book-keeping, geometry ... [etc.]. With examples ... With a memoir of the author. Longman, 1845. LEE

LOVECHILD, *Mrs., pseud. See* Fenn, Eleanor

LOVECHILD, Solomon, *pseud. See* Fenn, Eleanor

D844 LOWE, Solomon, *fl.* 1723–1737. (1737) Mnemonics delineated. *See* D570

D845 LOWRES, Jacob. (2nd ed., 1851) A system of English parsing and derivation, with the rudiments of English grammar ... For the use of schools. Specially adapted to the tuition of pupil-teachers. New ed., Longman, 1864. HU

D846 LUDLOW, George. (1836) The class reading book: designed to furnish youth with practical information on a variety of interesting subjects. 3rd ed., Parker, 1840. LEE

D847 LULLABY, *Mrs., pseud.* Nursery ditties from the lips of Mrs. Lullaby ... 1844. NoU

D848 [LUND, John]. (1777) Ducks and green peas; or, the Newcastle rider ... Alnwick, [18–?]. NoU

D849 LUNN, Joseph, 1784–1863. The shepherd of Derwent Vale, a drama ... [18–?]. NoU

D850 M., C. The child and the hermit; or, a sequel to The story without an end [by F. W. Carové]. By C.M. [possibly Clara Moore]. Darton & Clark, for the author, [*c.* 1840]. LEE

D851 M., J.E. (1816 or 1824?) The crocus, containing original poems for young people. By J.E.M. New ed., Birmingham, Cornish, 1899. LEI

M., T. *See* Morell, Thomas

M.C. *See* C., M.

M.P., *pseud. See* Kilner, Dorothy

D852 McCRINDELL, Rachel. (1840) The school girl in France. 3rd ed., Seeley, Burnside & Seeley, 1847. LEI

D853 M'CULLOCH, John Murray. (1827) A course of elementary reading in science and literature, compiled from popular writers; to which is added, a copious list of the Latin and Greek primitives which enter into the composition of the English language. For the use of Circus-Place School, Edinburgh. 5th ed., impr., Edinburgh, Oliver & Boyd; London, Simpkin, Marshall; 1834. HU

D854 M'CULLOCH, J. M. (1837) A third reading-book for the use of schools, containing simple pieces in prose and verse, with exercises on the more difficult words and sounds ... 19th ed., Edinburgh, Oliver & Boyd, 1853. NE

D855 McGUFFEY, William Holmes, 1800–1873. (1837) McGuffey's newly revised eclectic fourth reader: containing elegant extracts in prose and poetry ... Revised and improved. Cincinnati, W. B. Smith, [1853]. LEI

D856 M'LAREN, James. A collection from the most approved English authors, in prose and verse; for the use of schools and private classes. Dundee, A. Colville, pr., 1820. HU

D857 MACLEAR, George Frederick, 1833–1902. (1866) A shilling book of Old Testament history for national and elementary schools. Macmillan, rep. 1897. LEI

D858 MACLEOD, Norman, 1812–1872. (1861) The gold thread; a story for the young. 7th ed., Strahan, 1867. LEI

D859 MACLOC, J. New, complete and universal natural history of all the most remarkable quadrupeds, birds, fishes, reptiles, and insects, in the known world. 1813. NoU

D860 [M'QUIN, Ange Denis], 1756–1823. (1812) Compendium of zoology, being a description of more than three hundred animals ... ['Recomposed' by A. D. M'Quin]. New ed., rev. and corr., Baldwin, Cradock & Joy, 1818. LEI

D861 MACREDIE, Alexander, *publisher.* The select atlas for the use of schools. Edinburgh, Macredie, [182–?]. HU

D862 MAGAZINE for the young. Vols. 15, 16, 19, 22, 24–26, 28. Mozley, & Masters, 1856–1869. LEE

D863 The MAGIC legacy. Mozley, [18–?]. NoU

D864 [MAITLAND, Julia Charlotte, *formerly* Barrett], d. 1864. Historical charades: by the author of 'Letters from Madras' [i.e. J. C. Maitland]. Longmans, [etc.], 1847. LEE

D865 MALAHER, Louis. Poésies diverses: containing selections from the most celebrated French poets ... and the drama of 'Esther', by Racine. Accompanied by introductory arguments ... Whittaker, 1852. HU

D866 MALGAIGNE, Joseph François, 1806–1865. Conseils pour le choix d'une bibliothèque, écrits pour une jeune fille. [Stamford], Overbrook Pr., 1936. [First published in the life of Malgaigne by E. Pilastre.] LEI

D867 MAMMA's. (182–?) Mamma's lessons for her little boys and girls. First part. A series of reading lessons in words of three and four letters. Second part. Chiefly in monosyllables ... 4th ed., Harris, 1833. NoU; 9th ed., Grant & Griffith, 1846. LEI

D868 MANGNALL, Richmal, 1769–1820. (1798) Historical and miscellaneous questions. 5th ed., 1806. ReU; 6th ed., corr., Longman, [etc.], 1808. LEI; 7th ed., corr., Longman, 1809. NoU; new ed., Longman, Hurst, [etc.], 1825. LO; new ed., Longman, 1828. NoU; new ed., corr., Longman, 1834. HU; new ed., revised by William Birkin. Richardson, 1844. SH; new ed., corrected, enlarged and continued to the present time, by G. N. Wright. Tegg, [18–]. NoU; new ed., revised and corrected by Edward H. Riches. Milner & Sowerby, [187–?]. OX

D869 MANN, E. [Manuscript arithmetic book, giving methods and examples. Begun Jan. 1849, at 'Mr. Bartlett's private school'.] LEI

D870 MANN, Isaac, *bp. of Cork and Ross.* (Pre-1780) A familiar exposition of the Church catechism ... To which are added, Prayers, for the use of parents, children, and servants. 24th ed., Rivington for S.P.C.K., 1825. LEI

D871 MANSON, David. (c. 1760) A new spelling book: containing above six thousand familiar words, arranged in tables according to the tones of the vowels; with a variety of reading lessons... Dublin, T. Tegg, 1839. HU

D872 MANT, Alicia Catherine, fl. 1812–1825. (1822) The cottage in the chalk-pit. Harvey & Darton, 1822. LEE

D833 MANT, A. C. (1812) Ellen, or the young godmother. A tale for youth. 4th ed., Whittaker, 1826. LEI

D874 MANT, Richard, 1776–1848. A familiar and easy guide to the understanding of the Church catechism, in question and answer. For the use of children. 8th ed. Rivington for S.P.C.K., 1826. LEI

D875 MANUAL OF SACRED POETRY. Lessons intended for introduction into schools and cottages; consisting of descriptive hymns selected from A Manual of sacred poetry, for the use of public and private charities. 2nd ed., Birmingham, Smith, 1823. BI

D876 [MARCET, Mrs. Jane], 1769–1858. [?] Bertha's visit to her uncle in England. Murray, 1831. 3 vols. [Possibly by Mrs. Marcet.] ReU

D877 MARCET, Mrs. Jane. Conversations for children on land and water. Longman, 1838. LEE

D878 [MARCET, Mrs. Jane] [?] (1817) Conversations on botany. Longman, [etc.], 1817. LEI; 2nd ed., 1818. ReU; 8th ed., 1834. ReU [Also attributed to Elizabeth and Sarah Fitton.]

D879 [MARCET, Mrs. Jane]. (1806) Conversations on chemistry, in which the elements of that science are familiarly explained and illustrated by experiments. 5th ed., rev., corr. and enl., Longman, 1817. 2 vols. LEI; 1837. 2 vols. NoU

D880 [MARCET, Mrs. Jane]. (1819) Conversations on natural philosophy; in which the elements of that science are familiarly explained... By the author of 'Conversations on chemistry'. Longman, [etc.], 1819. ReU; 4th ed., rev. and corr., Longman, [etc.], 1824. LEE; [new ed.], with corrections, improvements, and considerable additions... questions and a glossary by Dr. Thomas P. Jones. Philadelphia, John Grigg, 1826. NE

D881 [MARCET, Mrs. Jane]. (1816) Conversations on political economy... By the author of 'Conversations on chemistry'. 2nd ed., 1817. NoU

D882 [MARCET, Mrs. Jane]. (1833) The seasons: stories for very young children. By the author of 'Conversations on chemistry', etc. Longman, 1833–1835. 4 vols. [Vols. 1 and 3, 2nd ed.] LEI; Longman, 1865–1868. 4 vols. NO

D883 MARCET, Mrs. Jane. (1845) Willy's grammar; interspersed with stories for the use of children. 3rd ed., Longman, 1850. LEI

D884 [MARCHETTI, Giuseppe]. A new, practical and easy method of learning the Italian language, by Franz Ahn [actually by Marchetti?]. Trubner, [etc.], 1863. LEI

MARKHAM, Mrs., pseud. See Penrose, Elizabeth

D885 MARKHAM, William. (1720?; 5th ed., 1738) An introduction to spelling and reading English: being the most plain and easy method of teaching young children to read... Morpeth, Blair, 1824. LEI

D886 MARRYAT, Frederick, 1792–1848. (1847) The children of the New Forest. 5th ed., Routledge, 1855. LEI

D887 MARRYAT, Frederick. (1841–1845) Masterman Ready; or, the wreck of the Pacific. Written for young people. New ed.... Bohn, 1857. LEI

D888 MARRYAT, Frederick. (1840) Poor Jack. With illustrations by Clarkson Stanfield. Longman, 1840. LEI

D889 [MARTIN, Sarah Catherine], 1768–1826. The adventures of old Mother Hubbard and her wonderful dog. See D960 Mother Hubbard

D890 [MARTIN, William], 1801–1867. (1858) The hatchups of me and my school-fellows, by Peter Parley. Edited by William Martin. [Actually by Martin.] Darton & co., 1858. LEI

D891 MARTIN, William. The parlour book; or, familiar conversations on science and the arts, for the use of schools and families. Darton, [1835?]. NoU

D892 MARTIN, William, ed. Peter Parley's annual. Darton, 1841. LEI; 1842. NoU; 1848. NE; 1862. LEI

D893 MARTINEAU, Harriet, 1802–1876. (1841) The Crofton boys. New ed., Routledge, 1864. NoU

D894 MARTINEAU, Harriet. (1841) Feats on the fiord. A tale of Norway. C. Knight, 1844. (Knight's weekly volume, viii). LEI; Routledge, 1856. NE

D895 MARTINEAU, Harriet. (1841) The settlers at home. Routledge, 1856. NE

D896 MARY Campbell; or, the affectionate granddaughter. Wellington (Salop), Houlston, 1828. ReU

D897 MASON, Charles Peter. (1858) English grammar; including the principles of grammatical analysis. 12th ed. Walton & Maberly, 1869. HU

D898 MATHEWS, Eliza Kirkham, 'Mrs. Charles Mathews', d. 1802. Ellinor; or, the young governess... York, T. Wilson, 1808. ReU

MAUNDER, Samuel, 1790?–1849. See Friend to youth, pseud.

D899 [MAURICE, Mary Atkinson]. (1829) Aids to development; or, mental and moral instruction exemplified: in conversations between a mother and her children. 4th ed., abridged. Seeley, Burnside & Seeley, 1844. [Also had title: Aids to mental development.] LEI

D900 MAVOR, William Fordyce, 1758–1837. (1798) The British Nepos: consisting of select lives of illustrious Britons... Written purposely for the use of schools, and carefully adapted to the situations and capacities of youth. 7th ed., R. Phillips, 1806. HU; new [13th] ed., impr. and enl., Longman, [etc.], 1829. LEI

D901 MAVOR, W. F. Catechism of general knowledge; or, a brief introduction to the arts and sciences. For the use of schools and families. New impr. ed., Lackington, [etc.], 1816. HU

D902 MAVOR, W. F. The catechism of universal history. For the use of schools and families. 3rd ed., Lackington, Allen, 1810. HU

D903 MAVOR, W. F. (1780?) The English spelling-book, accompanied by a progressive series of easy and familiar lessons... 32nd ed., rev., R. Phillips, 1806. HU; 136th ed., 1812. ReU; 352nd ed., rev., Longman, [etc.], 1829. LEI; 375th ed., Longman, 1831. NoU; 443rd ed., rev., Longman, 1838. HU; Bristol, —, 1840. NoU; new ed., Wood, [18–]. NoU; Routledge, 1885. ReU

D904 MAVOR, W. F. (1800) [Natural history]. The elements of natural history... 9th ed., 1816. NoU

D905 MAVOR, W. F. do. Histoire naturelle, à l'usage des écoles. Traduit de l'anglais. Londres, E. Newbery, [etc.], 1801. LEI

D906 MAVOR, W. F. Mavor's New universal primer. [1883]. LO

D907 MAVOR, W. F. (1801) The nursery garland, being a selection of short poems. 3rd ed., Harris, 1809. ReU

D908 MAVOR, W. F. (1780?) Universal stenography. Or a practical system of short hand. 8th ed., R. Phillips, 1807. LEI

D909 MAVOR, W. F., ed. and trans. (1800) Select lives of Plutarch, containing some of the most illustrious characters of antiquity; abridged from the original for the use of schools. New ed., R. Phillips, 1806. HU; new ed., rev., Longman, [etc.], 1823. LEI

D910 MAVOR, W. F., and PRATT, Samuel Jackson, comps. (1801) Classical English poetry for the use of schools, and young persons in general. New ed., collected by Dr. Mavor and Mr. Pratt. Longman, 1819. HU

D911 MAXWELL, Caroline. The juvenile edition of Shakespeare, adapted to the capacities of youth. Chapple, 1828. NoU

D912 MAY, A. A practical grammar of the Swedish language, with reading and writing exercises. 2nd ed., Stockholm, A. Bonnier, 1854. LO

D913 MAY, Robert, missionary. (1816) Lectures to the young on interesting subjects. 4th ed., Nisbet, 1820. NE

D914 MAYHEW, Henry, 1812–1887. (1854) The wonders of science; or, young Humphry Davy... Routledge, [1854]. LEI

D915 MAYHEW, Henry, and MAYHEW, Augustus Septimus, 1826–1875. (1847) The good genius that turned everything into gold; or, the queen bee and the magic dress: a fairy tale. New ed., D. Bogue, [185–?]. LEI

D916 MAYNARD, Samuel, ed. The complete measurer... by Thomas Keith... Enlarged by Samuel Maynard. New ed., Longman, [etc.], 1839. LEI

D917 The MECHANICS' magazine. Vol. 41, June–Dec. 1844, and vol. 55, July–Dec. 1851. LEI

D918 The MECHANIC'S weekly journal... Nos. 1–26, Nov. 15, 1823–May 8, 1824. LEI

Memoir of Naimbanna. *See* Gilpin, William

Memoirs of a peg top. *See* Kilner, Mary Jane

D919 MEMOIRS. (1801) Memoirs of Bob the spotted terrier. Grant & Griffith, [c. 1850]. [In Animal histories. Originally called 'The Dog of knowledge'.] LEI

D920 MEMOIRS. (1799?) Memoirs of Dick, the little poney... New ed., Tabart, 1806. ReU

D921 MEMORABLE spots in English history. [18–]. NoU

Metamorphoses. *See* Robson, Mary

MEULAN, Pauline de, *aft. Mme.* Guizot. *See* Guizot, Pauline

D922 MILLARD, John. The new art of memory, founded upon the principles taught by M. Gregor von Feinagle: and applied to chronology, history ... To which is added some account of the principal systems of artificial memory... 3rd ed., Sherwood, Neely & Jones, 1813. LEE

D923 MILLARD, John. (1811) The new pocket cyclopaedia; or, elements of useful knowledge, methodically arranged: designed for the higher classes in schools, and for young persons in general. Sherwood, Neely & Jones, 1811. ReU; 2nd ed., 1813. NoU

D924 MILLER, E. (New ed., 1822) Scripture history; with the lives of the most celebrated Apostles. Designed for the improvement of youth. New ed., T. Kelly, 1826. 3 vols. in 2. HU; Kelly, 1827. NoU

D925 MILLER, Thomas, 1807–1874. The boy's autumn book, descriptive of the season, scenery, rural life, and country amusements. 1847. NoU

D926 MILLER, Thomas. (1852) Original poems for my children. 2nd series. Ward, Lock & Tyler, [187–?]. LEI

D927 MILLS, Alfred, 1776–1833. Natural history of 48 birds, with elegant engravings, from drawings. 1810. NoU

D928 MILLS, Alfred. (1809) Pictures of Roman history, in miniature... with explanatory anecdotes. Darton, [etc.], 1817. NoU

D929 MILNER, Thomas. The history of England: from the invasions of Julius Caesar... For schools and families. R.T.S., 1860. LEI

D930 MILTON, John, 1608–1674. [Paradise lost]. The story of our first parents, selected from Milton's Paradise lost: for the use of young persons. By Mrs. Siddons. Murray, 1822. LEI

Ministering children. *See* Charlesworth, Maria Louisa

D931 MISTER, Mary. (1816) The adventures of a doll... Darton, Harvey & Darton, 1816. ReU

D932 [MISTER, Mary]. (1810) Mungo; or, the little traveller. To which are annexed, The Seven wonders of the world. Dublin, J. Jones, 1819. LEI

Mrs. Leicester's school. *See* Lamb, Charles and Mary Ann

D933 MITCHELL, James. (1819) Mitchell's easy introduction to the writing of Latin exercises. New ed., carefully corrected, altered, and improved, by J. W. Underwood. John Souter, 1838. HU

D934 MITCHELL, James, 1786?–1844. (1824?) The universal catechist; or, student's textbook of general knowledge; consisting of separate catechisms of the arts and sciences, and principal objects of a liberal education. Whittaker, 1824. ReU; new ed., *with title*: Conversations on general knowledge, or, universal catechist ... Whittaker, 1845. NE

D935 MITCHELL, John. The female pilgrim; or, the travels of Hephzibah; under the similitude of a dream. 2nd ed., Evans, 1814. LO

D936 [MOGRIDGE, George], 1787–1854. Half hours with Old Humphrey, [pseud.]. R.T.S., [1849?]. LEI

D937 [MOGRIDGE, George.] The new illustrated primer. By Old Humphrey. Revised by T.B.S. S. W. Partridge, [1870]. HU NE

D938 [MOGRIDGE, George]. (1844) Old Humphrey's country strolls. R.T.S., [1844?]. LEI

D939 [MOGRIDGE, George]. (1849) Old Humphrey's ripe fruit for youthful gatherers. R.T.S., [1867?]. LEI

D940 [MOGRIDGE, George]. Pleasant tales, for young people. By Old Humphrey. [1881?]. NoU

D941 [MOGRIDGE, George]. Peter Parley's Walks in the country, by the author of 'Ephraim Holding's domestic addresses', 'Old Humphrey', etc. W. Tegg, 1864. NE

D942 [MOGRIDGE, George], *ed.* Tales about Greece. By Peter Parley [i.e. S. G. Goodrich. Edited and abridged by G. Mogridge]. Tegg, 1837. LEI

D943 MOLINEUX, Thomas, 1759–1850. (1804) An introduction to Mr. Byrom's universal English short-hand ... Designed for the use of schools by T. Molineux. 3rd ed., Part 1 [and Part 2]. [1823?] [MS. copy, made 1833–1834 by W. H. Scott, of Bramley School, nr. Leeds.] LEI

D944 MONTEITH, A. H., *ed.* (1857?) A first Italian reading book, by Franz Ahn. With a vocabulary of the words, and copious notes, by A. H. Monteith. Allman, 1873. [Preface date, 1857.] LEI

D945 MOORE, Thomas, 1821–1887. The elements of botany, for families and schools. Published under the direction of the Committee of general literature and education appointed by the S.P.C.K. 10th ed. [revised] by T. Moore. Longmans, 1865. [First ed. of this work, 1833.] HU

D946 MORAND, C. Dialogues classiques, familiers, et autres, à l'usage des étudians des langues française et italienne ... 2e éd., Paris, Cormon & Blanc, 1833. LEI

D947 MORE, Hannah, 1745–1833. (1821) Bible rhymes, on the names of all the books of the Old and New Testaments: with allusions to some of the principal incidents and characters. T. Cadell, 1821. HU

D948 MORE, Hannah. (1777) Essays on various subjects, principally designed for young ladies. New ed., Sharpe & Hailes, 1810. LEI

D949 MORE, Hannah. (1782) Sacred dramas: chiefly intended for young persons: the subjects taken from the Bible. To which is added, Sensibility, a poem. 16th ed., Cadell & Davies, 1810. HU; *another ed.* With a memoir of the author. Chiswick, Whittingham, 1823. BR

D950 MORE, Hannah. The shepherd of Salisbury Plain, and other tales. N.Y., Derby & Jackson, 1858. LEI

More instructive lessons for children. *See* Barbauld, A. L.

D951 [MORELL, Thomas], 1703–1784, *ed.* Exempla minora; or, new English examples, to be rendered into Latin ... for the use of the lower forms. [By Joseph Pote, edited by T. Morell?] New ed., Eton, E. Williams, 1817. LO; new ed., York, 1821. NoU; new ed., Eton, 1831. NoU

D952 [MORELL, Thomas], *ed.* Exempla moralia; or, third book of new English examples, to be rendered into Latin ... New ed., rev., Eton, E. Williams, 1815. HU

MORGAN, Augustus de. *See* De Morgan, A.

D953 MORRIS, A. J. Glimpses of great men; or, biographic thoughts of moral manhood. Ward, 1853. LO

D954 MORRISON, James. A compendium of practical arithmetic: containing such rules only, as are applicable to mercantile transactions ... The whole adapted as a text-book, for the use of schools, and peculiarly adapted for preparing youth for commercial situations. 2nd ed., enl., Glasgow, W. Lang, 1814. HU

D955 [MORTIMER, *Mrs.* Favell Lee, *formerly* Bevan], 1802–1878. (1837) Line upon line; or, a second series of the earliest religious instruction the infant mind is capable of receiving ... By the author of the 'Peep of day'. Part 1 [and] 2. Hatchard, 1852–1853 rep. HU; Part 1 [only]. R.T.S., [19–?]. LEI

D956 [MORTIMER, *Mrs.* F. L.]. (1849) Near home; or, the countries of Europe described. With anecdotes ... By the author of 'The Peep of day', etc., etc. Hatchard, 1858. LEE

D957 [MORTIMER, *Mrs.* F. L.]. (1833) The peep of day; or, a series of the earliest religious instruction the infant mind is capable of receiving ... Rev. and corr. Hatchard, 1854. HU; Hatchard, 1866. LEE; Hatchard, 1876. LEI

D958 [MORTIMER, *Mrs.* F. L.]. (1850) Reading without tears; or, a pleasant mode of learning to read. By the author of 'Peep of day'. Hatchard, 1857. HU; Hatchard, 1861. LEI; Hatchard, 1870–1875. 2 vols. HU

D959 MORTIMER, Thomas, 1730–1810. (1810) A grammar illustrating the principles and practice of trade and commerce for the use of young persons. Phillips, 1810. NoU

Mother Goose in hieroglyphics. *See* Appleton, George S.

D960 MOTHER HUBBARD. The adventures of old Mother Hubbard and her wonderful dog. Darton & Clark, [*c.* 1840]. ReU

D961 MOTHER. (1812) The Mother's fables, in verse. Designed, through the medium of amusement, to correct some of the faults and follies of children. 1812. NoU

Mother's grammar. *See* Fenn, Eleanor

D962 MOZLEY's first book for children, or reading made perfectly easy. 69th ed., Derby, Mozley, 1824. NoU

D963 [MULLION, Mary]? New sacred dramas for young persons. London, Longman; Edinburgh, Constable; 1820. [Inscription suggests that Mary Mullion is author.] LEI

D964 MULTIPLICATION TABLE. [Card with engraving by A. Reid on verso.] Alnwick, Davison, [18–]. NoU

Mungo, or, the little traveller. *See* Mister, Mary

D965 MURE, Eleanor. The story of the three bears metrically related, with illustrations locating it at Cecil Lodge in September 1831. [Photographic copy of MS.] NoU

MURPHY, Anna Brownwell, *aft. Mrs.* Jameson. *See* Jameson, A. B.

D966 MURRAY, Lindley, 1745–1826. (1797) Abridgment of Murray's English grammar. With an appendix . . . Designed for the younger classes of learners. 57th ed., 1818. NoU; 86th ed., Harvey & Darton, 1825. HU; new ed., Derby, Mozley, 1846. LEI

D967 MURRAY, Lindley. (1798) English exercises, adapted to Murray's 'English grammar' . . . Designed for the benefit of private learners, as well as for the use of schools. 10th ed., York, 1806. NoU; 33rd ed., York, printed for Longman, [etc.], 1825. HU; 36th ed., York, T. Wilson, for Longman, [etc.], 1827. LEI

D968 MURRAY, Lindley. Key to the Exercises adapted to Murray's 'English grammar' . . . 30th ed., Longman, 1853. HU

D969 MURRAY, Lindley. (1795) An English grammar. 12th ed., York, 1805. NoU; new ed., Longman, [etc.], 1808. 2 vols. [Vol. 2 is English exercises.] LEI; 24th ed., York, T. Wilson for Longman [etc.], 1813. HU; 27th ed., York, for Longman, 1815. NoU; 4th ed. [*sic*], York, Wilson; London, Longman; 1819. 2 vols. LEE; 5th ed., York, Longman, 1824. 2 vols. BR

D970 MURRAY, Lindley. (1799) The English reader; or, pieces in prose and poetry, selected from the best authors . . . 8th ed., York, T. Wilson, for Longman, [etc.], 1809. HU

D971 MURRAY, Lindley. A first book for children . . . 13th ed., York, Wilson, 1818. NoU

D972 MURRAY, Lindley. (1807) Introduction au lecteur françois . . . 5e éd., York, Longman, 1826. LEE

D973 MURRAY, Lindley. (1801?) Introduction to the English reader; or, a selection of pieces, in prose and poetry . . . 25th ed., York, T. Wilson for Longman, [etc.], 1827. LEI

D974 MURRAY, Lindley. (1802) Lecteur françois: ou recueil de pièces en prose et en vers, tirées des meilleurs écrivains . . . 3e éd., York, T. Wilson for Longman, [etc.], 1814. LEI

D975 MURRAY, Lindley. The young man's best companion, and book of general knowledge . . . with lists of the most approved books on each subject. T. Kelly, 1822. HU; 1824. NoU

D976 MY grandfather Gregory. R.T.S., [184–]. HU

D977 NATIONAL SOCIETY FOR PROMOTING THE EDUCATION OF THE POOR. Central school book. No. 2. Rivington, 1820. LEI

D978 NATURAL history for children: being a familiar account of the most remarkable quadrupeds, birds, insects, fishes and reptiles, trees and plants. Baldwin, Cradock & Joy, 1819. 5 vols. LO

D979 The NATURAL history of reptiles and serpents. Dublin, C. Bentham, 1821. [Incomplete.] ReU

D979a NATURAL phenomena. S.P.C.K., 1855. LO

D980 [Die NATURLEHRE in Bildern, gemeinfassliche Darstellungen aus dem Gebiete der Naturlehre, enthaltend eine Beschreibung der allgemeinen Eigenschaften der Körper. Mit . . . erläuterndem Text. Schwäb. Hall., 1853.] NoU

D980a NEALE, John Mason, 1818–1896. (1843) Hymns for children. 3rd ed., 1848. NoU

Near home. *See* Mortimer, Favell Lee

D981 NESBIT, Anthony, 1778–1859. (1838) A treatise upon practical mensuration. York, [etc.], Wilson, [etc.], 1838. LEE; 14th ed., enl. To which is added, A treatise on levelling . . . Longman, [etc.], 1846. LEI; new ed., enl., Longman, [etc.], 1861. LEI

D981a A NEW and entertaining alphabet for young children . . . 1811. NoU

D982 The NEW cabinet album of entertainment and instruction. Embellished with fine plates. E. Lacey, [183–?]. LEI

D982a NEW. (1833?) New cobwebs to catch little flies. R.T.S., 1835. LEE

D983 The NEW estate; or, the young travellers in Wales and Ireland. By the author of 'Portugal', etc. Harvey & Darton, 1831. LEE

D983a The NEW expositor, containing tables of words from two to seven syllables . . . for the use of schools . . . 7th ed., Liverpool, —, 1806. NoU

D984 A NEW grammar of the French language. [*c.* 1810]. [Lacks t.p.] HU

New history of England. *See* Cooper, *Rev. Mr.*

D984a A NEW history of England, from the invasion of Julius Caesar to the present time. In two parts: part II. LEE

D985 A NEW introduction to arithmetic; containing a concise explanation of the simple rules; with the tables of money, weights, measures, etc. . . . Warminster, J. L. Vardy, 1819. [Cover title: Vardy's improved edition of arithmetical rules and tables.] HU

New method of learning with facility the Latin tongue. *See* Lancelot, C.

D985a The NEW reading made easy, consisting of a variety of useful lessons. Alnwick, Davison, [18–?]. NoU

D986 NEW sacred dramas for young persons. London, Longman, [etc.]; Edinburgh, Constable; 1820. [Possibly by Mary Mullion.] LEI

D986a NEW Testament biography, in the form of questions, with reference to Scripture for the answers. For the use of schools and private families. Stereotype ed., J. Wardlaw, [etc.], [183–?]. HU

D987 The NEW Tom Thumb, consisting of a series of easy and useful lessons adapted expressly for schools. Newcastle, —, [18–?]. NoU

D988 The NEW universal primer. Derby,—, [18–]. NoU

D989 The NEW week's preparation, for a worthy receiving of the Lord's Supper, as recommended and appointed by the Church of England. 1833. NoU

D990 The NEW year's gift, and juvenile souvenir. Edited by Mrs. Alaric Watts. Longman, 1830. NoU

D991 NEWCOMBE, Samuel Prout. (1850–1853) Pleasant pages for young people: a book of instruction and amusement on the infant school system. Vols. 3–5 [only, of 6]. Houlston & Wright, 1863–1866. LEI

D992 NEWMAN, Edward, 1801–1876. A history of British ferns. 4th or school edition, J. Van Voorst, [1866]. HU

D993 NICHOLSON, Henry Alleyne, 1844–1899. (1870) Advanced text-book of zoology, for the use of schools. 2nd ed., rev. and enl., Edinburgh, Blackwood, 1873. HU

D994 NICHOLSON, Peter, 1765–1844, and ROWBOTHAM, John. A practical system of algebra. 2nd ed., 1831. NoU

D995 NOEHDEN, Georg Heinrich, 1770–1826. (1809) Exercises for writing German, according to the rules of grammar. 5th ed., Longman, [etc.], 1829. HU

D996 NOVERRE, Elizabeth G. The little book of knowledge. New ed., Harvey & Darton, [18–]. [Inscription dated 1846.] LEI

D997 NUGENT, Thomas, 1700?–1772, trans. A new method of learning with facility the Latin tongue... Translated from the French of the Messieurs de Port Royal, and improved, by T. Nugent. New ed., rev. and corr., F. Wingrave, 1803. 2 vols. LEI; Wingrave & Collingwood, 1816. 2 vols. LO

D998 [NURSERY rhymes and children's stories series], 1–16. Otley, Yorkshire J.S. Publishing & Stationery Co. for the booksellers, [c. 1850?]. LEE

D999 NURSERY rhymes for good children. Hodgson, [18–]. NoU

D1000 The OBSERVING eye; or, letters to children on the three lowest divisions of animal life... By the author of 'Our world, its rocks and fossils'. 6th ed. [18–?]. NoU

D1001 O'KEEFE, Adelaide, 1776–1855? (1818) National characters exhibited in forty geographical poems. Darton, Harvey & Darton, 1818. ReU

O'KEEFE, Adelaide, joint author. See Taylor, Ann, and others

OLD HUMPHREY, pseud. See Mogridge, George

Old Mother Hubbard. See Mother Hubbard

D1002 OLD Testament biography, in the form of questions, with references to Scripture for the answers, for the use of schools and private families. 5th ed., Edinburgh, J. Wardlaw, [etc.], 1833. HU

D1003 The OLD woman of Stepney. Johnson, [18–]. NoU

D1004 OLIVER, Daniel. (1868) Lessons in elementary botany; the part of systematic botany based upon material left in manuscript by the late Prof. Henslow. New ed. Macmillan, 1886. HU

D1005 OLLENDORF, Heinrich Gottfried, 1803–1865. A key to the exercises in the New method of learning to read, write and speak a language in six months, adapted to the Italian. Whittaker, 1857. LO

D1006 OLLENDORF, H. G. (1848) Nouvelle méthode pour apprendre à lire, à écrire et à parler une langue en six mois, appliquée à l'anglais... 6e éd., rev., corr. et augm., Paris, Author, 1856. LEI

D1007 ORDER and disorder, a tale. Recommended to the perusal of all little girls who wish to be neat, notable and industrious. Harvey & Darton, 1825. LEI

Original poems for infant minds. See Taylor, Ann, and others

Ornaments discovered. See Robson, Mary

Orphan sailor boy. See Hedge, Mary Ann

D1008 OTTO, Emil. (1856) German conversation-grammar. A new and practical method of learning the German language. 18th ed., Sampson Low, 1879. LEI

D1009 OVID. Eclogae Ovidianae; being the fifth part of the Lateinisches Elementarbuch, by Professors Jacobs and Doering. Edited by Thomas Kerchever Arnold. 10th ed., Rivington, 1860. LEI

D1010 P., Gabrielle de. Les amis de collège, ou quinze jours de vacances. Paris, 1819. NoU

P., M., pseud. See Kilner, Dorothy

P., P. See Poiret, Pierre

D1011 PALEY, William, 1743–1805. (1790) Reading made completely easy; or, a necessary introduction to reading the Bible. Johnson, [c. 1855?]. [1790 ed. had title: The young Christian instructed in reading.] LEE

Parental instruction, in familiar dialogues. See Rees, C.

D1012 The PARENT's cabinet of amusement and instruction. [A serial.] Smith, Elder, 1836. LEI; [new ed.] Vol. 2 [only, of 12]. Smith, Elder, [1858]. NoU

D1013 [PARIS, John Ayrton], 1785–1856. (1827) Philosophy in sport made science in earnest... 6th ed., 1846. NoU; 8th ed., rev., Murray, 1857. LEI

D1014 PARK, A., publisher. Park's amusing fairy tale of the sleeping beauty. [c. 1840?]. ReU

PARLEY, Peter, pseud. See Clark, Samuel; Goodrich, Samuel Griswold; Martin, William; Mogridge, George

D1015 [PARTON, Sarah Payson]. Little ferns for Fanny's little friends. By the author of 'Fern leaves from Fanny's portfolio' . . . 1864. NoU

Pastoral advice to young persons. *See* Woodward, Josiah

Pastor's tales. *See* Bunbury, Selina

D1016 PATTERSON, Robert, 1802–1872. Introduction to zoology for the use of schools. 1848. 2 vols. NoU

D1017 PAYNE, Isaac. An atlas, for the use of schools, designed for the younger students in geography. Darton, Harvey & Darton, 1817. HU

D1018 PAYNE, Joseph, 1808–1876. (1845) Studies in English poetry: with short biographical sketches, and notes . . . Intended as a text book for the higher classes in schools . . . New ed., Arthur Hall, 1848. HU

D1019 [PEACOCK, Lucy], *fl.* 1785–1816. Patty Primrose; or, the parsonage house. Darton, Harvey & Darton, 1813. ReU

D1020 PEACOCK, Lucy. (1794) The visit for a week; or, hints on the improvement of time. Containing original tales, anecdotes from natural and moral history, etc., designed for the amusement of youth. 4th ed., Carpenter, [1804]. LEI; 8th ed., 1815. NoU

D1021 PEACOCK, Lucy. Visite d'une semaine. Ouvrage traduit de l'anglois de Lucie Peacock, par J. E. Le Febvre. 2e éd., Londres, Law & Whittaker, 1817. LEI

D1022 PEACOCK, Lucy, *trans.* (1796) Ambrose and Eleanor . . . Translated by Lucy Peacock. 3rd ed., Baldwin, Cradock & Joy, 1807. ReU

D1023 PEACOCK, Thomas Love, 1785–1866. (1814) Sir Hornbook. [in Cole, *Sir* H., Faery tales and ballads.] *See* D278

D1024 The PEACOCK and parrot, on their tour to discover the author of 'The Peacock at home . . .' 1816. NoU

Peacock at home. *See* Dorset, *Mrs.* Catherine Ann

D1025 PEASE, John. [Algebra exercise book. 1812.] HU

D1026 PEASE, John. [Arithmetic exercise books. 1810–1811. 5 vols.] HU

D1027 PEASE, John. [MS. copybook, 1812–1813.] HU

D1028 PEASE, John. [Logarithms exercise-book. 1811?] HU

Peep of day. *See* Mortimer, Favell Lee

D1029 PELHAM, Margaret, [pseud.?]. The London primer; or, a first book for children at a very early age. 40th ed. Phillips, [etc.], 1809. LEE

D1030 PELHAM, Margaret. The parents' and tutors' first catechism, of the dawning of juvenile knowledge . . . Revised and improved by the Rev. David Blair, [pseud., i.e. Sir Richard Phillips]. R. Phillips, 1827. [Margaret Pelham may be another pseudonym of Sir R. Phillips.] LEI

PELHAM, Mary, *pseud. See* Kilner, Dorothy

D1031 PENNY magazine of the Society for the diffusion of useful knowledge. June 1833–Dec. 1835. BI; Vols. 5–6, 1836–1837. LEI; Vols. 11–14, 1842–1845. BI

D1032 [PENROSE, *Mrs.* Elizabeth], 1780–1837. Historical conversations for young persons: containing, 1. The history of Malta and of the Knights of St. John, 2. The history of Poland, by Mrs. Markham, [pseud.]. Murray, 1836. LEI

D1033 [PENROSE, *Mrs.* Elizabeth]. (1823) A history of England, from the first invasion by the Romans to the end of the reign of George the Third. With conversations at the end of each chapter. By Mrs. Markham, [pseud.]. For the use of young persons. Constable, 1823. 2 vols. HU; new ed., with continuation to . . . 1869 by E. H. Riches. Milner, [1871?]. ReU; author's ed., carefully rev., Murray, 1872. LEI

D1034 [PENROSE, *Mrs.* Elizabeth]. (1828) A history of France, from the conquest of Gaul by Julius Caesar to the death of Louis Philippe; with conversations at the end of each chapter. By Mrs. Markham. For the use of young persons. New rev. ed., Murray, 1855. LEI; new ed., rev., Murray, 1863. HU

D1035 [PENROSE, *Mrs.* Elizabeth]. A history of Germany, from the invasion of Marius to the year 1850. On the plan of Mrs. Markham's histories. For the use of young persons. New ed., Murray, 1862. LEI

D1036 PENROSE, John, d. 1888. (Pre-1851) Easy exercises in Latin elegiac verse. 16th ed., Whitaker, [etc.], 1884. LEI

D1037 PERCIVAL, *Mrs.* T. W. An abstract of ancient history, from the earliest records to the time of Xerxes, intended as an introduction to the Grecian and Roman histories generally used in schools. Harvey & Darton, 1830. NoU

D1038 PERKINS, George Roberts, 1812–1876. (1844) The elements of algebra, designed for the use of common schools . . . N.Y., Appleton, 1850. HU

D1039 PERRIN, Jean Baptiste. (1774) The elements of French conversation, with familiar and easy dialogues . . . 18th ed., revised and corrected by C. Gros . . . Law & Whittaker, [etc.], 1815. LEI; 26th ed., revised by C. Gros. Longmans, 1833. LO

D1040 PERRIN, J. B. (1771) Fables amusantes, suivies d'une table générale et particulière des mots, et de leur signification en anglois. 16e éd., revue et corrigée par C. Gros . . . Londres, Law & Whittaker, [etc.], 1817. LEI

D1041 PERRIN, J. B. Fables, adapted to the Hamiltonian system. *See* D595 Hamilton, J.

D1042 PETER PARLEY's annual: a Christmas and New Year's present for young people. Edited by William Martin. Darton & Co., 1841. LEI; 1842. NoU; 1848. NE; 1862. LEI

Petit Grandisson. *See* Berquin, Arnaud

D1043 PHILIP, George, & *son, firm.* Philip's progressive series of copy books, arranged and written by A. Stewart. No. 7. Philip, [18–]. NoU

D1044 [PHILLIPS, *Sir* Richard], 1767–1840. (1820) The biographical class book; consisting of . . . [450] lives . . . arranged as lessons for every day of the year. For the use of schools. By the Rev. J. Goldsmith, [pseud.]. Sir R. Phillips, 1820. HU

D1045 [PHILLIPS, *Sir* Richard]. (1806) The class book; or, three hundred and sixty-five reading lessons, adapted to the use of schools, for every day in the year . . . By the Rev. David Blair, [pseud., i.e. Sir R. Phillips, but probably originally by Eliza Fenwick]. 10th ed., Sir R. Phillips, 1811. OX; 12th ed., Longman, 1814. HU

D1046 [PHILLIPS, *Sir* Richard]. An easy grammar of geography . . . New ed., by the Rev. J. Goldsmith, [pseud.]. Phillips, 1806. NoU; 1807. NoU

D1047 [PHILLIPS, *Sir* Richard]. An easy grammar of natural and experimental philosophy . . . By the Rev. David Blair . . . New ed., Phillips, 1808. NoU

D1048 [PHILLIPS, *Sir* Richard]. The first, or mother's catechism, containing common things necessary to be known at an early age. By the Rev. David Blair, [pseud.]. 34th ed., Wm. Darton, 1820. LEI; 45th ed., rev. and corr. with additions, Wm. Darton, 1825. HU; 96th ed., [*c.* 1847]. NoU

D1049 [PHILLIPS, *Sir* Richard]. (*c.* 1820?) The first step to knowledge; being an easy introduction to the various English spelling books. By the Rev. J. Goldsmith. New ed., Darton, [*c.* 1850?]. HU

D1050 [PHILLIPS, *Sir* Richard]. Five hundred questions and exercises on Murray's Abridgment and Murray's English grammar; also on Irving's Elements of English composition . . . by James Adair, [pseud., i.e. Sir R. Phillips]. [1824]. NoU

D1051 [PHILLIPS, *Sir* Richard]. (1802) Geography, illustrated on a popular plan; for the use of schools and young persons. By the Rev. J. Goldsmith, [pseud.]. 7th ed., Longman, [etc.], 1815. LEI

D1052 [PHILLIPS, *Sir* Richard]. (1803) A grammar of general geography, for the use of schools and young persons . . . By the Rev. J. Goldsmith, [pseud.]. New ed., Longman, 1819. LEE; new ed., 1823. ReU; new ed., corrected and modernized. Longman, [pref. 1824]. HU; Longman, [*c.* 1829]. LEI; new ed., revised and corrected by H. Murray. [*c.* 1840]. NoU; new ed., [18–]. NoU

D1053 [PHILLIPS, *Sir* Richard]. A grammar of the principles and practice of chemistry; for the use of schools . . . New ed., by the Rev. David Blair. Baldwin, Cradock & Joy, 1815. LEE

D1054 [PHILLIPS, *Sir* Richard]. (1827) A popular dictionary of facts and knowledge for the use of schools and students . . . By the Rev. S. Barrow, [pseud., i.e. Sir Richard Phillips]. Poole & Edwards, 1827. LO NoU; 4th ed., Poole & Edwards, 1831. LEI

D1055 [PHILLIPS, *Sir* Richard]. (4th ed., 1809) Practical grammar of the English language, accompanied by numerous exercises, and adapted throughout to the use of schools. By the Rev. David Blair. 10th ed. [No pub.]. 1820. RE

D1056 [PHILLIPS, *Sir* Richard]. (2nd ed., 1811) The universal preceptor; or, general grammar of arts, sciences, and useful knowledge, for the use of schools. By the Rev. David Blair. 65th ed., improved, Sherwood, Gilbert & Piper, 1835. LEI

D1057 [PHILLIPS, *Sir* Richard]? The wonders of the microscope, *and* The wonders of the telescope. *See* D1486–1487

PHILLIPS, *Sir* Richard. *See also* Pelham, Margaret, *pseud.*?

Philosophy in sport made science in earnest. *See* Paris, John Ayrton

D1058 PICTORIAL panoramic alphabet for very little folks. Thos. Dean & son, [18–]. (Amusing panoramas of animals . . . no. 12.) ReU

D1059 A PICTURE of the seasons; with anecdotes and remarks, on every month in the year. Davis, 1818. (Juvenile library.) LEE

D1060 PILKINGTON, *Mrs.* Mary, 1766–1839. (1807) The calendar; or, monthly recreations: chiefly consisting of dialogues between an aunt and her nieces. Designed to inspire the juvenile mind with a love of virtue, and of the study of nature. J. Harris, 1807. LEI

D1061 PILKINGTON, *Mrs.* Mary. (1798) Tales of the cottage; or, stories moral and amusing, for young persons. 5th ed., J. Harris, 1809. HU ReU

D1062 PILKINGTON, *Mrs.* Mary. (1798) Tales of the hermitage. 2nd ed., 1809. ReU

D1063 [PINCHARD, *Mrs.*]. (1791) The blind child; or, anecdotes of the Wyndham family. Written for the use of young people. By a lady. 9th ed., 1809. ReU; new ed., J. Harris & son, [etc.], [*c.* 1820?]. LEI

D1064 PINNOCK, George. (185–?) English grammar. Allman, n.d. (First steps to knowledge series). OX

D1065 [PINNOCK, William], 1782–1843. A catechism of ancient history . . . for young people . . . By a friend to youth. 1812. NoU

D1066 PINNOCK, William. A catechism of architecture. By a friend to youth. [18–]. NoU

D1067 [PINNOCK, William]. A catechism of astronomy. Revised . . . by W. H. Pinnock. Whittaker, [18–]. (Whittaker's improved editions of Pinnock's catechism.) NoU

D1068 PINNOCK, William. A catechism of botany. 7th ed., 1824. NoU

D1069 PINNOCK, William. Catechism of English grammar; with easy parsing lessons, etc. Whittaker, 1822. HU; *see also* D1078

D1070 PINNOCK, William. A catechism of music. 9th ed. (1822). NoU

D1071 PINNOCK, William. A catechism of natural history; or, the animal kingdom displayed . . . For the use and instruction of youth. 9th ed., Whittaker, 1822. NoU; 10th ed., Whittaker, [1822?]. LEI

D1072 [PINNOCK, William]. A catechism of perspective. By a friend to youth. [18–]. NoU

D1073 [PINNOCK, William]. A catechism of Roman history, from the origin of the name to its extinction . . . intended as an introduction to Pinnock's improved edition of Goldsmith's History of Rome . . . 11th ed., Whittaker, 1822. NoU

D1074 PINNOCK, William. (1818) A catechism of the history of America; in two parts . . . 3rd ed., Whittaker, 1823. 2 vols. LEE

D1075 PINNOCK, William. The catechism of the history of England from the earliest period to the reign of George the Fourth. 31st ed., Whittaker, 1822. LEE

D1076 PINNOCK, William. Catechism of the history of France; containing a clear outline of all the important changes which that country has undergone from its foundation to the year 1822. 4th ed., Whittaker, 1822. LEE

D1077 PINNOCK, William. A catechism of the history of Ireland, containing a brief outline of the principal occurrences which have taken place in that country, from the most distant period of its history to the year 1817. Pinnock & Maunder, [1817?]. LEE

D1078 [PINNOCK, William]. A catechism of the principles of English grammar . . . By a friend to youth. 18th ed., 1825. NoU

D1079 PINNOCK, William. A comprehensive grammar of the English tongue. Poole & Edwards, 1830. LO

D1080 PINNOCK, William. Epitome of classical geography. New ed., revised and improved by W. C. Taylor. 1827. NoU

D1081 PINNOCK, William. (1811) Exercises to the Elements of punctuation, accompanied with notes, critical and explanatory, for the use of young men and senior classes in schools. 2nd ed., Newbury, S. Maunder, pr., [1812?]. NE

D1082 PINNOCK, William. History of England made easy. [2 pts. in 1.] 1830. NoU; new ed. Continued to 1839. 1844. NoU

D1083 PINNOCK, William. The young lady's library of useful and entertaining knowledge; intended as a holiday or birth-day present . . . W. J. Sears for the proprietors, 1829. LEI

D1084 PINNOCK, William, ed. Pinnock's improved edition of Dr. Goldsmith's abridgment of the history of England. See D539

D1085 PINNOCK, William, ed. Pinnock's improved edition of Dr. Goldsmith's history of Greece. See D543

D1086 PINNOCK, William, ed. The guide to knowledge. [Shepherd & Sutton], 1838. 4 vols. [Published as a periodical, 1832–1836.] BI

D1087 PINNOCK, William Henry, 1813–1885, ed. Pinnock's Catechism of astronomy. Revised . . . by W. H. Pinnock. See D1067

D1088 PINNOCK, W. H. Pinnock's improved edition of Dr. Goldsmith's abridgment of the history of England . . . Continued by W. H. Pinnock. See D539

D1089 PITMAN, Sir Isaac, 1813–1897. A history of shorthand. Written in phonography. F. Pitman, 1852. LEI

D1090 PITMAN, Sir Isaac. A manual of phonography; or, writing by sound . . . 5th ed., impr., S. Bagster, 1842. LEI

D1091 PLATTS, John, 1775–1837. (1823) The female mentor; or, ladies' class-book: being a new selection of three hundred and sixty-five reading lessons, relating to the education, characteristics and accomplishments of young women. Adapted to the use of schools and private libraries. Derby, Mozley, 1823. LEI

D1092 [The PLEASANT verse and prose story book.] [No place], [18–?]. NoU

Pleasing instructor, or entertaining moralist. See Slack, Anne

D1093 PLEASING. (1789) The pleasing, interesting, and affecting history of Prince Lee Boo: with an account of the Pelew Islands. W. Darton, 1816. LEI; Banbury, —, [18–?]. NoU

D1094 PLUTARCH. Select lives of Plutarch, containing some of the most illustrious characters of antiquity; abridged from the original for the use of schools. By W. F. Mavor. New ed., R. Phillips, 1806. HU; new ed., rev., Longman, [etc.], 1823. LEI

D1095 POETAE. (176–?) Poetae Graeci . . . In usum regiae scholae Etonensis. Ed. nova, recognita et aucta. Eton, E. Williams, 1828. [Originally had title: Selecta ex Homeri, Odyss.] LEI; Pars II. Eton, E. P. Williams, 1849. LEI

Poetical epitome; or, elegant extracts. See Knox, V.

D1096 POETRY about birds and animals. Leeds, Webb & Millington, [c. 1840?] [Inscription dated 1843.] LEI

D1097 POETRY. (1856) A poetry book for National schools. New ed., Bell & Daldy, 1857. [Preface dated Christmas 1855.] HU NoU

D1098 A POETRY book for schools; illustrated with many engravings. New ed., Bell & Daldy, 1861. HU; new ed., Bell & Daldy, 1868. NE

D1099 The POLITE present, or child's manual of good manners. 4th ed., Glasgow, —, 1833. NoU

D1100 [POLLOK, Robert], 1798–1827. Helen of the glen: a tale for youth. 2nd ed. Glasgow, Chalmers & Collins, [etc.], 1825. LEI

D1101 POLN'II samouchitel, ili legchaishii sposob nauchit'sia rossiiskomu iaziku . . . Moscow, Stepanova, 1830. LEI

D1102 The POPULAR educator. [Edited by R. Wallace.] Cassell, 1852–1855. 6 vols. SH; Vols. 1–2. 1852–1853. LEE

PORQUET, Louis Philippe R. Fenwick de. See Fenwick de Porquet, L. P. R.

Port Royal grammars. See Lancelot, C.

D1103 PORTRAITS and characters of the kings of England, from William the Conqueror to George the Third. 1825. 2 parts. NoU

D1104 [POTE, Joseph], 1703?–1787. ? Exempla minora. See D420a

D1105 POTTS, Robert, 1805–1885. (1845) Euclid's elements of geometry, the first six books, and the portions of the eleventh and twelfth books read at Cambridge . . . designed for the use of the junior classes in public and private schools. Longman, 1866. CA

D1106 PRACTICAL. (1824) Practical wisdom; or, the manual of life. The counsels of eminent men to their children . . . Coburn, 1824. LEI

PRATT, Samuel Jackson, 1749–1814, joint compiler. See Mavor, W. F., and Pratt, S. J.

D1107 [PRENTISS, Elizabeth], 1818–1878. (185–) Little Susy's little servants. By the author of 'Stepping heavenwards' . . . etc. Nelson, 1879. LEI

D1108 [PRENTISS, Elizabeth]. Little Susy's six birthdays, little servants, and six teachers. By her Aunt Susan. 5th ed., Nisbet, 1865. NO

Present for an apprentice. *See* Barnard, *Sir* John

D1109 PRESENT. (1830?) A present for the young. 7th ed., R.T.S., 1839. LEE

D1110 PRETTY. (1762) Pretty book of pictures for little masters and misses, or Tommy Trip's history of beasts and birds . . . Written by Oliver Goldsmith[?] for John Newbery . . . 15th ed. . . . E. Pearson, 1867. LEI

D1111 The PRIMITIVE Methodist children's magazine. Vol. 7, new series, 1849. LEI

Prince and the page. *See* Yonge, Charlotte Mary

Prince Lee Boo. *See* Pleasing, interesting, and affecting history of Prince Lee Boo

D1112 The PRONUNCIATION of the French language. [Pref. 1820.] [Lacks t.p. Binder's title: French analogies.] HU

D1113 The PROVERBS of little Solomon. Edinburgh, Oliver & Boyd, [18–?]. NoU

Public buildings of the city of London described. *See* Johnstone, C. I.

Public school Latin primer. *See* Kennedy, B. H.

D1114 PULLEN, P. H. (1820) The mother's book; exemplifying Pestalozzi's plan of awakening the understanding of children in language, drawing, geometry, geography, and numbers. Black, 1820. BI; 2nd ed., Author, 1823. HU

D1115 PULLEN, P. H. Pestalozzi's intellectual or intuitive arithmetic: exemplifying the doctrine of mental calculation by means of tables . . . Black, Young & Young, pr., 1821. OX

D1116 PUNCH AND JUDY. The serio-comic drama of Punch and Judy. Devonport, Keys, [18–?]. NoU

Punch and Judy. *See also* Collier, John Payne

Punctuation personified, by Mr. Stops. *See* Stops, *Mr., pseud.*

D1117 PUZZLE. (2nd ed., 1803) A puzzle for a curious girl. 3rd ed., 1810. [Incomplete.] ReU; 5th ed., Baldwin, Cradock & Joy, 1818. LEI

Q.Q., *pseud. See* Taylor, Jane

D1118 QUINTILIAN. Institutionis oratoriae libri duodecim. Ad fidem codicum manuscriptorum recensuit E. Bonnell. Leipzig, Teubner, 1854. LO

D1119 [R., E.]. (2nd ed., 1794) Geography and history, selected by a lady for the use of her own children. 7th ed., enl., C. Law, [etc.], 1808. LEI; 10th ed., Law & Whittaker, 1815. LO

D1120 R.R. (1809) The assembled alphabet; or, acceptance of A's invitation. Being a sequel to the 'Invited alphabet'. By R.R. Darton, 1809. NoU

D1121 R.R. (1808) The invited alphabet; or, address of A to B, containing his friendly proposal for the amusement and instruction of good children . . . By R.R. Darton, 1809. NoU

D1122 RACHEL Johnson: a tale. By the author of 'The widow's son', 'Charlie Burton', etc. Published under the direction of the Committee of general literature and education . . . S.P.C.K., [*c.* 184–?] LEI

D1123 RAGONOT, L. C. Vocabulaire symbolique anglo-français, pour les élèves de tout âge et de tout degré: dans lequel les mots les plus utiles sont enseignés par des illustrations . . . 7th ed., London, Simpkin, Marshall; Paris, Galignani; [1858]. LEI; 8th ed., Lockwood, 1862. BR

Rambles of a rat. *See* Tucker, Charlotte Maria

D1124 RATIONAL recreations: the most marvellous scientific experiments, the most astounding feats of legerdemain, the most puzzling numerical exercises. Knight & Lacey, 1825. NoU

D1125 READ, Charles. [MS. Specimen book. Written by Charles Read, Mr. Rossiter's Academy, Norton St. Phillip. Dated Christmas, 1848.] BR

D1126 READING made easy; in a regular and speedy method of teaching young children to spell and read English . . . Dublin, Fox, 1811. LEI

Reading without tears. *See* Mortimer, Favell Lee

D1127 The RECREATION: MDCCCXLII. A gift-book for young readers . . . Edinburgh, J. Menzies, [etc.], [1841]. LEI

D1128 RECREATIONS in natural history; or, popular sketches of British quadrupeds: describing their nature, habits, and dispositions . . . Wm. Clarke, [etc.], 1815. LEI

D1129 [REES, C.]. Parental instruction, in familiar dialogues; intended principally for children of the Society of Friends. Bristol, T. Lane, pr., [1811]. HU

D1130 REID, Alexander, *LL.D.* (1837) Rudiments of modern geography, with an appendix containing an outline of ancient geography . . . For the use of schools. 31st ed., rev., Edinburgh, Oliver & Boyd; London, Simpkin, Marshall; 1868. NE

D1131 REID, Hugo, 1809–1872. Elements of physical geography . . . Edinburgh, 1850. NoU

D1132 REID, Hugo, *ed.* (1852) A system of modern geography: including sacred and classical geography . . . With exercises. To which are added, Treatises on astronomy and physical geography. Edinburgh, Oliver & Boyd, 1852. HU

D1133 RELIGIOUS TRACT SOCIETY. The canal boat; or, the orphan boy, [and 5 other tracts in 1 vol.]. R.T.S., [184–]. HU

D1134 RELIGIOUS TRACT SOCIETY. The servant's friend, and profitable companion: [a collection of tracts]. R.T.S., [*c.* 1840?]. LEI

D1135 RELIGIOUS TRACT SOCIETY. The watchmaker and his family, [and six other tracts in one vol.]. R.T.S., n.d. [post-1837]. HU

D1136 RENNIE, James, 1787–1867. Alphabet of physics, or natural philosophy for the use of beginners. 1833. NoU

D1137 REWARDS for attentive studies; or, stories moral and entertaining. 1801. NoU

Rhymes for the nursery. *See* Taylor, Ann, and Taylor, Jane

D1138 RICHARDSON'S British primer. Derby, Richardson, [18–]. NoU

D1139 RICHARDSON'S new arithmetical tables. Derby, Richardson, [18–?]. NoU

D1140 RICHARDSON'S new primer. Derby, Richardson, [18–]. NoU

D1141 RICHMOND, Legh, 1772–1827. (1814) Annals of the poor. Nelson, 1864. LEI

D1142 RICHMOND, Legh. (1809 in shorter form) The dairyman's daughter, (with considerable additions). A narrative from real life. Author, 1815. LEI

D1143 ROBERTS, George, d. 1860. The elements of modern geography. 1820. ReU

ROBIN GOODFELLOW, *pseud. See* Goodfellow, Robin

D1144 ROBIN HOOD. Robin Hood's garland. York, [1806?]. NoU

D1145 ROBIN HOOD. The history of Robin Hood. New ed., 1806. NoU

D1146 ROBINSON, J., *master of the free school of Bunny, Notts.* (1829) A manual of manners; or, hints for the proper deportment of school boys. Hamilton, Adams, 1829. LO NoU; 2nd ed., Hamilton, Adams, 1830. LEI

D1147 ROBINSON, John, 1774–1840. (New ed., 1817) Ancient history. New ed., 1824. NoU

D1148 ROBINSON, John. (1806) Grammar of history, ancient and modern; with questions for exercise . . . 24th ed., Whittaker, 1843. LEI

D1149 ROBINSON, W. L. The pronouncing reading book, for children from five to ten years of age, on a new plan . . . Longman, [etc.], 1862. SH

D1150 [ROBSON, Mary, *aft.* Mrs. Hughs], *fl.* 1813–1839. (1818) The alchemist. By the author of 'Ornaments discovered' . . . [etc.]. W. Darton, jr., 1818. ReU

D1151 [ROBSON, Mary]. (1813) Aunt Mary's tales, for the entertainment and improvement of little girls. 3rd ed., Darton, Harvey & Darton, 1815. ReU

D1152 [ROBSON, Mary]. (1818) The metamorphoses; or, effects of education: a tale. By the author of 'Aunt Mary's tales', . . . etc. Wm. Darton, jr., 1818. LO; Wm. Darton, 1822. LEI

D1153 [ROBSON, Mary]. (1815) The ornaments discovered: a story in two parts. By the author of Aunt Mary's tales. Wm. Darton, jr., 1815. ReU

D1154 [ROBSON, Mary]. (1819) Stories for children; chiefly confined to words of two syllables; by the author of 'Aunt Mary's tales'. . . . 2nd ed., rev., Wm. Darton, 1822. NE

D1155 RODWELL, M. M. The spoiled child reclaimed, or the advantages arising from good instruction. Chapman & Hall, 1835. LEI

Rollo at school. *See* Abbott, Jacob

D1156 ROSCOE, William, 1753–1831. (1807) The butterfly's ball and the grasshopper's feast. A facsimile reproduction of the [2nd] edition of 1808. With an introduction by C. Welsh. Griffith & Farran, 1883. LEI NO NoU

D1157 [ROSCOE, William]. The butterfly's ball and the grasshopper's feast. With prose versions by Comus, [*pseud.*, i.e. R. M. Ballantyne]. Nelson, 1857. LEI

D1158 ROSE and Ann. An easy first book for children. Monosyllables. 2nd ed., Chapman & Hall, 1840. LEE

D1159 ROSS, Robert. (1860) Outlines of English history for junior classes in schools; or, a first book for pupils preparing for public examinations. Rev. ed., Simpkin, Marshall, [1861]. NE NO

D1160 ROSSENDALE, A. History of the kings and queens of England in verse; from King Egbert to Queen Victoria. Souter & Law, 1846. NE

D1161 ROUND games for all parties: a collection of the greatest variety of family amusements for fireside or pic-nic . . . Adapted to the understandings of children from the ages of seven to seventy. David Bogue, 1854. HU

ROWBOTHAM, John, *joint author. See* Nicholson, Peter, and Rowbotham, John

D1162 The ROYAL primer: a good book to teach me how to read. London, Marlborough, Gould; Leicester, Winks; [186–?] [post 1861]. LEI

D1163 The ROYAL visitor. n.d. [pre-1840]. ReU

D1164 RUDDIMAN, Thomas, 1674–1757. (1714) The rudiments of the Latin tongue; or, a plain and easy introduction to Latin grammar. Corrected and revised by Andrew Dun. Aberdeen, J. Chalmers, pr., for A. Brown, 1803. LEI

D1165 RUDIMENTS of the Greek language. For the use of Charterhouse School. Wilkie, 1826. LEI; Taylor, 1826. LEE

D1166 RUDIMENTS of the Latin language. For the use of Charterhouse School. Wilkie, 1816. HU NoU; Wilkie, 1825. LEI

Rudimentum grammaticae Latinae metricum. *See* Busby, R.

D1167 RUSHER, J. G., *publisher.* The English primer; or, child's first book . . . Banbury, Rusher, [18–?]. NoU

D1168 RUSHER, J. G., *publisher.* The English spelling book improved . . . 2nd ed., Banbury, J. G. Rusher, [pref. 1830]. LEI

D1169 S., H. (1791?) The history of the Davenport family . . . Vol. 1 [only]. [18–?] NoU

S.S., *pseud. See* Kilner, Mary Jane

S.W. *See* W., S.

D1170 SABBATH occupations. Liverpool, R.T.S., n.d. [pre-1840]. ReU

SAINT-AUBIN, Stéphanie Félicité du Crest de, *comtesse de Genlis. See* Genlis, *comtesse de*

D1171 SAINTINE, Joseph Xavier, 1798–1865. (1863) La nature et ses trois règnes: causeries et contes d'un bon papa sur l'histoire naturelle . . . 6e éd. de 'La Mère Gigogne et ses trois filles'. Paris, Hachette, 1884. LEI

D1172 SAINTINE, J. X. (1837 France; 1844 Dubuc's ed.) Picciola. Edited by Dr. E. Dubuc. Whittaker, [&] Bell, 1881. LEI

D1173 SALISBURY. (1786) The Salisbury spelling-book, with historical and moral extracts from the New Testament . . . published for the use of Sunday schools. 12th ed., Salisbury, Easton, 1809. LEI

D1174 [SANDHAM, Elizabeth], *fl.* 1788–1815. (1810) Deaf and dumb! By the author of 'The twin sisters'. 1810. ReU

D1175 [SANDHAM, Elizabeth]. Juvenile drama. By the author of 'Summer rambles', 'A cup of sweets', . . . Longman, [etc.], 1808. 3 vols. LEI

D1176 SANDHAM, Elizabeth. (1818) The school-fellows: a moral tale. 2nd ed., J. Souter, 1819. LEI ReU

D1177 SANDHAM, Elizabeth. (1805?) The twin sisters; or, the advantages of religion. 4th ed., J. Harris, 1810. LEI

D1178 [SANDHAM, Elizabeth], trans. Select fables . . . Translated from the French of Mons. Florian, by the author of 'A cup of sweets' . . . J. Harris, 1806. ReU

D1179 SARGANT, Mrs. Jane Alice. (1821) Letters from a mother to her daughter, at or going to school, pointing out the duties towards her Maker, her governess, her schoolfellows, and herself . . . New ed., Wetton & Jarvis, [c. 1825]. [Contains also her 'A holiday letter, for a young lady'.] LEI

D1180 SARGEANT, Anne Maria. Papa and mamma's easy lessons in geography. [c. 1860?]. NoU

D1181 The SATURDAY magazine. Published under the direction of the Committee of general literature and education appointed by the S.P.C.K. Vols. 4–5, Jan.–Dec. 1834. J. W. Parker. LEI

D1182 SAVIGNY, Laurence de, abbé. (1844) La civilité en images et en action, ou, la politesse, les usages et les convenances enseignés aux enfants. 2e éd., Paris, Soulié, 1844. LEI

Scenes of industry. See Johnstone, C. I.

D1183 SCHMID, Johann Christoph von, 1768–1854. (German 182–?) The basket of flowers; or, piety and truth triumphant. A tale for the young. Translated by G. T. Bedell. Halifax, Milner & Sowerby, 1855. LEE

D1184 SCHOEDLER, Friedrich. Elements of botany. 2nd ed., translated from the 6th German ed. by Henry Medlock. London & Glasgow, R. Griffin, 1854. HU

School days at Rugby, by an old boy. See Hughes, Thomas

D1185 Der SCHWÄTZER, an amusing introduction to the German language. On the plan of 'Le babillard'. 2nd ed., Griffith & Farran, [1874?]. [Le Babillard first published 182–.] LEI

D1186 SCOTT, Sir Walter, 1771–1832. (1828–1830) The history of Scotland; from the earliest period to the close of the Rebellion, 1745–1746. Contained in Tales of a grandfather. Edinburgh, R. Cadell, [etc.], 1840. 2 vols. LEI

D1187 SCOTTISH SCHOOL BOOK ASSOCIATION. Principles of natural philosophy. Popularly explained and illustrated. No. VII, pt. 1. Edinburgh, Wm. Whyte, 1845. LO

D1188 SCRAGGS, Rev. George Glyn. (1802) English composition, in a method entirely new . . . To which are added, an essay on the advantages of understanding composition, and a list of select books for English readers . . . H. D. Symonds, 1802. HU LEI

D1189 The SEA-SHORE. Published under the direction of the Committee of general literature and education appointed by the S.P.C.K. S.P.C.K., [184–?]. LEI

D1190 SEAMAN, Meshach. The scientific monitor . . . Colchester, —, 1821. NoU

Seasons. See Marcet, Jane

D1191 SECOND book of lessons, for the use of schools. Published by direction of the Commissioners of national education in Ireland. Dublin, Falconer, 1855. LEI

D1192 SEDGWICK, Miss —. (1865) Arcturus; or, the bright star in Bootes; an easy guide to science. Wm. Macintosh, 1865. NE

D1193 SÉGUR, Sophie Rostopchine, comtesse de. (1862) Les deux nigauds. 6e éd., Paris, Hachette, 1872. LEI

D1194 SÉGUR, comtesse de. (1866) La fortune de Gaspard. Nlle. éd., Paris, Hachette, 1883. LEI

D1195 SÉGUR, comtesse de. (1859) Les malheurs de Sophie . . . 9e éd., Paris, Hachette, 1872. LEI; Nlle. éd., Paris, Hachette, 1904. HU

D1196 SÉGUR, comtesse de. (1860?) Mémoires d'un âne. Nlle. éd., Paris, Hachette, 1878. LEI

D1197 The SELECT atlas for the use of schools . . . Edinburgh, Alex. Macredie, [182–?]. HU

D1198 SELECTION of hymns and poetry, for the use of infant and juvenile schools and families. In five parts. Prepared at the request of the Committee of the Home and Colonial School Society. 6th ed., Groombridge, 1857. NO

D1199 SELECTIONS from the British poets . . . Vol. 1 [only, of 3]. Published by direction of the Commissioners of national education in Ireland. Dublin, Thom, 1858. LEI

D1200 SELF. (1807) The Self instructor, or, young man's best companion; being an introduction to all the various branches of useful learning and knowledge . . . Stereotype ed., Liverpool, Nuttall, Fisher & Dixon; [1813]. HU

D1201 SELLON, William, minister at Clerkenwell. (1784) An abridgment of the Holy Scriptures. New ed., Rivington, [c. 1820]. HU

D1202 SERIOUS thoughts on eternity. R.T.S., n.d. [pre-1840]. ReU; R.T.S., [183–?]. LEI

D1203 A SERMON on malt. Darton, n.d. [pre-1840]. ReU

D1204 The SERVANTS' magazine; or, female domestics' instructor. N.S. vol. 2 (whole series vol. 27), 1864. LEI

D1205 SHAKESPEARE, William. The juvenile edition of Shakespeare, adapted to the capacities of youth. By Caroline Maxwell. Chapple, 1828. NoU

D1206 SHAKESPEARE, William. Tales from Shakespeare. See D792 Lamb, C. and M. A.

D1207 [SHARPE, Mrs. —]. (1823) Dame Wiggins of Lee, and her seven wonderful cats: a humorous tale written principally by a lady of ninety, 1823. [Has also been ascribed to Richard Scrafton Sharpe and Mrs. Pearson.] ReU; another ed. Edited with additional verses, by John Ruskin. Orpington, Allen, 1885. NoU; Allen & Unwin, 1926. LEI

D1208 SHAW, John. [Five mathematics exercise books: the work of John Shaw from the age of 11 to 15, covering the years 1817 to 1821.] NoU

D1209 SHERWOOD, *Mrs.* Mary Martha, *formerly* Butt, 1775–1851. (1835) Caroline Mordaunt; or, the governess. Darton & Clark, [1845?]. LEI

D1210 SHERWOOD, *Mrs.* M. M. (1830?) Do your own work. Houlston, [18–]. ReU

D1211 SHERWOOD, *Mrs.* M. M. False colours. Houlston, [18–]. ReU

D1212 [SHERWOOD, *Mrs.* M. M.] (1839) The flowers of the forest. By the author of Little Henry and his bearer. 5th ed., R.T.S., 1839. ReU; 6th ed., R.T.S., [1840?]. NE

D1213 SHERWOOD, *Mrs.* M. M. The golden chain. Berwick, T. Melrose, 1830. ReU

D1214 SHERWOOD, *Mrs.* M. M. (1828) The hills. New ed., Houlston & Stoneman, 1847. HU

D1215 SHERWOOD, *Mrs.* M. M. (1822–1837) The history of Henry Milner, a little boy who was not brought up according to the fashions of this world. Hatchard, 1822–1837. 4 pts. LEE

D1216 SHERWOOD, *Mrs.* M. M. (1818–1847) The history of the Fairchild family . . . being a collection of stories calculated to show the importance and effects of a religious education. Part 1. Hatchard, 1818. NO ReU; 5th ed., Hatchard, 1822. ReU; 19th ed., Hatchard, 1853. LEI; Part 2. 4th ed., 1848. LEI; 5th ed., 1850. ReU; 6th ed., 1854. SO; Part 3. 1847. LEI ReU; 2nd ed., 1850. SO

D1217 SHERWOOD, *Mrs.* M. M. (1828) The idiot boy. 7th ed., Houlston & Stoneman, [*c.* 1850?]. LEI

D1218 SHERWOOD, *Mrs.* M. M. (1821) The infant's progress, from the Valley of Destruction to everlasting glory. 3rd ed., Wellington (Salop), F. Houlston, 1823. HU; *another ed. with title:* The infant pilgrim's progress . . . New ed., Houlston & Stoneman, 1856. NE

D1219 SHERWOOD, *Mrs.* M. M. (1818) The Indian pilgrim . . . Wellington (Salop), Houlston, 1818. ReU

D1220 SHERWOOD, *Mrs.* M. M. It is not my business. Houlston, [18–]. ReU

D1221 SHERWOOD, *Mrs.* M. M. Jack, the sailor boy. [18–?]. NoU

D1222 SHERWOOD, *Mrs.* M. M. Joan; or, trustworthy. Houlston, [18–]. ReU

D1223 SHERWOOD, *Mrs.* M. M. (1814 or 1815) [Little Henry and his bearer]. The history of Little Henry and his bearer. 18th ed., Wellington (Salop), Houlston, 1822. LEE; *with title* Little Henry and his bearer. Nelson, 1861. HU; Nelson, 1876. LEI

D1224 SHERWOOD, *Mrs.* M. M. (1818) The little woodman, and his dog Caesar. [18–]. NoU

D1225 SHERWOOD, *Mrs.* M. M. (1828) The rainbow. 7th ed., Houlston & Stoneman, [1847?]. HU

D1226 SHERWOOD, *Mrs.* M. M. (1835?) Social tales for the young. Wm. Darton & son, [1835?]. LEI

D1227 SHERWOOD, *Mrs.* M. M. Scenes from real life; being selections from 'Social tales'. Darton & Clark, [1838?]. ReU

D1228 SHERWOOD, *Mrs.* M. M. (1817?) Stories explanatory of the Church catechism. 4th ed., Wellington (Salop), Houlston, 1818. NoU

D1229 SHERWOOD, *Mrs.* M. M. The turnpike-house. Houlston, [18–]. 2 vols. ReU

D1230 SHERWOOD, *Mrs.* M. M. Uncle Manners; or, self-will cured. [18–?]. NoU

D1231 SHERWOOD, *Mrs.* M. M. The useful little girl, and the little girl who was no use at all. Berwick, T. Melrose, 1830. ReU

D1232 SHERWOOD, *Mrs.* M. M., and Kelly, Sophia. (1854) Boys will be boys; or, the difficulties of a schoolboy's life. A schoolboy's mission. Darton & co., 1854. LEI

D1233 SHOBERL, Frederic, 1775–1853, *ed.* Ackermann's juvenile forgetmenot: a Christmas, New Year's, and birth-day present, for youth of both sexes, 1832. Ackermann, 1832. LEI

D1234 SHORT. (1800) Short and easy rules for attaining a knowledge of English grammar. To which are added a few letters for the formation of juvenile correspondence. Wallis, 1801. NoU

D1235 SHORT. (1807) A short explanation of the different parts of the morning and evening prayer: written for the use of sunday-school scholars, in the villages of Great Durnford and Netton; by their sincere friend and well-wisher, [L.M.H.]. Salisbury, Wilks, 1807. [Inscription says 'Given to me by the author, my aunt Louisa'.] LEI

D1236 SHORT. (1728) A short introduction to the Latin grammar for the use of the lower forms in Westminster School. 1810. NoU

D1237 A SHORT system of polite learning, being an introduction to the arts and sciences, and other branches of useful knowledge. 3rd ed., 1804. NoU

D1238 SIDDONS, *Mrs.* Sarah, 1755–1831. (1822) The story of our first parents, selected from Milton's Paradise lost: for the use of young persons. Murray, 1822. LEI

D1239 SIEVRAC, J. H., *ed.* A theoretical and practical grammar of the French language, [by M. Lecoutz de Levizac]. 20th ed., Dulau, 1835. LO

SILLERY, *marquise de. See* Genlis, *comtesse de*

D1240 SIMPLE stories for children. 2nd ed., 1839. NoU

D1241 SIMPSON, John, *of Baldock Academy*. (1807) Quaestiones Graecae; or, questions adapted to the Eton Greek grammar. New ed., Eton, E. Williams, 1814. LO

D1242 SINCLAIR, Catherine, 1800–1864. (1839) Holiday House: a series of tales. Edinburgh, Wm. Whyte, 1856. LEI NE

D1243 SINNETT, Jane, 'Mrs. Percy Sinnett'. (1846) Hunters and fishers; or, sketches of primitive races in the lands beyond the sea. By Mrs. Percy Sinnett. Chapman & Hall, 1846. LEI

D1244 SINNETT, Jane. (1846) A story about a Christmas in the seventeenth century. By Mrs. Percy Sinnett. Chapman & Hall, 1846. LEI

D1245 SISSON, Joseph Lawson. The elements of Anglo-Saxon grammar: to which are added a praxis and vocabulary. Leeds, [etc.], Longman, 1819. LEE

D1246 Six histoires pour la première enfance . . . Par une mère. Londres, 1819. NoU

Sketch of the Greek accidence. *See* Hodgkin, John

Sketches of little boys and girls. *See* Fenn, E.

D1247 SKILLERN, R. S. A new system of English grammar . . . 2nd ed., Gloucester, 1808. NoU

D1248 SLACK, *Mrs.* Anne [*or* Ann], *formerly* Fisher, 1719–1778. (*c.* 1780?) The new English tutor, or modern preceptor; consisting of orthography . . . Also, a practical abstract of English grammar. By A. Fisher. 18th ed., enl. and impr., Newcastle, S. Hodgson, pr., 1821. HU

D1249 SLACK, *Mrs.* Anne [*or* Ann]. (1750) [A new grammar]. Fisher's Grammar improved; or, an easy guide to speaking and writing the English language . . . With exercises of bad English . . . 35th ed., enlarged and much improved, by a near relation of the late A. Fisher. Newcastle, S. Hodgson, [etc.], 1811. HU

D1250 SLACK, *Mrs.* Anne [*or* Ann], *ed.* (1756) The pleasing instructor or entertaining moralist . . . To which are prefixed New thoughts on education. New ed., J. Brambles, [etc.], 1805. NE; new ed., enl., Gainsborough, Mozley, 1809. LEI

D1251 SLATER, Eliza, 'Mrs. John Slater'. (1819) Sententiae chronologicae; or a complete system of ancient and modern chronology, contained in familiar sentences . . . Intended for the use of schools and private students. By Mrs. John Slater. E. Wallis, [1831?]. HU NoU

D1252 A SMALL book of history, intended to be useful. Arranged by a lady. Edwards, [etc.], 1838. HU LEI

D1253 SMART, Martin. The female class-book; or, three hundred and sixty-five reading lessons, adapted to the use of schools . . . selected principally from female writers, or on subjects of female education and manners. Lackington, Allen, [etc.], 1813. HU

D1254 SMITH, Barnard. (1854) Arithmetic for schools. Cambridge, Macmillan, 1858. HU

D1255 SMITH, Charles, *publisher.* Atlas of modern geography for the use of schools. Smith, 1828. NoU

D1256 [SMITH, Charlotte], 1749–1806, *ed.* (1804) Conversations introducing poetry, chiefly on subjects of natural history, for the use of young persons. Whittingham & Arliss, 1819. 2 vols. in 1. HU

D1257 SMITH, Henry D., *engraver.* Large text copies; Small text copies; Round hand copies; Small hand copies. (H. D. Smith's School copies, nos. 2, 3, 4 and 5.) C. Chabot, [*c.* 1850?]. HU; Large text copies; Small text copies. [*c.* 1850?]. NoU

D1258 SMITH, J. Pretty stories, with pretty pictures, to instruct and amuse little folks. Dean & Munday, [*c.* 1825?]. NoU

D1259 SMITH, James Hamblin, 1829–1901. Elementary hydrostatics. 2nd ed., rev. and enl., Rivingtons, 1870. CA

D1260 SMITH, John, *lecturer on education, fl.* 1830–1840. (1834) Lessons on words and objects, with easy and amusing experiments, for the parlour or school. Simpkin & Marshall, [etc.], 1834. LEE; 2nd ed., Simpkin & Marshall, 1834. OX

SMITH, John Brook-. *See* Brook-Smith, John

D1261 SMITH, Philip, 1817–1885. (1862) A smaller history of England, from the earliest times to the year 1878. 26th ed., Murray, 1887. LEI

SMITH, Sarah. *See* Stretton, Hesba, *pseud.*

D1262 SMITH, Thomas, 1775/6–1830, *of Spa Fields chapel.* (1806) The scientific library; or, repository of useful and polite literature. J. Wallis, & Harris, 1806. 6 vols. NoU

D1263 SMITH, Thomas, *ed.* Orthographical exercises, by James Alderson. 14th ed., revised and corrected by the Rev. Thomas Smith. Law & Whittaker, [etc.], 1818. LEI

D1264 SMITH, W. C., *writing master.* Principles of epistolary and mercantile writing; containing easy and infallible rules for facilitating the attainment of a free expeditious running hand . . . London, Gale, Curtis & Fenner; Bristol, W. Bulgin; [1811]. HU

D1265 SMITH, *Sir* William, 1813–1893. (1853?) A first Latin course, comprehending grammar, delectus, and exercise book, with vocabularies. For the use of the lower forms in public and private schools. 26th ed., Murray, 1884. LEI

D1266 SOCIETY FOR PROMOTING CHRISTIAN KNOWLEDGE. Religious tracts dispersed by the Society . . . C. & J. Rivington, 1827. 10 vols. LEI

D1266a SOCIETY FOR PROMOTING CHRISTIAN KNOWLEDGE. *Committee of general literature and education.* A little reading book for young children. [18–]. NoU

SOCIETY FOR PROMOTING CHRISTIAN KNOWLEDGE. do. For further publications under the direction of this committee, *see under* authors, or title when anonymous

D1266b SOCIETY FOR PROMOTING CHRISTIAN KNOWLEDGE, & NATIONAL SOCIETY. English history. S.P.C.K. & N.S., [1856]. (New reading series.) HU

D1267 SOCIETY FOR THE DIFFUSION OF USEFUL KNOWLEDGE. Drawing for young children. *See* D560 Grant, Horace

D1268 SOCIETY FOR THE DIFFUSION OF USEFUL KNOWLEDGE. Penny magazine of the Society . . . June 1833–Dec. 1835. BI; vols. 5–6, 1836–1837. LEI; vols. 11–14, 1842–1845. BI

Sorrows of selfishness. *See* West, *Mrs.* Jane

D1269 SOUTHEY, Robert, 1774–1843. (1832) The beauties of the prose works of Robert Southey . . . chiefly for the use of schools and young persons. [Edited by I.M.]. E. Moxon, 1833. [1832 ed. had title: Selections from the prose works . . .]. LEI

D1270 SPECIMENS of English poetry, for the use of Charterhouse School. 11th ed., S. Walker, 1855. LEI

D1271 SPECKTER, Otto, *illus.* Otto Speckter's Fable book. *See* D622 Hey, W.

SPHINX, *pseud.* *See* Fox, Sara

D1272 SPRAGUE, William Buell, 1795–1876. (2nd U.S. ed., 1831) Letters to a daughter, on practical subjects. R.T.S., [184–?]. NO

D1273 STAINTON, H. T. The educational sheet of butterflies: adapted for schools. Newman, 1856. LEE

STANHOPE, Philip Dormer, *4th earl of Chesterfield. See* Chesterfield, *earl of*

D1274 STEPS to sense verses; or, a set of exercises to be rendered into Latin hexameters and pentameters. For the use of schools. Law & Whittaker, 1815. HU

D1274a STEWART, A. Philip's progressive series of copy books, no. 7. Philip, [18–]. NoU

D1275 STEWART, J. A. The young man's companion; or, youth's instructor: being a guide to the various branches of useful knowledge ... 2nd ed., Oxford, Bartlett & Newman, 1814. OX

D1276 STOCKDALE, John Joseph, 1770–1847, *ed. and trans.* Encyclopaedia for youth; or, an abridgment of all the sciences ... 2nd ed., 1807. NoU

D1277 STONHOUSE, *Sir* James, 1716–1795. (*c.* 1780) Prayers for the use of private persons, families, children and servants. 21st ed., Rivington for S.P.C.K., 1825. LEI

D1278 STOPS, *Mr., pseud.* (*c.* 1820?) Punctuation personified; or, pointing made easy. Harris, [182–?]. NoU

D1279 STORIES. (1823) Stories from Roman history. By a lady. 2nd ed., Harvey & Darton, 1825. LEI

Stories of animals. *See* Hack, Maria

D1280 STORIES on 'my duty towards my neighbour'. By the author of 'Work for all' ... etc. Published under the direction of the Committee of general literature and education appointed by the S.P.C.K. S.P.C.K., [1864]. HU

D1281 STORIES. (1820) Stories selected from the history of Scotland, for children ... 3rd ed., J. Harris, 1825. HU

D1282 STOWE, Harriet Elizabeth, *formerly* Beecher, 1811–1896. Little foxes; or, the little failings which mar domestic happiness. Author's ed., rev., Bell & Daldy, [etc.], 1866. LEE

D1283 [STRETCH, L. M.]. (1770) The beauties of history; or, pictures of virtue and vice, drawn from real life; designed for the instruction and amusement of youth. T. Lewis, 1817. LEI

D1284 [STRETTON, Hesba, *pseud.*, i.e. Sarah Smith], 1832–1911. (1866 serial) Jessica's first prayer. By the author of 'Fern's Hollow', etc. R.T.S., [1867?]. [Inscription dated 1869.] LEI

D1285 STRICKLAND, Agnes, 1796–1874. Historical tales of illustrious British children. New ed., Jarrold & son, [1848?]. HU

D1286 STRICKLAND, Agnes, *ed.* Fisher's juvenile scrap-book, 1838. By Agnes Strickland and Bernard Barton. Fisher, [1837?]. LEI

D1287 STUBBS, Amelia. Family tales for children. Wm. Darton, [1824]. HU

Study of history rendered easy. *See* Fletcher, Ann, *and others*

D1288 SULLIVAN, Robert, 1800–1868. (17th ed., 1852) An attempt to simplify English grammar; with observations on the method of teaching it. 57th ed., Dublin, M. & J. Sullivan, 1864. HU

D1289 SULLIVAN, Robert. Geography generalized; or, an introduction to the study of geography on the principles of classification and comparison ... 12th ed., Dublin, W. Curry, jr., 1849. OX

D1290 SUMMER rambles, illustrative of the pleasures derived from the study of natural history. London, Hamilton, Adams & co.; Liverpool, D. Marples; 1834. LEI

D1291 SUNDAY afternoons with Mamma. A book for very little children. By the author of 'A visit to Aunt Agnes'. R.T.S., [1866]. LEI

Sunday enjoyments. *See* Lea, T.

D1292 SUNDAY. (1801) The Sunday school library, containing ... select tracts ... forming a series of religious instruction from infancy to youth ... Williams, 1801. ReU

D1293 SUNDAY SCHOOL UNION. The child's own magazine for 1864, 1865. The Union. LEI

D1294 SUNDAY SCHOOL UNION. Reading book. Part 1. [1830]. NoU

D1295 SUNDAY SCHOOL UNION. (182–?) Spelling book, published for the use of Sunday schools. Part 4. Davis, & Hamilton, [*c.* 1845?]. LEE

D1296 SUNDAY SCHOOL UNION. Sunday-school tracts, nos. 1–62. W. Kent, [1806–1811]. HU

D1297 SURENNE, Gabriel. A new pronouncing French primer. 1847. RE

D1298 SWEETS for leisure hours. Dean & Munday, [18–]. NoU

D1299 TAILLARD, Constant. Guide de la jeunesse, ou entretiens d'un professeur sur l'histoire et la morale. Paris, Caillot, 1834. LO

D1300 TAINSH, Edward Campbell. Mr. Johnston's school; or, the new master. Warne, [1867?]. LEI

D1301 TALES. (1821) Tales of the academy ... Series 1. Cowie, [etc.], 1821. LEI

Tales of the hermitage. *See* Pilkington, M.

D1302 TALLIS's illustrated scripture history for the improvement of youth. By the editor of Sturm's Family devotions, etc. [Part 1]. London & New York, J. Tallis, [*c.* 1850?]. LEI

D1303 TAYLOR, *Mrs.* Ann, 1757–1830. (1816) The present of a mistress to a young servant: consisting of friendly advice and real histories ... 7th ed., Taylor & Hessey, 1822. LO

D1304 TAYLOR, *Mrs.* Ann, and TAYLOR, Jane. (1817) Correspondence between a mother and her daughter at school. 2nd ed., Taylor & Hessey, 1817. HU LEI LO; 4th ed., Taylor & Hessey, 1818. LEE

D1305 [TAYLOR, Ann, *aft. Mrs.* Gilbert], 1782–1866, and TAYLOR, Jane. (1810?) Hymns for infant minds. By the authors of 'Original poems', ... etc. 12th ed., Holdsworth, 1820. LEE

D1306 [TAYLOR, Ann, and TAYLOR, Jane]. (1806) Rhymes for the nursery. By the authors of 'Original poems'. 6th ed. [incomplete]. ReU; new ed, rev., R. Clarke, 1852. HU; new ed., 1854. ReU

D1307 [TAYLOR, Ann] *and others.* (1804–1805) Original poems, for infant minds. By several young persons. Vol. 1 [only]. 11th ed., 1811. ReU; 1823. 2 vols. ReU; new ed., rev., Harvey & Darton, [1836?]. 2 vols. LEI; Vol. 1. New rev. ed., Harvey & Darton, 1839, [&] Vol. 2, 27th ed., Harvey & Darton, 1834. HU; 1854, 2 vols. ReU; new ed. Vol. 2. Hall, Virtue & co., 1856. NO; authors' complete ed., [1875]. NoU

D1308 TAYLOR, Charles. A familiar treatise on drawing, for youth . . . 1820. NoU

D1309 TAYLOR, Emily, 1795–1872. (1835) The boy and the birds. Harvey & Darton, 1840. LEI

D1310 TAYLOR, Emily. (1821) Historical prints, representing some of the most memorable events in English history . . . with descriptions by E. Taylor. Harvey & Darton, 1821. LEI NoU

D1311 TAYLOR, Isaac, 1759–1829, *of Ongar.* (1818) Advice to the teens; or, practical help towards the formation of one's character. 2nd ed., Fenner, 1818. LEE; 3rd ed., Baldwin, Cradock & Joy, [182–?]. LEI; 4th ed., Baldwin, Cradock & Joy, 1825. NoU SH

D1312 TAYLOR, Isaac. (1829) The mine. 4th ed., Harris, 1832. (The little library, vol. 1.) LEI; 5th ed., Harris, 1834. NoU

D1313 TAYLOR, Isaac. (1820) Scenes in Africa, for the amusement and instruction of little tarry-at-home travellers. 4th ed., Harris, 1824. LEE

D1314 TAYLOR, Isaac. (1821) Scenes in America . . . 2nd ed., Harris, 1822. ReU; 3rd ed., Harris, 1824. LEE

D1315 TAYLOR, Isaac. (1819) Scenes in Asia . . . 2nd ed., Harris, 1821. ReU

D1316 TAYLOR, Isaac. (1818) Scenes in Europe . . . 4th ed., Harris, 1821. LEI; 8th ed., Harris, 1825. LEE

D1317 TAYLOR, Isaac. (1830) Scenes of commerce, by land and sea; or, 'Where does it come from?' answered . . . 3rd ed., Harris, 1839. NoU; 4th ed., 1845. NoU

D1318 TAYLOR, Isaac. (1817) Self-cultivation recommended; or, hints to a youth leaving school. 5th ed., 1825. NoU

D1319 TAYLOR, Isaac. (1824) Beginnings of biography. Harris, 1824. 2 vols. NoU

D1320 TAYLOR, Jane, 1783–1824. (1824) The contributions of Q.Q. 10th ed., Jackson & Walford, 1845. [Contributions to *Youth's magazine.* Edited by Isaac Taylor, of Stanford Rivers.] LEI

D1321 TAYLOR, Jane. (1816) Essays in rhyme, on morals and manners. Taylor & Hessey, 1816. HU

TAYLOR, Jane, 1783–1824, *joint author. See* Taylor, *Mrs.* Ann, and Taylor, Jane; Taylor, Ann, and Taylor, Jane; Taylor, Ann, *and others*

D1322 TAYLOR, Jefferys, 1792–1853. (1818) Harry's holiday; or, the doings of one who had nothing to do. 2nd ed., Baldwin, Cradock & Joy, 1819. LEI; 3rd ed., Baldwin, Cradock & Joy, 1822. ReU

D1323 TAYLOR, Jefferys. (1832) A new description of the earth. 1832. ReU

D1324 TAYLOR, Jefferys. (1822) Tales and dialogues, in prose and verse. Holdsworth, 1822. HU

D1325 TAYLOR, Joseph, 1761/2–1844. Anecdotes of remarkable insects; selected from natural history, and interspersed with poetry. Baldwin, Cradock & Joy, 1817. LEI

D1326 TAYLOR, Samuel, *fl.* 1786–1816. (1786) Taylor improved. Universal stenography, or a new and practical system of short hand writing . . . By William Harding. For the use of schools . . . New [10th] ed., enl. and impr., Simpkin & Marshall, [pref. 1830]. LEI

D1327 TAYLOR, William Cooke, 1800–1849, *ed.* Pinnock's Epitome of classical geography. New ed., revised and improved by W. C. Taylor. 1827. NoU

D1328 TAYLOR, W. C., *ed.* Pinnock's improved edition of Dr. Goldsmith's History of Greece . . . Revised . . . By W. C. Taylor. 13th ed., Whittaker, 1838. BI

D1329 TAYLOR, W. C., *ed.* Whittaker's improved edition of Pinnock's Goldsmith's History of England . . . by W. C. Taylor, continued by W. H. Pinnock . . . 43rd ed., Whittaker, 1854. LO; new rev. ed., Whittaker, 1865. LEI

D1330 The TEACHER'S offering; or, Sunday school monthly visitor. Edited by J. Campbell. New series. Vol. 1 [Jan.–Dec. 1828]. Westley & Davis, 1828. [Imperfect.] NoU

D1331 The TEACHING parrot for children. 1802. NoU

TEACHWELL, *Mrs., pseud. See* Fenn, Eleanor

D1332 TEGETMEIER, William Bernhard, 1816–1912. First lines of botany, comprising the structure of plants, and the tribes of plants. Darton & co., [*c.* 1860?]. [Inscription dated 1862.] LEI

D1333 TEGG, Thomas, 1776–1845. The young man's book of knowledge . . . 6th ed., enl., Sherwood, [etc.], 1817. LEI

D1334 TEGG's magazine of knowledge and amusement. Vol. 1, 1844. [First two numbers have title: Tegg's London magazine.] LEI

D1335 The TEN commandments. [A child's writing sheet.] [18–?]. NoU

D1336 THACKWRAY, *Mrs.* A grammatical catechism. 2nd ed., 1813. NoU

Théâtre pour servir à l'éducation. *See* Genlis, *comtesse de*

D1337 THIRD book of lessons for the use of schools. Routledge, 1826. (Irish national school books.) HU

D1338 THOMSON, Andrew. Elements of chronology and history. 1827. NoU

D1339 THREDDER, *Master.* [Manuscript arithmetic book, written at Morden Hall boarding school, Surrey, conducted by Mr. Thomas N. White. With view of school. *c.* 1820?] LEI

D1340 THREE. (1812) The Three birth-days. 4th ed., J. & E. Wallis, [181–?]. ReU

THURTLE, Frances, *aft. Mrs.* Jamieson. *See* Jamieson, F.

D1341 TIARKS, Johann Gerhardt. (1835) A progressive German reader. 7th ed., Nutt, 1852. LO

D1342 TIBBINS, J. The learner's first book. Nach dem ... Werke J. Tibbins für Deutsche bearbeitet von H. Jensch. Arnsberg, Ritter, 1845. LEI

D1343 [TIMPSON, *Rev.* Thomas]. Companion to the Bible. Intended for Bible classes, families, and young persons in general. New ed., R.T.S., [*c.* 1845?]. [Maps dated 1845.] HU

D1344 TODD, John, 1800–1873. The daughter at school. Nelson, 1853. LEI; Nelson, 1860. HU

D1345 TODD, John. (1834–1858; series 1–2) Lectures to children, familiarly illustrating important truth. Second series. Routledge, [pref. 1859]. LEI

D1346 TODD, John. (G.B. ed. 1836) The student's guide: designed ... to aid in forming and strengthening the intellectual and moral characters and habits of students in every profession. Revised by the Rev. Thomas Dale. 2nd ed., Seeley, 1837. [Also has title: The student's manual.] LEI

D1347 TODHUNTER, Isaac, 1820–1884. (1858) Algebra for the use of colleges and schools ... New ed., Macmillan, 1879. LEI

D1348 TODHUNTER, Isaac. (1859) Plane trigonometry for the use of colleges and schools ... 7th ed., Macmillan, 1878. LEI

D1349 TODHUNTER, Isaac. (1866) Trigonometry for beginners; with numerous examples. Macmillan, repr. 1889. HU

Tom Brown at Oxford. *See* Hughes, Thomas

D1350 TOM THUMB. The surprising adventures of Tom Thumb. Glasgow, [18–?]. NoU

D1351 TOM THUMB's play book. New ed., Alnwick, [18–?]. NoU

D1352 TOMKINS, Thomas, 1743–1816. (1806) Rays of genius, collected to enlighten the rising generation. Longman, [etc.], 1806. 2 vols. LEI

D1353 TOWN. (1824) Town and country tales. Intended for the amusement and moral instruction of youth. Territt, 1824. LEE

D1354 TOY-SHOP. (*c.* 1788?) The Toy-shop; or, sentimental preceptor. 1830. ReU [Based on the farce by R. Dodsley.]

D1355 TRAVELLER. (1820) The Traveller; or, an entertaining journey round the habitable globe; being a novel and easy method of studying geography ... 2nd ed. J. Harris, [1820]. HU; 3rd ed., J. Harris. [1820.] BR

Travels at home. *See* Lloyd, Charles

D1356 TRAVELS in Africa. 1831. NoU

D1357 TRAVELS in Northern Asia; compiled from authentic sources. Dublin, Bentham, 1823. LEE

D1358 TRAVELS in South-Eastern Asia, compiled from the most authentic and recent sources. Dublin, Jones, 1823. LEE

Travels of Rolando. *See* Jauffret, L. F.

D1358a A TREATISE on mensuration for the use of schools. Published by direction of the Commissioners of national education in Ireland. 2nd ed., Dublin, The Commissioners, 1850. BR

D1359 TREDGOLD, Thomas, 1788–1829. Elementary principles of carpentry. Weale, 1840. LO

D1360 TRIAL. (1822) The trial of skill; or, which is the best story? N. Hailes, 1822. 2 vols. [Preface signed Humphrey Arden.] LEI

D1361 TRIMMER, Jane. (1820?) Miscellaneous stories for children. Collected by Jane Trimmer. Lacey, [*c.* 1820]. LEE LEI

D1362 TRIMMER, *Mrs.* Mary, *pseud.* A natural history of the most remarkable quadrupeds, birds, fishes, serpents, reptiles, and insects. Chiswick, Whittingham for T. Tegg, [etc.], 1826. 2 vols. [Portion dealing with quadrupeds was published 1803. Largely adapted from Bewick.] HU; Chiswick, Whittingham, pr., 1830. 2 vols. NoU

D1363 TRIMMER, *Mrs.* Sarah, 1741–1810. (1786) The charity school spelling book. Part 1. 10th ed., Rivington, 1807. RE; Part 1, for girls. New ed., Rivington, 1818. LEI; Part 1, for boys. New ed., Rivington, 1818. LEI

D1364 TRIMMER, *Mrs.* Sarah. The charity school spelling book. Part 2. New ed., Rivington, 1818. LEI

D1365 TRIMMER, *Mrs.* Sarah. (1780) An easy introduction to the knowledge of nature and reading of the Holy Scriptures, adapted to the capacities of children. 11th ed., J. Johnson, 1802. ReU; 17th ed., 1825. NoU

D1366 TRIMMER, *Mrs.* Sarah. Introduction à la connaissance de la nature, et à la lecture de l'écriture sainte. Traduite de la 3ème éd. par C. Gros ... Londres, 1837. NoU

D1367 TRIMMER, *Mrs.* Sarah. (1786) Fabulous histories. Designed for the instruction of children, respecting their treatment of animals. 8th ed., 1809. ReU; 11th ed., Rivington, 1821. NoU; new ed., 1838. ReU; Scott, Webster & Geary, 1840. LEE

D1368 TRIMMER, *Mrs.* Sarah. do., *with title:* The story of the robins, designed to teach children the proper treatment of animals. Warne, 1870. LEI; Warne, 1873. NO; Griffith & Farran, [187–?]. NE

D1369 TRIMMER, *Mrs.* Sarah. The history of England written for young persons. New edition by Mrs. Milner. 1849. NoU

D1370 TRIMMER, *Mrs.* Sarah. (1788–1789 serial) Instructive tales. 3rd ed., Rivington, 1815. HU

D1371 TRIMMER, *Mrs.* Sarah. A selection from Mrs. Trimmer's Instructive tales. Rivington for S.P.C.K., 1823. 6 vols. LEI

D1372 TRIMMER, *Mrs.* Sarah. (1786–1788) (Prints with descriptions, as below):

(*a*) [Ancient history]. A new series of prints, accompanied by easy lessons, containing a general outline of antient history. 1803. 2 vols. NoU

(*b*) [do.] A series of prints designed to illustrate the ancient history. Baldwin, Cradock & Joy, 1828. LEI

(*c*) [do.] A description of a set of prints of ancient history, contained in a set of easy lessons. 1817. NoU

(*d*) [do.] New and comprehensive lessons; containing a general outline of antient history. Harris, 1814. BR; Harris, 1820. NoU; Harris, 1825. LEI

(e) [English history]. A series of prints designed to illustrate the English history. Baldwin, Cradock & Joy, 1821. LEI

(f) [do.] A description of a set of prints of English history, contained in a set of easy lessons. Baldwin, Cradock & Joy, 1823. 2 vols. LEI

(g) [Roman history]. A new series of prints, accompanied by easy lessons, containing a general outline of Roman history. 1803–1804. 2 vols. NoU

(h) [do.] New and comprehensive lessons; containing a general outline of the Roman history; with forty engravings. J. Harris, [etc.], 1835. LEI

(i) [Scripture. O.T.]. A new series of prints, accompanied by easy lessons; being an improved edition of the first set of scripture prints from the Old Testament. J. Harris, [etc.], 1808. 2 vols. LEI

(j) [do. do.] Scripture lessons: designed to accompany a series of prints from the Old Testament. Baldwin, Cradock & Joy, [etc.], 1821. BR

(k) [Scripture. N.T.]. A new series of prints, accompanied by easy lessons: consisting of subjects taken from the New Testament. 1811. 2 vols. HU

(l) [do. do.] A series of prints taken from the New Testament... 1817. 2 vols. ReU

D1373 TRIMMER, Mrs. Sarah. (1782–1784?) Sacred history, selected from the Scriptures... 7th ed., Rivington, [etc.], 1817. 6 vols. LEI

D1374 TRIMMER, Mrs. Sarah. (2nd ed., 1787) The servant's friend, an exemplary tale; designed to reinforce the religious instruction given at Sunday and other charity schools... New ed., Rivington for S.P.C.K., 1824. LEI

D1375 TRIMMER, Mrs. Sarah. [Teacher's assistant] Lessons extracted from The Teacher's assistant. By Mrs. Trimmer. Designed for the use of the National Society's central and other schools. Rivington, 1826. LEI

D1376 TRIMMER, Mrs. Sarah. Questions adapted to Lessons extracted from The Teacher's assistant ... Rivington, 1821. LEI

D1377 TRIMMER, Mrs. Sarah. (1787) The two farmers, an exemplary tale... New ed., corr., Rivington for S.P.C.K., 1826. LEI

D1378 TRIMMER, Mrs. Sarah, ed. (1805?) The ladder to learning: a collection of fables; arranged progressively in words of one, two, and three syllables; with original morals. Edited and improved by Mrs. Trimmer. 16th ed., Harris, 1841. LEI; 17th ed., Grant & Griffith, 1845. HU

D1379 TROTTER, Alexander. (1858) Arithmetic for advanced classes... New ed., Edinburgh, Oliver & Boyd, [1883?]. LEI

True stories, or interesting anecdotes. See Frank, Elizabeth

True stories from English history. See Budden, Maria E.

TRUEMAN, Thomas, pseud. See Hanway, Jonas

D1380 TRUSLER, John, 1753–1820. (1775?) The accomplished gentleman; or, principles of politeness, and of knowing the world... Dublin, Richardson, [1847?]. [Abridgment of Chesterfield's Letters.] HU

D1381 [TUCKER, Charlotte Maria], 1821–1893. (1866?) Fairy Know-a-bit. By A.L.O.E. Nelson, 1867. [Cover title: A nut-shell of knowledge.] NE

D1382 [TUCKER, C. M.]. (1857) The rambles of a rat. By A.L.O.E. Nelson, 1857. HU

D1383 [TURNER, Elizabeth], d. 1846. (1811) The cowslip; or, more cautionary stories, in verse. 16th ed., 1836. ReU; 26th ed., [1885?]. NoU; Leadenhall Pr., [1899?]. NoU

D1384 [TURNER, Elizabeth]. (1807) The daisy; or, cautionary stories in verse. Adapted to the ideas of children from four to eight years old. 18th ed., [183–]. ReU; Leadenhall Press, 1899/1900. LEI

D1385 TURNER, Richard, 1753–1788. (1783?) An easy introduction to the arts and sciences... 10th ed. with additions, Johnson, [etc.], 1804. LEI NoU

D1386 TURNER, Richard. (1780) A new and easy introduction to universal geography and the use of globes... 14th ed. Rivington, [etc.], 1810. SH

D1387 TURNER, William Coham. [Two copybooks, completed at Bray's Academy, Barnstaple, in 1836 and 1838.] HU

D1388 TYTLER, Alexander Fraser, lord Woodhouselee, 1747–1813. (1801) Elements of general history, ancient and modern... A new edition... brought down to the commencement of the year 1862. For the use of schools and private students. Edinburgh, Oliver & Boyd, [etc.], 1862. LEI

D1389 TYTLER, Ann Fraser. (1838) Mary and Florence; or, grave and gay. 7th ed., Hatchard, 1844. LEI

Uncle Philip's conversations with children. See Hawks, Francis Lister.

D1390 UNDERWOOD, J. W., ed. Mitchell's easy introduction to the writing of Latin exercises. New ed., carefully corrected, altered, and improved, by J. W. Underwood. J. Souter, 1838. HU

D1391 UTILITY. (1815) Utility; or, sketches of domestic education. By the author of 'Simple pleasures', the 'Young botanists', etc. Darton, Harvey & Darton, 1815. HU LEI

D1392 [VALPY, Edward], 1764–1832. (1803) Elegantiae Latinae; or, rules and exercises illustrative of elegant Latin style; intended for the use of the higher classes of grammar schools. 2nd ed., Reading, R. Snare & co., 1804. HU

VAN BEMMELEN, J. See Bemmelen, J. van

D1393 VAUX, Frances Bowyer. (1816) Domestic pleasures; or, the happy fire-side Illustrated by interesting conversations. Darton, Harvey & Darton, 1816. HU

D1394 VAUX, F. B. (1817) The happy travellers; or, a trip to France. For the amusement of young persons. Darton, Harvey & Darton, 1817. LEI

Veillées du château. See Genlis, comtesse de

D1395 VENERONI, Giovanni [otherwise Jean Vigneron], 1642–1708. (Eng. 1729) The complete Italian master; containing the best and easiest rules for attaining that language. Wingrave, 1814. LO

D1396 VENERONI, Giovanni. Grammaire française et italienne de Véneroni . . . corrigée et augmentée . . . par Romualdo Zotti. London, Author [i.e. editor], 1804–1805. 2 vols. LO

D1397 VENNING, Mary Anne. (1817) A geographical present; being descriptions of the principal countries of the world. 3rd ed. Harvey & Darton, 1820. ReU

D1398 VERSES and hymns for little children. W. Foster, & C. Gilpin, [c. 1840?] [pre-1845]. LEI

D1399 VIEYRA, Antonio. (1767) A new Portuguese grammar. 7th ed. Wingrave, 1809. LO

VIGNERON, Jean. See Veneroni, Giovanni

Village school. See Kilner, Dorothy

D1400 VINES, C. A key to Keith's Treatise on the globes . . . S. Brooke, pr., for the author, 1820. LEI

D1401 VIRGILIUS MARO, Publius. Opera; ad fidem optimorum exemplarium castigata. Ed. nona. A. J. Valpy for G. B. Whittaker, [etc.], 1828. LEI

Visit. See Grierson, Miss

D1402 VISIT. (1804) A visit to a farm house . . . By S.W. See D1408 W., S.

D1403 VISIT. (1808) A visit to London . . . by S.W. See D1409 W., S.

D1404 VISITS to an infant school. J. Mardon, 1832. LEI

D1405 VOYAGE autour du monde, ou, revue pittoresque des différentes nations qui peuplent le globe. Tome troisième: Afrique. 2e éd. Paris, A. René, pr., [1820?]. LEI

D1406 [W., E.]. A history of my pet animals, during a year's residence in the country; in a series of letters, addressed to my niece Selina. 2nd ed., rev. and corr., W. Darton, [c. 1830]. LEE

D1407 [W., S.]. (2nd ed., 1803) A puzzle for a curious girl . . . 3rd ed., Phillips, 1810. [Incomplete.] ReU; 5th ed., Baldwin, Cradock & Joy, 1818. LEI

D1408 W., S. (1804) A visit to a farm house . . . 5th ed., Phillips, 1811. NoU; 6th ed., W. Darton, jr., 1815. ReU

D1409 W., S. (1808) A visit to London; by the author of A Visit to a farm-house. New ed., 1813. NoU

W.B. See B., W.

D1410 WAKEFIELD, Eliza. Five hundred charades, from history, geography, and biography. J. W. Parker, 1835. LEI

D1411 WAKEFIELD, Mrs. Priscilla, 1751–1832. Domestic recreation; or, dialogues illustrative of natural and scientific subjects. 1805. ReU; 1806. NoU

D1412 WAKEFIELD, Mrs. Priscilla. (1811) Instinct displayed in a collection of well authenticated facts. 2nd ed., Darton, Harvey & Darton, 1814. ReU; 4th ed., 1821. NoU

D1413 WAKEFIELD, Mrs. Priscilla. (1796) An introduction to botany, in a series of familiar letters. 5th ed., Darton & Harvey, 1807. LEE; 7th ed., Darton, Harvey & co., [etc.], 1816. LEI

D1414 WAKEFIELD, Mrs. Priscilla. (1801) The juvenile travellers; containing the remarks of a family during a tour through the principal states and kingdoms of Europe . . . 6th ed., Darton & Harvey, 1808. LEI; 14th ed., Harvey & Darton, 1824. ReU; 16th ed., 1832. NoU

D1415 WAKEFIELD, Mrs. Priscilla. (1794–1796) Leisure hours; or, entertaining dialogues . . . designed as lessons of morality for youth. 5th ed., Darton, 1812. LEI NoU; 7th ed., Harvey & Darton, 1821. ReU

D1416 WAKEFIELD, Mrs. Priscilla. (1794) Mental improvement; or, the beauties and wonders of nature and art. Three volumes in one, arranged as a series of instructive conversations. New ed., improved by Edward Emerson. G. Bingley, [18–]. LEI

D1417 WALKER, John, 1732–1807. (1801) The teacher's assistant in English composition; or, easy rules for writing themes and composing exercises on subjects proper for the improvement of youth of both sexes at school. Printed for the author, and sold by G. G. & J. Robinson, and Cadell & Davies, 1801. HU

D1418 WALKER, John. [do., with title]: English themes and essays; or, the teacher's assistant in composition . . . 2nd ed., enl., J. Johnson, [etc.], 1805. LEI; 8th ed., Cadell, [etc.], 1832. HU

D1419 WALKER, John, 1759–1830. (3rd ed., 1800) Elements of geography, and of natural and civil history . . . 4th ed. carefully revised and enlarged by . . . Thomas Smith. J. Walker, [etc.], 1805. BR

D1420 WALKER, John. [Atlas of maps engraved for Walker's Geography]. No place, [c. 1800]. NoU

D1421 WALKER, John, 1768–1833. The philosophy of arithmetic, (considered as a branch of mathematical science) and the elements of algebra: designed for the use of schools, and in aid of private instruction. Dublin, R. Napper, pr., 1812. HU

D1422 WALKINGAME, Francis, 1723?–1783. A treatise on arithmetic . . . Revised by R. Langford . . . 1824. NoU

D1423 WALKINGAME, Francis. (1751) The tutor's assistant: being a compendium of arithmetic . . . 55th ed., with additions and corrections. Scatcherd & Letterman, 1818. HU; 62nd ed., 1823. NoU; another ed., 1826. ReU; 71st ed., Longman, 1832. NoU; 74th ed. . . . by J. Fraser. 1837. NoU; new ed., [ed.] by T. Crosby. York, T. Wilson, 1840. HU; Crosby's new ed., with considerable additions. York, Wilson, 1841. LEE; new ed., [18–]. NoU

D1424 [WALLACE, R.], ed. Cassell's Popular educator. See D214 Cassell, pub.

D1425 WALLIS, E., publisher. European travellers: an instructive game. E. Wallis, n.d. [between 1818 and 1840?]. LEI

D1426 WALLIS, E. (1794) Wallis's Tour through England and Wales, a new geographical pastime. Wallis, [1802?]. NoU

D1427 WALLIS, J., *publisher*. Wallis's new geographical game exhibiting a tour through Europe. J. Wallis, 1811. [Map in case only.] LEI

D1428 WANOSTROCHT, Nicolas, 1745–1812. (1780) A grammar of the French language, with practical exercises. 10th ed., corr., J. Johnson, [etc.], 1807. HU

D1429 WANOSTROCHT, Nicolas. (5th ed., 1797) Recueil choisi de traits historiques et de contes moraux; avec la signification des mots en anglois au bas de chaque page. A l'usage des jeunes gens . . . qui veulent apprendre le françois. Nlle. éd., revue, corrigée et augmentée par Vincent Wanostrocht. Londres, Longman, [etc.], 1833. LEI

D1430 [WARD, Mr. —]. (1860?) The guide to English literature; with an account of the principal English writers and their works, arranged in simple language in the form of question and answer. 2nd ed., Simpkin, Marshall, [etc.], 1862. LEI

D1431 WARD, *Mrs.* Catherine G. Cottage stories; or, tales of my grandmother. For the amusement and improvement of young ladies . . . Newman, 1817. LEI

D1432 [WARD, E.]. (1853) Boys and their rulers; or, what we do at school. N. Cooke, 1853. LEI

D1433 [WARD, John], *grammarian, ed.* (1732) A short introduction of grammar generally to be used . . . Printed for W. Lily and John Ward, [actually printed by Edward Baines, Leeds], [*c.* 180–]. LEI

D1434 WARD, *Hon. Mrs.* M. Microscopic teachings: descriptions of various objects of especial interest and beauty adapted for microscopic observation . . . Groombridge, 1864. HU

D1435 [WARD, *Mrs.* R.]. (1828) The child's guide to knowledge: being a collection of useful and familiar questions and answers on every-day subjects . . . By a lady. [1st ed. had title: 262 questions and answers.] 7th ed., 1836. NoU; 9th ed., 1839. NoU; 37th ed., enl., Simpkin, Marshall, 1865. LEI; 44th ed., 1870. NoU; 49th ed., Simpkin, Marshall, 1875. HU; 57th ed., enl., Simpkin, Marshall, 1888. LEI

WARNER, Susan, 1819–1885. *See* Wetherell, Elizabeth, *pseud.*

D1436 [WATKINS, Henry George]. Affectionate advice to apprentices, on their being bound. Presented by the bailiffs, wardens, and assistants of the worshipful company of weavers. Weavers' co., [183–?]. LEI

D1437 WATKINS, H. G. Affectionate advice to apprentices and other young persons engaged in trades or professions. 10th ed., Seeleys, 1852. BI

D1438 WATKINS, John, *fl.* 1792–1831, *ed.* Goldsmith's History of England . . . With a continuation to . . . 1825 by J. Watkins. Fisher, 1832. LEI

D1439 WATSON, William. (1829) Watson's Tutor's assistant; or, complete school arithmetic: on a plan peculiarly calculated to facilitate the improvement of the pupil, and reduce the labour of the teacher . . . New ed., London, Simpkin, Marshall; Beverley, W. B. Johnson; [1845]. HU

D1440 WATTON, Timothy. [10 historical charts, in 1 vol. Birmingham, 185–?]. NoU

D1441 WATTON, Timothy. Chief events of English history. Whittaker, [1868?]. [Folding chart.] HU

WATTS, *Mrs.* Alaric. *See* Watts, Priscilla Maden

D1442 WATTS, Isaac, 1674–1748. (1715) Divine and moral songs for children. Stereotype ed., A. Wilson, 1811. HU; R.T.S., 1841. LEE

D1443 WATTS, Isaac. Divine songs attempted in easy language for the use of children. Rivington for S.P.C.K., 1821. LEI

D1444 WATTS, Isaac. The first set of catechisms and prayers; or, the religion of little children under seven years of age. Collected out of the larger book of Prayers and catechisms for children and youth. Wellington (Salop), Houlston, [*c.* 1810]. LEI; Derby, —, 1839. NoU

D1445 WATTS, Isaac. The golden rule. Abridged from Dr. Watts. R.T.S., [183–?] (Tract no. 13). LEI; The golden rule: an abstract from Dr. Isaac Watts. Liverpool, R.T.S., [185–?]. ReU

D1446 WATTS, Isaac. The historical catechism for children and youth. Woodbridge, Pite, 1851. LEI

D1447 WATTS, Isaac. (1728) Prayers composed for the use and imitation of children; suited to their different ages and their various occasions. Together with Instructions to youth in the duty of prayer . . . Derby, H. Mozley, [*c.* 1820?]. LEI

D1448 WATTS, Priscilla Maden, 'Mrs. Alaric Watts', 1797–1873, *ed.* The New year's gift, and juvenile souvenir, 1830. Edited by Mrs. Alaric Watts. Longman, [etc.], 1830. NoU

D1449 WAUTHIER, J. M. (1815) The geographical institutions; or, a set of classical and analytical tables; forming a complete course of gradual lessons in ancient and modern geography. First part . . . 3rd ed., G. Schulze, pr., for the author, 1820. [With] A short treatise on the sphere . . . Adapted to the capacity of youth. Second part. Schulze & Dean, pr., 1815. LEI

D1450 The WAY to reading made easy, or the child's first book . . . New ed., Birmingham, —, 1811. NoU

D1451 A WEEK well spent. Liverpool, R.T.S., [18–]. (Tract no. 107.) ReU

D1452 WEIR, Harrison, *illus. See* D246 Children's picture fable-book

D1453 WESLEY, John, 1703–1791. Works . . . Vol. 14. 11th ed., J. Mason, 1856. [Contents include: A short English grammar; A short French grammar; A short Latin grammar; A short Greek grammar; A short Hebrew grammar; A compendium of logic.] HU

D1454 WEST, Henry Aspinall, *ed.* Dr. Calcott's [*sic*] Grammar of music . . . 12th ed., carefully revised by H. A. West. Davidson, [*c.* 1860?]. LEI

D1455 [WEST, *Mrs.* Jane], 1758–1852. The sorrows of selfishness; or, the history of Miss Richmore. By Mrs. Prudentia Homespun, [pseud.]. Harris, 1812. NoU

D1456 WETHERELL, Elizabeth, *pseud.* [i.e. Susan Warner]. (1860) Say and seal, by the author of 'Wide, wide world' and 'Dollars and cents'. Bentley, 1860. NE

D1457 [WHITAKER, George], *ed.* Florilegium poeticum. 1840. *See* D477 Florilegium

D1458 WHITE, Henry, 1812–1880. (1849) History of Great Britain and Ireland; with an account of the present state and resources of the United Kingdom and its colonies. For the use of schools and private students. 7th ed., Edinburgh, Oliver & Boyd, 1855. HU

D1459 WHITE, John, *teacher, of Edinburgh.* (c. 1830) An abstract of general geography, comprehending a more minute description of the British Empire; and of Palestine . . . For the use of junior classes. 141st ed., rev., Edinburgh, W. Whyte & co., [etc.], [185–]. HU

D1460 WIGGINS, Richard. The New-York expositor, or fifth book; being a collection of the most useful words in the English language . . . New York, Wood, 1811. LEI

D1461 WILKINS, Henry Musgrave. (1857) A manual of Latin prose composition for the use of schools and private students. 9th ed., Longmans, 1874. HU

D1462 WILKS, Samuel Charles. Rosebuds rescued, and presented to my children. [Poems.] J. W. Parker, 1835. LEI

D1463 WILLCOLKES, *Dr. —.* Dr. Willcolkes's new and much admired system of arithmetic and mental calculations. Derby, Mozley, 1832. NoU

D1464 WILLCOLKES, *Dr. —.* The united new and much admired system of arithmetic and mental calculations, of Dr. Willcolkes and Messrs. T. and T. W. Fryer . . . 7th ed., enl. and rev., Derby, Mozley, pr.; London, Longmans; 1840. HU

D1465 WILLIAM Bryant, or the folly of superstitious fears. W. Kent, 1806. (Sunday school tracts, 4.) HU; [1806?]. NoU

D1466 [WILLIAMS, Charles], 1796–1866. (1836) The adventures of a coal-mine. By Henry Harcourt, [pseud.]. Westley & Davis, 1836. BI

D1467 WILLIAMS, Charles. Visible history: England. Westley & Davis, 1835. LEE

D1468 WILLIAMS, E. A catalogue of schoolbooks . . . printed by E. Williams . . . at Eton College . . . Eton, Williams, [18–]. NoU

D1469 WILLIAMS, *Mrs.* Helen Maria, 1762–1827. (1817) A summary method of teaching children to read; upon the principle originally discovered by the Sieur Berthaud . . . Author, 1817. LEE

D1470 WILLIAMS, *Mrs.* H. M. [do., *with title*]: Syllabic spelling; or, a summary method of teaching children to read . . . 5th ed., Whittaker, Treacher & co., 1830. LEI

D1471 WILLIAMS, Jackson Muspratt, *ed.* (1827?) The elements of Euclid; containing the first six, and the eleventh and twelfth books, chiefly from the text of Dr. Simson. London, C. Tilt; Cambridge, T. Stevenson; 1829. OX

D1472 WILLIAMS, W., *of High Beech collegiate school, Essex.* The new mathematical demonstrations of Euclid, rendered clear and familiar to the minds of youth, with no other mathematical instruments than the triangular pieces commonly called the Chinese puzzle. Author, 1817. LEI

D1473 WILLIE's first drawing lessons. Simple lines of nature, by a lady . . . Bosworth, 1855. LO

WILLIS, Sarah Payson. *See* Parton, Sarah Payson, *Mrs.*

D1474 WILSON, Alexander, *principal of the National Society's training inst., London.* Outlines of English grammar, compiled for the use of National and other schools. 1844. NoU

WILSON, Caroline, *formerly* Fry. *See* Fry, Caroline

D1475 WILSON, J. The youth's reader; or, second book for children . . . 2nd ed., Nottingham, —, 1822. NoU

WILSON, *Mrs.* Sarah, *formerly* Atkins. *See* Atkins, Sarah

WILSON, *Rev.* T., *pseud. See* Clark, Samuel

D1476 WILSON, W. A new dictionary of music. Wm. Hughes, [182–]. HU

D1477 WILSON, *Rev.* William, 1774–1831. (Written 1815) The history of Mr. Moland and little Henry, 1815. Edited and issued . . . by the author's grandson . . . Sir Guy Fleetwood Wilson. Cassell, 1923. LEI

D1478 WILSON, William Carus, 1791–1859, *ed.* The children's friend. Vol. 2, 1825; vols. 12–13, 1835–1836. Kirkby Lonsdale, Foster. LEI

D1480 WINKS, Joseph Foulkes, *comp.* (1834) The British school book, for reading and recitation; being selections of prose and poetry . . . London, Simpkin, Marshall; Leicester, Winks; [1834]. LEI

D1481 WINKS, J. F., *ed.* The little child's picture magazine, in easy words. Vol. 6, 1859. [Lacks first no.] London, Simpkin, Marshall; Leicester, Winks; 1859. LEI

D1482 WISDOM. (3rd ed., 1791) Wisdom in miniature; or, the pleasing instructor; being a collection of sentences, divine, moral, and historical. W. Simpkin & R. Marshall, 1821. LEI

D1483 WITT, Henriette de, *formerly* Guizot, 1829–1908. Enfants et parents: petits tableaux de famille. Paris, Hachette, 1868. LO

D1485 The WONDERS of nature. Nelson, 1857. NO

D1486 The WONDERS of the microscope. [By Sir Richard Phillips?]. R. Phillips, 1811. NoU

D1487 WONDERS. (1805) The Wonders of the telescope; or, a display of the wonders of the heavens and of the systems of the universe . . . adapted particularly to the perusal of young persons . . . [By Sir Richard Phillips?]. R. Phillips, 1805. LEI NoU; new ed., R. Phillips, 1809. NE

D1488 WOOD, James, 1760–1839. (1798) The elements of algebra: designed for the use of students in the university. 3rd ed., Cambridge, Deighton, 1801. [1st ed. had title: The principles of mathematics and natural philosophy.] NoU; 7th ed., Cambridge, Deighton, 1820. LEI

D1489 WOOD, John, b. c. 1850. [Exercise book in arithmetic and mensuration, worked first at Shepley Church School, Yorks., 1864, and then at Shepley British School.] HU

D1490 WOOD, John George, 1827–1889. (1860) The boy's own book of natural history. Routledge, 1904. LEI

D1491 WOOD, J. G., *ed.* Beeton's annual: a book for the young. Edited by S. O. Beeton and the Rev. J. G. Wood. F. Warne & co., 1866. LEI

D1492 [WOODD, Basil], *ed.* (1820) The faith and duty of a Christian ... chiefly selected from the Christian institutes of Bishop Gastrell, designed for the use of young people. New ed., enl., Rivington for S.P.C.K., 1825. LEI

WOODHOUSELEE, Alexander Fraser Tytler, *lord. See* Tytler, Alexander Fraser

D1493 WOODLAND, M. Bear and forbear; or, the history of Julia March. Intended for the use of young ladies. 2nd ed., M. J. Godwin, 1814. LEI

D1494 [WOODWARD, Josiah], *D.D., supposed author.* (1702) Pastoral advice to young persons in order to their being confirmed by the bishop. 20th ed., 1809. NoU

D1495 The WORD book; or, twenty-four stories ... for children under four years of age ... 4th ed. [18–?]. NoU

D1496 A WORD in season. Liverpool, R.T.S., [18–]. ReU

D1497 The WORKING man's friend and family instructor. Vols. 1–2, Jan.–June 1850; vol. 4, Oct.–Dec. 1850; vol. 7, July–Sept. 1851. Cassell. LEI

D1498 WORSLEY, Israel, 1768–1836. (1814) A French delectus; or, sentences and passages ... designed to facilitate a knowledge of the French tongue. 2nd ed., Longman, 1816. LEE

D1499 WRIGHT, George Newenham, 1790?–1877, *ed.* Historical and miscellaneous questions, [by Richmal Mangnall]. New ed., corrected, enlarged and continued to the present time, by G. N. Wright. Tegg, [18–]. NoU

D1500 WRIGHT, G. N., *ed.* A new treatise on the use of globes ... by Thomas Keith. New ed., enlarged and improved by G. N. Wright. Tegg, 1857. LEI

D1501 WRIGHT, Richard, 1764–1836. (1803–1804) Instruction for youth, in a series of lectures on moral and religious subjects ... 2nd ed., Liverpool, Wright, 1819. LEI

D1502 WRIGLEY, Alfred. (1845) A collection of examples and problems in pure and mixed mathematics, with answers and occasional hints. 8th ed., corr., Longmans, 1871. [1st ed. was by A. Wrigley and William H. Johnstone.] HU

D1503 [YONGE, Charlotte Mary], 1823–1901. (1858) The instructive picture book; or, lessons from the vegetable world, by the author of 'The heir of Redclyffe' ... 5th ed., Edinburgh, Edmonston & Douglas, [188–?]. LEI

D1504 [YONGE, C. M.]. (1866) The prince and the page: a story of the last crusade, by the author of 'The heir of Redclyffe'. Macmillan, 1866. NE

York House. *See* Kent, Anna

D1505 YOUNG, John Radford, 1799–1885. An elementary treatise on algebra, theoretical and practical ... Intended for the use of students. J. Souter, 1826. HU

D1506 YOUNG, J. R. Elements of plane and spherical trigonometry, with its applications to the principles of navigation and nautical astronomy ... To which are added some original researches in spherical geometry, by T. S. Davies. J. Souter, 1833. HU

D1507 The YOUNG ladies' useful pocket book, for the year 1811. J. Johnson, [1810]. [Wants some of the diary pages.] HU

D1508 YOUNG. (1809) The young lady's and gentleman's library, consisting of voyages, travels, tales and stories ... Vol. 3 [only, of 6]. Edinburgh, Deas, 1809. NoU

D1509 [The YOUNG man's best companion, and book of general knowledge.] [1813?]. [T.p. wanting. Incomplete.] LEI

D1510 YOUNG. (1837) Young man's own book; a manual of politeness, intellectual improvement, and moral deportment. Halifax, Pohlman, [etc.], 1837. LEI

Young travellers. *See* Jamieson, *Mrs.* Frances

D1511 YOUNG woman's companion and instructor. Manchester, Aston, 1806. LO

D1512 YOUTH'S compendium of information on the arts and advances in life and society. Fletcher, [18–]. [Inscription dated Xmas, 1838.] LEI

D1513 The YOUTH's drawing book complete. No place, [18–?]. NoU

D1514 The YOUTH's instructor and guardian. Vol. 8, 1824; N.S. vol. 9, 1845. LEI

D1515 The YOUTH's magazine; or, evangelical miscellany for the years 1816–1822. New series, vols. 1–7; 4th series, vol. 14, 1851. LEI

D1516 ZOOLOGICAL sketches consisting of descriptions of one hundred and twenty animals. Published under the direction of the Committee of general literature and education. S.P.C.K., 1844. BI

D1517 ZORLIN, Rosina Maria. (1840) Recreations in physical geography ... 2nd ed., rev., Parker, 1842. LEI

SECTION E

Government publications up to and including 1918

Plan of arrangement:

1. British publications:
   - (*a*) Acts of Parliament, individual Acts arranged chronologically;
   - (*b*) Collected legislation;
   - (*c*) Parliamentary debates;
   - (*d*) Sessional papers (except serial publications) arranged chronologically;
   - (*e*) Serial publications and departmental publications, arranged by department.

2. Foreign publications, arranged by country.

1. British publications

Individual Acts, arranged chronologically

E1   1654   An ordinance for the ejecting of scandalous, ignorant and insufficient ministesr [*sic*] and school-masters. Tuesday August 29, 1654.   LEE

E2   1748/49   An act for explaining and amending an act passed in . . . [1743], intituled, 'An act for raising and establishing a fund for a provision for the widows and children of the ministers of the Church of Scotland, and of the heads, principals and masters of the universities of Saint Andrews, Glasgow, and Edinburgh.   22 Geo. II, ch. 21. 1749.   LEI

E3   1802/03   An act for making better provision for the parochial schoolmasters, and for making further regulations for the better government of the parish schools in Scotland.   43 Geo. III, ch. 54. 1803.   SO

E4   1843   Poor law amendment act.   An act for the amendment and better administration of the laws relating to the poor in England and Wales. 4 & 5 Will. IV, ch. 76.   1834.   LO

E5   1847/48   Public health act.   An act for promoting the public health.   11 & 12 Vict., ch. 63. 1848.   LEI

E6   1857/58   Universities (Scotland) act, 1858. An act to make provision for the better government and discipline of the universities of Scotland.   21 & 22 Vict., ch. 83.   LEI;   *see also* E73

E7   1860   Industrial schools (amendment) act. An act to amend the Industrial schools act, 1857.   23 & 24 Vict., ch. 108.   1860.   LEE

E8   1861   Durham university act.   An act for making provision for the good government and extension of the University of Durham.   24 & 25 Vict., ch. 82.   1861.   LEE

E9   1861   Industrial schools act.   An act for amending and consolidating the law relating to industrial schools.   24 & 25 Vict., ch. 113.   1861. LEE

E10   1862   Industrial schools (continuation) act. An act for continuing for a further limited time, etc., orders made under the Industrial schools act, 1861, and the Industrial schools (Scotland) act, 1861.   25 & 26 Vict., ch. 10.   1862.   LEE

E11   1862   Poor law (certified schools) act.   An act to provide for the education and maintenance of pauper children in certain schools and institutions.   25 & 26 Vict., ch. 43.   1862.   LEE

E12   1866   Reformatory schools act.   An act to consolidate and amend the acts relating to reformatory schools in Great Britain.   29 & 30 Vict., ch. 117.   1866.   LEE;   The Reformatory schools act . . . with memorandum, appendices, and index, by F. V. Hornby.   H.M.S.O., 1897.   BR

E13   1866   Industrial schools act.   An act to consolidate and amend the acts relating to industrial schools in Great Britain.   29 & 30 Vict., ch. 118. 1866.   LEI

E14   1867/68   Public schools act.   An act to make provision for the good government and extension of certain public schools in England.   31 & 32 Vict., ch. 118.   1868.   LEE

E15   1868/69   Endowed schools act.   An act to amend the law relating to endowed schools, etc. 32 & 33 Vict., ch. 56.   1869.   LEE LO;   *see also* E71

E16   1870   Elementary education act.   An act to provide for public elementary education in England and Wales.   33 & 34 Vict., ch. 75.   1870.   HU LO OX;   do., edited by F. Adams.   Simpkin, Marshall, 1870.   BR;   do., edited by W. A. Houldsworth. Routledge, 1870.   LO;   do., edited by T. Preston. W. Amer, 1870.   CA LEI;   do., edited by H. Owen, jr.   Knight, 1870.   LEE;   do., edited for the National education union.   Manchester and London, N.E.U., 1870.   HU;   *see also* E74–75, E78–80, E92

E17   1872   Education (Scotland) act.   35 & 36 Vict., ch. 62.   *See* E86

E18   1873   Elementary education act.   36 & 37 Vict., ch. 86.   1873.   LO OX;   *see also* E74, E78

E19 1873 Endowed schools act. An act to continue and amend the Endowed schools act, 1869. 36 & 37 Vict., ch. 87. 1873. LEE LO; *see also* E71

E20 1874 Elementary education (orders) act. 37 & 38 Vict., ch. 90. 1874. OX

E21 1875 Public health act. 38 & 39 Vict., ch. 55. 1875. *See* E88

E22 1876 Elementary education act. 39 & 40 Vict., ch. 79. 1876. LO OX; do., edited by H. Owen. Knight, 1876. LEI; 3rd ed., Knight, 1877. HU NE; *see also* E74–75

E23 1878 Endowed institutions (Scotland) act. 41 & 42 Vict., ch. 48. 1878. *See* E86

E24 1878 Education (Scotland) act. 41 & 42 Vict., ch. 78. 1878. *See* E86

E25 1878 Free Church of Scotland school properties act. 41 & 42 Vict., ch. 220. *See* E86

E26 1879 Elementary education (Industrial schools) act. 42 & 43 Vict., ch. 48. 1879. LO; *see also* E74

E27 1880 Elementary education act. 43 & 44 Vict., ch. 23. 1880. OX; *see also* E74

E28 1884/85 School boards act. 48 & 49 Vict., ch. 38. *See* E74

E29 1889 Welsh intermediate education act. 52 & 53 Vict., ch. 40. 1889. LO; *see also* E71

E30 1890 Education code (1890) act. 53 & 54 Vict., ch. 22. 1890. LO OX; *see also* E74

E31 1890 Education of blind and deaf-mute children (Scotland) act. 53 & 54 Vict., ch. 43. LO

E32 1891 Army schools act. 54 & 55 Vict., ch. 16. 1891. LEE

E33 1891 Elementary education act. 54 & 55 Vict., ch. 56. 1891. LO OX; *see also* E74

E34 1893/94 Elementary education (blind and deaf children) act. 56 & 57 Vict., ch. 42. 1893. BR LO OX; *see also* E74

E35 1893/94 Elementary education (school attendance) act. An act to amend the Elementary education acts with respect to the age for attendance at school. 56 & 57 Vict., ch. 51. 1893. LO OX; *see also* E74

E36 1893/94 Local government act. 56 & 57 Vict., ch. 73. 1894. LO

E37 1897 Voluntary schools act. 60 & 61 Vict., ch. 5. 1897. LO OX; *see also* E74

E38 1897 Elementary education act. 60 & 61 Vict., ch. 16. 1897. OX

E39 1897 School board conference act. 60 & 61 Vict., ch. 32. 1897. OX; *see also* E74

E40 1898 Elementary school teachers (superannuation) act. 61 & 62 Vict., ch. 57. 1898. LO OX; do., published with annuity tables and an explanatory memorandum to the act. 1899. BR; *see also* E74, E76

E41 1899 Elementary education (school attendance act, 1893) amendment act. An act to amend the law respecting the employment and education of young children. 62 & 63 Vict., ch. 13. 1899. LO OX; *see also* E74

E42 1899 Elementary education (defective and epileptic children) act. 62 & 63 Vict., ch. 32. 1899. LO OX; *see also* E74

E43 1899 Board of Education act. 62 & 63 Vict., ch. 33. 1899. LEE LO OX; *see also* E74, E84

E44 1900 Elementary education act. An act to amend the Elementary education acts, 1870–1893. 63 & 64 Vict., ch. 53. 1900. LO OX; *see also* E74

E45 1901 Education (Scotland) act. 1 Edw. VII, ch. 9. 1901. LEE

E46 1901 Education act. 1 Edw. VII, ch. 11. 1901. LO; *see also* E74–75

E47 1902 Education act, 1901 (renewal) act. 2 Edw. VII, ch. 19. 1902. LO

E48 1902 Education act. 2 Edw. VII, ch. 42. HU LO OX; School board chronicle & School government chronicle. The Education act, 1902. 3rd ed., 1903. BR; *see also* E72, E74–75, E89

E49 1903 Education (provision of working balances) act. An act to provide for the borrowing by local education authorities for certain purposes. 3 Edw. VII., ch. 10. 1903. LO OX

E50 1903 Elementary education amendment act. 3 Edw. VII, ch. 13. LO OX

E51 1903 Education (London) act. An act to extend and adapt the Education act, 1902, to London. 3 Edw. VII, ch. 24. 1903. LEE LO OX; *see also* E84

E52 1903 Employment of children act. 3 Edw. VII, ch. 45. 1903. BR

E53 1904 Education (local authority default) act. An act to make provision for the case of default on the part of local authorities in the performance of their duties as respects elementary schools. 4 Edw. VII, ch. 18. 1904. LO OX

E54 1906 Education of defective children (Scotland) act. 6 Edw. VII, ch. 10. 1906. LO

E55 1906 Education (provision of meals) act. 6 Edw. VII, ch. 57. 1906. LO OX

E56 1907 Education (administrative provisions) act. 7 Edw. VII, ch. 43. 1907. LEE LO OX

E57 1908 Endowed schools (masters) act. 8 Edw. VII, ch. 39. 1908. LO OX

E58 1908 Education (Scotland) act. 8 Edw. VII, ch. 63. 1908. LEE

E59 1908 Children act. 8 Edw. VII, ch. 67. 1908. BR LO; do., *reprinted* 1950. LEI

E60 1909 Local education authorities (medical treatment) act. An act to provide for the recovery by local education authorities of costs for medical treatment of children attending public elementary schools in England and Wales. 9 Edw. VII, ch. 13. 1909. LO OX

E61 1909 Education (administrative provisions) act. 9 Edw. VII, ch. 29. 1909. LO OX

E62 1910 Education (choice of employment) act. 1 Geo. V, ch. 37. 1910. OX

E63 1911 Education (administrative provisions) act. 1 & 2 Geo. V., ch. 32. 1911. OX

E64 1912/13 Elementary school teachers (superannuation) act. 2 & 3 Geo. V, ch. 12. 1912. LEE OX; *see also* E76

E65 1913 Mental deficiency act. 3 & 4 Geo. V, ch. 28. 1913. BR LEE LO; *see also* E77

E66 1913 Mental deficiency and lunacy (Scotland) act. 3 & 4 Geo. V, ch. 38. LO

E67 1914 Elementary education (defective and epileptic children) act. 4 & 5 Geo. V, ch. 45. 1914. LO OX

E68 1918 Education act. 8 & 9 Geo. V, ch. 39. 1918. LEE LO OX RE; do., edited by Sir M. Barlow and R. Holland. Nat. soc., [1918]. LEI; do. [*in* Clarke, J. J. Outlines of local government]. Pitman, 1919. LO

E69 1918 Education (Scotland) act. 8 & 9 Geo. V, ch. 48. 1918. LEE OX; do., edited by John Strong . . . [and others]. Edinburgh, Oliver & Boyd, 1919. LEI

E70 1918 School teachers' (superannuation) act. 8 & 9 Geo. V, ch. 55. LO OX

Collected legislation

E71 CHARITY COMMISSIONERS. The Charitable trust acts, 1853–94; the Endowed schools acts, 1869, 1873–74, Welsh Intermediate education act, 1889. 1896. LO [Contains: Charitable trusts act, 1853. Charitable trusts amendments act, 1855. Charitable trusts act, 1860; do., 1862; do., 1869. Endowed schools act, 1869; do., 1873; do. 1874. Charitable trusts act, 1887. Welsh intermediate education act, 1889. Charitable trusts (recovery) act, 1891. Charitable trusts (places of religious worship) amendments act, 1894.]

E72 CARSON, W. A., and WHITELEY, G. C. The Education act, 1902, fully explained . . . with sections of the Education acts, 1870–1900, and other statutes. Knight, 1903. NE

E73 CLAPPERTON, A. E., *ed.* The Universities (Scotland) act, 1858, together with ordinances of Commissioners under said act . . . Glasgow, MacLehose, 1916. LEI

E74 DRURY, J. F. W. Manual of education . . . Manchester & London, Heywood, [1903]. CA LEI [Contains: Elementary education act, 1870; do., 1873; do., 1876. Elementary education (industrial schools) act, 1879. Elementary education act, 1880. School boards act, 1885. Education code (1890) act, 1890. Elementary education act, 1891. Elementary education (blind and deaf children) act, 1893. Elementary education (school attendance) act, 1893. Voluntary schools act, 1897. School board conference act, 1897. Elementary school teachers (superannuation) act, 1898. Elementary education (school attendance) act (1893) amendment act, 1899. Elementary education (defective and epileptic children) act, 1899. Board of Education act, 1899. Elementary education act, 1900. Education act, 1901; do., 1902.]

E75 EDUCATION acts, 1890–1919. [Separate acts bound together.] LO

E76 ELEMENTARY school teachers superannuation pamphlet. 1912. LO [Contains: Elementary school teachers (superannuation) act, 1898. Elementary school teachers superannuation rules, 1899; do., 1904, 1905, 1907, 1909 and 1911. Elementary school teachers (superannuation) act, 1912, etc.]

E77 FRY, D. P. The law relating to lunacy and mental deficiency, comprising the Lunacy acts, 1890 to 1911, the Mental deficiency act, 1913 . . . the Education of epileptic and defective children acts . . . 4th ed. by J. Lithiby. Knight, 1914. LEI

E78 GLEN, W. C., *ed.* The Elementary education acts, 1870 and 1873, with introduction . . . [etc.]; and appendix containing the incorporated statutes . . . 4th ed., Shaw, 1874. HU

E79 OWEN, *Sir* H., *ed.* The Elementary education act, 1870, and Elementary education (elections) act, 1871. 7th ed., Knight, 1872. RE

E80 OWEN, *Sir* H., *ed.* The Education acts, 1870–1902, and other acts . . . Knight, 1903. NE

E81 PUBLIC general statutes, 1870–86. ReU

E82 PUBLIC general acts, 1887 to date. ReU

E83 SCHOOL government chronicle, *periodical.* The Education acts, 1870–1901, as remaining after the total and partial repeals enacted by the Education act, 1902. 2nd ed., S.G.C., 1903. BR

E84 SCHOOLMASTERS yearbook and directory, 1910/11. LEI [Contains: Board of Education act, 1899. Education act, 1902. Education (London) act, 1903. Education (local authority default) act, 1904. Education (administrative provisions) act, 1907. Endowed schools (masters) act, 1908. Education (administrative provisions) act, 1909.]

E85 SCOTLAND. *General register house.* Acts of the Parliament and of the Privy Council of Scotland relative to the establishing and maintaining of schools from the year MCCCCXCVI to the year MDCXCVI. [Edinburgh], General register house, [1839?]. BR LEI

E86 SELLAR, A. C., *ed.* Manual of the Education acts for Scotland. 7th ed., Edinburgh, Blackwood, 1879. LEI [Contains: Education (Scotland) act, 1872; do., 1878. Industrial schools act, 1866. Free Church of Scotland school properties act, 1878. Endowed institutions (Scotland) act, 1878, etc.]

E87 SHADWELL, L. L., *ed.* Enactments in Parliament concerning the universities of Oxford and Cambridge, the colleges and halls therein and the colleges of Winchester, Eton and Westminster. Oxford, Clarendon Pr., 1912. 4 vols. [Vol. 1: 37 Edward III–13 Anne. Vol. 2: 1 George I–11 George IV. Vol. 3: 11 George IV–31 & 32 Victoria. Vol. 4: 32 & 33 Victoria–1 & 2 George V.] SH

E88 STRATTON, F., *ed.* The Public health act, 1875, and other statutes and parts of statutes relating to public health . . . Knight, 1901. LO; 1904 ed., edited by F. Stratton and G. Metcalfe. Knight, 1904. LO

E89 TAYLOR, G. R. S., *ed.* The Education acts of 1902 (England and Wales) and 1903 (London), with notes . . . With the revised text of the Education acts, 1870–1899. Routledge, 1903. LEI

E90 UNIVERSITIES (Scotland) act, 1889. Ordinances. [1890, nos. 1–3: St. Andrews. 1891, nos. 4–6: General; no. 7: Glasgow and Aberdeen; no. 8: St. Andrews, Aberdeen and Edinburgh; no. 10: General.] LO

Parliamentary debates

E91 BUCKMASTER, J. C. The education question in Parliament; being a digest of proceedings, from 1816 to the publication of the Revised code. Chapman & Hall, [1862]. HU

E92 NATIONAL EDUCATION UNION. A verbatim report, with indexes, of the debate in Parliament during the progress of the Elementary education bill, 1870, together with a reprint of the Act... Manchester and London, N.E.U., [1870]. BI BR CA HU LEE LEI NE RE

E93 NATIONAL EDUCATION UNION. A verbatim report of the debate in Parliament during the progress of the Elementary education bill, 1876. N.E.U., [1876]. LEI LO SH

E94 PARLIAMENTARY debates. New series. Vol. 11, June 27th–Sept. 7th 1820. LO [Includes debate on the Education of the poor bill.]

E95 PRESIDENT OF THE BOARD OF EDUCATION, [i.e. H. A. L. Fisher]. Speech [in the House of Commons] upon the introduction of the [Education] bill, 10th August 1917. H.M.S.O., 1917. NE

Note: For speeches of individuals in the House of Commons and House of Lords *see* entries under the following names in Section C: Blomfield, C. J.; Brougham, H. P., *baron*; Bruce, H. A.; Dixon, G.; Goschen, G. J. G., *visct.*; Henley, J. W.; Lansdowne, H. Petty-Fitzmaurice, *marquis*; Lowe, R.; Maltby, E.; Pakington, J.; Phillpotts, H.; Richard, H.; Roebuck, J. A.; Shaftesbury, A. Ashley Cooper, *earl of*; Walpole, S. H.

Sessional papers (House papers, command papers, bills)

Note: For Annual reports and other serial publications *see* separate sub-sections.

Figures in round brackets are House paper numbers for the House of Commons, unless preceded by H.L., for House of Lords. Figures in square brackets are command paper numbers. Entries are arranged chronologically, with minor exceptions (to keep related material together).

E96 1813 (243?) Committee on the apprentice laws. Report on the several petitions presented respecting the apprentice laws... 1813. [Chairman: George Rose.] LEI

E97 1815 (440) Home Office. Copies of memorials or statements of charitable donations delivered in the several offices of the Clerks of the Peace... in pursuit of... an Act for registering and securing charitable donations (52 Geo. 3, ch. 102)... 1815. HU

E98 1816 (498, 427, 469, 495, 497) Select committee to inquire into the education of the lower orders of the metropolis. [Chairman: H. P. Brougham.] First [to] Fourth reports, with mins. of ev. 1816. LEI ReU

E99 1818 (428) do., Fifth report... viz. Appendix (B) documents. 1818. ReU

E100 1817 (?) Committee on climbing boys. Copy of report presented to the House of Commons by the committee appointed to examine the several petitions against the employment of boys in sweeping chimneys. 1817. LEI

E101 1818 (426) Select committee on the education of the lower orders. [Chairman: H. P. Brougham.] Third report. 1818. HU

E102 1825–28 Commission of Irish education inquiry. [Commissioners: T. F. Lewis, J. Glassford, A. R. Blake, J. L. Foster, W. Grant.] First to Ninth reports, with correspondence. 1825–27. LO; First report, 30th May 1825. (400) LEI; Eighth report, 1828. (509) LI

E102a 1862/67 (281) Charity Commissioners. General index to reports 1–14. 1827. HU LO ReU

E103 1831 (310) R. Commission on state of universities of Scotland. [Chairman: Lord Rosebery.] Report. 1831. LEI ReU

E104 1831/32 (63) Charity Commissioners. Return: An analytical digest of the reports made to Parliament by the Commissioners upon the public charities... 1832. BI HU ReU

E105 1834 (44) R. Commission on administration and practical operation of the Poor laws. [Chairman: Sir E. Chadwick.] Report, answers to questions, index. 1834. LEE

E106 1834 (572) Select committee on the state of education. Report, with mins. of ev. and index. 1834. OX

E107 1835 (62) Education enquiry, England and Wales. Abstracts of the answers and returns. 1835. Vol. 1: England, Bedford–Lancaster. BI BR; Vol. 2: England, Leicester–Suffolk. BI; Vol. 3: England and Wales, Surrey–Radnor. BI

E108 1835 (115) Charity Commissioners. Public charities. Analytical digest of the Commissioners' reports, in continuation of Digest printed in 1832... 1835. LEI

E109 1835 (465) Select committee on education in England and Wales. [Chairman: Earl of Kerry.] Reports, mins. of ev., appendix, index. 1835. LO

E110 1835 (479) Select committee on the British Museum. [Chairman: T. C. B. Estcourt.] [First] report, mins. of ev., appendix, index. 1835. LO

E111 1835 (598) Select committee on arts and manufactures. [Chairman: W. Ewart.] Report, mins. of ev., etc. 1835. LO

E112 1835 [45] Commissioners of public instruction, Ireland. [First] report on the state of religious and other instruction now existing in Ireland. 1835. LO

E113 1835 [46] do. Appendix. 1835. LO

E114 1835 [47] do. Second report. 1835. LO ReU

E115 1835 (630) Select committee on diocesan, royal, and other schools of public foundation in Ireland. [Chairman: Sir T. Wyse.] Report, mins. of ev., etc. Part 1. 1835. LI ReU

E116 1836 (586) do. Report, etc. Part 2. 1836. LI ReU

E117 1836 [35] R. Commission on the condition of the poorer classes in Ireland. Appendix C. Pts. I, II. Charitable institutions. 1836. LO

E118 1836 [36] do. Appendix D. Baronial examinations on the earnings of labourers. 1836. LO

E119 1836 [37] do. Appendix E. Baronial examinations on food, cottages, etc. 1836. LO

E120 1836 [38] do. Appendix F. Landlord, tenants, etc. 1836. LO

E121 1836 [39] do. Suppt. II to apps. D, E, F. 1836. LO

E122 1836 [41, 42] do. Appendix H, pts. I, II. Voluntary associations, etc.; Remarks on evidence. 1836. LO

E123 1836 (440) Select committee on the British Museum. [Chairman: T. C. B. Estcourt.] [Second] report, mins. of ev., etc. 1836. LO

E124 1837 (133) Education enquiry, Scotland. Abstract of the answers and returns . . . Scotland. 1837. ReU

E125 1837 (543-I-II) Select committee on the progress and operation of the plan of education in Ireland. Report; together with the minutes of evidence, etc. 1837. 2 vols. LO ReU; Vol. 1 only. LI

E126 1837 (485) do. [2nd] Report. 1837. LO ReU

E127 1837 [92–95] R. Commission on the universities of Scotland. [Chairman: Lord Aberdeen.] Minutes of evidence. 1837. 4 vols. [Vol. 1: Edinburgh. Vol. 2: Glasgow. Vol. 3: St. Andrews. Vol. 4: Aberdeen.] BI LO

E128 1837 (42) R. Commission on religious instruction, Scotland. [Chairman: W. H. Johnstone.] First report. 1837. LO

E129 1837/38 (113) do. Third report. 1838. LO

E130 1837/38 (122) do. Fourth report. 1838. LO

E131 1837/38 (589) Select committee on education of the poorer classes in England and Wales. Report, mins. of ev., etc. 1838. LO ReU

E132 1837/38 (701) Select committee on schools of public foundation in Ireland. [Chairman: Sir T. Wyse.] Report, etc. 1838. LO ReU

E133 1837/38 [123] R. Commission for visiting the universities of King's College and Marischal College, Aberdeen. [Chairman: Lord Erroll.] First report. 1837. LO

E134 1839 [176] do. Second report. 1839. LO

E135 1839 [175] R. Commission for visiting the university of Glasgow. [Chairman: Lord Melville.] Report. 1839. LO ReU

E136 1839 (42) Educational provisions of the Factories act. Reports by four factory inspectors. 1839. LO

E137 1838 (284) Report of the Committee of Council appointed to superintend the application of any sums voted by Parliament for the purpose of promoting public education. 1839. [Xerox copy.] LO

E138 1840 (124) Education. A return of applications for portion of the sum granted for promotion of public education in 1839 . . . 17th March 1840. LEI

E139 1840 (470) do. 10th July 1840. LEI

E140 1840 (279) Charity Commissioners. Index to reports. 1840. HU LO ReU

E141 1841 — Poor Law Commissioners. [E. Chadwick, J. P. Kay, E. C. Tufnell, etc.] Report on the training and education of pauper children, with appendices. 1841. BI BR HU LEE OX ReU SH

E142 1842 [433–434] Charity Commissioners. Public charities. I. Analytical digest of the reports. 1842. 2 vols. ReU; vol. 2 *only*. LO

E143 1842 [435] Charity Commissioners. do. II. Digest of schools and charities for education. 1842. LEI LO ReU

E144 1842 [436] Charity Commissioners. do. III. Return of charities to be distributed to the poor. 1842. LO ReU

E145 1843 Factories Bill, 1843. An analytical digest of the education clauses . . . [by James Dinnis?]. 1843. *See* C369

E146 1843 (444) Education. Returns of lists of applications for grants out of the sums voted for education in the years 1840, 1841, and 1842. 1843. ReU

E147 1842 [380] and 1843 [430] R. Commission on the employment of children in mines and manufactures. [1st and 2nd reports.] The physical and moral condition of the children and young persons employed in mines and manufactures. Illustrated by extracts from the reports of the Commissioners. Parker for H.M.S.O., 1843. LEI

E148 1843 [510] Poor Law Commissioners. Reports of special assistant Poor Law Commissioners on the employment of women and children in agriculture. 1843. HU LEE LEI

E149 1844 [557] R. Commission for inquiring into administration and practical operation of the poor laws in Scotland. Report. 1844, repr. 1906. LO

E150 1844 [543–544?] do. Parts I–III; part VI, Answers to questions 57–70 . . .; part VII, Analytical index. LO

E151 1845/46 [717] R. Commission for visiting St. Andrews University. [Chairman: Lord Melville.] Report and appendix. 1846. LO

E152 1847 [835] Special committee of the council of the Government School of Design. Report on the state and management of the school, with appendix. 1847. LO

E153 1847 [850] Second special committee of the council of the Government School of Design. Report on measures for carrying out the recommendations of the special report. LO

E154 1847 [870] R. Commission of inquiry into the state of education in Wales. Report. Part I, Carmarthen, Glamorgan and Pembroke. 1847. LO; 1848 reprint [abbreviated version]. BI ReU SH

E155 1847 [871] do. do. Part II, Brecknock, Cardigan, Radnor, and Monmouth. 1847. BI; 1848 reprint [abbreviated version]. BI ReU SH

E156 1847 [872] do. do. Part III, North Wales. 1848 reprint [abbreviated version]. BI ReU SH

E157 1849 (426) Education commission in Ireland. Special report relative to the endowed school at Clonmel. 1849. LO

E158 1851 [1373] Charity Commissioners. Report of the Commissioners, 1849, for inquiring into those cases which were investigated by and reported upon, but not certified to the Attorney-General. 1851. LO

E159 1852 (?) Returns of translated copies of all charters or letters patent granting certain lands for the promotion of education in Ireland during the reign of Queen Elizabeth . . . and subsequently; also, of all grants of money or other funds . . . over which the Commissioners of Education have control. 1852. BI

E160 1852/53 (571) Select committee on education (Manchester, Salford, etc.). Report, proceedings, mins. of ev., etc. 1853. BI ReU

E161 1852/53 (674) Select committee to inquire into the treatment of criminal and destitute children. Report, mins. of ev., etc. 1853. LO

E162 1852/53 [1482] R. Commission to inquire into the state, discipline, studies and revenues of the university and colleges of Oxford. [Chairman: Samuel Hinds.] Report, mins. of ev., etc. 1852. LO OX ReU

E163 1852/53 (1017-I) do. do. Index. 1852. ReU

E164 1852/53 [1559] R. Commission to inquire into the state, discipline, studies and revenues of the university and colleges of Cambridge. [Chairman: John Graham.] Report, mins. of ev., etc. 1852. LO OX ReU

E165 1852/53 (1017) do. do. Index. 1852. ReU

E166 1852/53 [1637] R. Commission to inquire into the state, discipline, studies and revenues of the university of Dublin and Trinity College. Report, etc. 1853. ReU

E167 1854 (?) Correspondence respecting the proposed measures of improvement in the universities of Oxford and Cambridge. 1854. 6 vols. [1. University and colleges of Oxford. 2. University and colleges of Cambridge. 3. Pembroke coll., Oxford. 4. Snell foundation, Balliol coll., Oxford. 5. Corpus Christi and Emmanuel colls., Cambridge. 6. Christ Church, Oxford.] BI

E168 1854 (525) Select committee of the House of Lords on practical working of the system of national education in Ireland. A review and compendium of the minutes of evidence . . . Edited by an advocate of Lord Stanley's plan. 1855. See C1214

E169 1854/55 [1957] Committee of Council on Education. Report on the Kneller Hall training school, by the Rev. Henry Moseley, H.M.I. 1855. LEI LO

E170 1854/55 A Bill for the better encouragement and promotion of education in England. 16 March 1855. SH

E171 1854/55 [1993] Report of the Commissioner [H. S. Tremenheere] appointed to inquire into the state of the population in the mining districts. 1855. LO

E172 1856 (338) Committee of Council on Education. Copy of the correspondence between the committee of the Model Secular School of Manchester and the Committee of Council on Education, on participation of the school in the parliamentary grant for education. 1856. BI

E173 1857/58 (487) do. [Further] Correspondence. 1858. BI; see also C835

E174 1856 (387) Churches and schools. Return of all sums which have been granted by any public department of the government within the last ten years, in aid of the erection of churches or schools. 1856. LEI

E175 1857 (57) Report of Commissioners appointed to consider the best mode of re-organising the system for training officers for the scientific corps; together with an account of foreign and other military education, [with appendices]. 1857. LO

E176 1857 (?) Charity Commissioners. Copy of the report of an inquiry made by an inspector [Walter Skirrow] in 1854 into the state and management of the estates and property of the Charterhouse. 1857. LO

E177 1857/58 (343) Oxford University Commission. Report. LO

E178 1857/58 [2336-I] R. Commission on endowed schools, Ireland. [Chairman: Lord Kildare.] Report on endowments, funds, and actual condition of all schools endowed . . . in Ireland. Part I. Report. BI LO

E179 1857/58 [2336-II-III] do. Parts II and III. Minutes of evidence. BI LO

E180 1857/58 [2336-IV] do. Part IV. Tables. BI LO

E181 1857/58 [2368] R. Commission on state of the universities of Aberdeen, with a view to their union. [Chairman: W. Mure.] Report, mins. of ev. LO

E182 1859, session 2 (82) Cambridge University Commission. Report. 1859. [Photo-copy.] LO

E183 1860 (181) Select committee on public institutions (hours of opening). [Chairman: Sir John Trelawny.] Report, mins. of ev., etc. 1860. LEI

E184 1860 (252) Committee of Council on Education. Copy of minutes and regulations of the Committee reduced into the form of a code. 1860. HU

E185 1860 (540) Select committee on the British Museum. [Chairman: W. H. Gregory.] Report, with proceedings, mins. of ev., etc. 1860. LO

E186 1861 [2852] Cambridge University Commission. General report. 1861. LO

E187 1861 [2794-I-VI] R. Commission on the state of popular education. [Chairman: Duke of Newcastle.] Report, etc. 1861. 6 vols. [Vol. 1: Report. Vol. 2: Education in rural and other districts. J. Fraser, etc. Vol. 3: Education in the Metropolis and other districts. J. Wilkinson, W. B. Hodgson, etc. Vol. 4: Education in Central Europe. M. Arnold, M. Pattison, etc. Vol. 5: Answers to the circular of questions. Vol. 6: Minutes of evidence.] LEI LO NE ReU SH; Vols. 2–3 and 5–6 *only*. BI; Vol. 1 *only*. BR; Vols. 5–6 *only*. OX; [Abstract of report], Popular education in England ... by H. S. Skeats. *See* C1314

E188 1861 (231) do. Letter by J. K. Shuttleworth on the report of the Commission. 1861. SH

E189 1861 (354) do. Paper by H. S. Tremenheere submitted to the Commission. 1861. SH

E190 1862 (120 and 120-I) do. Copy of two papers submitted to the Commission by Mr. Chadwick, one entitled Communications on half-time teaching and on military drills, the other a letter to Mr. Senior explanatory of the former paper. 1862. BI LO SH

E191 1862 (510) Education of pauper children. Return containing copies of reports made to the Poor Law Board by W. H. T. Hawley, Robert Weale, Sir John Walsham and Andrew Doyle, Poor Law inspectors. 1862. LEI LO

E192 1863 [3174] Commission on Scottish universities. General report of the Commissioners under the Universities (Scotland) act, 1858; with appendix. 1863. BI LEI LO

E193 1863 [3173] and (77) Durham University Act, 1861. Report of Commissioners, with mins. of ev. 1863. LO

E194 1864 (468) Select committee on education (Inspectors' reports). Report, with proceedings, mins. of ev., etc. 1864. BI; photographic reprint, lacking appendix. HU

E195 1864 [3288] R. Commission on revenues and management of certain colleges and schools. [Chairman: Earl of Clarendon.] Report, mins. of ev., etc. 4 vols. [Vol. 1: Report. Vol. 2: Appendix. Vols. 3–4: Minutes of evidence.] LEE LEI LO ReU; Vols. 1–2 *only*. BI OX; Vol. 2 *only*. BR

E196 1865 (481) Select committee of the House of Lords on the Public schools bill. [Chairman: Lord Clarendon.] Report, with proceedings, mins. of ev. 1865. OX

E197 1866 (487) Education (conscience clause). Return, copy of correspondence between the Archbishop of Canterbury and Earl Granville. 1866. LEI LO

E198 1867 (287) Sir John Port's hospital and school. Copy of report of F. O. Martin, inspector of charities, in the matter of Sir John Port's hospital in Etwall and school in Repton. 1867. LEI

E199 1867 (497) Select committee on the Oxford and Cambridge universities education bill. Special report, with proceedings, mins. of ev., etc. 1867. HU ReU

E200 1865 [3483] R. Commission on schools in Scotland. First report. 1865. LO

E201 1867 [3858] do. Appendix to first report. 1867. LO

E202 1867 [3845] do. Second report, etc. Elementary schools. 1867. BI LO

E203 1867 [3845-I-V] do. Reports and statistics on country districts, etc. 1867. 5 vols. [I. Lowland country districts. II. Glasgow. III. Country districts. IV. Hebrides. V. Statistics.] LO; III *only*. BI

E204 1867 [3796] Children's employment commission. Sixth report, with appendix. 1867. HU

E205 1867 [3857] Report by James Fraser to the [Schools inquiry commission and the Schools in Scotland commission] on the common school system of the United States and of the provinces of upper and lower Canada. 1867. BI LO

E206 1867 [3898] Schools inquiry commission. [Chairman: Lord Taunton.] Report relative to technical education. 1867. LEI LO

E207 1867/68 [3966 and 3966-I-XX] do. Report, etc. 1868–69. 21 vols. [Vol. 1: Report. Vol. 2: Misc. papers. Vol. 3: Answers to questions. Vols. 4–5: Mins. of ev. Vol. 6: Burgh schools in Scotland and Secondary education in foreign countries, by D. Fearon and M. Arnold. Vol. 7: General report, southern counties. Vol. 8: do., midland counties, Northumberland. Vol. 9: do., northern counties. Vol. 10: Special report, London div. Vol. 11: Special report of assistant commissioners, south-eastern counties. Vol. 12: do., south-midland counties. Vol. 13: do., eastern counties. Vol. 14: do., south-western counties. Vol. 15: do., west-midland counties. Vol. 16: do., north-midland counties. Vol. 17: do., north-western counties. Vol. 18: do., Yorkshire. Vol. 19: do., northern counties. Vol. 20: do., Monmouthshire and Wales. Vol. 21: Tables.] LO ReU; vols. 1–12 and 18 *only*. NE; vols. 1–10 and 12 *only*. BI; vols. 2–9 *only*. LEE; vols. 1, 2, 4 and 8 *only*. LEI; vol. 1 *only*. BR CA; vol. 6 *only*. RE SH; vol. 18 *only*. HU; *see also* C125 Report on King Edward's grammar school, Birmingham

E208 1867/68 [3967] French Imperial commission on technical instruction. Translation of report and notes. 1868. BR HU

E209 1867/68 [3967-I] do. Abstract of evidence. [Trans.] 1868. BR

E210 1868/69 [4207] do. Report on technical instruction in Sweden, together with trans. of the report of the Select committee appointed to examine the draft of the bill on technical education in France, etc. 1869. LEI

E211 1868/69 [?] do. Report on technical instruction in Germany and Switzerland, together with documents laid before the Commission. 1869. BR LEI SH

E212 1867/68 (432) Select committee on scientific instruction. [Chairman: B. Samuelson.] Report, mins. of ev., etc. BI LO

E213 1867/68 (433-10) Endowed charities. Return, general digest of endowed charities. County of Leicester. 15 July 1868. LEI

E214 1867/68 (433-19) do. County of Rutland. 15 July 1868. LEI

E215 1868/69 [4103-I] R. Commission on the Science and art department in Ireland. Vol. II. Minutes of evidence, appendix, etc. 1869. ReU

E216 1868/69 [4202-I] R. Commission on the employment of children, young persons and women in agriculture. Second report, appendix pt. 2. 1869. LEI

E217 1870 C.221 and 221-I do. Fourth report, with appendices. 1870. 2 vols. LEI

E218 1870 C.6-A and C.6-I-VII R. Commission on primary education (Ireland). Report, etc. Vol. 1, pt. 2-vol. 8. Dublin, 1870. [Vol. 1, pt. 2: Special reports. Vol. 2: Assistant commissioners' reports. Vols. 3-4: Minutes of evidence. Vol. 5: Analysis of evidence. Vol. 6: Educational census. Vol. 7: Returns. Vol. 8: Misc. papers.] BI

E219 1870 C.25 R. Commission on military education. [Chairman: Earl de Grey and Ripon.] Report of the commission appointed to inquire into the education and training of cadets for commissions in the army. 1870. LO

E220 1870 C.47 do. Accounts of the systems of military education in France, Prussia, Austria, Bavaria and the United States. 1870. LO SH

E221 1871 C.318 R. Commission on scientific instruction and the advancement of science. [Chairman: Duke of Devonshire.] First report. 1871. LEI

E222 1872 C.536 do. First report (reprint), supplementary and second reports, analysis of ev., etc. 1872. BI LO OX

E223 1873 C.868 do. Third report, etc. 1873. BI LO OX

E224 1874 C.884 do. Fourth report, etc. 1874. BI LO OX

E225 1874 C.958 do. Mins. of evidence, etc. BI LO OX

E226 1874 C.1087 do. Fifth report. 1874. BI LO OX

E227 1875 C.1279 do. Sixth report. 1875. LO OX

E228 1875 C.1297 do. Seventh report, etc. 1875. LO OX

E229 1875 C.1298 do. Eighth report, etc. 1875. LO OX

E230 1875 C.1363 do. Minutes of evidence, indexes, etc. 1875. LO

E231 1872 C.524 Endowed schools commissioners. [Chairman: Lord Lyttelton.] Report to the Committee of Council on Education. 1872. BI ReU

E232 1875 C.1142 do. Report. 1875. BI

E233 1873 (25-1) Endowed charities. Return, general digest of endowed charities. County of Northampton. 13 Feb. 1873. LEI

E234 1873 (101) School fees. Return from each school board in England and Wales of the number of cases in which, during the year 1872, the school fees of any children have been paid. March 1873. LEI

E235 1873 (254) Select committee on Endowed schools act, 1869. [Chairman: W. E. Forster.] Report, mins. of ev., etc. 1873. BI LO ReU

E236 1873 C.755 R. Commission on endowed schools and hospitals (Scotland). [Chairman: Sir E. Colebrooke.] First report, with mins. of ev., etc. 1873. BI LEI LO

E237 1874 C.976 do. Second report, mins. of ev., etc. 1874. BI LEI LO

E238 1875 C.1123 and 1123-I-II do. Third report, with mins. of ev., statistics. 1875. 3 vols. BI LEI LO

E239 1874 C.856 and C.856-I-II R. Commission on the property and income of the universities of Oxford and Cambridge. [Chairman: Duke of Cleveland.] Report, returns, etc. 1874. 3 vols. [Vol. 1: Report. Vol. 2: Returns, Oxford. Vol. 3: Returns, Cambridge.] BI LO OX ReU; Vol. 3 only. LEI

E240 1877 (261) Endowed charities. Return, general digest of endowed charities. Explanatory memorandum and tabular statements. 12 June 1877. LEI

E240a 1877 C.1764 Correspondence respecting the introduction into, and employment in this country of, Italian children. 1877. LO

E241 1878 C.1935 and C.1935-I-III R. Commission on the universities of Scotland. [Chairman: Lord Justice Inglis.] Report, mins. of ev., returns, etc. 1878. BI; Vol. 4 only, Returns and documents. LEI

E242 1878 C.1971 Commercial no. 4 (1878) Further correspondence respecting the attitude of the state towards the fine arts in Great Britain and the foreign countries of Europe. 1878. NE

E243 1878/79 (160) Elementary schools. Return relative to elementary schools, cost per child, London, April 1879. 1879. LEI NE

E244 1878/79 (?) School Board schools (religious teaching), Return, etc. 1879. LEE

E245 1880 (82) Musical education abroad. Return. Copy of Mr. Hullah's report on musical education abroad. 1880. LEI LO NE

E246 1880 C.2522 R. Commission on City of London parochial charities. Vol. 1: Report. Appendix I. 1880. LEI

E247 1880 C.2493 R. Commission on endowed institutions in Scotland. [Chairman: Lord Moncrieff.] First report, mins. of ev. 1880. BI LO SO

E248 1881 C.2790 do. Second report, mins. of ev. 1881. BI LO

E249 1881 C.3076 do. Third report, etc. 1881. BI LO SO

E250 1881 C.2831 and C.2831-I Commission on endowed schools (Ireland). [Chairman: Earl of Rosse.] Vol. 1: Report. 1881. BI; Vol. 2: Evidence and index. 1881. LO

E251 1881 C.2868 R. Commission on Oxford University. [Chairman: Lord Selborne.] Minutes of evidence, appendix, etc. Pts. 1 and 2. 1881. LO

E252 1882 C.3171 R. Commission on technical instruction. [Chairman: Sir B. Samuelson.] First report. 1882. BI CA LEI RE ReU

E253 1884 C.3981 and C.3981-I-IV do. Second report. 1884. 5 vols. [Vol. 1: Report. Vol. 2: Report on agricultural education, by H. M. Jenkins. Vol. 3: Misc. and mins. of ev. Vol. 4: Evidence relating to Ireland. Vol. 5: Foreign reports, appendices, etc.] LEI LO ReU; Vols. 1, 2, 4, 5 *only*. BI NO; Vols. 1, 2, 4 *only*. OX; Vols. 1, 2, 5 *only*. SO; Vols. 1–2 *only*. NE; Summary of the report, by F. C. Montague. Cassell, [1887]. HU

E254 1883 ? do. Notes of Mr. Swire Smith. 1883. 22 parts in 1 vol. HU

E255 1884 (293) Elementary schools (Dr. Crichton-Browne's report). Return, copy of report of Dr. Crichton-Browne to the Education department upon the alleged over-pressure of work in public elementary schools, [and] Copy of Mr. Fitch's memorandum relating to Dr. Crichton-Browne's report . . . July–August 1884. LEI LO NE

E256 1884 (312) Select committee on education, science and art (administration). [Chairman: Mr. Childers.] Report, etc. 1884. LO OX

E257 1884 C.3876 R. Commission on reformatories and industrial schools. [Chairman: Lord Aberdare.] Report, etc. Vol. 1 *only*. LO NE

E258 1884 C.3980 R. Commission of inquiry into the conditions of the crofters and cottars in the Highlands and Islands of Scotland. Report, appendices. 1884. LO

E259 1884 C.3995 R. Commission on educational endowments (Scotland). [Chairman: Lord Balfour.] First report, mins. of ev., etc. 1884. BI

E260 1884/85 C.4329 do. Second report, mins. of ev., etc. 1885. BI

E261 1886 C.4664 do. Third report, mins. of ev., etc. 1886. BI

E262 1887 C.4981 do. Fourth report, mins. of ev., etc. 1887. BI

E263 1888 C.5312 do. Fifth report, mins. of ev., etc. 1888. BI

E264 1889 C.5641 do. Sixth report, mins. of ev., etc. 1889. BI

E265 1884/85 C.4308 Cathedral commission. Report upon the cathedral church of Peterborough. 1885. [Includes the cathedral school.] LEI

E266 1886 C.4639 Education Department. H.M.I.'s reports on the education of deaf and dumb children in the Metropolitan, Manchester and Swansea inspection districts. 1886. LEI LO NE

E267 1886 C.4752 Education Department. Special report on certain points connected with elementary education in Germany, Switzerland, and France. [By Matthew Arnold.] 1886. BI LEI LO RE

E268 1886 C.4885 Admiralty. Committee on the education of naval executive officers. Report, mins. of ev., etc. 1886. BI

E269 1886 sess. 1 (191) Select committee on endowed schools acts. [Chairman: Sir Lyon Playfair.] Report, mins. of ev., etc. 1886. LEE; Index. 1886. BI LO

E270 1887 (120) do. Report, mins. of ev., appendix. 1887. LEE LEI LO NE

E271 1887 (335) do. Report. 1887. OX

E272 1886 C.4863 R. Commission on the Elementary education acts (England and Wales). [Chairman: Lord Cross.] First report, mins. of ev., etc. 1886. BI HU LEE LO OX

E273 1887 C.5056 do. Second report, mins. of ev., etc. 1887. BI CA HU LEE LO NO OX

E274 1887 C.5158 do. Third report, mins. of ev., etc. BI CA HU LEE LO NO OX

E275 1888 C.5485 do. Final report. 1888. BI CA HU LEE LEI LO OX; 1913 reprint. NO; Summary. National Society, 1888. BR

E276 1888 C.5329 do. Digest of evidence. 1888. BI CA HU LEE LO NO

E277 1888 C.5485-I do. Foreign, etc., returns. 1888. BI HU LEE LO NE OX

E278 1888 C.5485-II do. Statistical report. 1888. BI CA HU LEE LO

E279 1888 C.5485-III do. Training college returns. 1888. BI HU LEE LO

E280 1888 C.5485-IV do. Appendix to final report. 1888. BI HU LEE LO

E281 1887 C.5285 Departmental commission on agricultural and dairy schools. [Chairman: Sir R. H. Paget.] First report. 1887. LEI LO

E282 1888 C.5313 do. Final report. 1888. LEI LO

E283 1888 C.5313-I do. Minutes of evidence. 1888. LEI

E284 1888 C.5336 Committee of Council on Education in Scotland. Committee to inquire into certain questions relating to education in Scotland (training colleges, etc.). First and second reports, etc. 1888. BI

E285 1888 C.5425 do. Third report, mins. of ev., etc. 1888. BI

E286 1888 C.5341 Elberfeld Poor law system. Reports on the Elberfeld Poor law system and German workmen's colonies, by J. S. Davy, C. S. Loch and A. F. Hanewinkel. 1888. LO

E287 1888 C.5453 Science and Art Department. Report . . . on the action of light on water colours. 1888. ReU

E288 1889 C.5709 and C.5709-I R. Commission on a university for London. [Chairman: Earl Selborne.] Report of the commissioners appointed to inquire whether any and what kind of new university or powers is or are required for the advancement of higher education in London, with appendix, [and] Minutes of evidence. 1889. 2 vols. LO; Vol. 1, Report, *only*. CA NE OX

E289 1889 C.5781 R. Commission on the blind, the deaf and dumb, etc., of the United Kingdom. [Chairman: Lord Egerton.] Report, etc. [Vol. 1] *only*. 1889. BR LEI

E290 1890 Teachers' registration and organisation bill. 1890. OX

E291 1890 (346) Select committee on Infant life protection bill. Index to the Report. [1890]. LEI

E292 1890/91 (24) Charities commission. City of London parochial charities act, 1883. Scheme for the management of charities. 1890. LO

E293 1890/91 (25) Endowed schools act, 1869, and amending acts. Schemes for the management of (1) Alleyne's college, Dulwich, (2) Corporation for middle class education in the metropolis, (3) Bishopsgate ward schools, (4) St. Ethelburga's society, (5) Central foundation schools of London. 1890. LEI LO

E294 1890/91 (102) Endowed charities. Supplementary digest. County of Northampton. 17 Feb. 1891. LEI

E295 1890/91 (111) do. County of Derby. 1891. LO

E296 1890/91 (275) Elementary education (schemes). Return by counties of schemes for schools made since the year 1870. 1891. LEI OX

E297 1890/91 (335) Select committee on Teachers' registration and organisation bill. [Chairman: Sir W. Hart Dyke.] Special report, with proceedings of the committee. 1891. OX

E298 1892 (99) Return, Endowed schools acts foundations (England). 1892. OX

E299 1892 C.6790 Commissioners on Scottish universities. Report as to the subscription of tests by principals, professors and other university officers in the Scottish universities. Vol. 1: Report. Edinburgh, [1892]. BI

E300 1893/94 Teachers' registration bill. 1893. OX

E301 1893/94 (244) Endowed schools acts (schemes). Return, by counties, of schemes approved between Jan. 1, 1887, and Dec. 31, 1892. 1893. LEI LO

E302 1893/94 (311) Departmental committee on the conditions of school attendance and child labour. Report. 1893. BI

E303 1893/94 C.6889 General report on the wages of the manual labour classes in the United Kingdom, with tables of the average rates of wages in 1886 and 1891. 1893. LO

E304 1893/94 C.6894-I-VI. R. Commission on labour. The agricultural labourer. Vol. 1: England. Reports. [Pt. I, by W. E. Bear. Pt. II, by C. M. Chapman. Pt. III, by A. W. Fox. Pt. IV, by R. C. Richards. Pt. V, by A. J. Spencer. Pt. VI, by E. Wilkinson.] 1893. LO; Pts. I and IV *only*. LEI

E305 1893/94 C.6894-X-XII do. do. Digest of evidence, groups A–C. LO

E306 1893/94 C.6894-XIV do. do. Vol. 2, Wales. Reports. LO

E307 1893/94 C.6894-XV-XVII do. do. Vol. 3, Scotland. [Pts. I–II, Reports. Pt. III, Index.] LO

E308 1893/94 C.6894-XVIII-XXII do. do. Vol. 4, Ireland. [Pts. 1–IV, Reports. Pt. V, Index.] LO

E309 1893/94 C.7118 Home Office. General rules and regulations for the management of certified industrial schools. 1893. LEI

E310 1893/94 C.7119 Home Office. General rules and regulations for the management of certified reformatory schools. 1893. LEI

E311 1893/94 C.7259 R. Commission on draft charter for the proposed Gresham University in London. [Chairman: Lord Cowper.] Report, etc. Vol. 1: Report. 1894. LEI LO OX

E312 1894 C.7335 Education Department. Minute of the 2nd April 1894 by the Committee of Council on education, providing for grants on account of the education of blind and deaf children. 1902. LEI

E313 1894 C.7373 Committee to inquire into the entrance examinations (in non-military subjects) of candidates for commissions in the army. [Chairman: Lord Sandhurst.] Report, mins. of ev., etc. 1894. LO

E314 1894 C.7517 Educational endowments (Ireland) commission. Final report, with abstracts of the minutes, mins. of ev., etc. 1894. LO

E315 1895 (235 and 235-I) Charities Commission. Endowed charities (county of London). Returns. Bermondsey; Limehouse, St. Anne. 1895. LO

E316 1895 (304) do. do. Woolwich Bow. LO

E317 1895 (392) do. do. Lee. LO

E318 1895 (425 and 425-I-VI) do. do. Charleton-next-Woolwich; Christchurch, Spitalfields; Greenwich; Kidbrooke; Poplar All Saints; St. George in the East; Stepney. LO

E319 1895 (261) Departmental committee on the Charity Commission. [Chairman: Sir Robert Hamilton.] Report. 1895. LO

E320 1895 C.7684 R. Commission on the aged poor. [Chairman: Lord Aberdare.] Report of the commission appointed to consider whether any alteration in the system of poor relief is desirable in the case of persons whose destitution is occasioned by incapacity for work resulting from old age. Vol. 1. 1895. LO

E321 1895 C.7705 Scotch education department. Report by J. Struthers on sloyd and kindergarten occupations in the elementary school. 1895. BI LEI NE

E322 1895 C.7711 Foreign office. Reports from H.M. representatives abroad on the educational standard for the Merchant Navy. 1895. BI

E323 1895 C.7778 Science and art department. Drawing in elementary schools. Illustrated syllabus of the course of instruction. 1895. LEI; [Photocopy.] NE

E324 1895 C.7862 and C.7862-I-VIII R. Commission on secondary education. [Chairman: James Bryce.] Report, etc. 1895. 9 vols. [Vol. 1: General report. Vols. 2–4: Minutes of evidence. Vol. 5: Memoranda and answers to questions. Vols. 6–7: Reports of the assistant commissioners. Vol. 8: Summary of, and index to, minutes of evidence. Vol. 9: Appendix, statistical tables.] BI BR CA LEE LEI LO NE NO OX ReU; Vols. 1–4 *only*. SO; Summary of recommendations, prepared for the Conference on secondary education, Cambridge, 1896. C.U.P., 1896. HU

E325 1896 (144 and 144-I-II) Charities commission. Endowed charities (county of London). Returns. Bromley St. Leonard; St. John of Wapping; Whitechapel. 1895. LO

E326 1896 C.8027 Departmental committee on the maintenance and education of children in the metropolis. [Chairman: A. J. Mundella.] Report. Vol. 1. 1896. NE

E327 1896 C.8032 and 8033 do. Report and mins. of ev. Vols. 2–3. 1896. NE

E328 1896 C.8151 Education department. Report on the vision of children attending elementary schools in London, by R. Brudenell Carter. 1896. LEI

E329 1896 C.8204 Departmental committee on reformatory and industrial schools. Report, etc. Vol. 1: Report and appendices. 1896. BR

E330 1897 (86) Charities commission. Endowed charities (county of London). Returns. St. Botolph without Aldgate. 1897. LO

E331 1897 (222 and 222-II-III) do. Chelsea; St. Nicholas and St. Paul, Deptford; St. Leonard, Shoreditch. 1897. LO

E332 1897 (393) do. Christchurch. 1897. LO

E333 1897 (245) Treasury. University colleges, Great Britain. Grant in aid returns. Treasury minutes and reports. 1897. LO

E334 1897 C.8420 Education department. Minute of the Committee of Council on education dated 9th April 1897 [on the] Voluntary schools act, 1897. 1897. LEI

E335 1897 C.8447 [and succeeding vols.] Education department. Special reports on educational subjects. *See* E518

E336 1897 C.8477 Committee appointed to inquire into the distribution of science and art grants. Report, in which is included a revised edition of the Science and art directory, embodying the recommendations of the committee. 1897. OX

E337 1897 C.8492 Scotch education department. Return by counties, for each school district in Scotland, of rateable value, school rate, population, number of children of school age, and amount of accommodation in [different types of school]. 1897. BI

E338 1897 C.8647 and C.8648 Departmental committee on the working of the Universities and college estate acts, 1858 to 1880. Report and mins. of ev. 1897. 2 vols. BI; Vol. 1, Report [*only*]. LO

E339 1897 C.8618 R. Commission on manual and practical instruction in primary schools in Ireland. [Chairman: Earl Belmore.] Third report. Dublin, 1897. LEI

E340 1897 C.8619 do. Minutes of evidence, appendix. 1897. LEI LO

E341 1898 C.8923 do. Final report. 1898. LEI LO

E342 1898 C.8924 do. Minutes of evidence, etc. 1898. LEI LO

E343 1898 C.8925 do. Further appendix. 1898. LEI LO

E344 1898 (112 and 112-I) Charities commission. Endowed charities (county of London). Returns. Clerkenwell; St. Sepulchre (without city). 1898. LO

E345 1898 (201) Endowed schools act, 1869, and amending acts. Schemes for the management of (1) Parochial schools (St. Botolph's, Aldgate), (2) Charity of Henry Petter, Aldgate. 1898. LO

E346 1898 (246) Technical education (France). Return, copy of report on French technical education by Mr. Charles Copland Perry, recently issued by the Science and art department. 1898. LEI

E347 1898 C.8746 Departmental committee on defective and epileptic children. [Chairman: T. W. Sharpe.] Vol. 1: Report. 1898. BR LEE

E348 1898 C.8747 do. Vol. 2: Minutes of evidence, appendices, etc. 1898. LEI

E349 1898 C.8761 Departmental committee on the pupil-teacher system. [Chairman: T. W. Sharpe.] Vol. 1: Report. 1898. BI LEI LO OX

E350 1898 C.8762 do. Vol. 2: Minutes of evidence, etc. 1898. BI LEI LO OX SO

E351 1898 C.9116 and C.9117 R. Commission on intermediate education (Ireland). First report and Appendix. Dublin, 1898. BI

E352 1899 C.9512 and C.9513. do. Appendix to Final report, containing mins. of ev., etc. 1899. 2 vols. BI

E353 1899 (234) Voluntary schools closed, etc., 1897. Return of schools closed or transferred to school boards since the commencement of the Voluntary schools act, 1897. 1899. LEI LO

E354 1899 (239) Education (fees for pauper children). Return, copy of letters of Education department sanctioning the imposition of fees on pauper children. 1899. LEI LO

E354a 1899 (307) Endowed charities. Supplementary digest. County of Rutland. 28 July 1899. LEI

E355 1900 (335) Return: county council scholarships. 1900. OX

E356 1900 Cd. 276 Commissioners on Scottish universities. General report; with appendix containing ordinances, minutes, etc. Edinburgh, 1900. BI

E357 1900 Cd. 419 Board of education. Report on technical and commercial education in East Prussia, Poland, Galicia, Silesia and Bohemia, by James Baker. 1900. BR OX RE SO

E358 1901 Cd. 430-XVI Foreign office. Report on chemical instruction in Germany and the growth and present condition of the German chemical industries. 1901. BI

E359 1901 Cd. 787-II Foreign office. Report on the technical, agricultural, commercial and art schools of Wurtemberg. 1901. BI

E360 1902 Education (England and Wales) bill (Bill 138). 1902. LO; do., with amendments, the Bill as amended in committee, etc. HU

E361 1902 (171) Statement showing non-county boroughs (population over 10,000) and other urban districts (population over 20,000) in England and Wales, [in connection with the Education bill]. HU

E362 1902 (252) Treasury. University colleges (Great Britain) (Grant in aid). Return, copy of Treasury minute(s) [and] report(s) . . . 1902. LEI

E363 1902 Cd. 895 Inter-departmental committee on employment of school children. [Chairman: H. H. S. Cunynghame.] Minutes of evidence, with appendices and index. 1902. LEI

E364 1902 Cd. 982–983 Committee on military education. [Chairman: A. Akers-Douglas.] Report of the committee on the education and training of officers of the army, [with] minutes of evidence. 1902. 2 vols. LEI LO

E365 1902 Cd. 1229 R. Commission on university education in Ireland. [Chairman: Lord Robertson.] Appendix to the third report. Minutes of evidence. 1902. LO

E366 1903 Cd. 1483 and Cd. 1484 do. Final report and appendix. 1903. LO

E367 1903 Cd. 1507 R. Commission on physical training (Scotland). [Chairman: Lord Mansfield.] Vol. 1: Report and appendix. 1903. LEI LO

E368 1903 Cd. 1508 do. Vol. 2: Minutes of evidence, etc. 1903. LEI

E369 1903 Cd. 1602 Board of education. Papers relating to the resignation of the Director of special inquiries and reports [Sir Michael Sadler]. 1903. BR

E370 1904 Cd. 2032 Inter-departmental committee on the model course of physical exercises. [Chairman: J. Struthers.] Report. 1904. LEE LO

E371 1904 Cd. 2175 Interdepartmental committee on physical deterioration. [Chairman: A. W. Fitzroy.] Vol. 1: Report and appendix. 1904. LEI NE

E372 1904 Cd. 2210 do. Vol. 2: List of witnesses and mins. of ev. 1904. LEI

E373 1905 Cd. 2526 Trinity College, Dublin, estates commission. [Chairman: G. Fitzgibbon.] Report. 1905. LO

E374 1905 Cd. 2726 Board of education. Reports on children under five years of age in public elementary schools, by women inspectors of the Board of education. 1905. BI BR HU LEE LEI LO NE OX

E375 1905 Cd. 2779 Inter-departmental committee on medical inspection and feeding of children attending public elementary schools. [Chairman: H. W. Simpkinson.] Vol. 1: Report and appendices. 1905. BR LO

E376 1905 Cd. 2784 do. Vol. 2: Minutes of evidence. 1905. BR

E377 1905 Cd. 2729 Board of education. Administrative county of Stafford endowed charities (elementary education). Report made to the Board of education. 1905. ReU

E378 1906 (178-XIX and 178-XXXIV) Education (England and Wales) (Non-provided schools). Return of the schools in England and Wales recognised as non-provided public elementary schools. Lincolnshire; Yorkshire. [Photocopies.] HU

E379 1906 (—) Board of education. Return showing provision by local education authorities for enabling scholars of public elementary schools to proceed to secondary schools, [etc.], by means of exhibitions, scholarships, [etc.]. 1906. HU

E380 1906 (H.L. 115 and 115-I) Return. Education (Religious instruction in council schools). 1906. 2 vols. BI LEI

E381 1906 Cd. 2941 Board of education. Administrative county of Northampton endowed charities (elementary education). Report made to the Board of education. 1906. ReU

E382 1907 Cd. 3313 Departmental committee on education rates. [Chairman: H. W. Primrose.] Report, with appendices. 1907. BI

E383 1907 Cd. 3530 Board of education. County of Cornwall endowed charities (elementary education). Report made to the Board of Education. 1907. ReU

E384 1907 Cd. 3768 do. Administrative county of Kent. 1907. ReU

E385 1907 Cd. 3582 Board of education. General report on the instruction and training of pupil-teachers, 1903–1907, with historical introduction. 1907. BI HU NE OX ReU

E386 1908 Elementary education (England and Wales) bill. 1908. OX

E387 1908 Cd. 3723 Departmental committee on the supply and training of British boy seamen for the mercantile marine. [Chairman: H. E. Kearley.] Minutes of evidence, with appendices, etc. 1908. LEI

E388 1908 Cd. 3952 Board of education. Consultative committee. [Chairman: A. H. D. Acland.] Report on devolution by county education authorities. 1908. BI NE

E389 1908 Cd. 3990 Board of education. Public elementary schools in single-school parishes, as defined in section 3 (6) of the Elementary education (England and Wales) bill, 1908. 1908. BI

E390 1908 Cd. 4132 Board of education. Statement as to the age at which compulsory education ceases in certain foreign countries and British colonies. 1908. BI

E391 1908 Cd. 4202 R. Commission on the care and control of the feeble-minded. [Chairman: Lord Radnor.] Vol. 8: Report. 1908. BR LO

E392 1908 Cd. 4215–4218 do. Vols. 1–4: Minutes of evidence. 1908. BR; Vol. 1 only. LO

E393 1908 Cd. 4219 do. Vol. 5: Appendices to mins. of ev. 1908. BR LO

E394 1908 Cd. 4220 do. Vol. 6: Reports of the medical investigators. 1908. BR LO

E395 1908 Cd. 4221 do. Vol. 7: Report on visit to American institutions. 1908. BR LO

E396 1908 Cd. 4259 Board of education. Consultative committee. [Chairman: A. H. D. Acland.] Report upon the school attendance of children below the age of five. 1908. BI HU LEE LO ReU SH

E397 1908 Cd. 4271 Board of education. Memorandum giving an outline of the successive legislative and administrative conditions affecting the relation of the Board of education to agricultural education in England and Wales, with appendices. 1908. ReU

E398 1909 Cd. 4499 R. Commission on the poor laws and relief of distress. [Chairman: Lord George Hamilton.] Majority report. Separate minority report. 1909. LO

E399 1910 Cd. 5037 do. Appendix vol. XVIII: Report on the condition of children who are in receipt of various forms of poor law relief in England and Wales, by Miss E. M. N. Williams, Miss M. Longman and Miss M. Phillips. 1910. LO

E400 1910 Cd. 5199 do. Appendix vol. XXXII: Reports on visits paid by the Labour colonies committee to certain institutions in Holland, Belgium, Germany and Switzerland. 1910. BR

E401 1909 Cd. 4569 Board of education. Tables of expenditure for agricultural education. 1909. LEI ReU

E402 1909 Cd. 4757 Board of education. Consultative committee. [Chairman: A. H. D. Acland.] Report on attendance, compulsory or otherwise, at continuation schools. Vol. 1: Report and appendices. 1909. BR LEE LEI LO NE OX

E403 1909 Cd. 4758 do. Vol. 2: Summaries of evidence. 1909. LEE LEI NE OX

E404 1910 Cd. 5131 Board of education. Report on the working of the Education (provision of meals) act, 1906, up to 31st March 1909. 1910. BR NO

E405 1910 Cd. 5230 Departmental committee on the Employment of children act, 1903. [Chairman: J. A. Simon.] Minutes of evidence, with appendices, etc. 1910. LEI

E406 1911 Cd. 5534 Departmental committee on the cost of school buildings. [Chairman: L. A. Selby-Bigge.] Report and abstracts of evidence. 1911. BI BR LEE

E407 1911 Cd. 5662 Departmental committee on educational endowments. [Chairman: C. Trevelyan.] Reports on the administration of (a) endowments applicable to elementary education, and (b) small educational endowments other than the above. Vol. 1: Report. 1911. ReU

E408 1911 Cd. 5747 do. Vol. 2: Minutes of evidence, etc. 1911. ReU

E409 1911 Cd. 5666 Imperial education conference, 1911. Report. 1911. NE OX ReU

E410 1911 Cd. 5726 Board of education. Further papers relating to the registration of teachers and the proposed Registration Council (in continuation of Cd. 4185 and Cd. 4402). 1911. OX SH

E411 1911 Cd. 6004 Board of education. Consultative committee. [Chairman: A. H. D. Acland.] Report on examinations in secondary schools. 1911. BI BR LEE LO OX ReU SO

E412 1910 Cd. 5166 R. Commission on university education in London. [Chairman: Lord Haldane.] Appendix to First report, mins. of ev., appendix, index. 1910. LO

E413 1911 Cd. 5527 and Cd. 5528 do. Second report and appendix. 1911. 2 vols. LO

E414 1911 Cd. 5910 do. Third report. 1911. LO

E415 1911 Cd. 5911 do. Appendix to Third report. 1911. BI LO

E416 1911 Cd. 6015 do. Fourth report. 1911. LO

E417 1912 Cd. 6311 do. Fifth report. 1912. LO

E418 1913 Cd. 6717 do. Final report (with reprint of Fourth report). 1913. BI BR LEI LO ReU SH

E419 1913 Cd. 6718 do. Appendix to Final report. 1913. BI LO ReU

E420 1912 Cd. 6463 Departmental committee on playgrounds of public elementary schools. [Chairman: J. C. Iles.] Report, with abstracts of evidence. 1912. BI CA HU LEE LO NE

E421 1912 [Cd. 6209] and Cd. 6210 R. Commission on the civil service. [Chairman: Lord MacDonnell.] First report, and Appendix to first report. 1912. LO

E422 1913 Cd. 6739 and Cd. 6740 do. Third report and Appendix to third report. 1913. LO

E423 1914 Cd. 7339 and Cd. 7340 do. First appendix to fourth report, and Appendix to fourth report. 1914. LO

E424 1913 Cd. 6849 Board of education. Consultative committee. [Chairman: A. H. D. Acland.] Report on practical work in secondary schools. BI BR LEE LO OX

E425 1913 Cd. 6933 Board of education. Public elementary schools in England and Wales. Tabular statement of staffing ... expenditure on teachers per unit of average attendance and ... salaries. 1913. BI

E426 1916 Cd. 8291 Board of education. Consultative committee. [Chairman: Sir A. H. D. Acland.] Interim report on scholarships for higher education. 1916. BI BR OX

E427 1917 Cd. 8512 Departmental committee on juvenile education in relation to employment after the war. [Chairman: J. H. Lewis.] Final report. Vol. 1: Report. 1917. HU OX

E428 1917 R. Commission on university education in Wales. [Chairman: Lord Haldane.] Appendix to first report. 1917. OX

E429 do. Appendix to second report. OX

E430 1918 Cd. 8991 do. Final report. 1918. BI HU LEE OX

E431 1918 Education (No. 2) bill, [and] Notes on the Education (No. 2) bill. 1918. OX

E432 1918 Cd. 8669 Board of Education. Distribution of exchequer grants to university colleges in England, 1913–1918. Third report of the Advisory committee. 1918. OX

E433 1918 Cd. 8939 Departmental committee on the principles determining the construction of scales of salary for teachers in elementary schools. [Chairman: Sir H. Stephen.] Vol. 1: Report. 1918. BI HU LO

E434 1918 Cd. 8999 do. Vol. 2: Summaries of evidence and memoranda. 1918. HU LO NE

E435 1918 Cd. 9011 Committee on the position of natural science in the educational system of Great Britain. [Chairman: Sir J. J. Thomson.] Report. 1918. BI BR HU LEE LEI LO NE OX RE ReU; *with title:* Natural science in education. [1918.] DU LEI LO NE SO

E436 1918 Cd. 9036 Committee on the position of modern languages in the educational system of Great Britain. [Chairman: Stanley Leathes.] Report. 1918. CA LEE LEI OX RE ReU SH; 1928 reprint. NE; *with title:* Modern studies. 1918. BI DU LO OX

E437 1918 Cd. 9107 Ministry of reconstruction. Committee on adult education. Interim report: Industrial and social conditions in relation to adult education. 1918. BI LEE OX

E438 1918 Cd. 9124 Board of education. Some notes on medical education in England. A memorandum by Sir George Newman. 1918. LEI ReU

E439 1918 Cd. 9140 Board of education. Departmental committee on the principles determining the construction of scales of salary for teachers in secondary and technical schools, schools of art, training colleges and other institutions for higher education (other than university institutions). Vol. 1: Report. 1918. BI NE OX; [xerox copy.] LO

E440 1918 Cd. 9168 do. Vol. 2: Summaries of evidence. 1918. LEI OX

E441 1918 Cd. 9225 Ministry of reconstruction. Committee on adult education. Second interim report: Education in the army. 1918. OX

E442 1918 Cd. 9230 Ministry of reconstruction. Machinery of government committee. Report. 1918. LEE

Serial publications and departmental publications, arranged by department:

England, including England and Wales together

E443 AGRICULTURE, Board of. Report on the distribution of grants to agricultural and dairy schools in Great Britain, 1890/91. LO

E444 AGRICULTURE, Board of. Annual report on the distribution of grants for agricultural education and research. 1900/01; 1910/11; 1914/15. BI

E445 AGRICULTURE, Board of. Education in rural districts of England and Wales. 1906. BR

E446 AGRICULTURE, Board of, and EDUCATION, Board of. Report of the Rural education conference. [Chairman: H. Hobhouse.]

1. County staffs of instructors in agricultural subjects. 1910 ReU

2. The qualifications of teachers of rural subjects. 1911. BI OX ReU

3. A suggested type of agricultural school. 1911. BI ReU

4. The consolidation of rural elementary schools. 1912. OX ReU

5. Courses in agricultural colleges. 1912. BI ReU

6. Co-ordination of agricultural education. 1912. BI ReU

7. Manual instruction in rural elementary schools. 1913. BI OX ReU

8. Manual processes of agriculture. 1913. BI ReU

E447 AGRICULTURE, Board of, and EDUCATION, Board of. Rural education conference. Return, 1910, for the minutes constituting a Rural education conference. 1910. BI

E448 CHANCERY, Court of. Attorney-General *v.* the Governors of the free grammar-school in Wimborne Minster. Scheme for the administration of the charity, approved by the report of N. W. Senior. E. G. Atkinson, pr., 1848. ReU

E449 CHANCERY, Court of. Scheme for the management and regulation of the charity of Seckford hospital, and the grammar school, at Woodbridge, in the county of Suffolk. Order dated June 14th, 1861. Roworth, 1861. LEI

CHARITY COMMISSIONERS:

E450 Reports of the Commissioners to enquire concerning charities in England for the education of the poor. Reports 1–32, 1819–40. 32 vols. in 39. ReU; Reports 1–31. 1819–37. 31 vols. HU; Reports 1–29. 1819–35. 29 vols. BI; Reports 1–2. 1819. LEE; Report 1, and appendix. 1819. 2 vols. SH; Report 3. 1820. LEI; Report 6. 1821. NE; Report 31. 1837. LEI; Further report, pts. 1–2. 1836. LO

E451 General index to first 14 reports. *See* E102a; Index to the reports. 1840. *See* E142; Analytical digest. 1832. *See* E104; Digests and returns. 1842. *See* E142–144

E452 An account of public charities in England and Wales, abridged from the reports of His Majesty's commissioners . . . with notes and comments. By the editor of 'The cabinet lawyer' [i.e. John Wade]. Simpkin & Marshall, 1828. LEI

E453 Reports relating to the county of Cambridge. [1839?] LEI

E454 Report relating to the county of Devon. Vol. 2. Exeter, Besley, 1828. LEI

E455 Reports relating to the county of Hampshire, 1819–37. Gray, [1839?]. SO

E456 Reports relating to the county of Leicestershire, 1819–37. Gray, [1839?]. LEI

E457 Reports relating to the county of Lincoln, 1815–39. [1839?] HU

E458 The endowed charities of the city of London; reprinted . . . from seventeen reports of the Commissioners . . . Sherwood, 1829. LEI

E459 Public charities of Frome. *See* C652

E460 Annual reports. 20th, 1872. LO; 26th, 1878. LO; 36th. 1889. BI; 1895. OX; 1900. OX

E461 General digest of endowed charities. 1868–. *See* E213–214; E233; E240

E462 Endowed charities, supplementary digest. 1891–. *See* E294–295; E354a

E463 Endowed charities, county of London. *See* E315–318; E325; E330–332; E344

E464 Scheme for the regulation and management of the school and charities in the township of Hartwith, as ordered by the Board of Charity Commissioners . . . 16 November 1866. Ripon, [no pub.], 1866. LEE

E465 CONTROL, Board of. The despatch of 1854 on general education in India. *See* E842

COMMISSIONERS FOR THE EXHIBITION OF 1851. *See* London international exhibition

EDUCATION. Arrangement is as follows: Publications of:

   (1) Education, Committee of Council on.
   (2) Education Department.
   (3) Education, Board of.

EDUCATION, Committee of Council on:

E466 *Circulars and memoranda.* Apprenticeship of pupil teachers. [1860]. BI

E467 do. Books and maps, explanatory circular. [1855?]. LEI

E468 do. Memorandum respecting the organization of schools in parallel groups of benches and desks. 1851. BR LEE

E469 *Codes.* Minutes and regulations reduced into the form of a code. 1860. (1860, H.C.252). HU SH

E470 do. Revised code of the minutes and regulations. 1861. BI SH

E471 do. Revised code of education. [*c.* 1862]. BI

E472 do. The modified revised code of education. School managers. 1862. BI

E473 do. Supplementary rules, revised code. 1864. (1864, H.C. 293). LO

E474 do. Revised code of regulations (1867), incorporating the minute of 11th June 1866, with a schedule of all articles cancelled or modified, and of all new articles. 1867. HU

E475 do. New code of regulations. 1873–81. 9 vols. ReU; 1875 *only.* RE

E476 do. Evening continuation schools code. Minute modifying certain provisions of the Evening continuation schools code (1893). 1897. [*C.* 7090]. LEI

E477 do. do. Minutes dated 4th August 1899, modifying articles 13 and 15 of the Evening continuation schools code, 1899. [*C.* 9455]. LO

E478 *Correspondence.* Correspondence, etc. 1848/49. HU

E479 do. Copy of a letter from C. A. Stevens on the educational statistics given in the reports for 1863 and 1866 of the Committee ... 1868. BI

E480 do. Letter from the Rev. Henry Moseley, enclosing scheme of examination for students in training colleges, May 2, 1854. [1855?]. LEI

E481 *Inspectors.* [Instructions for the inspectors of schools.] 1840. [Lacks t.p.] HU

E482 do. [General reports of inspectors for 1852, England and Wales.] [Lacks t.p.] BR

E483 do. Matthew Arnold's Reports on elementary schools, 1852–82. *See* C48

E484 *Minutes.* Minutes, with appendices. 1839/40–1857/58. 26 vols. LEE LO ReU; 1839/40, 1841/42, 1844, vol. 1, 1846, 1847/48, 1848/49, 1850/51–1852/53, 1857/58. 13 vols. BI; 1839/40, 1840/41, 1842/43, 1852/53, vol. 1, 1853/54. BR; 1839/40–1841/42, 1844–46, 1847/48, 1848/50, 1850/51–1857/58. HU; 1839/40, 1841/42, 1844, vol. 1, 1845, vol. 2, 1846, 1847/48, vol. 2, 1854/55, 1857/58. LEI; 1839/40, 1842/43, 1847/48, 1856/57, 1857/58. NE; 1839/40, 1842/43, 1845, 1847/48, 1848/49, 1851/52–1852/53, 1853/54, vol. 1, 1854/55–1857/58. NO; 1841/42. OX; 1839/40–1848/49, 1851/52–1852/53, 1856/57–1857/58. 18 vols. SH; 1839/40. SO; *continued as Reports*

E485 do. Minutes, with appendices. Schools of parochial unions. 1847/48, vol. 2. SO; 1847/48/49. LEI; 1848/50, 1850/52, 1852/53–1856/57. HU

E486 *Plans.* Plans of school houses. [No t.p. Revised from Minutes for 1839/40 and 1845.] HU

E487 *Reports.* Reports, with appendices. 1858/59–1898/99. 45 vols. LO; 1866/67–1897/98. 38 vols. BI; 1861/62, 1869/70–1898/99. BR; 1859/60, 1861/62–1898/99, appendix 2, 1871/72, appendix 5, 1872/73–1876/77. HU; 1858/59–1864/65, 1870/71–1898/99. LEE; 1858/59, 1866/67–1872/73, vol. 1, 1893/94, 1895/96, vol. 1, 1897/98, vol. 1. LEI; 1861/62, 1897/98. NE; 1858/59–1860/61, 1862/63–1866/67, 1868/69–1898/99. NO; 1882/83–1898/99. OX; 1858/59–1887/88, 1891/92–1893/94, 1896/97, 1898/99. ReU; 1867/68, 1871/72–1872/73, 1879/80–1884/85, 1891/92, 1895/96. SH; 1869/70, 1871/72–1897/98. SO

E488 *Teachers' certificates.* Teacher's certificate of the third class, awarded to Margaret Schoffield, mistress of the Donington Cowleys endowed school. [1879]. HU

E489 do. Teacher's certificate awarded to student at Chichester Training college, 1889–90. LO

EDUCATION DEPARTMENT:

E490 *Building regulations.* The Elementary education act, 1870, [edited] by Hugh Owen, [with] an appendix containing the provisions of the revised code with regard to grants for the building of schools. Knight, 1870. LEE

E491 do. Rules to be observed in planning and fitting up public elementary schools. 1900. LEI

E492 *Codes, etc.* The Elementary education act, 1870, popularly explained by W. A. Holdsworth, together with the various Orders in Council issued by the Education Department. Routledge, 1870. LO

E493 do. The Elementary education acts, 1870 and 1873. [Edited] by W. C. Glen ... [with] the rules, regulations, and code of the Education Department. 4th ed. Shaw, 1874. HU

E494 do. Code of regulations. 1878, 1880, 1886, 1888. LEI; 1887–89. CA; 1893–95, 1899–1900. ReU; 1893. LO

E495 do. Handbook of the new code of regulations, 1880, and other official instructions, orders, and circulars of the Education Department, by J. F. Moss. Isbister, 1880. LEI

E496　do.　Code of regulations for day schools. 1894, 1895, 1896. OX; 1894, 1897, 1899, 1900. LO

E497　do.　Code of regulations for evening continuation schools. 1898. (C.8839.) LO

E498　do.　Revised instructions to Her Majesty's inspectors and applicable to code 1894. (C.7321.) LO; do., code 1899. (C.9199.) LO

E499　do.　Revised regulations as to certificates of age, school attendance and proficiency. 1876. NE; 1879. LEI; 1898. LEI

E500　Elementary school teachers (superannuation) act, 1898, published together with Annuity tables, and an explanatory memorandum to the Act. 1899. BR

E501　*Grant returns.*　Returns relative to elementary schools. (1) Total cost per child in London School board schools defrayed by rates. (2) Total cost per child in London voluntary schools defrayed by voluntary subscriptions. 1876. (1876, H.C.160.) LO

E502　do.　Elementary education (Schools receiving special grants). Return, year ending 31st August, 1891. 1892. (1892, H.C.336.) HU

E503　do.　Return showing (1) expenditure in England and Wales upon annual grants to elementary schools, and (2) elementary schools on the grant list. 1885, 1899. OX; 1892. LEI; 1900. BI HU

E504　do.　(1) Schools in receipt of parliamentary grants, (2) Grants paid to school boards, (3) School board accounts and lists of loans. 1895/96–1899/1900. ReU; 1895/96. OX

E505　do.　Technical education: return. Application of funds by local authorities. 1896, 1898, 1899. OX

E506　*Inspectors' reports.*　Matthew Arnold's reports on elementary schools, 1852–82. *See* C48

E507　do.　East-central division. General report by the Chief Inspector. 1887, 1891, 1893, 1895, 1897, 1899. OX

E508　do.　Eastern division. General report by the Chief Inspector. 1886, 1888, 1890, 1892, 1896, 1898. OX

E509　do.　North-central division. General report by the Chief inspector. 1886, 1888, 1890, 1892, 1894, 1896, 1898. OX

E510　do.　North-eastern division. General report by the Chief inspector. 1888, 1890, 1892, 1894, 1896, 1898. OX

E511　do.　North-western division. General report by the Chief inspector. 1887, 1889, 1891, 1893, 1895, 1897, 1899. OX

E512　do.　South-eastern division. General report by the Chief inspector. 1887, 1889, 1891, 1893, 1895, 1897, 1899. OX

E513　do.　South-western division. General report by the Chief inspector. 1886, 1888, 1890, 1892, 1894, 1896, 1898. OX

E514　do.　West-central division. General report by the Chief inspector. 1887, 1889, 1891, 1893, 1895, 1899. OX

E515　*List* of school boards and school attendance committees in England and Wales, 1st April 1884. CA; 1885. CA HU; 1886. HU; 1891. LEI; 1st January 1900. BI

E516　*Reports* from university colleges. 1896, 1899. OX; 1899. ReU

E517　*Return* of the pupils in public and private secondary and other schools . . . and of the teaching staff in such schools on 1st June 1897. OX

E518　*Special reports on educational subjects.* Vols. 1–3. 1897–98. 3 vols. BI CA LEE LEI LO NE OX RE ReU SH; vols. 2–3. 1898. DU NO; vol. 2. 1898. HU

E519　do.　Special reports on secondary education in France. [Reprinted from vol. 2 of the above.] 1899. ReU

E520　do.　Special reports on secondary education in Prussia. [Reprinted from vol. 3 of Special reports.] 1899. LEI

E521　*Training colleges.* Reports for the years 1887 and 1891. LEI; 1891. LO; 1896. OX

EDUCATION, Board of:

E522　*Circulars.* No. 547: Manual instruction in secondary schools. 1908. RE

E523　do.　No. 552: Education (provision of meals) act. 1906. OX

E524　do.　No. 555. *See* E532 Circular no. 707

E525　do.　No. 561: Regulations for secondary schools. Geography. 1907. RE

E526　do.　No. 563: Elementary school teachers' superannuation pamphlet. 1907. OX

E527　do.　No. 573: Memorandum on the history and prospects of the pupil-teacher system. 1907. LEE

E528　do.　No. 574: Teaching of Latin in secondary schools. 1907. BI NE OX RE

E529　do.　No. 577: Education (administrative provisions) act. 1907. OX

E530　do.　No. 599: Teaching of history in secondary schools. 1908. BI LO NE OX RE SO

E531　do.　No. 705: Memorandum on language teaching in state-aided secondary schools in England. 1909. BI LO OX RE

E532　do.　No. 707: Regulations for secondary schools. Pronunciation of Latin. [Formerly issued as Circular 555, Feb. 1907.] 1909. BI NE OX RE

E533　do.　No. 711: Teaching of geometry and graphic algebra in secondary schools. 1909. RE

E534　do.　No. 717: Grants for educational experiments. Employment of French and German assistant teachers in English secondary schools. 1909. HU LEI NE RE

E535　do.　No. 718: Conditions of employment of French and German assistant teachers in English secondary schools. 1909. HU LEI NE RE

E536　do.　No. 719: Teaching of needlework in secondary schools. 1909. BI OX

E537　do.　No. 746: Suggestions for the teaching of gardening. [2nd ed.] 1910, repr. 1911. BI

E538 do. No. 753: The teaching of English in secondary schools. 1910. BI LEI LO OX

E539 do. No. 779: Memorandum on physical training in secondary schools. 1911. BI

E540 do. No. 791: Memoranda on teaching and organisation in secondary schools: pronunciation of Latin. 1913. BI

E541 do. No. 797: Memoranda on teaching and organisation in secondary schools: modern languages. 1912. BI OX ReU

E542 do. No. 819: Suggestions for the consideration of teachers in public elementary schools: winter work for school-gardening classes. 1913. NE

E543 do. No. 826: Memoranda on teaching and organisation in secondary schools: curricula of secondary schools. 1916. BI

E544 do. No. 832: Memoranda on teaching and organisation in secondary schools: music. 1914. LEE NE

E545 do. No. 851: Memoranda on teaching and organisation in secondary schools: geometry. 1914. BI LEE LO NE

E546 do. No. 869: Memoranda on teaching and organisation in secondary schools: modern European history. 1914. BI

E547 do. No. 883: Memoranda on teaching and organisation in secondary schools: curricula of ruralised secondary schools. 1914. LO NE

E548 do. No. 884: Memoranda on teaching and organisation in secondary schools: the place and use of graphs in mathematical teaching. 1914. BI

E549 do. No. 891: Memoranda on teaching and organisation in secondary schools: manual instruction in secondary schools for boys. 1915. BI NE

E550 do. No. 940: Education and infant welfare. 1916. LO

E551 do. No. 1012: Papers read at a conference on the Choice of employment act, with an address by H. A. L. Fisher. 1917. BR

E552 do. No. 1086: Report of the Committee to consider buildings which will be required for compulsory continuation schools. 1918. NE

E553 *Codes of regulations, etc.* [Bound sets of Regulations for] 1902/03; 1903/04; 1904/05; 1905/06; 1906/07; 1907/08; 1908/09; 1909/10; 1910/11; 1911/12; 1914/15. LO

E554 do. *Buildings.* Building regulations: being principles to be observed in planning and fitting up new buildings for public elementary schools. 1907. OX

E555 do. do. Building regulations for public elementary schools. In force from 1st September 1914. 1914. (Cd. 7516.) NE OX RE; 1930 reprint. BI

E556 do. do. Building regulations for secondary schools. 1914. (Cd. 7535.) NE OX

E557 do. *Day schools.* Code of regulations for day schools. 1901, 1902. LO ReU; 1902 *only*. NO OX

E558 do. do. Revised instructions applicable to the code of 1902. 1902. (Cd. 1120.) BI LO ReU

E559 do. *Public elementary schools, etc.* Provisional code of regulations for public elementary schools and training colleges, with schedules. 1903. LO NO

E560 do. do. Code of regulations for public elementary schools. 1904. (Cd. 2074.) DU LEI LO NO OX RE; 1906. (Cd. 3043.) LO NO OX ReU

E561 do. do. Code of regulations for public elementary schools in England. 1907. HU NO OX; 1909. (Cd. 4735.) HU LEE LO NE; 1911. (Cd. 6262.) LO; 1912. HU; 1912 (with modifying minutes 1913/14). LEI

E562 do. *Secondary schools.* Regulations for secondary day schools. 1902. (Cd. 1102.) BI LO OX; Supplementary regulations. 1902/03. LO; Regulations for secondary schools. 1903. (Cd. 1668.) BI LO NO OX; 1904. (Cd. 2128.) BI DU LEI LO NO OX; 1905. (Cd. 2492.) BI LO NO OX; 1906. (Cd. 2998.) BI LO NO OX; 1907. (Cd. 3592.) BI HU NO OX; 1908. (Cd. 4037.) BI OX; 1909. (Cd. 4691.) BI HU LEI LO

E563 do. do. Regulations for secondary schools in England. 1917. (Cd. 8541.) BI BR LO; 1918. (Cd. 9076.) LO OX

E564 do. do. Regulations for secondary schools, memoranda re. Roman Catholics and secondary school regulations, [1907–09], 'waiver resolutions'. [Xerox copies.] LO

E565 do. do. Regulations for secondary schools, 1909/10: correspondence between Sir J. Bromley, G. H. Murray and T. L. Heath. [Xerox copy.] LO

E566 do. *Certified efficient schools.* Regulations and conditions, certified efficient schools. 1908. (Cd. 3944.) HU LEI

E567 do. *Evening schools, technical and vocational education.* Directory, with regulations for establishing and conducting science and art schools and classes, 1900. (Cd. 190.) LO; 1901. NO; Pt. 2, comprising syllabuses and lists of apparatus, etc., for use in schools and classes in connection with the Board of Education. 1901. NO

E568 do. do. Regulations for evening schools, technical institutions, and schools of art and art classes. 1902. [Typescript copy.] LO; 1903 (Cd. 1669.) BI LO; 1904. (Cd. 2172.) BI LEI LO; 1905. (Cd. 2574.) BI; 1906. (Cd. 3067.) BI; 1907. (Cd. 3555.) BI HU LO; 1908. (Cd. 4187.) BI

E569 do. do. Regulations for technical schools, schools of art, and other forms of provision of further education in England and Wales. 1909. HU; do. Grant regulations [*only*]. BI; 1910. HU; do. Grant regulations [*only*]. BI; 1914. (Cd. 7531.) LEI; Amending regulations. 1914. (Cd. 7731.) LEI

E570 do. *Museums and institutions* Code of regulations for museums and institutions 1902. (Cd. 1218.) LO

E571 do. do. Regulations relating to the Royal College of Science, the Royal College of Art, and to museums under the Board of Education. 1903. (Cd. 1840.) BI LO; 1904. (Cd. 2303.) BI

E572 do. *Special education, health and welfare.* Mental deficiency (notification of children) regulations, 1914. 1914. (Cd. 7322) BR

E573 do. do. Model arrangements under section 1 (1) of the Elementary education (defective and epileptic children) act, 1899, and section 31 (1) of the Mental deficiency act, 1913. [1914.] BR

E574 do. do. Regulations, July 11th 1904, providing for grants on account of the education of defective and epileptic children. 1904. (Cd. 2152.) LEI

E575 do. do. Regulations: schools for blind, deaf [etc.] children. 1907, 1909. HU; 1909 with modifying minute 1910. HU; do., with modifying minutes, 1909–14. LEI; modifying minute. 1915. (Cd. 7787.) BR

E576 do. do. Regulations: grants in respect of medical treatment, 1912/13. BR HU; 1914/15. LEI

E577 do. do. Regulations: grants for provision of meals for children attending public elementary schools, year ending 31st March 1915. 1914. (Cd. 7461.) BR LEI

E578 do. do. Regulations for evening play centres for the year ending 31st July 1917. (Cd. 8453.) BR; do., in force from 1st August 1917. (Cd. 8730.) BR

E579 do. do. Regulations: grants to day nurseries in England and Wales, year ending on 31st March 1915. (Cd. 7702.) LEI

E580 do. *Superannuation.* The elementary school teachers superannuation rules, 1898. Published together with the additional rules of 1904 and 1905. 1906. BR; The elementary school teachers superannuation pamphlet. 1912. LO; 1918. OX

E581 do. *Teacher training, etc.* Regulations for the instruction and training of pupil teachers and students in training colleges. 1903. (Cd. 1666.) BR LO NO ReU; 1904. (Cd. 2140.) LEI LO NO ReU; 1905. (Cd. 2607.) NO ReU; 1906. (Cd. 3012.) NE NO ReU

E582 do. do. Regulations for the preliminary education of elementary school teachers. 1907. (Cd. 3444.) HU LO NO ReU; 1908. (Cd. 4038.) ReU; 1909. (Cd. 4628.) BR HU LO ReU; 1913. (Cd. 7003.) BI LEI OX ReU

E583 do. do. Regulations for the training of teachers and for the examination of students in training colleges. 1904. (Cd. 2134.) BI LEI; 1905. NO; 1906. (Cd. 3049.) ReU; 1907. (Cd. 3597.) BI BR HU LEE LO; 1908. (Cd. 4169.) LO

E584 do. do. Regulations for the training of teachers for elementary schools. 1909. (Cd. 4737.) BI BR HU LO; 1910. (Cd. 5239.) BI LO; 1911. (Cd. 5781). BI LO; 1912. (Cd. 6350.) BI HU LO ReU; 1913. (Cd. 6795.) BI LEE LEI; 1915. (Cd. 7988.) LO

E585 do. do. Regulations for the training of teachers for secondary schools. 1909. HU; 1913. LEI; 1916. OX

E586 do. do. Regulations for the training of teachers in force from 1st October 1918. (Cd. 9176.) BR OX

E587 do. do. Regulations for the training of teachers of domestic subjects. 1907. HU; 1909. (Cd. 4603.) HU; do., reprinted. 1913. LEI; 1915. OX

E588 do. do. Regulations and syllabuses [Teachers' examinations]. 1905/06. LEI; 1908/09. HU

E589 do. do. Regulations and syllabus for the preliminary examination for the elementary school teachers' certificate, 1907. [1906.] ReU

E590 do. *Miscellaneous.* Regulations for special grants-in-aid in 1909/10, 1912. HU

E591 do. do. Regulations providing for grants in aid of local authorities in England and Wales exercising powers under the Education (choice of employment) act, 1910. 1913. LEI

E592 do. do. Special regulations for grants in aid of instruction for men serving with the colours. 1914. (Cd. 7712.) LEI

E593 *Educational pamphlets.* No. 3: The modern side at Harrow: the working of an educational experiment, [by G. T. Warner]. [1905]. BI LO

E594 do. No. 4: School doctors in Germany, [by W. H. Dawson]. [1906]. BI BR RE

E595 do. No. 8: Modern sides of public schools: 3. Eton, [by A. A. Somerville]. [1907]. BI

E596 do. No. 10: Modern sides of public schools: 4. Dulwich, [by A. K. Gilkes]. [1907]. BI

E597 do. No. 11: The organisation of physical training in Sweden, with a note on the system adopted in Denmark, [by G. M. Fox, C. J. Phillips and W. H. Salmon]. [1907]. NE

E598 do. No. 13: The problem of rural schools and teachers in North America, [by E. H. Spalding]. [1908]. BI OX

E599 do. No. 18: Compulsory continuation schools in Germany, [by H. A. Clay]. 1910. BI LEE NE

E600 do. No. 19: The course system in evening schools, [by H. T. Holmes]. [1910]. BI LEE NE SH

E601 do. No. 20: The teaching of Latin at the Perse School, Cambridge. 1910. (Educational experiments in secondary schools, no. 1). BI LO

E602 do. No. 21: A school week in the country. Bradford, Grange Road secondary school, girls' department. By Mary A. Johnstone. 1910. (Educational experiments in secondary schools, no. 2.) BI ReU

E603 do. No. 22: Syllabus of mathematics for the Austrian gymnasien, [translated by E. A. Price]. 1910. LEE

E604 do. No. 23: The training of women teachers for secondary schools: a series of statements from institutions concerned. 1912. BI LO NE OX RE SO

E605 do. No. 24: The Montessori system o education, [by E. G. A. Holmes]. 1912. BI LEE LO SH

E606 do. No. 26: Education and peasant industry: some state and state-aided trade schools in Germany, [by Edith Edlmann]. 1912. BI HU LEE LO ReU

E607 do. No. 27: The playground movement in America and its relation to public education, [by Walter Wood]. 1913. BI BR HU LEE

E608 do. No. 28: Report on the teaching of Greek at the Perse School, Cambridge. 1914. (Educational experiments in secondary schools, no. 3.) BI BR LEE NE ReU

E609 do. No. 29: The experiment in rural secondary education conducted at Knaresborough. 1915. (Educational experiments in secondary schools, no. 4.) OX ReU

E610 do. No. 30: An experiment in industrial research, [by T. L. Humberstone]. 1915. BR

E611 do. No. 31: A rural special subjects centre. 1915. BI DU NE ReU

E612 do. No. 33: The universities of the United Kingdom. A handbook compiled by the Universities Bureau of the British Empire. 1918. BI ReU

E613 *Grant returns, etc.* 1. Associations constituted under the Voluntary schools act, 1897; 2. Associated schools and amount of aid grant paid; 3. Unassociated schools and amount of aid grant paid, 1899/1900. (Cd. 212.) BI HU; 1901/02. (Cd. 1143.) BI; 1902/03. (Cd. 1615.) BI

E614 do. 1. Schools in receipt of parliamentary grants; 2. Grants paid to school boards; 3. School board accounts and list of loans, 1899/1900. (Cd. 332.) BI NE ReU; 1900/01. ReU

E615 do. 1. Grants paid to school boards; 2. School board accounts; 3. List of loans, 1901/02. (Cd. 1276.) HU NE; 1902/03. (Cd. 1751.) BI

E616 do. Return for public elementary schools, name and denomination of school; number of scholars; annual grant paid; and particulars of school income and expenditure for the year ended 31st August 1899. 1901. (Cd. 315.) BI

E617 do. Return, higher education, England and Wales: application of funds by local authorities during the year 1903/04. BI NO; 1905/06. BI; 1906/07. BI

E618 do. Return, technical education; application of funds by local authorities. 1900–03. 4 vols. OX; 1902/03–1904/05. 2 vols. BI

E619 do. Tables of expenditure for agricultural education (apart from secondary schools and elementary schools), comprising tables of grants-in-aid from the Board of Agriculture and the Board of Education, and of the expenditure of county councils, with explanatory memorandum. 1909. OX

E620 do. Statement of grants available from the Board of Education in aid of technological and professional work in universities in England and Wales. 1911. HU NO; 1912. HU

E621 *Inspectors' and examiners' reports.* Reports on elementary schools, 1852–82, by Matthew Arnold. New edition, with an introduction by F. S. Marvin. H.M.S.O., 1908. *See* C48

E622 do. General report for the year 1899: East Central division; Metropolitan division; North Western division; South Eastern division; West Central division. 1900. 5 vols. BI

E623 do. General report for the year 1900: Eastern division; North Central division; North Eastern division; South Western division. 4 vols. OX

E624 do. General reports of H.M. Inspectors on elementary schools and training colleges for the year 1901. (Cd. 1159.) BI HU NE OX; for the year 1902. (Cd. 1706.) BR OX

E625 do. General reports of H.M. Inspectors on science and art schools and classes, and evening schools, and of examiners in science and art for the year 1901. (Cd. 1214.) BI NE OX

E626 do. Art examinations, reports of the examiners, 1906–09. 4 vols. in 1. BI

E627 do. Science examinations: reports, summaries of results, names of successful candidates. 1907–09. 3 vols. in 1. BI

E628 do. Science examinations: examination papers and examiners' reports. 1910–12, 1914–15. 5 vols. in 3. BI

E629 do. General report by Mr. H. Ward, H.M.I., upon elementary education in Lancashire and Cheshire. [Reprinted from the Board's Annual report, 1913/14.] OX

E630 do. General report of H.M. Inspectors on the technical schools and evening schools in the administrative county of Wilts, for the period ending on the 31st July 1914. 1914. BR

E631 do. General report of H.M. Inspectors on Swindon and North Wilts technical institute for the period ending on the 31st July 1914. BR

E632 do. Swindon and North Wilts technical institute school of art: report of detailed inspection held on the 4th–9th May, 1914. BR

E633 do. General reports on higher education for the year 1902. (Cd. 1738.) BI LO OX

E634 do. General report on the teaching of domestic subjects to public elementary school children in England and Wales, by the chief woman inspector. 1912. OX

E635 do. Report by the chief woman inspector on the teaching of needlework in public elementary schools, 1912. 1913. BI; do., repr. 1919. LEI

E636 do. Special report on the teaching of cookery to public elementary school children in England and Wales, by the chief woman inspector. 1907. NE NO OX

E637 do. Report of an enquiry into the teaching of French in London secondary schools, conducted by the Board's inspectors, during parts of the spring and summer terms, 1916. 1916. BI OX

E638 do. Report on the teaching of literary subjects in some secondary schools, by J. W. Headlam. 1902. [Typescript.] LO

E639 do. Special reports on the instruction and training of pupil teachers. [Confidential.] 1903. ReU

E640 *Lists.* Abstracts of accounts of secondary schools on the grant list in England. (List 69.) 1911–12. (Cd. 7043.) BI; 1912/13. BI HU

E641 do. Abstract of school attendance by-laws in force in England and Wales on 1st Jan. 1910. LO

E643 do. List of school boards and school attendance committees in England and Wales, 1st Jan. 1902. (Cd. 1038.) HU

E644 do. List of schools under the administration of the Board, 1901/02. (Cd. 1277.) BI NE

E645 do. List of public elementary schools and training colleges under the Board, 1902/03. (Cd. 1490.) BI; 1903/04. (Cd. 2011.) BI

E646 do. List of public elementary schools in England and Wales, 1st Jan. 1906. (Cd. 3182.) HU; 1st Aug. 1907. (Cd. 3901.) HU

E647 do. List of public elementary schools and certified efficient schools in England, excluding Monmouthshire. (List 21.) Years 1907–12, 1919. 7 vols. BI

E648 do. List of secondary schools, science and art schools and classes, and evening schools under the administration of the Board, 1902/03. (Cd. 1752.) BI

E649 do. List of secondary schools in England recognised as efficient. (List 60). Years 1907/08–1913/14. BI; 1909/10, 1913/14, 1917/18 index. LO; 1911/12. NE

E650 do. List of the schools in England and Wales recognised on 1st Jan. 1906 as voluntary public elementary schools. (List 32.) 1906, repr. 1907. BI RE

E651 do. List of certified schools for blind, deaf, defective and epileptic children. (List 42.) At July 1912. (Cd. 6570.) NE

E652 do. List of training colleges, and hostels, for the training of teachers for elementary schools in England and Wales, with particulars for 1912/13 and accounts for 1911/12. (List 175.) BI

E653 do. Medical officers recognised under the Elementary school teacher (superannuation) act, 1898. (List 11.) 1915. LO

E654 do. National competition; lists of students rewarded, with the report of the examiners. 1905–1910. 6 vols. BI

E655 do. National competition; lists of successful competitors and reports of examiners. (List 108.) 1912–16. 5 vols. BI

E656 do. National competitions, retrospective exhibition, 1908. Unillustrated list of works for which gold or silver medals have been awarded, 1897 to 1906. 1908. BI

E658 *Memoranda.* Interim memorandum on the teaching of housecraft in girls' secondary schools. 1911. OX

E659 do. Memorandum in explanation and expansion of the Board's circular on the teaching of history in secondary schools. [1908]. BI RE

E660 do. Memorandum on closure of and exclusion from school. 1909. BR

E661 do. Memoranda on 'common form deprivation clause' with reference to scholarships and free places. 1909. [Xerox copy.] LO

E662 do. Memorandum on defining the powers of the Advisory committee. (Office memorandum no. 36, 1910), [by W. N. Bruce]. [Xerox copy.] LO

E663 do. Memorandum on the need of a new Advisory committee on curricula, etc. (Office memorandum no. 35, 1910), [by R. L. Morant]. [Xerox copy.] LO

E664 do. Memorandum on the full inspections of secondary schools, 1906–07. (Office memorandum no. 20, 1908) [Xerox copy.] LO

E665 do. Memorandum on the principles and methods of rural education. 1911. BI NE

E666 do. Physical training. Memorandum on gymnasium equipment. 1914. NE

E667 *Reports, Annual.* Report for the years 1899/1900–1917/18. SO; do. [wanting vols. 1 and 3 of 1900/01, 1903/04, and 1906/07]. BI; do. [wanting 1904/05 and 1909/10]. BR; 1901/02, 1908/09, 1910/11–1917/18. LEE; 1900/01–1903/04, 1905/06, 1907/08–1908/09, 1910/11–1911/12, 1913/14–1918/19. LO; 1899/1900 [wanting vol. 2], 1900/01, 1907/08, 1911/12, 1912/13. NE; 1899/1900 [wanting vol. 2], 1903/04, 1904/05, 1908/09, 1910/11, 1914/15, 1915/16. NO; 1908/09, 1909/10, 1911/12, 1912/13. MA; 1899/1900, 1902/03 [vol. 2 *only*], 1903/04, 1909/10, 1911/12–1917/18. OX; 1916/17, 1917/18. RE; 1899/1900, 1900/01, 1901/03, 1904/07, 1909/10, 1911/12, 1913/14, 1915/16, 1916/17. ReU

E668 do. Report on the museums, colleges and institutions under the administration of the Board, year 1901. (Cd. 1266.) BI NE; year 1902. (Cd. 1737.) BI

E669 do. Reports from university colleges in receipt of grant, *continued as* Reports from universities and university colleges. 1899–1913/14. OX ReU; 1900–02 (Cd. 331, 845, 1510), 1906/07, 1907, 1907/08–1909/10 (Cd. 4440, 3885, 4875, 5246, 5872). BI; 1910/11–1913/14 [vol. 2 *only* for 1911/12 and 1912/13]. LEI; 1905, 1906/07, 1907, 1907/08, 1911/12–1913/14. LO; 1907, 1912/13, 1913/14. NE; 1906, 1907/08–1910/11 (Cd. 3409, 4875, 5246, 5872, 6245–6). SH

E670 do. Annual report of the Chief medical officer for the years 1909–18. LO OX; 1908–1910, 1912, 1916–17. NE; 1910, 1912–18. ReU; 1908. HU; 1909. LEI

E671 *Special reports on educational subjects.* [*For vols. 1–3 see* E518–E520.] Vol. 4–5: Educational systems of the chief colonies of the British Empire. 1901. (Cd. 416–417.) BI HU LEE LEI NE NO OX RE ReU SH; vol. 5 *only.* SO

E672 do. Vol. 6: Preparatory schools for boys: their place in English secondary education. 1900. (Cd. 418.) BI CA LEE LEI LO NE NO OX RE ReU SH SO

E673 do. Vol. 7: Rural education in France. 1902. (Cd. 834.) BI CA HU LEE LEI LO NE NO OX RE ReU SH

E674 do. Vol. 8: Education in Scandinavia, Switzerland, Holland, Hungary, etc. 1902. (Cd. 835.) BI CA DU HU LEE LEI LO NE NO OX RE ReU SH SO

E675 do. Supplement 1 to Vol. 8: A short account of education in the Netherlands. 1902. (Cd. 1157.) BI LEE NE RE ReU SO

E676 do. Supplement 2 to Vol. 8: Report on the school training and early employment of Lancashire children. 1903. (Cd. 1867.) BI CA LEE RE

E677 do. Vol. 9: Education in Germany. 1902. (Cd. 836.) BI CA HU LEE LEI LO NE NO OX RE ReU SH

E678 do. Vols. 10–11: Education in the United States of America. 1902. (Cd. 837 and 1156.) BI CA HU LEE LEI LO NE NO OX RE ReU SH; vol. 11 only. DU

E679 do. Vols. 12–14: Educational systems of the chief Crown colonies. 1905. (Cd. 2377–9.) BI LEE LEI NO RE ReU SH; vols. 12–13 only. LO; vols. 13–14 only. OX

E680 do. Vols. 15–16: School training for the home duties of women. 1905–06. (Cd. 2498 and 2963.) BI LEE LEI LO NO OX RE ReU SH; vol. 15 only. NE; vol. 16 only. SO

E681 do. Vol. 17: Schools public and private in the north of Europe. 1907. (Cd. 3537.) BI LEE LEI LO NO OX RE ReU SH SO

E682 do. Vol. 18: The education and training of the French primary school teacher. 1907. (Cd. 3777.) BI CA LEE LEI LO NO OX RE ReU SH SO

E683 do. Vol. 19: School training for the home duties of women. Pt. 3. 1907. (Cd. 3860.) BI LEE LEI LO NO OX RE ReU SH SO

E684 do. Vol. 20: The teaching of classics in secondary schools in Germany. 1909. (Cd. 4997.) BI LEE LEI LO NO OX RE ReU SH SO

E685 do. Vol. 21: School excursions and vacation schools. 1907. (Cd. 3866.) BI HU LEE LEI NE NO OX RE ReU SH SO

E686 do. Vol. 22: Provision made for children under compulsory school age in Belgium, France, Germany and Switzerland. 1909. (Cd. 4477.) BI LEE LEI NO OX ReU SH SO

E687 do. Vol. 23: Education in Russia. 1909. (Cd. 4812.) BI LEE LEI NO OX ReU SH

E688 do. Vol. 24: Secondary education in France. 1911. BI CA LEE LEI LO ReU SH

E689 do. Vol. 25: Universities in the overseas dominions. 1912. BI CA LEE LEI OX ReU SH

E690 do. Vols. 26–27: The teaching of mathematics in the United Kingdom. 1912. BI HU LEE LEI NO OX RE ReU SH

E691 do. Vol. 28: School and employment in the United States. 1914. BI HU LEE OX ReU

E692 *Statistics.* Statistics of public education in England and Wales, 1903/04/05 (Cd. 2782). BI LO OX; 1904/05/06. LO NO

E693 do. Statistics of public education in England and Wales. Part 1: Educational statistics. 1905/06/07. (Cd. 3886.) BI LO; 1906/07/08. (Cd. 4288.) BI HU LO NO; 1907/08. (Cd. 4885.) BI HU LO OX; 1908/09. (Cd. 5355.) BI LO NO; 1909/10. (Cd. 5843.) BI LO NO OX ReU; 1910/11. (Cd. 6338.) BI HU LEI LO NO; 1911/12. (Cd. 6934.) BI HU LEI LO NO; 1912/13. (Cd. 7674.) BI LO OX ReU; 1913/14. (Cd. 8097.) BI HU LEI LO NO OX ReU

E694 do. Statistics of public education in England and Wales. Part 2: Financial statistics. 1907/08/09. (Cd. 5147.) BI HU NO OX ReU; 1908/09/10. (Cd. 5506.) BI NO OX ReU; 1909/10/11. (Cd. 6018.) BI HU NO OX; 1910/11/12. (Cd. 6551.) BI NO; 1911/12/13. (Cd. 7204.) BI HU NO OX; 1912/13. (Cd. 8054.) BI OX ReU; 1910/14. NO

E695 do. Statistics of elementary day schools, evening continuation schools and training colleges, 1900/01. NE

E696 do. Statistics of public elementary schools, pupil teacher centres and training colleges, 1901/02. (Cd. 1476.) BI OX; 1902/03. (Cd. 2000.) HU LO NO OX; 1903/04–1913/14. LO

E697 do. Public elementary schools in England and Wales: tabular statement showing, for the area of each local education authority for elementary education in England and Wales, the number of departments of ordinary public elementary schools with an average attendance not exceeding 100. 1914. OX

E698 do. Elementary education (England and Wales): statistics relating to the receipts and expenditure of local education authorities in the financial year 1913/14. OX

E699 *Suggestions and syllabuses.* Manual instruction in public elementary schools. 1910. NE

E700 do. Model course of physical training for use in the upper departments of public elementary schools, 1902. 1902. BI

E701 do. Syllabus of physical exercises for public elementary schools. 1904. LO; do. 1909. BR LO OX; 1909, repr. 1914. LO

E702 do. Outline scheme for teaching hygiene and temperance to the scholars attending public elementary schools. 1905. ReU

E703 do. Syllabus of lessons on temperance for scholars attending public elementary schools. [1909]. BI

E704 do. Suggestions for the consideration of teachers and others concerned in the work of public elementary schools. 1905. (Cd. 2638.) LO NO OX ReU SO; *with* Rev. ed., Instalment no. 1, Suggestions for the teaching of needlework, 1909. HU; *with* Rev. ed., Instalments nos. 1 and 2, Needlework and gardening. 1912. BI LO NE; 4th ed. 1918. BI NE ReU

E705 do. Suggestions for the consideration of teachers . . . Revised ed. Instalment no. 1: Suggestions for the teaching of needlework, 1909, repr. 1911. LO; Instalment no. 2: Suggestions for the teaching of gardening. 1910. LO; Instalment no. 3: Suggestions for the teaching of arithmetic. 1912. LO; Instalment no. 4: Suggestions for the teaching of English. 1912. LO; Instalment no. 6: Suggestions for the teaching of history. 1914. LO; Instalment no. 8: Suggestions for the teaching of singing. 1914. LO

E706 do. Suggestions on rural education, by T. S. Dymond . . . together with some specimen courses of nature study, gardening, and rural economy. 1908. NO ReU

E707 do. Syllabuses and lists of apparatus applicable to schools and classes other than elementary, 1903/04. LO; 1904/05. LO; 1906/07. BI; *see also* E567

E708 do. Syllabuses and lists of apparatus applicable to technical schools, schools of art, and other forms of provision of further education in England and Wales. 1907/08–1908/09. BI

E709 do. Syllabuses applicable to technical schools, schools of art . . . [etc.] in England and Wales. 1909/10. BI LEI; 1910/11. BI

E710 do. Syllabuses of the preliminary examination for the Elementary school teachers' certificate. (Syllabus 1, 1910.) 1908. HU; 1915 syllabus. 1913. LEI; 1916 syllabus. 1914. LEI; *see also* E588–589

E711 do. Syllabus of the Certificate examination for teachers in elementary schools. (Syllabus 2, 1910.) [1908]. HU; 1914 syllabus. 1912. LEI; 1916 syllabus. 1914. LEI; 1918 syllabus. 1916. BI

E712 *Miscellaneous.* Form 125: Music in secondary schools. 1906. BI OX RE

E713 do. Scheme for a new Teachers' registration council proposed to the Board of Education by the representatives of certain educational associations. 1908. OX

E713a EDUCATION, Board of. Consultative committee. Conferences held on 8th and 9th May 1903, with representatives of universities on the subject of a system of leaving certificate examinations. 1903. (Paper no. 60.) LEI

E714 do. Minutes, 1st–45th meetings, Nov. 7, 1900–June 1, 1905. [Lacks 36 and 38.] LEI

E715 do. Report of the consultative committee upon questions affecting higher elementary schools. 1906. BI OX

E716 do. Standing orders of the consultative committee constituted under the Board of Education act, 1899. [1901.] LEI

E717 FOREIGN OFFICE. Technical and primary education: circular of Lord Stanley to Her Majesty's representatives abroad, together with their replies. 1868. SH

E718 GENERAL REGISTER OFFICE. Census, 1851. Education: England and Wales. Report and tables. 1854. HU LEE ReU

E719 GENERAL REGISTER OFFICE. Census, 1851. Education in Great Britain. Being the official report of Horace Mann, with selected tables. Routledge, 1854. LEI

E720 HOME OFFICE. Libraries for reformatory and industrial schools. 1916. LEE

E721 HOME OFFICE. Inspector of reformatory schools. 1st report. 1858. BR; 2nd report. 1859. HU

E722 HOME OFFICE. Inspector of reformatory and industrial schools. 28th report, for the year 1884. LEI; 40th–54th reports, for the years 1896–1910. [Lacks nos. 41–43, 52.] LEE

E723 IMPERIAL EDUCATION CONFERENCE, 1911. Conditions of recognition, classification and payment of teachers in the self-governing dominions. No. 8: Dominion of Canada—Saskatchewan. 1914. No. 11: Commonwealth of Australia—New South Wales. 1914. No. 15: do., Western Australia. 1913. No. 16: do., Tasmania. 1913. No. 18: Union of South Africa—Cape of Good Hope. 1914. No. 19: do., Natal. 1914. No. 20: do., Transvaal. 1913. No. 21: do., Orange Free State. 1913. BR; No. 21 *only*. NE

E724 IMPERIAL EDUCATION CONFERENCE, 1911. Educational systems of the chief colonies. British Honduras, 1915; Falkland Islands, Fiji, St. Helena. 1915. Federated Malay States. 1913. Northern Nigeria. 1913. Southern Nigeria. 1913. Straits Settlements. 1913. Trinidad and Tobago. 1913. NE

E725 IMPERIAL EDUCATION CONFERENCE, 1911. Report. 1911. *See* E409

E726 IMPERIAL INSTITUTE. English education exhibition, January 5th to 27th, 1900. Catalogue of exhibits. 2nd ed., [1900]. LEI

E727 IMPERIAL INSTITUTE. Year-book, 1893. Murray, 1893. LEI

INSPECTOR OF REFORMATORY AND INDUSTRIAL SCHOOLS. *See* Home Office

E728 LOCAL GOVERNMENT BOARD. Annual local taxation returns, year 1883/84. Part V, [sections] 20–24. 1885. (H.C.250-IV.) [Section 24: School board accounts.] LEI

E729 LOCAL GOVERNMENT BOARD. Annual reports, nos. 9–12, 1879/80–1882/83, and no. 14, 1884/85. LEI; no. 25, 1895/96; no. 30, 1900/01; no. 32, 1902/03; no. 39, 1909/10. LO

E730 LOCAL GOVERNMENT BOARD. Supplement to the annual report, containing the report of the medical officer. Suppt. to report no. 16, 1886/87; suppt. to report no. 39, 1909/10; suppt. to report no. 43, 1913/14; suppt. to report no. 45, 1915/16. LEI

E731 LOCAL GOVERNMENT BOARD. Reports on public health and medical subjects. New series. Nos. 40, 53, 63, 64, 66, 78, 85, 88. 1910–14. 8 vols. LEI; No. 100. 1914. NE

E732 LOCAL GOVERNMENT BOARD. Education of girls in pauper schools: report, by Jane E. Senior. 1874. [In Hughes, D. M. Memoir of Jane Elizabeth Senior. Boston, 1916.] HU

E733 LONDON INTERNATIONAL EXHIBITION, 1871. Official reports on the various sections of the exhibition, ed. by Lord Houghton. Division II, Educational works and appliances. Part VIII. *Also* Part IX, Reports on specimens of school work. [n.d.] HU

E734 POOR LAW COMMISSIONERS. Annual report, with appendices. 1st. 1835. LEI; 2nd. 1836. LEI LO; 9th. 1843. HU; 13th. 1847. LO

E735 POOR LAW COMMISSIONERS. The training of pauper children: a report by James Phillips Kay, published by the Poor Law Commissioners in their fourth annual report. 1839. HU

E736 PRACTICAL ART, Department of. (Board of Trade.) First report, 1852/53. [1615-iv.] LO; [Second report is included in the First report of the Science and art department, Board of Trade, q.v.]

E737 PUBLIC ACCOUNTS, Committee of. First report. 1905. (H.C.176.) LO

E737a SCHOOL OF DESIGN COUNCIL. (Board of Trade.) 2nd–5th reports, 1842–46. LO

E738 SCHOOL OF DESIGN COUNCIL. Schools of design. Government reports and documents exhibiting the progress of the head and branch schools of design in the year 1850/51. [1423.] LO

SCIENCE AND ART DEPARTMENT. (Board of Trade):

E739 Industrial instruction on the continent, by Sir Lyon Playfair. Introductory lecture of the session 1852/53, Museum of practical geology, Government school of mines. HU

E740 Prospectus of the Metropolitan school of science applied to mining and the arts, 4th session, 1854/55. LEI

E741 Reports 1–3, 1854–56. HU ReU; 1–2 only. LO; 2–3 only. NO; 1–2 and 4, 1854–57. SH; see also E750

SCIENCE AND ART DEPARTMENT. (Committee of Council on Education):

E742 Art directory, containing regulations for promoting instruction in art. Rules revised to: Aug. 1878, Apr. 1879, Aug. 1879, Aug. 1880, Aug. 1881, Aug. 1882, Aug. 1883, Aug. 1884, Sept. 1885. LEI; see also E336

E743 Calendar and general directory, for the years 1885–87, 1889–91. BI; years 1884, 1886–87, 1890. LEI; years 1890–92. LO

E744 Calendar, history and general summary of regulations for 1893–99. 7 vols. LO; 1894–1900. OX; 1894. HU; 1900. NO

E745 Directory, with regulations for establishing and conducting science and art schools and classes for the years 1890–93, 1896. BI; 1889–1901. LO; 1901. NO

E746 Certificates. Certificates for examinations in Mathematics, stages 1, 2, 3: 2nd class, 1st stage; Human physiology: 2nd class, advanced stage; Hygiene: 2nd class, advanced stage. LO

E747 do. Certificate for training college examinations, Geometrical drawing, 1889: Pass; Freehand drawing, 1889: 2nd grade, 1st class; Botany, 1889: 2nd class, elementary stage; Model drawing with chalk on blackboard, 1890: Pass; Perspective, 1890: 2nd grade, 1st class; Botany, 1890: 2nd class, advanced stage; Drawing in light and shade, 1891: Pass. LO

E748 Drawing for elementary schools, by Ellis A. Davidson. See C348

E749 Prospectus of Sir Joseph Whitworth's scholarships and exhibitions for mechanical science. Regulation for the competition in 1890 (24th ed.), 1900 (34th ed.). HU

E750 Reports. Reports, with appendices. Nos. 17, 19–20, 22, 26, 31, 33–34, 36, 38–39. 1870–92. 11 vols. BI; nos. 1–2, 18–20, 22, 26, 29, 31, 33–34, 36, 38–39. 1854–92. HU; nos. 6, 13, 15, 17–20, 22, 25, 28, 34, 36–40, 42–46. 1859–99. LEI; nos. 6–8, 10–11, 13–29. 1859–82. LO; nos. 2–3, 18–22, 25–27, 29, 31–39. 1855–92. NO; nos. 41, 43, 45–46. 1894–99. OX; nos. 1–3, 12. 1854–65. ReU; nos. 11–12, 19–20, 28. 1864–81. SH; [N.B.: Dates are given for first and last in the run only.]

E751 Supplement to reports 40–45, with title: Drawing and manual instruction in elementary schools. 1893–99. LEI

E752 Return to the Department of science and art, showing the manner in which . . . councils . . . are devoting funds to the purposes of science, art, technical and manual instruction, 1894, 1895. OX

E753 South Kensington Museum. Catalogue of of the education library in the South Kensington Museum. 1893. LEI

E754 do. Catalogue of the special loan collection of scientific apparatus at the South Kensington Museum. 3rd ed. 1877. LEI

E755 do. An address to teachers by William Ellis . . . delivered at the South Kensington Museum, Oct. 1859. See C422

TRADE, BOARD OF:

E756 Commercial, labour and statistical dept. Statistical abstract for the United Kingdom in each of the last fifteen years from 1894 to 1908. 1909. (Cd. 4805.) LO; do. for each of the fifteen years from 1910 to 1924. 1926. (Cmd. 2620.) LO

E757 do. Statistical abstract for the British Empire in each year from 1893 to 1907. 1909. (Cd. 4486.) LO

E758 Labour dept. Foreign labour statistics, fourth abstract. 1911. [Cd. 5415.] LO

E759 Dept. of labour statistics. Labour statistics of the United Kingdom, seventeenth abstract. 1915. (Cd. 7733.) LO

E760 TREASURY. Estimates, etc., civil services. Class IV: Education, science, and art, year ending 31 March 1892. (Session 1890/91, H.C.50-iv.) LEI

E761 [WAR OFFICE.] Manual of physical training. 1908. NE

E762 WAR OFFICE. Council of military education. General report no. 2. [1865.] (C.3502.) BI

E763 WAR OFFICE. do. First report on army schools. 1862. SH

E764 WAR OFFICE. do. Reports on army schools, libraries and recreations. Nos. 2–4, years 1864–66; no. 6, year 1868/69. 1865–70. 4 vols. BI; no. 5, year 1867. 1868. SH

E765 WAR OFFICE. Director-general of military education. Report on army schools, 1889. 1889. (C.5805.) BI

Serial publications and departmental publications, arranged by department: Ireland

E766 BELFAST. Queen's College. Report of the President for the session 1885/86. (C.4867.) LO

E767 CENSUS OF IRELAND, 1875. Part I, vol. 2: Province of Munster, nos. 1–6, summary index. 1875. (C.873-I-vii.) LO

E768 CENSUS OF IRELAND, 1875. Part II, vol. 1: Vital statistics report—disease. 1875. (C.876.) LO

E769 CENSUS OF IRELAND, 1875. Part II, vol. 2: Vital statistics report—deaths. 1875. (C.1000.) LO

E770 COMMISSION ON EDUCATIONAL ENDOWMENTS (Ireland). Annual report of the commissioners for the years 1885/86–1888/89, together with abstract of the minutes of the commission, minutes of evidence and appendices. Dublin, 1886–89. 4 vols. (C.4903, C.5232, C.5546, C.5838.) BI

E771 COMMISSIONERS OF THE BOARD OF EDUCATION IN IRELAND. Reports 1–14, 1809–12. Dublin, 1813. [1: Free schools of royal foundation. 2: Schools of private foundation. 3: Protestant charter schools. 4: Diocesan free schools. 5: Wilson's Hospital. 6: Blue Coat Hospital. 7: Hibernian School. 8: Foundling Hospital. 9: Erasmus Smith's schools. 10: Hibernian Marine School. 11: Parish schools. 12: Classical schools of private foundation. 13: English schools of private foundation in Ireland. 14: General remarks.] BR; 11th report *only*. 1811. ReU; 12th report *only*. 1812. NE

COMMISSIONERS OF NATIONAL EDUCATION IN IRELAND:

E772 Correspondence of Messrs. Longman and Co. with the Rt. Hon. Lord John Russell, M.P., on the publication of school books by Government at the public expense: the statement of the commissioners in reference thereto; and the reply of Lord John Russell. Dublin, 1851. LEI; *another ed.*, London, Longman, & J. Murray, 1851. HU

E773 An introduction to the art of reading, with suitable accentuation and intonation, for the use of teachers. 3rd ed., Dublin, 1857. BI

E774 Manual of needlework for the use of national schools. Dublin, 1873. LEI

E775 Reports 1–15, years 1834–45; 21, vols. 1–2, year 1854. BR; Reports 1–15, years 1834–45. HU; Reports 1–16, 1834–49; 17, vol. 1, 1850; 18, vols. 1–2, 1851; 19, vol. 1, 1852; 20, vol. 2, 1853; 21, vol. 1, 1854; 32, vols. 1–2, 1865; *also* Appendix to 3rd report, 1836. LO; Reports 1–16, 1834–49; 17, vol. 1, 1850; 18, vols. 1–2, 1851; 19, vol. 1, 1852; 21, vol. 1, 1854; 58–59, 1891–92. ReU; Reports 1–9, 1834–42. SH; Report 31, vols. 1–2, year 1864. LEI; Report 66, 1899, with appendices. 4 vols. BI

E776 Rules and regulations. From the 21st report. Dublin, 1855. BI

E777 Selections from the Rules and regulations, bearing on the subject of religious instruction, for the information of the parents of the children attending national schools. [In E773]

E778 *Textbooks*. Agricultural classbook. 1853. *See* D15

E779 do. Chemistry and chemical analysis. 1861. *See* D235

E780 do. First book of arithmetic. 1857. *See* D460

E781 do. Second book of lessons. 1855. *See* D1191

E782 do. Selections from the British poets. 1858. *See* D1199

E783 do. Third book of lessons. 1862. *See* D1337

E784 do. Treatise on mensuration. 2nd ed. 1850. *See* D1358a

E785 COMMISSIONERS OF EDUCATION IN IRELAND. Annual report for the years 1885/86, 1886/87. Dublin. LEI; year 1904. (Cd. 2502.) LO; year ending 1916. (Cd. 8557.) LO

E786 BOARD OF INTERMEDIATE EDUCATION IN IRELAND. 2nd report, for the year 1880. (C.2919); 6th report, for the year 1884. (C.4464.) LO

E787 IRISH OFFICE. Copy of correspondence relative to the proposed charter to a Roman Catholic university in Ireland. 1868. BI

E788 IRISH OFFICE. Copy of further correspondence relative to the proposed charter to a Roman Catholic university in Ireland. 1868. BI

Serial publications and departmental publications, arranged by department: *Scotland*

E789 CHURCH OF SCOTLAND. *General Assembly*. Reports of the Committee for increasing the means of education and religious instruction in Scotland, particularly in the Highlands and Islands, submitted . . . 1829–36. Edinburgh, 1829–36. 8 vols. in 1. BI

E790 CHURCH OF SCOTLAND. do. Statement by the education committee of deficiencies in the means of education for the poor in certain of the large towns of Scotland. Edinburgh, 1836. SH

EDUCATION:

E791 Board of Education for Scotland. Annual reports 1–6. Edinburgh, 1874–79. 6 vols. BI LO; Reports 1–2. 1874–75. ReU

E792 Committee of Council on Education. Minute dated 10th June, 1897, providing for the distribution of the sum available for secondary education under section 2 (1) (b) of the Education and Local Taxation Account (Scotland) Act, 1892. 1897. (C.8515.) LO

E793 Committee of Council on Education in Scotland. Reports, etc. 1873/74–1907/08 [wants 1899/1900]. LO; 1877/78–1904/05 and 1907/08 [1894/95 no appendix]. 29 vols. BI; 1874/75, 1875/76, 1904/05–1906/07. NE; 1875/76, 1899/ 1900–1900/01, 1902/03–1905/06, 1907/08, 1909/10– 1910/11, 1915/16–1917/18. LEE; 1895/96, 1899/ 1900, 1907/08, 1918/19, 1919/20. OX; 1875/76. LEI; 1896/97–1898/99. SH

E794 do. Report on the inspection of higher class schools and the examination for leaving certificate, with appendix, 1894, 1895, 1896, 1906. OX

E795 Scotch [later Scottish] Education Department. *Circulars*. Circulars relating to the inspection of higher class schools, and papers set at the examination for leaving certificates, 1888. (C.5496.) LEI

E796 do. do. A selection of circular letters of the Scotch Education Department, 1898–1904, with explanatory memorandum. 1904. OX

E797 do. *Codes of regulations, etc.* Code of regulations, 1874. (C.930.) LEI; 1891. (C.6280.) LEI

E798 do. do. Code of regulations for day schools, with appendixes, 1908. (Cd. 3948.) BI

E799 do. do. Code of regulations for continuation classes, 1901, with memorandum, 1904– 15. LO; 1911–13. LEI

E800 do. do. Regulations for the preliminary education, training and certification of teachers for various grades of schools, 1915. (Cd. 8061.) NE

E801 do. Leaving certificate examination: examination papers, 1918. LEI

E802 do. *Memoranda.* Memorandum on the teaching of English in Scottish primary schools. 1907. (Cd. 3410.) BI; do., 1911 reprint. LEE

E803 do. do. Memorandum on the teaching of arithmetic in primary schools. 1907. (Cd. 3448.) BI

E804 do. do. Memorandum on the study of languages. 1907. (Cd. 3546.) BI

E805 do. do. Memorandum on the teaching of drawing. 1907. (Cd. 3662.) BI LO

E806 do. do. Memorandum on the study of history in Scottish schools. 1907. (Cd. 3843.) LEE LEI

E807 do. do. Memorandum on nature study and the teaching of science in Scottish schools. 1908, repr. 1911. (Cd. 4024.) LEI

E808 do. *Reports, etc.* Reports and statistics relating to continuation classes and central institutions for the year 1906/07. LO

E809 do. do. Secondary education (Scotland). Report for the year 1915. OX

E810 do. do. Training of teachers. Report, statistics, etc., 1901/02. (Cd. 1514.) BI

E811 GENERAL REGISTER OFFICE. Census, 1851. Religious worship and education. Scotland. Report and tables. 1854. LEE

E812 LOCAL GOVERNMENT BOARD FOR SCOTLAND. Annual reports 1, for the year 1894/95; 13–14, 1907–08; 18–25, 1912–19. LO

Serial publications and departmental publications, arranged by department: *Wales*

E813 EDUCATION DEPARTMENT. Welsh division. General report for the year 1886. LEI; year 1894. OX; year 1898. ReU

E814 EDUCATION, Board of. Code of regulations for public elementary schools in Wales, 1909. HU; 1912. OX

E815 EDUCATION, Board of. Regulations for secondary schools (Wales), 1909. HU

E816 EDUCATION, Board of. Regulations for the preliminary education of elementary school teachers (Wales), 1909. HU

E817 EDUCATION, Board of. Education in Wales: directory, 1911. OX

E818 EDUCATION, Board of. Report on the administration of schools under the Welsh Intermediate Education Act for the years 1901–07, 1911–15, 1917–24. OX; year 1916. ReU

E819 EDUCATION, Board of. Statistics of public education in Wales (with Monmouthshire). 1912/13, pts. 1 and 2, 1913/14, 1919/20. OX; Educational statistics, 1913/14. BI HU LO

2. Foreign publications, arranged by country

E820 ARGENTINE. Dictamos en lo administrativo de los procuradores generales de la nacion. S. Kier, 1892–1905; J. Botel, 1905–17. Buenos Aires, 1949. LO

E821 AUSTRALIA. *New South Wales.* The treatment of neglected and delinquent children in Great Britain, Europe, and America, with recommendations as to amendment of administration and law in New South Wales, by Sir Charles Mackellar. Sydney, 1913. LEI

E822 do. *South Australia.* An act to consolidate and amend the law relating to public education. Adelaide, 1915. LO

E823 do. *Tasmania.* Report of the Minister of Education for the years 1895/96, 1898/99, 1904/05, 1907/09, 1911, 1913–18. LO

E824 BAHAMAS. Annual report of the Board of education, 1913–14, 1916–17. Nassau, 1914–18. 4 vols. LEI

E825 BELGIUM. Ministry of the Interior. Projet de loi pour l'enseignement public en Belgique. Brussels, Rémy, 1832. LO

E826 CANADA. Royal commission on industrial training and technical education. Report. Ottawa, 1913. 3 vols. BI; do., Parts 1–4. 4 vols. LEI

E827 do. *Alberta.* Annual report of the Department of Education, no. 3, 1908, nos. 8–9, 1913–14. Edmonton, 1909–15. LEI

E828 do. *Lower Canada.* Rapport du Surintendant de l'éducation dans le Bas-Canada pour l'année 1858, [and] 1859. Toronto, 1859. 2 vols. LO

E829 do. *Nova Scotia.* Annual report of the Superintendent of education on the public schools of Nova Scotia for the year ended 31st July 1898. Halifax, 1899. LEI

E830 do. *Ontario.* Archaeological report, 1898: being part of Appendix to the report of the Minister of education. Toronto, 1898. LEI

E831 CEYLON. Dept. of public instruction and Central school commission. 20th report, 1862/63. 24th report, 1866/67; 26th report, 1868/69; 27th report, 1869/70. Colombo, 1863–70. LO

E832 do. do. Report of sub-committee to inquire into education. Colombo, 1867. LO

E833 do. do. Special report on the state of public instruction. Colombo, 1869. LO

E834 do. do. Administrative reports of the Director of public instruction, 1871, 1873, 1874. Colombo, 1871–74. LO

E835 FRANCE. *Imperial council of state.* A system of education for the infant king of Rome and other French princes of the blood. 1820. *See* C471

E836 do. *Laws, etc.* Recueil des lois et règlements sur l'enseignement supérieur, comprenant les décisions de la jurisprudence, par A. de Beauchamp. Paris, Delalain, 1880–85. LO

E837 do. Ministry of public instruction. De l'enseignement secondaire en Angleterre et en Ecosse. Rapport addressé à Son Exc. le Ministre de l'Instruction Publique par J. Demogeot et H. Montucci. Paris, Imprimerie impériale, 1868. LO

E838 do. do. Manuel d'exercices gymnastiques et de jeux scolaires. Paris, Imprimerie nationale, 1891. LO

E839 do. do. [Reports by Victor Cousin on the state of public instruction in Holland and in Prussia.] *See* C325–326

E840 do. National Assembly. Rapport fait au nom de la Commission de l'assistance et de la prévoyance publique par M. Thiers. Paris, 1850. HU

E840a do. Technical instruction commission. Reports. *See* E208–211

E841 INDIA. *Governor General.* Indian educational policy, being a resolution issued by the Governor General in council on the 11th March, 1904. Calcutta, 1904. LO

E842 do. Education, General council on. The despatch of the Board of Control on general education in India. Reprinted from the return to the House of Commons dated 18 July, 1854. [Wood despatch.] [With] Appendix: Summary of the despatch by Arthur Howell for a return to the House of Commons in 1870. [*c.* 1880.] SH

E843 do. Education, Bureau of. Indian education, 1913/14, 1917/18. Calcutta, 1915–19. LO

E844 do. do. Progress of education in India. Quinquennial reviews, 1907–12, 1917–22. Calcutta, 1912–22. LO

E845 do. do. *Occasional reports.* No. 1: Rural schools in the Central Provinces, by H. Sharp. Calcutta, 1904. LEI

E846 do. do. do. No. 2: Vernacular reading in the Bombay Presidency, by J. G. Covernton. Calcutta, 1906. LO

E847 do. do. do. No. 3: The educational system of Japan, by W. H. Sharp. Bombay, 1906. LEI

E848 do. do. do. No. 5: Training of secondary teachers, by H. R. James, H. Sharp, J. Nelson Fraser. Calcutta, 1909. [In the U.K., Prussia, U.S.A. and Bombay.] LEI

E849 do. do. Selections from educational records. Part 1: 1781–1839, by H. Sharp. Part 2: 1840–59, by J. A. Richey. Calcutta, 1920–22. 2 vols. LO

E850 do. Conference of directors of public instruction. Report of the conference held at Delhi, January 1917. Delhi, 1917. LO

E851 do. Conference on the education of the domiciled community, held at Simla, July 1912. Report. Calcutta, 1912. LO

E852 do. Home Department. Papers relating to discipline and moral training in schools and colleges. Calcutta, 1896. (Serial no. 8.) LO

E853 do. *Bengal.* Dept. of education. Code of regulations for European schools in Bengal, 1908. Calcutta, 1908. LO

E854 do. do. General report on public instruction in the Bengal presidency, 1842/43, 1843/44, 1845/46–1852/55, Jan.–April 1855, 1856/57–1858/59, 1860/61–1863/64, 1866/67, 1868/69, 1869/70, 1870/71. Calcutta, 1844–71. LO; 1872/73. Calcutta, 1874. LEI

E855 do. do. Dept. of education. Progress of education in Bengal, 1902/03 to 1906/07, 3rd quinquennial review, by W. W. Hornell. Calcutta, 1907. LO

E856 do. do. do. Technical and industrial instruction in Bengal, 1888–1908. Calcutta, 1908. LO

E857 do. do. Calcutta university commission, 1917–19. Report. Calcutta, 1919. 5 vols. ReU

E858 do. *Bengal (Eastern) and Assam.* Report of the progress of education in Eastern Bengal and Assam during the years 1901/02 to 1906/07. Shillong, 1907. 2 vols. LO

E859 do. *Bombay.* Report of the Director of public instruction in the Bombay Presidency for the years 1886/87, 1887/88, 1889/90. Bombay, 1887–90. LO

E860 do. *Northwestern Provinces.* Dept. of public instruction. Report on the progress of education in the Northwestern Provinces for the years 1867/69 to 1884/85. Allahabad, 1869–85. LO

E861 do. *Punjab.* Dept. of education. Report on public instruction in the Punjab and its dependencies, 1905/06, 1906/07, 1907/08. Lahore, 1906–08. LO

E862 ITALY. Jullien, M. A. Esprit de la méthode d'éducation de Pestalozzi. Milan, Imprimerie royale, 1812. *See* C726

E863 JAPAN. Dept. of education. History of Japanese education, prepared for the Japan-British Exhibition, 1910. Tokyo, 1910. LO

E864 NETHERLANDS. Règlement sur l'organisation de l'enseignement supérieur dans les provinces méridionales du royaume des Pays-Bas. Ghent, 1817. LEI

E865 NEW ZEALAND. Education department. Public schools. Regulations for inspection, and syllabus of instruction. (Education act, 1908.) Wellington, 1914. BI

RHODESIA, Southern. *See* Southern Rhodesia

E866 RUSSIA. Ministry of public instruction. *School medical service.* Schème pour l'appréciation sanitaire du banc d'école, par le Dr. A. Nikitine. [St. Petersburg, *c.* 1910?] LEI

E867 SIERRA LEONE. Education ordinance, 1895. [Photocopy.] LO

SOUTH AFRICA. *See* Union of South Africa

E868 SOUTHERN RHODESIA. Education committee. Report of the committee appointed by the Administrator to enquire into and report upon laws and system under which education is at present provided . . . Salisbury, 1908. LO

E869 SWITZERLAND. Diet. Rapport sur L'Institut de M[r.] Pestalozzi à Yverdon, présenté à S.E. M[r.] de Landamann et à la haute Diète des dix-neuf cantons de la Suisse. Fribourg, 1810. LO

E870 UNION OF SOUTH AFRICA. Commission on higher education. Report of a commission appointed to enquire into and report upon matters concerning higher education in the Union. Pretoria, 1911. LO

E871 UNITED STATES. Bureau of education. Abnormal man, being essays on education and crime and related subjects, with digests of literature and a bibliography, by Arthur MacDonald. Washington, 1893. (Circular of information no. 4, 1893.) LEI

E872   do.   do.   College libraries as aids to instruction. Washington, 1880. (Circulars of information, no. 1.)   LEI

E873   do.   do.   Library instruction in universities, colleges, and normal schools, compiled by H. R. Evans. Washington, 1914. (Bulletin 1914, no. 34, whole no. 608.)   BI

E874   do.   do.   [Education in New England and Prussia.]   [186–?]   [Cover title.]   LI

E875   do.   do.   Report of the Commissioner of education for the years ended June 30th 1884–99, 1905–07, 1908–13, 1917. Washington, 1886–1917. 42 vols. LO;   1881–1905, 1911–15.   [Lacks vol. 2 of 1915 report.]   48 vols.   LEE;   1881–1900, 1912. 33 vols. BI;   1870, 1883, 1889, vol. 2 *only*.   HU; 1897, vol. 2, 1898, 1899, vol. 2, 1901, 1903, 1904, 1905, vol. 2, 1908–14, 1915, vol. 1.   23 vols.   LEI; 1888–1909 [lacks vol. 2 of 1899, 1900, 1905–07], 1912–13, 1914, vol. 1.   NE

E876   do.   do.   Report of the inquiry into the administration and support of the Colorado school system. Washington, 1917. (Bulletin 1917, no. 5.) BI

E877   do.   do.   Studies in higher education in Ireland and Wales; with suggestions for universities and colleges in the United States. By George Edwin MacLean. Washington, 1917. (Bulletin 1917, no. 15.)   HU

E878   do.   do.   Studies in higher education in England and Scotland, with suggestions for universities and colleges in the United States. By George Edwin MacLean. Washington, 1917. (Bulletin 1917, no. 16.)   HU

E879   do.   Department of labor.   25th annual report of the Commissioner of labor, 1910: Industrial education. Washington, 1911.   LEI

E880   do.   *District of Columbia.*   Board of education. Report, 1904/05. Washington, USGPO, 1906.   LO

E881   do.   *New York, state.*   Dept. of education. (*For the U.S. Commission to the Paris exposition of* 1900.) Monographs on education in the United States, edited by Nicholas Murray Butler. Albany, N.Y., 1900. 10 vols. LO; Monographs nos. 1–20. In 3 vols. LEI; Monograph no. 1: Educational organization and administration, by A. S. Draper. ReU; Monograph no. 2: Scientific, technical and engineering education, by T. C. Menderhall.   ReU

NOTE: *Numbers beginning with A represent works published 15th–17th centuries; those beginning with B 18th-century works; C 19th-century works on education; D Text and children's books of the 19th century; E Government publications.*

CAMBRIDGESHIRE. Charities, E453; Education, *see* Cambridge

CAMPAN, Jeanne Louise Henriette. School in Paris, D292

CANADA. Education, E205, E598, E671, E826–30; Education, universities, E689

CANTERBURY. Union chapel sunday school, C1288

CARPENTER, John, 1370?–1441?, C160

CATHEDRAL SCHOOLS, C576; Peterborough, E265; St. Paul's, C577

CATHERINE II, empress of Russia, B118, B151

CENTRAL SOCIETY OF EDUCATION, C242–5, C1376

CEYLON. Education, E671, E831–4

CHARITIES, B683–4, B759, C151, C153, C177–8, C755, C1458, E97, E102a, E104, E108, E140, E142–4, E158, E240, E450–63; Legislation, E71; Cambridgeshire, E453; Derbyshire, E295; Devonshire, E454; Hampshire, E455; Leicestershire, B488, E213, E456; Lincolnshire, E457; London, C610, C639, C811, E246, E292, E315–8, E325, E330–2, E344, E458; Northamptonshire, E233, E294; Rutland, E214, E354a; Somerset, C652

CHARITY COMMISSION, Departmental committee on, E319

CHARITY SCHOOLS, B181, B683–4, B793, B982–4, B989, B1016, B1044, C230, C921; Sermons, B122, B142, B166, B197, B214, B217, B227, B230, B266, B277–8, B302, B410, B436, B517, B558, B581, B672, B685, B723, B748, B801, B878, B883, B937, B946, B973, B979, B995, B997, B1017, B1073, B1133, B1145–6, B1149, C22, C683, C845, C1377, C1526; Textbooks for, B986–7, B1033–4, D766

CHARTERHOUSE, A212, C253, C1246, E176; Textbooks for, D1165–6, D1270

CHARTISTS, C810

CHEAM, Surrey. Pestalozzian school, C870–1, C1204–5

CHELTENHAM. College, C1469; Grammar school, C599–600

CHEMICAL ENGINEERING. Germany, E358

CHEMISTRY. *See* Science

CHESHIRE. Education, C67, E629

CHICHESTER. National schools, C508

CHILD CARE AND TRAINING, A344, B304, B516, B758, C83, C372, C655–6, C1318, C1471; *see also* Nursery education

CHILD WELFARE, E59, E550, E821; *see also* Day nurseries; Destitute; Orphans and orphanages

CHILDREN IN LITERATURE, C750

CHILDREN'S BOOKS, before 1801. (For nineteenth century *see* section D passim.) A318, B18–9, B34, B37, B61, B102, B104–10, B123, B178, B208, B238, B279, B297, B313, B323, B328, B330, B355, B376, B389, B414, B416, B422, B424, B426, B451, B471–2, B504, B559, B585, B603–4, B642, B644, B675, B697, B713, B715, B796–7, B804, B806–7, B827–9, B832, B834, B880–1, B928, B977, B1018, B1038, B1075, B1155

CHILDREN'S PERIODICALS, B209, B645, B1115, D244, D249, D252, D749, D751, D825, D862, D1111, D1330, D1334, D1514–5; *see also* Annuals and keepsakes

CHILDREN'S WRITINGS, C6

CHIMNEY SWEEPS, E100

CHRISTIAN SCHOOLS, Brothers of, C375

CHRIST'S HOSPITAL, C1199, C1429, C1524; Textbooks for, B27, B802

CHRONOLOGY. Textbooks, B467–8, B648, B1119–20, D84, D172, D296, D672, D800, D1251, D1338; Charts, D234, D484–6, D1440–1; *see also* History. Textbooks

CHURCH AND EDUCATION, C258–9, C361–2, C692, C855, C885, C1268, C1478; Bath and Wells diocese, C1353; Exeter diocese, C434; London diocese, C804; Salisbury diocese, C1264; *see also* National Society; Religious education; Voluntary schools

CHURCH EDUCATION SOCIETY, C1420

CHURCH LANGTON, Leics. Charities, B488

CIVIL SERVICE, E421–3

CLARE HALL, Cambridge, B1

CLASSICAL EDUCATION, C29, C221, C658, C1315; *and* sections A and B *passim*

CLASSICAL EDUCATION ABROAD, E684

CLASSICAL LANGUAGES. Textbooks, A3, A5, B125, B573, B872, B933, D663; *see also* Greek language; Hebrew language; Latin language

CLASSICAL MYTHOLOGY. Textbooks, B845, D521, D670

CLERGY, Education of, A345, C278, C344, C431; Abroad, C1235

CLIMBING BOYS, E100

CLONMEL. Endowed school, E157

CODES, Educational. See Education codes

COLET, John, B590, C762

COLLEGIATE EDUCATION, C1175, C1178; *see also* University education

COLORADO. Education, E876

COLUMBIA, District of. Education, E880

COMENIUS, John Amos, A448, A453; *see also* author entries, sections A and B

COMMERCIAL EDUCATION, C29, C445; Abroad, E357, E359

COMMON SCHOOLS (U.S.A.), C300, C1313, E205; Textbooks for, D1038

COMPARATIVE EDUCATION, C729–31

COMPOSITION. *See* English language; Latin language

COMPULSORY EDUCATION ABROAD, E390

CONDUCT AND ETIQUETTE. Textbooks, D2, D81, D124, D566, D766, D1099, D1146, D1303, D1311, D1380, D1436–7, D1510, Foreign, D1182; *see also* Courtesy books; Parents' advice

CONSCIENCE CLAUSE, C1452, E197

CONTINUATION SCHOOLS. *See* Further education

COOKERY. *See* Domestic subjects

COPY BOOKS. *See* Writing

CORNWALL. Charities, E383

CORPUS CHRISTI COLLEGE, Cambridge, B706

COURTESY BOOKS, A69, A73–4, A198, A359, A438–40, B186, B1030

CRIME AND CRIMINALS, C108, C332, C875, E871; *see also* Juvenile delinquency; Penology

CROYDON. Friends' school, C575; Whitgyft foundation, B721

CURRICULUM. *See* Teaching methods and curricula

DAVIES, James, 1765–1849, C503, C1042

DAVIES, Richard, d. 1762, B779

DAY, Thomas, B576

DAY NURSERIES, E579

DEAF (including deaf and dumb), E289; Education, B640, C1015, C1050, C1301–2, C1432, C1453, C1474, D743, E31, E34, E266, E312; Schools for, C127, C400, C1418, E575; Schools abroad, C606

DEBTORS' CHILDREN. Education, B1012

DEFECTIVE CHILDREN. *See* Feeble-minded; *and also* Blind; Deaf; etc.

DENMARK. Education, C566, E597, E681

DENMARK. Text and children's books, B34

DERBYSHIRE. Charities, E295

DESCARTES, René, A263

DESIGN, Schools of, E152–3, E737a–8

DESTITUTE, C912, C1201–2, C1516, E161; *see also* Paupers; Ragged schools; Vagrants; Wildlings

DEVONSHIRE. Charities, E454; Education, *see* Barnstaple; Exeter

DICK BEQUEST (Scotland), C883

DISCIPLINE, A266, B474, B626, C574, C744, E852

DISTRICT OF COLUMBIA. Education, E880

DISTRICT VISITORS, C650

DODDRIDGE, Philip, C1368

DOMESTIC SUBJECTS. Teacher training, E587; Abroad, E680, E683

DOMESTIC SUBJECTS. Teaching, E634; Cookery, E636; Housecraft, E658; Needlework, E536, E635, E704–5, E774

DOMESTIC SUBJECTS. Textbooks, D15, D458; Cookery, A432

DORSET. Education, C371; *see also* Wimborne Minster

DRAWING. *See* Art education

DUBLIN. Education, C270, C1401; St. Patrick's school – Textbooks, B275; Trinity College, B9, C1428, E166, E373; University, C1400, E166

DULWICH. Alleyn's school, E293, E596

DUMB, C356, C1316; *see also* Deaf (for deaf and dumb)

DUMFRIES. Mechanics' Institution, C11, School, B195–6; Mechanics' Institution – Textbooks for, B1049

DURHAM. Grammar school – Textbooks for, B162; University, E8, E193

DURHAM, county. Education, C972; *see also* Barnard Castle; Bishop Auckland; Durham; Gateshead

DURSLEY, Glos. Charity school, B558

DURY, John, A448

EAST INDIA COLLEGE, C411, C1183

EASTBOURNE. Industrial school, C982

ECCLESIASTICAL COMMISSION, C135

EDGEWORTH, Richard Lovell, C397–8, C1183, C1327

EDINBURGH. Education, C400–10, C1231, C1533; Academy, C407–8; Academy – Textbooks for, D161; Circus Place School – Textbooks for, D853; Heriot foundations, C1364; High school, C1049; Infant School Society, C105; Philosophical Institution, C813

EDUCATION, Finance of, C142, E49, E137–9, E243, E382, E760; *see also* Education grants; State aid for education

EDUCATION, History of, C25–7, C207, C373, C502, C620, C687, C1008, C1186, C1358, C1414, C1447a

EDUCATION, Social influence of, C227, C293, C378, C423

EDUCATION CODE ACT, E30

EDUCATION CODES, E184, E469–77, E492–9, E553–79; Scotland, E797–800; Wales, E814–6; Revised code of 1862 (as subject), C41, C50, C54, C123–4, C169–70, C303, C435, C454, C476, C511, C546, C548, C564, C675, C688, C742, C815, C848–9, C882, C1193, C1207, C1222, C1234, C1237, C1263, C1320, C1449, C1482, C1538

EDUCATION GRANTS, E137, E146, E174, E501–5, E613–20; for special education, E312; for science and arts, E336; for universities, E432, E620

EDUCATIONAL GAMES AND DEVICES, B689, C357a, D346, D517, D703, D710, D864, D1410, D1425–7, D1472

EDUCATIONAL LAWS AND LEGISLATION. Education bills – *1820*, C803, C980, C1053, E94; *1838*, C384; *1843, see* Factories bill, 1843; *1855*, C618, C1001, E170; *1870*, C370, C938, C941, C974, C1219; *1876*, E93; *1902*, E360; *1908*, E386; *1917*, E95; *1918*, E431; Education acts, E1–90

ELEMENTARY EDUCATION ACTS, Royal commission on, E272–83

ELEMENTARY SCHOOLS, E644–7; Pressure of work, E255; Schemes, E296

ELOCUTION, B703, B952, C1293

ELOCUTION. Textbooks, B325–6, B936, B1078, B1116, D117, D401, D419, D784; *see also* Rhetoric

EMBLEM BOOKS, B323

EMPLOYMENT OF CHILDREN AND YOUNG PEOPLE, E204, E302, E363, E405, E427, E676; Legislation, E41, E52; Special employments – Agriculture, E148, E216–7; Special employments – Chimney sweeps, E100; Special employments – Mines and manufactures, E147; *see also* Apprentices

ENDOWED SCHOOLS, C427, C555–60, C1361, E207, E231–2, E235, E293, E298, E301; Ireland, C851, E157, E159, E178–80, E250, E314; Scotland, E236–8, E247–9, E259–64

ENDOWED SCHOOLS ACTS, E15, E57; Select committee on, E269–71

ENDOWMENTS, Educational, E377, E381, E383–4, E407–8; Ireland, E770; *see also* Charities

ENGLISH EDUCATION, German views on, C1504–5; U.S. views on, E878

ENGLISH LANGUAGE. Pronunciation, B413, B884, C1177; Punctuation, B994, D1081, D1278; Spelling, B676, C1051

ENGLISH LANGUAGE. Teaching, B884, C1000, E538, E705, E802

ENGLISH LANGUAGE. Textbooks – General, B146, B152, B291, B308, B348, B750, D368, D423, D756; *see also* Anglo-Saxon language

ENGLISH LANGUAGE. Textbooks – Composition, D70, D708, D1081, D1188, D1278, D1417–8; *see also* Letter writing

ENGLISH LANGUAGE. Textbooks – Dictionaries, B50, B233, B235, B256, B331, B565, B690, B767, D222, D404, D598, D713, D726, D731

ENGLISH LANGUAGE. Textbooks – Etymology, etc., D207, D488, D555

ENGLISH LANGUAGE. Textbooks – Grammar, B3, B44, B159, B241, B287, B347, B462, B507, B589, B669, B767, B866, B960, B968, B976, B1002, B1153, D33, D35, D272, D297, D305, D314a, D343, D371, D442, D475, D481, D582, D688, D801, D813–4, D845, D883, D897, D966–9, D1050, D1055, D1064, D1069, D1078–9, D1234, D1247–9, D1288, D1336, D1453, D1474

ENGLISH LANGUAGE. Textbooks – Reading. *See* Reading

ENGLISH LANGUAGE. Textbooks – Spelling, A231, B22, B296, D28, D92, D176, D210, D226c, D416, D422, D583, D669, D983a, D1460

ENGLISH LANGUAGE ABROAD. Textbooks, B35, D719, D1006

ENGLISH LITERATURE. Textbooks – Anthologies, B8, B596–9, B705, B753, B1101, D72, D117, D412, D444, D837, D853–6, D970, D973, D1250, D1337, D1480; *see also* Elocution – Textbooks; English poetry for children; Reading

ENGLISH LITERATURE. Textbooks – Appreciation, D19, D208, D295, D388, D1018, D1430

ENGLISH POETRY FOR CHILDREN, B72, B90, B257, B974, B1104, D23, D95, D121, D667, D699, D791, D907, D910, D1096–8, D1199, D1270

EPILEPTICS. Education, E42, E67, E347–8, E573–4

ERASMUS, Desiderius, B592; *see also* author entries, sections A and B

ESSEX. Education. *See* Felsted school; Woodford

ETHICS. Textbooks, B339; *see also* Conduct and etiquette; Moral education

ETON COLLEGE, B652, C331, C513, C798, C1003, C1345, E595; Exercises, D406; Sermons, B1122; Textbooks for, A322, B2, B11, B215, B352, B556, B568, B770, B774, B939, B991, B1147, D52; Textbooks for, Catalogue of, D1468

EUROPE. Child welfare, E821

EUROPE. Educational systems, C49, C59, C836, E674, E681, E686; Education of girls and women, E680; Elementary education, C416, C738–9; Military education, E220; Technical education, E357; *see also under* the names of the various countries of Europe

EUROPE. History of education, C1447a

EVENING SCHOOLS. *See* Further education

EXAMINATIONS, C9–10, C41, C144; Science and art, E625–8; Secondary schools, C603, E411, E713a, E794–5, E801; Teacher training, E480, E588–9, E710–1, E747; University and university scholarships, C223, C1062; Women, C209, C1378

EXETER. Grammar school – Sermons, B246

EXHIBITIONS. *See* Scholarships

FACTORIES ACT, 1843, E136

FACTORIES BILL, 1843, C15, C30, C382, C470

FAIRY TALES, B47–8, B806–7; *see also under* authors' and collectors' names in section D

FARM SCHOOLS, C457, C820, C887, C890, C1038–40; *see also* Mettray

FARNHAM. Commercial Academy – Textbooks for, D372

FEEBLE-MINDED, C381, C708–9, C1285, E65–6, E77, E347–8, E391–5, E572; Education, E42, E54, E67, E573–4

FEINAGLE, Gregor von, D922

FELLENBERG, Philipp Emanuel von, C82, C218, C229, C388, C411, C444

FELSTED SCHOOL. Sermons, B957

GRANT, Horace, C247
GRANTS FOR EDUCATION. *See* Education grants
GREAT GREENFORD, Middx. Free school, B554
GREEK LANGUAGE. Pronunciation, A190, B1079
GREEK LANGUAGE. Teaching, E608
GREEK LANGUAGE. Textbooks – Dictionaries and vocabularies, B503, B573
GREEK LANGUAGE. Textbooks – Grammar, A55, A64, A144, A300, B70, B163–4, B175–7, B457, B526, B613–6, D352, D430, D640, D730, D1165, D1241, D1453
GREEK LANGUAGE. Readers, A4, A330, A419, B11, B38, B344–5, B840, B939, B991, B1129, D8, D41, D1095; for Italian schools, D125; *see also* Greek literature
GREEK LITERATURE, A3, A5, A233–4, A264, A361, B333, D281, D399
GREENWICH ACADEMY. Textbooks, B1130
GRESHAM COLLEGE, B1096
GRESHAM UNIVERSITY, E311
GUERNSEY. Mechanics' Institute, C380
GUTHRIE, Thomas, C571, C970
GYMNASTICS. *See* Physical education
HALLE, Saxony, B402–3
HAMILTONIAN SYSTEM, C590, D596–7
HAMPSHIRE. Charities, E455
HAMPSHIRE. Education, C337, C352, C705
HANDWORK. Teaching, E321, E424, E446, E522, E549, E699, E751; Ireland, E339–43
HANDWORK. Text and children's books, D795, D1359
HARROW SCHOOL, C506, C602–5, C1448, C1450, E593; Textbooks for, D430
HARTLIB, Samuel, A448
HARTWITH, Yorks. Endowed school, C1271
HASTINGS, *Lady* Elizabeth, B74
HEALTH EDUCATION, A43, C850, E702–3; *see also* Physique; Public health
HEATH, nr. Wakefield, Yorks. Academy, B868
HEBREW LANGUAGE, A5, A58, A60, B174, B673, D1453
HEREFORDSHIRE. *See* Ross-on-Wye
HERTFORDSHIRE. Education. *See* Bishop's Stortford
HIEROGLYPHIC BOOKS, D43, D109–10
HILL, Matthew Davenport, C645
HISTORY. Study and teaching, A352, B637, C1321, E806; Elementary schools, E705; Secondary schools, E530, E546, E659
HISTORY. Textbooks – General, A260, B518, B648, B686, B744, B868, B923, B1011, B1135, D90, D172, D223, D473, D510, D528, D552, D616, D864, D868, D902, D1148, D1252, D1283, D1338, D1388, D1419, D1440; French, D254, D1299
HISTORY, Ancient and biblical. Textbooks, A135, A188, A196, A398, B173, B346, B399–400, B447, B662, B1042a–b, d–f, B1137, B1165, D133, D217, D259, D485, D530, D537, D542–3, D550, D618, D672, D783, D857, D924, D928, D986a, D1002, D1037, D1065, D1073, D1147, D1279, D1372a–d, g–h, D1373, D1446; French, D838–9
HISTORY OF AMERICA. Textbooks, D1074
HISTORY OF ASIA. Textbooks, D220
HISTORY OF EUROPE. Textbooks, B384, B638, D304, D496, D625, D1032, D1034–5, D1076; in French, D276, D793
HISTORY OF GREAT BRITAIN. Textbooks, A314, A332, B240, B248, B445, B467, B555, B661, B707, B1042c, D10, D54, D114, D145, D149–51, D157, D181, D234, D245, D298, D300–3, D326, D332, D345, D366, D484, D532, D536, D538–41, D627, D671, D687, D692, D827, D921, D929, D984a, D1033, D1057, D1077, D1082, D1103, D1159–60, D1186, D1261, D1266b, D1281, D1285, D1310, D1369, D1372e–f, D1441, D1458, D1467
HISTORY OF THE BRITISH EMPIRE. Textbooks. D152. D286, D486
HOFWYL. *See* Fellenberg, P. E.
HOLLAND. *See* Netherlands
HOMER, A361

HOME EDUCATION, C2, C36–7, C203, C694, C825, C852, C1396, C1410; Methods, B21, B40, C343; *see also* Governesses; Nursery education
HOOK, Walter Farquhar, C204, C265
HOSPITALS, B539, E236–8; Children's, C805
HOUSECRAFT. *See* Domestic subjects
HULL. Charity school, B58; Ragged schools, C685
IMPERIAL EDUCATION CONFERENCE, 1911, E409, E723–4
INCORPORATED SOCIETY FOR PROMOTING PROTESTANT SCHOOLS IN IRELAND. Sermons, B75, B228, B303, B938
INDIA. Education, C466, C973, C1422, E841–61; Girls and women, C653; Secondary education, C220
INDIA. Textbooks, D220
INDUSTRIAL ARTS. Children's books, D130–1, D164
INDUSTRIAL EDUCATION, C143, C279, C1254, C1343, C1441
INDUSTRIAL EDUCATION ABROAD, C1055, E606
INDUSTRIAL SCHOOLS, C217, C406, C410, C685, C701, C982, C1501, E257, E309, E329, E720, E722; Legislation, C1329, E7, E9–10, E13, E26; *see also* Ragged schools
INDUSTRY, E111
INFANT BAPTISM. *See* Baptism, Infant
INFANT SCHOOLS, A122, B824, B1164, C77, C224, C409, C411, C667, C696, C868–9, C1057, C1238, C1370, C1372, C1508–13, C1527–8; *see also* Froebel, F.; Home education; Nursery education
INFANT SCHOOLS ABROAD, C276–7
INFANT SCHOOL TEXTBOOKS. General, D115, D667, D991
INSPECTION OF SCHOOLS, C353, E194, E481, E498, E664, E795; Inspectors' reports, C48, E482, E507–14, E622–39, E794
INSTITUTE OF BROTHERS OF THE CHRISTIAN SCHOOLS. *See* Brothers of the Christian schools
INTELLECT, C3, C61
INTERMEDIATE EDUCATION, E715; Ireland, E351–2, E786; Wales, E818
IPSWICH. Charity schools, B266; School of industry, C701
IRELAND. Education, B9, B200, B548–52, C31, C92, C112, C216, C231–2, C270, C294, C459–61, C528, C533, C636, C821, C839, C952, C978–9, C1044–5, C1059, C1061, C1208, C1214, C1323, C1335–6, C1401, C1420–1, C1467, C1489–90, E102, E112–22, E125–6, E132, E766–88; Elementary education, C1230, E218, E772–7; Endowed schools, C851, E157, E159, E178–80, E250, E314, E785; Higher education, C608, C789, C1059, C1380, C1400, C1415, C1428, E365–6, E766, E787–8, E877; Intermediate education, E351–2, E786; Science and Art Department, E215; Sunday schools, C707, C1382; Technical education, E253
ISLE OF WIGHT. Education, C961
ITALIAN LANGUAGE. Textbooks, B108, B617, D16, D18, D77, D292, D453, D557, D946, D1005, D1395–6; Dictionaries, D436
ITALIANS IN GREAT BRITAIN, E240
ITALY. Education, B349, C288, C854
ITALY. Text and children's books, B255, D5, D125
JACOTOT, Jean Joseph, C86, C318–9, C364, C390, C430, C713–4, C760, C800, C884, C1217
JAPAN. Education, E847, E863
JEWS. Religious education – Textbooks, D331
JUVENILE DELINQUENCY, C5, C16, C20, C71–2, C89–90, C108, C236–8, C787–8, C1249, C1257, C1334, C1440, C1506, C1543, E161, E821
JUVENILE DELINQUENCY ABROAD. France, C275; U.S.A., C35
KANT, Immanuel, C735–6
KAY-SHUTTLEWORTH, *Sir* James Phillips, C84, C411
KEEPSAKES. *See* Annuals and keepsakes
KENNINGTON. Nesbit's Academy, C949
KENSINGTON. Academy, B320
KENT. Charities, E384; Education, *see* Canterbury; Rainham; Tonbridge
KILDARE STREET EDUCATION SOCIETY, C270

PROFESSIONAL EDUCATION, C396, C411; France, C1260
PRUSSIA. *See* Germany
PSYCHOLOGY, B877, C60–1, C168, C219, C324, C433, C1203, C1352
PSYCHOLOGY, Educational, A229, B396, B540, C239–40, C443, C465, C622–33, C718
PUBLIC HEALTH, E730–1; Legislation, E5, E88; *see also* School health services
PUBLIC SCHOOLS (British), C17, C280, C285, C292, C411, C1209, C1361, C1454, E195–6; Legislation, E14, E87; *see also* under the names of individual public schools
PUNJAB. Education, E861
PUPIL TEACHERS. *See* Teacher training
PUPPETS AND PUPPET PLAYS, D285, D1116
PUSEY, Edward Bouverie, C507
QUATT, Salop. Industrial school, C1501
QUEEN'S COLLEGE, Belfast. *See* Belfast
RAGGED SCHOOLS, C236, C320, C403–4, C410, C571–3, C579, C685, C822, C970, C1188–90, C1195, C1516
RAINHAM, Kent. National school, C1191
READING. Teaching, C1051, D502, E773
READING. Textbooks – Primers and easy readers, A2, B62, B68, B211, B274, B311, B368, B511, B639, B647, B695, B762, B1033–5, D7, D42, D73–5, D83, D250–1, D253, D333, D402–3, D438a, D439, D448–9, D502, D534, D580, D609, D674–5, D694–5, D701, D722, D804, D828–30, D832, D834, D867, D871, D885, D903, D906, D937, D958, D962, D971, D977, D982a, D985a, D987–8, D1011, D1029, D1049, D1126, D1138, D1140, D1154, D1158, D1162, D1167–8, D1173, D1266a, D1294–5, D1363–4, D1378, D1450, D1469–70, D1495; second stage, D1191, D1475
READING. Textbooks – France, B660, D806
READING. Textbooks – Germany, A7, D456; later stage, D63
READING. Textbooks – U.S.A., A315–6, B1113
RECREATION, C81
REDHILL. Philanthropic farm school, C1038–40
REED, Andrew, C1200
REFORMATORIES, C16, C20, C130, C238, C306, C504, C646, C697, C820, C1201–2, C1473, C1492, C1551, E12, E257, E310, E329, E720, E722; Ireland, C1329; *see also* Farm schools
REFORMATORIES ABROAD, C35, C893; *see also* Mettray
RELIGIOUS EDUCATION, B299, B670, B729, B843, B1103, B1140, C22, C58, C119, C295, C472, C498, C514–6, C529, C798, C872, C1367, E244, E380; Ireland, E777; Scotland, E128–30; Conscience clause, C1452, E197
RELIGIOUS EDUCATION. Textbooks, A330, A447, B119, B138, B202, B261, B749, B1032, B1036, B1042f, D109–11, D216, D267–8, D350, D361, D513, D803, D870, D874, D947, D955, D957, D989, D1201, D1228, D1235, D1291–2, D1343, D1365–6, D1372i–l, D1444–5, D1494; Jewish, D331; Hymns, D31, D71, D667, D757, D817, D980a; Prayers, B579, B987, D1277, D1447; *see also* Geography, Ancient and biblical; History, Ancient and biblical
RELIGIOUS EDUCATION ABROAD. France, C207; U.S.A., C1439
REPTON SCHOOL, E198
REVISED CODE. *See* Education codes
RHETORIC. Textbooks, A79, A145, A320, A356, A368, A413, B351, B524, B611, B942, B1003, B1069, D70, D120a; France, D356
RHODESIA, Southern. *See* Southern Rhodesia
RICHMOND, Legh, C499
ROLLIN, Charles, B435
ROMAN CATHOLIC CHURCH, C260, C405, C737, C977, C1197, C1269, C1551, E564
ROME. Education, B863–4, C687
ROSS-ON-WYE, Herefordshire. Blue Coat school, C159
ROTHERHAM, Yorks. Grammar school – Textbooks, B530
ROTTERDAM. Gymnasium – Textbooks, A285
ROUSSEAU, Jean Jacques, B433–4
ROYAL COLLEGE OF ART, E571
ROYAL COLLEGE OF SCIENCE, E571

ROYAL SOCIETY, A369
RUGBY SCHOOL, C544, C959; Sermons, C52; Textbooks, D48
RURAL EDUCATION, C19, C388, C538, C1058, C1347, C1354, E445–7, E547, E609, E611, E665, E706
RURAL EDUCATION ABROAD, B610, E598, E673, E845
RUSSIA. Education, B118, B1172, E687
RUSSIA. Textbooks, D1101
RUSSIAN LANGUAGE. Textbooks, D1101
RUTLAND. Charities, E214, E354a
RUYSSELEDE. Reformatory, C893
SADLER, Sir Michael, E369
SAINT ANDREWS. University, B1173, E151; Addresses, C895
SAINT CYR (Girls' school), B183, C785–6
SAINT CYRAN, Jean du Vergier de Hauranne, abbé de, B612
SAINT PAUL'S SCHOOL, C577; History, B590, C762; Prize essays, etc., C1262; Sermons, A299, A321, A335
SALFORD. Education, E160
SCARBOROUGH, Yorks. Lancasterian schools, C351
SCHOLARSHIPS. Higher education, B1, C520, C1062, E426; Secondary education, E355, E379, E661; Technical education, E749
SCHOOL AND UNIVERSITY DRAMA, A382, B912
SCHOOL ATTENDANCE, E302, E499, E641
SCHOOL ATTENDANCE ACTS, E35, E41
SCHOOL BOARDS, E515, E643; Finance, E504, E728; Payments of school fees, E234
SCHOOL BOARDS ACT, 1884, E74
SCHOOL BUILDINGS, C74–5, C264, C753, E406, E486; Regulations, E490–1, E554–6
SCHOOL HEALTH SERVICES, E60, E375–6, E576, E653, E670; Germany, E594; Russia, E866
SCHOOL JOURNEYS AND EXPEDITIONS, E602, E685
SCHOOL LIBRARIES, C131, E720
SCHOOL MEALS, E55, E375–6, E404, E523, E577
SCHOOLS, C1179; Directories, C519; *see also* Endowed schools; Grammar schools; Public schools; and names of individual schools
SCHOOLS IN FICTION, B585, D9, D306, D429, D588, D683, D771, D890, D1176, D1232, D1300–1, D1404, D1432; France, D852
SCHOOLS OF DESIGN. *See* Design, Schools of
SCIENCE. Teaching, C157, C166, C198, C359, C442, C479, C1007, C1252, C1292, C1438, C1442; Scotland, E807; *see also* Object lessons; Scientific education
SCIENCE. Textbooks – General, D146, D164, D226b, D799, D1190, D1192
SCIENCE. Textbooks – Astronomy, A310, B46, B89, B454, B492, B525, B569, B629, B1000, B1001, B1119, D119, D128, D464, D527, D603, D1067, D1487; *see see also* Geography. Textbooks – General – Use of globes
SCIENCE. Textbooks – Biology and nature study, B15, B135, B709, B763–4, B838, B905, B1036, B1074, D118, D178, D289, D330, D362, D364–5, D389, D483, D515, D544, D551, D562, D594, D602, D620, D628, D635, D702, D707, D714, D774, D820, D823–4, D840–1, D859–60, D878, D904–5, D927, D945, D978–80, D992–3, D1004, D1016, D1071, D1128, D1184, D1273, D1290, D1309, D1325, D1332, D1362, D1365–6, D1411–3, D1485, D1490, D1503, D1516; Microscopy, D1434, D1486; French texts, D1171
SCIENCE. Textbooks – Chemistry, D80, D218, D235, D424, D738, D879, D1053
SCIENCE. Textbooks – Physics, B46, B535, B629, D78, D739–40, D880, D1013, D1047, D1136, D1187, D1259
SCIENCE AND ART DEPARTMENT, C198, E739–55; Ireland, E215
SCIENTIFIC APPARATUS, E754
SCIENTIFIC EDUCATION, C323, C344–6, C781, C965, E212, E221–30, E435, E739–41, E743–6, E749–50, E752, E754; Inspectors' and examiners' reports, E625, E627–8

SCOTLAND. Education, A445, B306, C133, C401–10, C539, C751, C883, C902, C1231, E124, E200–3, E337, E789–812; Endowed schools, E236–8, E247–9, E259–264; Higher education, E878; Legislation, E2–3, E6, E17, E31, E45, E54, E58, E69, E85–6; Parochial schools, C313, C1006, C1048, E3; Physical education, E367–8; Religious education, E128–30; Secondary education, E809, E837; Teacher training, C526; Universities, C248, E6, E73, E90, E103, E127, E192, E241, E299, E356

SCOTLAND. Highlands and Islands, C1192, C1339, E258, E789

SCOTT, Walter, C159

SECONDARY EDUCATION, E324, E609, E648; Curricula, E543, E547; Codes, E562–5; Finance, E640; Statistics, E517; Teacher training, E585, E604, E848; see also Grammar schools

SECONDARY EDUCATION ABROAD, E519–20, E688; see also names of countries

SECULAR EDUCATION, C132, C295, C302, C355, C514–5, C834–5, C918, E172–3; see also National Education League

SEDGLEY PARK SCHOOL, Staffs., C691

SELF EDUCATION, C251, C465, C617, C1319, D1318; Textbooks for, D91, D843; see also Adult education, Periodicals for; General knowledge; Study

SERVANTS, Books for, D600, D1134, D1204, D1303

SEWING. See Domestic subjects. Needlework

SHARP, John, 1812–1853, C575

SHEFFIELD. Mechanics institute, C1291; Milk St. Academy, C6

SHEPLEY, Yorks. School books, D1489

SHERIDAN, Thomas, B651

SHERWOOD, Mrs Mary Martha, C752

SHORTHAND. Textbooks, D604, D908, D943, D1089–90

SHREWSBURY. Grammar school, C214; Classical exercises, C1299

SHROPSHIRE. Education. See Quatt; Shrewsbury

SIERRA LEONE. Education, E867

SIMPSON, James, C928

SINGING. See Music education

SLOYD, E321

SOCIAL SCIENCES. Teaching, C422, C1252

SOCIAL STUDIES. Textbooks, D20, D373; Commerce, D959; Political economy, D881

SOCIETY CORRESPONDING WITH THE INCORPORATED SOCIETY FOR PROMOTING ENGLISH PROTESTANT SCHOOLS IN IRELAND. Sermons, B117, B502, B510, B674, B771, B956, B1026, B1136

SOCIETY FOR PROMOTING CHRISTIAN KNOWLEDGE, B214, B302, B985, C1333

SOCIETY FOR PROMOTING FEMALE EDUCATION IN THE EAST, C653

SOCIETY OF ARTS, C144; Lectures, C824, C1341

SOCIETY OF FRIENDS. See Friends, Society of

SOMERSET. Education. See Bath; Frome

SOUTH AFRICA. See Union of South Africa

SOUTH KENSINGTON MUSEUM, C422, E753–4

SOUTHERN RHODESIA. Education, E868

SOUTHWARK. Free schools – Sermons, B185, B723

SPAIN. Education, A307

SPANISH LANGUAGE. Textbooks, B835, D478

SPECIAL SCHOOLS, E651; see also Blind, Schools for; Deaf, Schools for; Feeble-minded. Education

SPELLING, B289; see also English language. Textbooks – Spelling

STAFFORDSHIRE. Education, C556, E377; see also Sedgley Park school; Tamworth

STAINES, Middx. Literary and scientific institution, C816

STANMORE, Middx. Pestalozzian school, C1068

STATE AID FOR EDUCATION. See section C passim

STATE AID FOR THE ARTS, E242

STATISTICS OF EDUCATION. England and Wales, E718–9, E819; Elementary education, E425, E692–8

STOW, David, C477

STUDY, A185, B385, B1102; see also Libraries; Self education

SUFFOLK. Education. See Bury St. Edmunds; Ipswich; Woodbridge

SUNDAY SCHOOL UNION, C1475

SUNDAY SCHOOLS, B10, B96, B99, B537, B1041, B1047, C1288, C1381–6, C1426, C1462; History, C1475; Ireland, C707; Scotland, C654; Teaching methods, C291, C1369, C1402, C1416; Textbooks for, D1235, D1292–6, D1330

SUPERANNUATION, See Pensions

SURREY. Education. See Cheam; Croydon; Farnham; Redhill

SURVEYING. See Mathematics. Textbooks – Mensuration, Surveying and Trigonometry

SUSSEX. Education. See Chichester; Eastbourne

SWEDEN. Education, E210, E597, E681

SWEDEN. Textbooks, D912

SWEDISH LANGUAGE. Textbooks, D912

SWINDON, Wilts. Technical college, E631–2

SWITZERLAND. Education, A365, C82, E211, E267, E686

SWITZERLAND. Textbooks, A3, A58, A60, A331, A336, B103

TAMWORTH, Staffs. Grammar school – Textbooks, B948

TASMANIA. Education, E823

TEACHER TRAINING, C282, C439, C1171, C1265, C1307, C1538, E279; Colleges, E521, E624, E645, E652; Examinations, E480, E710–11; in Scotland, C477, C526, E284–5, E800, E810; in Wales, E816; Pupil teachers, E349–50, E385, E446, E527, E639; Pupil teachers, Textbooks for, D117, D845; Regulations, E581–9; Secondary school teachers, E585, E604, E848; Women, E604

TEACHER TRAINING ABROAD, E682, E848

TEACHERS, B1016, C1, C242, C284, C1233, C1389, C1402, C1407, C1416, C1530; Certificates, E488–9; Fiction, C379, C554, C905; Registration, E290, E297, E300, E410, E713; Salaries, E433–4, E439–40; Scotland, C883; Teachers of rural subjects, E446; Women teachers, B932; see also Governesses; Teacher training

TEACHERS ABROAD. Germany, B747, C368, C1356, C1553; Switzerland, C542–3

TEACHING METHODS AND CURRICULA, A221, B40, B71, B195–6, B262, B320, B610, B689, B875, B914, B1082, C163–5, C193, C208, C291, C352, C355, C385, C455, C521, C667, C703–5, C724, C881, C913, C1048, C1236, C1393, C1446

TEACHING METHODS AND CURRICULA ABROAD. France, C276–7; Germany, B782, C966, C1522; U.S.A., C997

TECHNICAL EDUCATION, C1258, E206, E252–4; Finance, E505, E618; Handbooks, C1404; Regulations and syllabuses, E567–9, E571, E707–9; see also Further education

TECHNICAL EDUCATION ABROAD, E208–11, E346, E357–9, E717

TEMPERANCE EDUCATION, E702–3

TEXTBOOKS. Publication and supply, C809, E467; for particulars of textbooks see under subject names

THROPTON, Northumberland. School, C1347

TONBRIDGE SCHOOL, C304, C1176, C1228

TOWNSEND, John, C1418

TOYNTON, Lower, Lincs. Christian Union school, C458

TRAVEL. Educational, B545

TRIGONOMETRY. See Mathematics. Textbooks – Mensuration, etc.

TRIMMER, Mrs Sarah, C1427

TRINITY COLLEGE, Dublin. See Dublin

TROTTER, Robert, B664

UNION OF SOUTH AFRICA. Education, E671, E689, E870

UNITED STATES. Education, B560, C25, C73, C146, C300, C411, C719, C819, C837, C971, C1312–3, C1399, C1439, E205, E678, E691, E871–81; Adult education, C951; Educational periodicals, C23–27; Military education, E220; Rural education, E598; Universities, C187; Women and girls, E680

UNITED STATES. Social welfare – Child welfare, E821; Feeble-minded, E395; Playgrounds, E607

UNITED STATES. Textbooks, D599, D692, D1038

UNIVERSAL INSTRUCTION. See Jacotot, J. J.

196